P9-DDL-095

2018
EDITION

NATIONAL DESIGN SPECIFICATION®
for Wood Construction with Commentary

National Design Specification (NDS) for Wood Construction with Commentary 2018 Edition

First Electronic Version: May 2018
Second Electronic Version: April 2019
Third Electronic Version: October 2021

First Print Version: June 2018
Second Print Version: October 2021

ISBN 978-1-940383-45-3
ISBN 978-1-940383-51-4 (2 volume set)

Copyright © 2018 by American Wood Council
All rights reserved. No part of this publication may be reproduced, distributed, or transmitted in any form or by any means, including, without limitation, electronic, optical, or mechanical means (by way of example and not limitation, photocopying, or recording by or in an information storage retrieval system) without express written permission of the American Wood Council. For information on permission to copy material, please contact:

Copyright Permission
American Wood Council
222 Catoctin Circle, SE, Suite 201
Leesburg, VA 20175
info@awc.org

FOREWORD

The *National Design Specification® for Wood Construction (NDS®)* was first issued by the National Lumber Manufacturers Association (now the American Wood Council) (AWC) in 1944, under the title *National Design Specification for Stress-Grade Lumber and Its Fastenings*. By 1971, the scope of the Specification had broadened to include additional wood products. In 1977, the title was changed to reflect the new nature of the Specification, and the content was rearranged to simplify its use. The 1991 edition was reorganized in an easier to use "equation format", and many sections were rewritten to provide greater clarity.

In 1992, the American Forest & Paper Association (AF&PA) – formerly the National Forest Products Association – was accredited as a canvass sponsor by the American National Standards Institute (ANSI). The Specification subsequently gained approval as an American National Standard designated ANSI/NF$_{o}$PA NDS-1991 with an approval date of October 16, 1992.

In 2010, AWC was separately incorporated, rechartered, and accredited by ANSI as a standards developing organization. The current edition of the Standard is designated ANSI/AWC NDS-2018 with an approval date of November 16, 2017.

In developing the provisions of this Specification, the most reliable data available from laboratory tests and experience with structures in service have been carefully analyzed and evaluated for the purpose of providing, in convenient form, a national standard of practice.

It is intended that this Specification be used in conjunction with competent engineering design, accurate fabrication, and adequate supervision of construction. Particular attention is directed to Section 2.1.2, relating to the designer's responsibility to make adjustments for particular end uses of structures.

Since the first edition of the *NDS* in 1944, the Association's Technical Advisory Committee has continued to study and evaluate new data and developments in wood design. Subsequent editions of the Specification have included appropriate revisions to provide for use of such new information. This edition incorporates numerous changes considered by AWC's ANSI-accredited Wood Design Standards Committee. The contributions of members of this Committee to improvement of the Specification as a national design standard for wood construction are especially recognized.

Acknowledgement is also made to the Forest Products Laboratory, U.S. Department of Agriculture, for data and publications generously made available, and to the engineers, scientists, and other users who have suggested changes in the content of the Specification. AWC invites and welcomes comments, inquiries, suggestions, and new data relative to the provisions of this document.

It is intended that this document be used in conjunction with competent engineering design, accurate fabrication, and adequate supervision of construction. AWC does not assume any responsibility for errors or omissions in the document, nor for engineering designs, plans, or construction prepared from it.

Those using this standard assume all liability arising from its use. The design of engineered structures is within the scope of expertise of licensed engineers, architects, or other licensed professionals for applications to a particular structure.

American Wood Council

TABLE OF CONTENTS FOR THE NDS

TABLE OF CONTENTS FOR THE NDS COMMENTARY

LIST OF TABLES FOR THE NDS

Contents

LIST OF TABLES FOR THE NDS COMMENTARY

LIST OF FIGURES FOR THE NDS

LIST OF FIGURES FOR THE NDS COMMENTARY

GENERAL REQUIREMENTS FOR STRUCTURAL DESIGN

1.1 Scope

1.1.1 Practice Defined

1.1.1.1 This Specification defines the methods to be followed in structural design with the following wood products:

- visually graded lumber
- mechanically graded lumber
- structural glued laminated timber
- timber piles
- timber poles
- prefabricated wood I-joists
- structural composite lumber
- wood structural panels
- cross-laminated timber

It also defines the practice to be followed in the design and fabrication of single and multiple fastener connections using the fasteners described herein.

1.1.1.2 Structural assemblies utilizing panel products shall be designed in accordance with principles of engineering mechanics (see References 32, 33, 34, and 53 for design provisions for commonly used panel products).

1.1.1.3 Structural assemblies utilizing metal connector plates shall be designed in accordance with accepted engineering practice (see Reference 9).

1.1.1.4 Shear walls and diaphragms shall be designed in accordance with the *Special Design Provisions for Wind and Seismic* (see Reference 56).

1.1.1.5 This Specification is not intended to preclude the use of materials, assemblies, structures or designs not meeting the criteria herein, where it is demonstrated by analysis based on recognized theory, full-scale or prototype loading tests, studies of model analogues or extensive experience in use that the material, assembly, structure or design will perform satisfactorily in its intended end use.

1.1.2 Competent Supervision

The reference design values, design value adjustments, and structural design provisions in this Specification are for designs made and carried out under competent supervision.

1.2 General Requirements

1.2.1 Conformance with Standards

The quality of wood products and fasteners, and the design of load-supporting members and connections, shall conform to the standards specified herein.

1.2.2 Framing and Bracing

All members shall be so framed, anchored, tied, and braced that they have the required strength and rigidity. Adequate bracing and bridging to resist wind and other lateral forces shall be provided.

1.3 Standard as a Whole

The various Chapters, Sections, Subsections and Articles of this Specification are interdependent and, except as otherwise provided, the pertinent provisions of each Chapter, Section, Subsection, and Article shall apply to every other Chapter, Section, Subsection, and Article.

1.4 Design Procedures

This Specification provides requirements for the design of wood products specified herein by the following methods:

(a) Allowable Stress Design (ASD)

(b) Load and Resistance Factor Design (LRFD)

Designs shall be made according to the provisions for Allowable Stress Design (ASD) or Load and Resistance Factor Design (LRFD).

1.4.1 Loading Assumptions

Wood buildings or other wood structures, and their structural members, shall be designed and constructed to safely support all anticipated loads. This Specification is predicated on the principle that the loading assumed in the design represents actual conditions.

1.4.2 Governed by Codes

Minimum design loads shall be in accordance with the building code under which the structure is designed, or where applicable, other recognized minimum design load standards.

1.4.3 Loads Included

Design loads include any or all of the following loads or forces: dead, live, snow, wind, earthquake, erection, and other static and dynamic forces.

1.4.4 Load Combinations

Combinations of design loads and forces, and load combination factors, shall be in accordance with the building code under which the structure is designed, or where applicable, other recognized minimum design load standards (see Reference 5 for additional information). The governing building code shall be permitted to be consulted for load combination factors. Load combinations and associated time effect factors, λ, for use in LRFD are provided in Appendix N.

1.5 Specifications and Plans

1.5.1 Sizes

The plans or specifications, or both, shall indicate whether wood products sizes are stated in terms of standard nominal, standard net or special sizes, as specified for the respective wood products in Chapters 4, 5, 6, 7, 8, 9 and 10.

1.6 Notation

Except where otherwise noted, the symbols used in this Specification have the following meanings:

A = area of cross section, in.^{2}

$A_{critical}$ = minimum shear area for any fastener in a row, in.^{2}

A_{eff} = effective cross-sectional area of a cross-laminated timber section, in.^{2}/ft of panel width

$A_{group-net}$ = critical group net section area between first and last row of fasteners, in.^{2}

A_m = gross cross-sectional area of main member(s), in.^{2}

A_n = cross-sectional area of notched member, in.^{2}

A_{net} = net section area, in.^{2}

$A_{parallel}$ = area of cross section of cross-laminated timber layers with fibers parallel to the load direction, in.^{2}/ft of panel width

A_s = sum of gross cross-sectional areas of side member(s), in.^{2}

C_D = load duration factor

C_F = size factor for sawn lumber

C_I = stress interaction factor for tapered glued laminated timbers

C_L = beam stability factor

C_M = wet service factor

C_P = column stability factor

C_T = buckling stiffness factor for dimension lumber

C_V = volume factor for structural glued laminated timber or structural composite lumber

C_b = bearing area factor

C_c = curvature factor for structural glued laminated timber

C_{cs} = critical section factor for round timber piles

C_{ct} = condition treatment factor for timber poles and piles

C_d = penetration depth factor for connections

C_{di} = diaphragm factor for nailed connections

C_{dt} = empirical constant derived from relationship of equations for deflection of tapered straight beams and prismatic beams

C_{eg} = end grain factor for connections

C_{fu} = flat use factor

C_g = group action factor for connections

C_i = incising factor for dimension lumber

C_{ls} = load sharing factor for timber piles

C_r = repetitive member factor for dimension lumber, prefabricated wood I-joists, and structural composite lumber

C_{rs} = empirical load-shape radial stress reduction factor for double-tapered curved structural glued laminated timber bending members

C_s = wood structural panel size factor

C_{st} = metal side plate factor for 4" shear plate connections

C_t = temperature factor

C_{tn} = toe-nail factor for nailed connections

C_{vr} = shear reduction factor for structural glued laminated timber

C_y = tapered structural glued laminated timber beam deflection factor

C_Δ = geometry factor for connections

COV_E = coefficient of variation for modulus of elasticity

D = dowel-type fastener diameter, in.

D_H = fastener head diameter, in.

D_r = dowel-type fastener root diameter, in.

E = length of tapered tip of a driven fastener, in.

E, E' = reference and adjusted modulus of elasticity, psi

E_{axial} = modulus of elasticity of structural glued laminated timber for extensional deformations, psi

E_{min}, E_{min}' = reference and adjusted modulus of elasticity for beam stability and column stability calculations, psi

$(EI)_{min}$, $(EI)_{min}'$ = reference and adjusted EI for beam stability and column stability calculations, psi

$(EI)_{app}$, $(EI)_{app}'$ = reference and adjusted apparent bending stiffness of cross-laminated timber including shear deflection, lbs-in.²/ft of panel width

$(EI)_{app\text{-}min}$, $(EI)_{app\text{-}min}'$ = reference and adjusted apparent bending stiffness of cross-laminated timber for panel buckling stability calculations, lbs-in.²/ft of panel width

EI_{eff} = effective bending stiffness of the CLT section, lbs-in.²/ft of panel width

E_m = modulus of elasticity of main member, psi

E_s = modulus of elasticity of side member, psi

E_x = modulus of elasticity of structural glued laminated timber for deflections due to bending about the x-x axis, psi

$E_{x\ min}$ = modulus of elasticity of structural glued laminated timber for beam and column stability calculations for buckling about the x-x axis, psi

E_y = modulus of elasticity of structural glued laminated timber for deflections due to bending about the y-y axis, psi

$E_{y\ min}$ = modulus of elasticity of structural glued laminated timber for beam and column stability calculations for buckling about the y-y axis, psi

F_b, F_b' = reference and adjusted bending design value, psi

F_b^* = reference bending design value multiplied by all applicable adjustment factors except C_L, psi

F_b^{**} = reference bending design value multiplied by all applicable adjustment factors except C_V, psi

F_{b1}' = adjusted edgewise bending design value, psi

F_{b2}' = adjusted flatwise bending design value, psi

F_{bE} = critical buckling design value for bending members, psi

F_{bx}^+ = reference bending design value for positive bending of structural glued laminated timbers, psi

F_{bx}^- = reference bending design value for negative bending of structural glued laminated timbers, psi

F_{by} = reference bending design value of structural glued laminated timbers bent about the y-y axis, psi

F_c, F_c' = reference and adjusted compression design value parallel to grain, psi

$F_c{}^*$ = reference compression design value parallel to grain multiplied by all applicable adjustment factors except C_p, psi

F_{cE} = critical buckling design value for compression members, psi

F_{cE1}, F_{cE2} = critical buckling design value for compression member in planes of lateral support, psi

$F_{c\perp}$, $F_{c\perp}'$ = reference and adjusted compression design value perpendicular to grain, psi

$F_{c\perp x}$ = reference compression design value for bearing loads on the wide face of the laminations of structural glued laminated timber, psi

$F_{c\perp y}$ = reference compression design value for bearing loads on the narrow edges of the laminations of structural glued laminated timber, psi

F_e = dowel bearing strength, psi

F_{em} = dowel bearing strength of main member, psi

F_{es} = dowel bearing strength of side member, psi

$F_{e\parallel}$ = dowel bearing strength parallel to grain, psi

$F_{e\perp}$ = dowel bearing strength perpendicular to grain, psi

$F_{e\theta}$ = dowel bearing strength at an angle to grain, psi

F_{rc} = reference radial compression design value for curved structural glued laminated timber members, psi

F_{rt} F_{rt}' = reference and adjusted radial tension design value perpendicular to grain for structural glued laminated timber, psi

F_s, F_s' = reference and adjusted shear in the plane (rolling shear) design value for wood structural panels and cross-laminated timber, psi

F_t, F_t' = reference and adjusted tension design value parallel to grain, psi

F_v, F_v' = reference and adjusted shear design value parallel to grain (horizontal shear), psi

F_{vx} = reference shear design value for structural glued laminated timber members with loads causing bending about the x-x axis, psi

F_{vy} = reference shear design value for structural glued laminated timber members with loads causing bending about the y-y axis, psi

F_{yb} = dowel bending yield strength of fastener, psi

F_θ' = adjusted bearing design value at an angle to grain, psi

G = specific gravity

G_v = reference modulus of rigidity for wood structural panels, psi

GA_{eff} = effective shear stiffness of the CLT section, lbs/ft of panel width

I = moment of inertia, in.^{4}

I_{eff} = effective moment of inertia of a cross-laminated timber section, in.^{4}/ft of panel width

$(Ib/Q)_{eff}$ = effective panel cross sectional shear constant of cross-laminated timber, lbs/ft of panel width

K, K' = reference and adjusted shear stiffness coefficient for prefabricated wood I-joists

K_D = diameter coefficient for dowel-type fastener connections with $D < 0.25$ in.

K_F = format conversion factor

K_M = moisture content coefficient for sawn lumber truss compression chords

K_T = truss compression chord coefficient for sawn lumber

K_{bE} = Euler buckling coefficient for beams

K_{cE} = Euler buckling coefficient for columns

K_{cr} = time dependent deformation (creep) factor

K_e = buckling length coefficient for compression members

K_f = column stability coefficient for bolted and nailed built-up columns

K_{rs} = empirical radial stress factor for double-tapered curved structural glued laminated timber bending members

K_s = shear deformation adjustment factor for cross-laminated timber

K_t = temperature coefficient

K_x = spaced column fixity coefficient

K_θ = angle to grain coefficient for dowel-type fastener connections with $D \geq 0.25$ in.

K_ϕ = empirical bending stress shape factor for double-tapered curved structural glued laminated timber

L = span length of bending member, ft

L = distance between points of lateral support of compression member, ft

L_c = length from tip of pile to critical section, ft

M = maximum bending moment, in.-lbs

M_r, M_r' = reference and adjusted design moment, in.-lbs

N, N' = reference and adjusted lateral design value at an angle to grain for a single split ring connector unit or shear plate connector unit, lbs

P = total concentrated load or total axial load, lbs

P, P' = reference and adjusted lateral design value parallel to grain for a single split ring connector unit or shear plate connector unit, lbs

P_r = parallel to grain reference timber rivet capacity, lbs

P_w = parallel to grain reference wood capacity for timber rivets, lbs

Q = statical moment of an area about the neutral axis, in.^{3}

Q, Q' = reference and adjusted lateral design value perpendicular to grain for a single split ring connector unit or shear plate connector unit, lbs

Q_r = perpendicular to grain reference timber rivet capacity, lbs

Q_w = perpendicular to grain reference wood capacity for timber rivets, lbs

R = radius of curvature of inside face of structural glued laminated timber member, in.

R_B = slenderness ratio of bending member

R_d = reduction term for dowel-type fastener connections

R_m = radius of curvature at center line of structural glued laminated timber member, in

R_r, R_r' = reference and adjusted design reaction, lbs

S = section modulus, in.^{3}

S_{eff} = effective section modulus for cross-laminated timber, in^3/ft of panel width

T = temperature, °F

V = shear force, lbs

V_r, V_r' = reference and adjusted design shear, lbs

W, W' = reference and adjusted withdrawal design value for fastener, lbs per inch of penetration

W_H, W_H' = reference and adjusted pull-through design value, lbs

Z, Z' = reference and adjusted lateral design value for a single fastener connection, lbs

Z_{GT}' = adjusted group tear-out capacity of a group of fasteners, lbs

Z_{NT}' = adjusted tension capacity of net section area, lbs

Z_{RT}' = adjusted row tear-out capacity of multiple rows of fasteners, lbs

Z_{RTi}' = adjusted row tear-out capacity of a row of fasteners, lbs

$Z_{||}$ = reference lateral design value for a single dowel-type fastener connection with all wood members loaded parallel to grain, lbs

$Z_{m\perp}$ = reference lateral design value for a single dowel-type fastener wood-to-wood connection with main member loaded perpendicular to grain and side member loaded parallel to grain, lbs

$Z_{s\perp}$ = reference lateral design value for a single dowel-type fastener wood-to-wood connection with main member loaded parallel to grain and side member loaded perpendicular to grain, lbs

$Z_\perp$ = reference lateral design value for a single dowel-type fastener wood-to-wood, wood-to-metal, or wood-to-concrete connection with wood member(s) loaded perpendicular to grain, lbs

Z_α' = adjusted design value for dowel-type fasteners subjected to combined lateral and withdrawal loading, lbs

a = support condition factor for tapered columns

a_{char} = char depth, in

a_{eff} = effective char depth, in.

a_p = minimum end distance load parallel to grain for timber rivet joints, in.

a_q = minimum end distance load perpendicular to grain for timber rivet joints, in.

b = breadth (thickness) of rectangular bending member, in.

c = distance from neutral axis to extreme fiber, in.

d = depth (width) of bending member, in.

d = least dimension of rectangular compression member, in.

d = pennyweight of nail or spike

d = representative dimension for tapered column, in.

d_c = depth at peaked section of double-tapered curved structural glued laminated timber bending member, in.

d_e = effective depth of member at a connection, in.

d_e = depth of double-tapered curved structural glued laminated timber bending member at ends, in.

d_e = depth at the small end of a tapered straight structural glued laminated timber bending member, in.

d_{equiv} = depth of an equivalent prismatic structural glued laminated timber member, in.

d_{max} = the maximum dimension for that face of a tapered column, in.

d_{min} = the minimum dimension for that face of a tapered column, in.

d_n = depth of member remaining at a notch measured perpendicular to the length of the member, in.

d_y = depth of structural glued laminated timber parallel to the wide face of the laminations when loaded in bending about the y-y axis, in.

d_1, d_2 = cross-sectional dimensions of rectangular compression member in planes of lateral support, in.

e = eccentricity, in.

e = the distance the notch extends from the inner edge of the support, in.

e_p = minimum edge distance unloaded edge for timber rivet joints, in.

e_q = minimum edge distance loaded edge for timber rivet joints, in.

f_b = actual bending stress, psi

f_{b1} = actual edgewise bending stress, psi

f_{b2} = actual flatwise bending stress, psi

f_c = actual compression stress parallel to grain, psi

f_c' = concrete compressive strength, psi

$f_{c\perp}$ = actual compression stress perpendicular to grain, psi

f_r = actual radial stress in curved bending member, psi

f_t = actual tension stress parallel to grain, psi

f_v = actual shear stress parallel to grain, psi

g = gauge of screw

h = vertical distance from the end of the double-tapered curved structural glued laminated timber beam to mid-span, in.

h_a = vertical distance from the top of the double-tapered curved structural glued laminated timber supports to the beam apex, in.

h_{lam} = lamination thickness (in.) for cross-laminated timber

ℓ = span length of bending member, in.

ℓ = distance between points of lateral support of compression member, in.

ℓ_b = bearing length, in.

ℓ_c = clear span, in.

ℓ_c = length between tangent points for double-tapered curved structural glued laminated timber members, in.

ℓ_e = effective span length of bending member, in.

ℓ_e = effective length of compression member, in.

ℓ_{e1}, ℓ_{e2} = effective length of compression member in planes of lateral support, in.

ℓ_e/d = slenderness ratio of compression member

ℓ_m = length of dowel bearing in main member, in.

ℓ_n = length of notch, in.

ℓ_s = length of dowel bearing in side member, in.

ℓ_u = laterally unsupported span length of bending member, in.

ℓ_1, ℓ_2 = distances between points of lateral support of compression member in planes 1 and 2, in.

ℓ_3 = distance from center of spacer block to centroid of group of split ring or shear plate connectors in end block for a spaced column, in.

m.c. = moisture content based on oven-dry weight of wood, %

n = number of fasteners in a row

n_{lam} = number of laminations charred (rounded to lowest integer) for cross-laminated timber

n_R = number of rivet rows

n_c = number of rivets per row

n_i = number of fasteners in a row

n_{row} = number of rows of fasteners

p = length of fastener penetration into wood member, in.

p_{min} = minimum length of fastener penetration into wood member, in.

p_t = length of fastener penetration into wood member for withdrawal calculations, in.

r = radius of gyration, in.

s = center-to-center spacing between adjacent fasteners in a row, in.

$s_{critical}$ = minimum spacing taken as the lesser of the end distance or the spacing between fasteners in a row, in.

s_p = spacing between rivets parallel to grain, in.

s_q = spacing between rivets perpendicular to grain, in.

t = thickness, in.

t = exposure time, hrs.

t_{gi} = time for char front to reach glued interface (hr.) for cross-laminated timber

t_m = thickness of main member, in.

t_{ns} = net side member thickness, in.

t_s = thickness of side member, in.

t_v = thickness for through-the-thickness shear of cross-laminated timber, in.

x = distance from beam support face to load, in.

Δ_H = horizontal deflection at supports of symmetrical double-tapered curved structural glued laminated timber members, in.

Δ_{LT} = immediate deflection due to the long-term component of the design load, in.

Δ_{ST} = deflection due to the short-term or normal component of the design load, in.

Δ_T = total deflection from long-term and short-term loading, in.

Δ_c = vertical deflection at mid-span of double-tapered curved structural glued laminated timber members, in.

α = angle between the wood surface and the direction of applied load for dowel-type fasteners subjected to combined lateral and withdrawal loading, degrees

β_t = non-linear char rate (in./hr.$^{0.813}$) adjusted for exposure time, t

β_n = nominal char rate (in./hr.), linear char rate based on 1-hour exposure

γ = load/slip modulus for a connection, lbs/in.

λ = time effect factor

θ = angle of taper on the compression or tension face of structural glued laminated timber members, degrees

θ = angle between the direction of load and the direction of grain (longitudinal axis of member) for split ring or shear plate connector design, degrees

ϕ = resistance factor

ϕ_B = angle of soffit slope at the ends of double-tapered curved structural glued laminated timber member, degrees

ϕ_T = angle of roof slope of double-tapered curved structural glued laminated timber member, degrees

ω = uniformly distributed load, lbs/in.

DESIGN VALUES FOR STRUCTURAL MEMBERS

AMERICAN WOOD COUNCIL

2.1 General

2.1.1 General Requirement

Each wood structural member or connection shall be of sufficient size and capacity to carry the applied loads without exceeding the adjusted design values specified herein.

2.1.1.1 For ASD, calculation of adjusted design values shall be determined using applicable ASD adjustment factors specified herein.

2.1.1.2 For LRFD, calculation of adjusted design values shall be determined using applicable LRFD adjustment factors specified herein.

2.1.2 Responsibility of Designer to Adjust for Conditions of Use

Adjusted design values for wood members and connections in particular end uses, shall be appropriate for the conditions under which the wood products are used, taking into account conditions such as the differences in wood strength properties with different moisture contents, load durations, and types of treatment. Common end use conditions are addressed in this Specification. It shall be the final responsibility of the designer to relate design assumptions with design values, and to make design value adjustments appropriate to the end use conditions.

2.2 Reference Design Values

Reference design values and design value adjustments for wood products in 1.1.1.1 are based on methods specified in each of the wood product chapters. Chapters 4 through 10 contain design provisions for sawn lumber, glued laminated timber, poles and piles, prefabricated wood I-joists, structural composite lumber, wood structural panels, and cross-laminated timber, respectively. Chapters 11 through 14 contain design provisions for connections. Reference design values are for normal load duration under the moisture service conditions specified.

2.3 Adjustment of Reference Design Values

2.3.1 Applicability of Adjustment Factors

Reference design values shall be multiplied by all applicable adjustment factors to determine adjusted design values. The applicability of adjustment factors to sawn lumber, structural glued laminated timber, poles and piles, prefabricated wood I-joists, structural composite lumber, wood structural panels, cross-laminated timber, and connection design values is defined in 4.3, 5.3, 6.3, 7.3, 8.3, 9.3, 10.3, and 11.3, respectively.

2.3.2 Load Duration Factor, C_D (ASD Only)

2.3.2.1 Wood has the property of carrying substantially greater maximum loads for short durations than for long durations of loading. Reference design values apply to normal load duration. Normal load duration represents a load that fully stresses a member to its allowable design value by the application of the full design load for a cumulative duration of approximately ten years. When the cumulative duration of the full maximum load does not exceed the specified time period, all reference design values except modulus of elasticity, E, modulus of elasticity for beam and column stability, E_{min}, and compression perpendicular to grain, $F_{c\perp}$, based on a deformation limit (see 4.2.6) shall be multiplied by the appropriate load duration factor, C_D, from Table 2.3.2 or Figure B1 (see Appendix B) to take into account the change in strength of wood with changes in load duration.

2.3.2.2 The load duration factor, C_D, for the shortest duration load in a combination of loads shall apply for that load combination. All applicable load combinations shall be evaluated to determine the critical load combination. Design of structural members and connections shall be based on the critical load combination (see Appendix B.2).

2.3.2.3 The load duration factors, C_D, in Table 2.3.2 and Appendix B are independent of load combination factors, and both shall be permitted to be used in design calculations (see 1.4.4 and Appendix B.4).

Table 2.3.2 Frequently Used Load Duration Factors, C_D[1]

Load Duration	C_D	Typical Design Loads
Permanent	0.9	Dead Load
Ten years	1.0	Occupancy Live Load
Two months	1.15	Snow Load
Seven days	1.25	Construction Load
Ten minutes	1.6	Wind/Earthquake Load
Impact[2]	2.0	Impact Load

1. Load duration factors shall not apply to reference modulus of elasticity, E, reference modulus of elasticity for beam and column stability, E_{min}, nor to reference compression perpendicular to grain design values, $F_{c\perp}$, based on a deformation limit.
2. Load duration factors greater than 1.6 shall not be used in the design of structural members pressure-treated with water-borne preservatives (see Reference 30), or fire retardant chemicals. Load duration factors greater than 1.6 shall not be used in the design of connections or wood structural panels.

2.3.3 Temperature Factor, C_t

Reference design values shall be multiplied by the temperature factors, C_t, in Table 2.3.3 for structural members that will experience sustained exposure to elevated temperatures up to 150°F (see Appendix C).

2.3.4 Fire Retardant Treatment

The effects of fire retardant chemical treatment on strength shall be accounted for in the design. Adjusted design values, including adjusted connection design values, for lumber and structural glued laminated timber pressure-treated with fire retardant chemicals shall be obtained from the company providing the treatment and redrying service. Load duration factors greater than 1.6 shall not apply to structural members pressure-treated with fire retardant chemicals (see Table 2.3.2).

2.3.5 Format Conversion Factor, K_F (LRFD Only)

For LRFD, reference design values shall be multiplied by the format conversion factor, K_F, specified in Table 2.3.5. The format conversion factor, K_F, shall not apply for designs in accordance with ASD methods specified herein.

2.3.6 Resistance Factor, ϕ (LRFD Only)

For LRFD, reference design values shall be multiplied by the resistance factor, ϕ, specified in Table 2.3.6. The resistance factor, ϕ, shall not apply for designs in accordance with ASD methods specified herein.

2.3.7 Time Effect Factor, λ (LRFD Only)

For LRFD, reference design values shall be multiplied by the time effect factor, λ, specified in Appendix N.3.3. The time effect factor, λ, shall not apply for designs in accordance with ASD methods specified herein.

Table 2.3.3 Temperature Factor, C_t

Reference Design Values	In-Service Moisture Conditions[1]	C_t		
		T≤100°F	100°F<T≤125°F	125°F<T≤150°F
F_t, E, E_{min}	Wet or Dry	1.0	0.9	0.9
F_b, F_v, F_c, and $F_{c\perp}$	Dry	1.0	0.8	0.7
	Wet	1.0	0.7	0.5

1. Wet and dry service conditions for sawn lumber, structural glued laminated timber, prefabricated wood I-joists, structural composite lumber, wood structural panels and cross-laminated timber are specified in 4.1.4, 5.1.4, 7.1.4, 8.1.4, 9.3.3, and 10.1.5 respectively.

Table 2.3.5 Format Conversion Factor, K_F (LRFD Only)

Application	Property	K_F
Member	F_b	2.54
	F_t	2.70
	F_v, F_{rt}, F_s	2.88
	F_c	2.40
	$F_{c\perp}$	1.67
	E_{min}	1.76
All Connections	(all design values)	3.32

Table 2.3.6 Resistance Factor, ϕ (LRFD Only)

Application	Property	Symbol	Value
Member	F_b	ϕ_b	0.85
	F_t	ϕ_t	0.80
	F_v, F_{rt}, F_s	ϕ_v	0.75
	F_c, $F_{c\perp}$	ϕ_c	0.90
	E_{min}	ϕ_s	0.85
All Connections	(all design values)	ϕ_z	0.65

3

DESIGN PROVISIONS AND EQUATIONS

AMERICAN WOOD COUNCIL

3.1 General

3.1.1 Scope

Chapter 3 establishes general design provisions that apply to all wood structural members and connections covered under this Specification. Each wood structural member or connection shall be of sufficient size and capacity to carry the applied loads without exceeding the adjusted design values specified herein. Reference design values and specific design provisions applicable to particular wood products or connections are given in other Chapters of this Specification.

3.1.2 Net Section Area

3.1.2.1 The net section area is obtained by deducting from the gross section area the projected area of all material removed by boring, grooving, dapping, notching, or other means. The net section area shall be used in calculating the load carrying capacity of a member, except as specified in 3.6.3 for columns. The effects of any eccentricity of loads applied to the member at the critical net section shall be taken into account.

3.1.2.2 For parallel to grain loading with staggered bolts, drift bolts, drift pins, or lag screws, adjacent fasteners shall be considered as occurring at the same critical section if the parallel to grain spacing between fasteners in adjacent rows is less than four fastener diameters (see Figure 3A).

Figure 3A Spacing of Staggered Fasteners

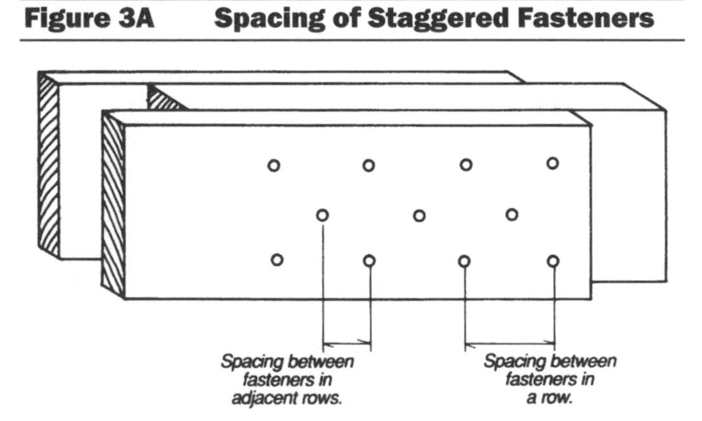

3.1.2.3 The net section area at a split ring or shear plate connection shall be determined by deducting from the gross section area the projected areas of the bolt hole and the split ring or shear plate groove within the member (see Figure 3B and Appendix K). Where split ring or shear plate connectors are staggered, adjacent connectors shall be considered as occurring at the same critical section if the parallel to grain spacing between connectors in adjacent rows is less than or equal to one connector diameter (see Figure 3A).

Figure 3B Net Cross Section at a Split Ring or Shear Plate Connection

grooves for split ring or shear plate connector
bolt hole

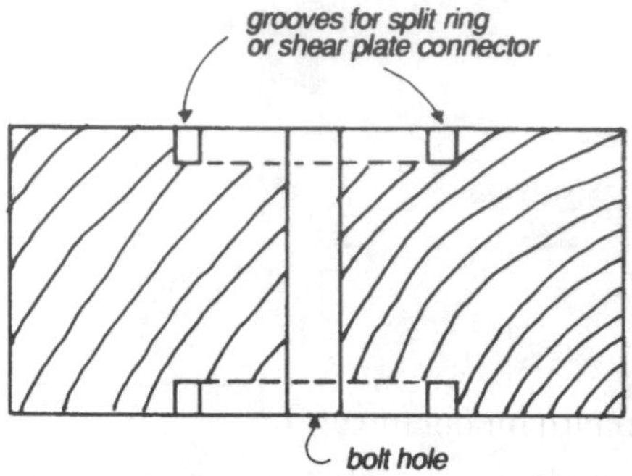

3.1.3 Connections

Structural members and fasteners shall be arranged symmetrically at connections, unless the bending moment induced by an unsymmetrical arrangement (such as lapped joints) has been accounted for in the design. Connections shall be designed and fabricated to insure that each individual member carries its proportional stress.

3.1.4 Time Dependent Deformations

Where members of structural frames are composed of two or more layers or sections, the effect of time dependent deformations shall be accounted for in the design (see 3.5.2 and Appendix F).

3.1.5 Composite Construction

Composite constructions, such as wood-concrete, wood-steel, and wood-wood composites, shall be designed in accordance with principles of engineering mechanics using the adjusted design values for structural members and connections specified herein.

3.2 Bending Members – General

3.2.1 Span of Bending Members

For simple, continuous and cantilevered bending members, the span shall be taken as the distance from face to face of supports, plus ½ the required bearing length at each end.

3.2.2 Lateral Distribution of Concentrated Load

Lateral distribution of concentrated loads from a critically loaded bending member to adjacent parallel bending members by flooring or other cross members shall be permitted to be calculated when determining design bending moment and vertical shear force (see 15.1).

3.2.3 Notches

3.2.3.1 Bending members shall not be notched except as permitted by 4.4.3, 5.4.5, 7.4.4, and 8.4.1. A gradual taper cut from the reduced depth of the member to the full depth of the member in lieu of a square-cornered notch reduces stress concentrations.

3.2.3.2 The stiffness of a bending member, as determined from its cross section, is practically unaffected by a notch with the following dimensions:

notch depth $\leq$ (1/6) (beam depth)
notch length $\leq$ (1/3) (beam depth)

3.2.3.3 See 3.4.3 for effect of notches on shear strength.

3.3 Bending Members – Flexure

3.3.1 Strength in Bending

The actual bending stress or moment shall not exceed the adjusted bending design value.

3.3.2 Flexural Design Equations

3.3.2.1 The actual bending stress induced by a bending moment, M, is calculated as follows:

$$f_b = \frac{Mc}{I} = \frac{M}{S} \quad (3.3\text{-}1)$$

For a rectangular bending member of breadth, b, and depth, d, this becomes:

$$f_b = \frac{M}{S} = \frac{6M}{bd^2} \quad (3.3\text{-}2)$$

3.3.2.2 For solid rectangular bending members with the neutral axis perpendicular to depth at center:

$$I = \frac{bd^3}{12} = \text{moment of inertia, in.}^4 \quad (3.3\text{-}3)$$

$$S = \frac{I}{c} = \frac{bd^2}{6} = \text{section modulus, in.}^3 \quad (3.3\text{-}4)$$

3.3.3 Beam Stability Factor, C_L

3.3.3.1 When the depth of a bending member does not exceed its breadth, $d \leq b$, no lateral support is required and $C_L = 1.0$.

3.3.3.2 When rectangular sawn lumber bending members are laterally supported in accordance with 4.4.1, $C_L = 1.0$.

3.3.3.3 When the compression edge of a bending member is supported throughout its length to prevent lateral displacement, and the ends at points of bearing have lateral support to prevent rotation, $C_L = 1.0$.

3.3.3.4 Where the depth of a bending member exceeds its breadth, $d > b$, lateral support shall be provided at points of bearing to prevent rotation. When such lateral support is provided at points of bearing, but no additional lateral support is provided throughout the length of the bending member, the unsupported length, ℓ_u, is the distance between such points of end bearing, or the length of a cantilever. When a bending member is provided with lateral support to prevent rotation at intermediate points as well as at the ends, the unsupported length, ℓ_u, is the distance between such points of intermediate lateral support.

3.3.3.5 The effective span length, ℓ_e, for single span or cantilever bending members shall be determined in accordance with Table 3.3.3.

Table 3.3.3 Effective Length, ℓ_e, for Bending Members

Cantilever[1]	where $\ell_u/d < 7$		where $\ell_u/d \geq 7$
Uniformly distributed load	$\ell_e=1.33\ \ell_u$		$\ell_e=0.90\ \ell_u + 3d$
Concentrated load at unsupported end	$\ell_e=1.87\ \ell_u$		$\ell_e=1.44\ \ell_u + 3d$
Single Span Beam[1,2]	where $\ell_u/d < 7$		where $\ell_u/d \geq 7$
Uniformly distributed load	$\ell_e=2.06\ \ell_u$		$\ell_e=1.63\ \ell_u + 3d$
Concentrated load at center with no intermediate lateral support	$\ell_e=1.80\ \ell_u$		$\ell_e=1.37\ \ell_u + 3d$
Concentrated load at center with lateral support at center		$\ell_e=1.11\ \ell_u$	
Two equal concentrated loads at 1/3 points with lateral support at 1/3 points		$\ell_e=1.68\ \ell_u$	
Three equal concentrated loads at 1/4 points with lateral support at 1/4 points		$\ell_e=1.54\ \ell_u$	
Four equal concentrated loads at 1/5 points with lateral support at 1/5 points		$\ell_e=1.68\ \ell_u$	
Five equal concentrated loads at 1/6 points with lateral support at 1/6 points		$\ell_e=1.73\ \ell_u$	
Six equal concentrated loads at 1/7 points with lateral support at 1/7 points		$\ell_e=1.78\ \ell_u$	
Seven or more equal concentrated loads, evenly spaced, with lateral support at points of load application		$\ell_e=1.84\ \ell_u$	
Equal end moments		$\ell_e=1.84\ \ell_u$	

1. For single span or cantilever bending members with loading conditions not specified in Table 3.3.3:
   - $\ell_e = 2.06\ \ell_u$ where $\ell_u/d < 7$
   - $\ell_e = 1.63\ \ell_u + 3d$ where $7 \leq \ell_u/d \leq 14.3$
   - $\ell_e = 1.84\ \ell_u$ where $\ell_u/d > 14.3$
2. Multiple span applications shall be based on table values or engineering analysis.

3.3.3.6 The slenderness ratio, R_B, for bending members shall be calculated as follows:

$$R_B = \sqrt{\frac{\ell_e d}{b^2}} \quad (3.3\text{-}5)$$

3.3.3.7 The slenderness ratio for bending members, R_B, shall not exceed 50.

3.3.3.8 The beam stability factor shall be calculated as follows:

$$C_L = \frac{1+\left(F_{bE}/F_b^*\right)}{1.9} - \sqrt{\left[\frac{1+\left(F_{bE}/F_b^*\right)}{1.9}\right]^2 - \frac{F_{bE}/F_b^*}{0.95}} \quad (3.3\text{-}6)$$

where:

F_b^* = reference bending design value multiplied by all applicable adjustment factors except C_{fu}, C_V (when $C_V \leq 1.0$), and C_L (see 2.3), psi

$$F_{bE} = \frac{1.20\, E_{min}'}{R_B^{\ 2}}$$

3.3.3.9 See Appendix D for background information concerning beam stability calculations and Appendix F for information concerning coefficient of variation in modulus of elasticity (COV_E).

3.3.3.10 Members subjected to flexure about both principal axes (biaxial bending) shall be designed in accordance with 3.9.2.

3

DESIGN PROVISIONS AND EQUATIONS

3.4 Bending Members – Shear

3.4.1 Strength in Shear Parallel to Grain (Horizontal Shear)

3.4.1.1 The actual shear stress parallel to grain or shear force at any cross section of the bending member shall not exceed the adjusted shear design value. A check of the strength of wood bending members in shear perpendicular to grain is not required.

3.4.1.2 The shear design procedures specified herein for calculating f_v at or near points of vertical support are limited to solid flexural members such as sawn lumber, structural glued laminated timber, structural composite lumber, or mechanically laminated timber beams. Shear design at supports for built-up components containing load-bearing connections at or near points of support, such as between the web and chord of a truss, shall be based on test or other techniques.

3.4.2 Shear Design Equations

The actual shear stress parallel to grain induced in a sawn lumber, structural glued laminated timber, structural composite lumber, or timber pole or pile bending member shall be calculated as follows:

$$f_v = \frac{VQ}{Ib} \quad (3.4\text{-}1)$$

For a rectangular bending member of breadth, b, and depth, d, this becomes:

$$f_v = \frac{3V}{2bd} \quad (3.4\text{-}2)$$

3.4.3 Shear Design

3.4.3.1 When calculating the shear force, V, in bending members:

(a) For beams supported by full bearing on one surface and loads applied to the opposite surface, uniformly distributed loads within a distance from supports equal to the depth of the bending member, d, shall be permitted to be ignored. For beams supported by full bearing on one surface and loads applied to the opposite surface, concentrated loads within a distance, d, from supports shall be permitted to be multiplied by x/d where x is the distance from the beam support face to the load (see Figure 3C).

Figure 3C Shear at Supports

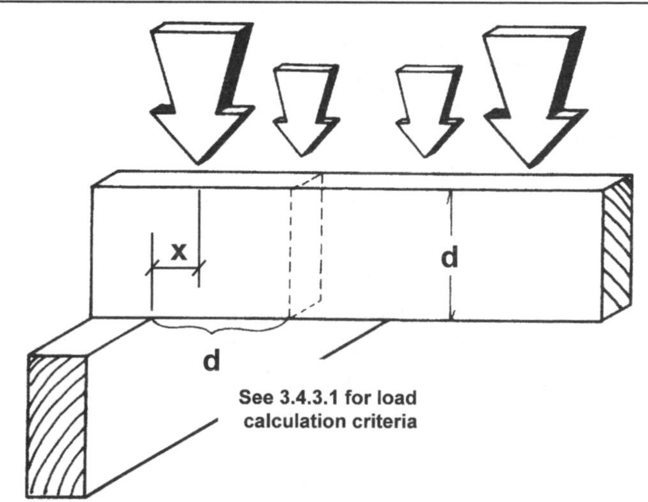

(b) The largest single moving load shall be placed at a distance from the support equal to the depth of the bending member, keeping other loads in their normal relation and neglecting any load within a distance from a support equal to the depth of the bending member. This condition shall be checked at each support.

(c) With two or more moving loads of about equal weight and in proximity, loads shall be placed in the position that produces the highest shear force, V, neglecting any load within a distance from a support equal to the depth of the bending member.

3.4.3.2 For notched bending members, shear force, V, shall be determined by principles of engineering mechanics (except those given in 3.4.3.1).

(a) For bending members with rectangular cross section and notched on the tension face (see 3.2.3), the adjusted design shear, V_r', shall be calculated as follows:

$$V_r' = \left[\frac{2}{3}F_v'bd_n\right]\left[\frac{d_n}{d}\right]^2 \quad (3.4\text{-}3)$$

where:

d = depth of unnotched bending member, in.

d_n = depth of member remaining at a notch measured perpendicular to length of member, in.

F_v' = adjusted shear design value parallel to grain, psi

(b) For bending members with circular cross section and notched on the tension face (see 3.2.3), the adjusted design shear, V_r', shall be calculated as follows:

$$V_r' = \left[\frac{2}{3}F_v'A_n\right]\left[\frac{d_n}{d}\right]^2 \quad (3.4\text{-}4)$$

where:

A_n = cross-sectional area of notched member, in^2

(c) For bending members with other than rectangular or circular cross section and notched on the tension face (see 3.2.3), the adjusted design shear, V_r', shall be based on conventional engineering analysis of stress concentrations at notches.

(d) A gradual change in cross section compared with a square notch decreases the actual shear stress parallel to grain nearly to that computed for an unnotched bending member with a depth of d_n.

(e) When a bending member is notched on the compression face at the end as shown in Figure 3D, the adjusted design shear, V_r', shall be calculated as follows:

$$V_r' = \frac{2}{3}F_v'b\left[d - \left(\frac{d-d_n}{d_n}\right)e\right] \quad (3.4\text{-}5)$$

where:

e = the distance the notch extends from the inner edge of the support and must be less than or equal to the depth remaining at the notch, $e \leq d_n$. If $e > d_n$, d_n shall be used to calculate f_v using Equation 3.4-2, in.

d_n = depth of member remaining at a notch meeting the provisions of 3.2.3, measured perpendicular to length of member. If the end of the beam is beveled, as shown by the dashed line in Figure 3D, d_n is measured from the inner edge of the support, in.

Figure 3D Bending Member End-Notched on Compression Face

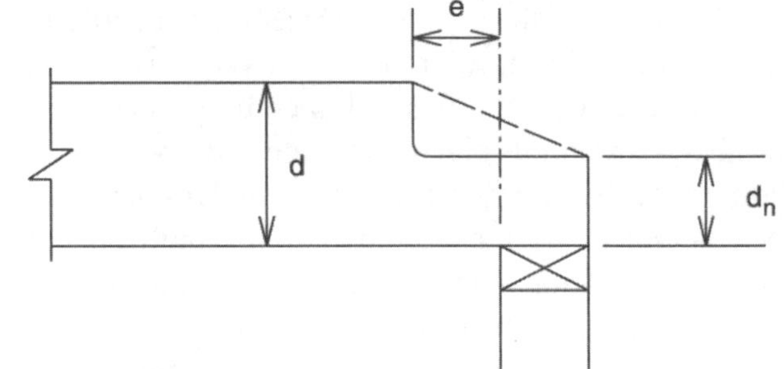

3.4.3.3 When connections in bending members are fastened with split ring connectors, shear plate connectors, bolts, or lag screws (including beams supported by such fasteners or other cases as shown in Figures 3E and 3I) the shear force, V, shall be determined by principles of engineering mechanics (except those given in 3.4.3.1).

(a) Where the connection is less than five times the depth, 5d, of the member from its end, the adjusted design shear, V_r', shall be calculated as follows:

$$V_r' = \left[\frac{2}{3}F_v'bd_e\right]\left[\frac{d_e}{d}\right]^2 \quad (3.4\text{-}6)$$

where:

for split ring or shear plate connections:

d_e = depth of member, less the distance from the unloaded edge of the member to the nearest edge of the nearest split ring or shear plate connector (see Figure 3E), in.

for bolt or lag screw connections:

d_e = depth of member, less the distance from the unloaded edge of the member to the center of the nearest bolt or lag screw (see Figure 3E), in.

(b) Where the connection is at least five times the depth, 5d, of the member from its end, the adjusted design shear, V_r', shall be calculated as follows:

$$V_r' = \frac{2}{3} F_v' b d_e \quad (3.4\text{-}7)$$

(c) Where concealed hangers are used, the adjusted design shear, V_r', shall be calculated based on the provisions in 3.4.3.2 for notched bending members.

Figure 3E Effective Depth, d_e, of Members at Connections

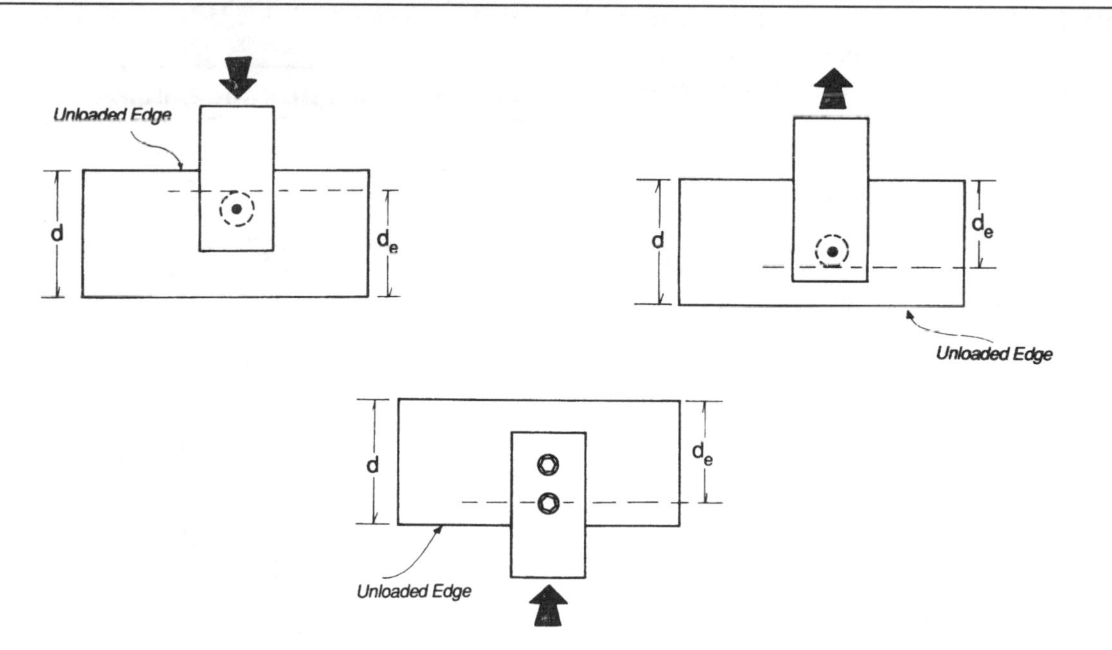

3.5 Bending Members – Deflection

3.5.1 Deflection Calculations

If deflection is a factor in design, it shall be calculated by standard methods of engineering mechanics considering bending deflections and, when applicable, shear deflections. Consideration for shear deflection is required when the reference modulus of elasticity has not been adjusted to include the effects of shear deflection (see Appendix F).

3.5.2 Long-Term Loading

Where total deflection under long-term loading must be limited, increasing member size is one way to provide extra stiffness to allow for this time dependent deformation (see Appendix F). Total deflection, Δ_T, shall be calculated as follows:

$$\Delta_T = K_{cr}\,\Delta_{LT} + \Delta_{ST} \quad (3.5\text{-}1)$$

where:

K_{cr} = time dependent deformation (creep) factor

= 1.5 for seasoned lumber, structural glued laminated timber, prefabricated wood I-joists, or structural composite lumber used in dry service conditions as defined in 4.1.4, 5.1.4, 7.1.4, and 8.1.4, respectively.

= 2.0 for structural glued laminated timber used in wet service conditions as defined in 5.1.4.

= 2.0 for wood structural panels used in dry service conditions as defined in 9.1.4.

= 2.0 for unseasoned lumber or for seasoned lumber used in wet service conditions as defined in 4.1.4.

= 2.0 for cross-laminated timber used in dry service conditions as defined in 10.1.5.

Δ_{LT} = immediate deflection due to the long-term component of the design load, in.

Δ_{ST} = deflection due to the short-term or normal component of the design load, in.

3.6 Compression Members – General

3.6.1 Terminology

For purposes of this Specification, the term "column" refers to all types of compression members, including members forming part of trusses or other structural components.

3.6.2 Column Classifications

3.6.2.1 Simple Solid Wood Columns. Simple columns consist of a single piece or of pieces properly glued together to form a single member (see Figure 3F).

3.6.2.2 Spaced Columns, Connector Joined. Spaced columns are formed of two or more individual members with their longitudinal axes parallel, separated at the ends and middle points of their length by blocking and joined at the ends by split ring or shear plate connectors capable of developing the required shear resistance (see 15.2).

3.6.2.3 Built-Up Columns. Individual laminations of mechanically laminated built-up columns shall be designed in accordance with 3.6.3 and 3.7, except that nailed or bolted built-up columns shall be designed in accordance with 15.3.

3.6.3 Strength in Compression Parallel to Grain

The actual compression stress or force parallel to grain shall not exceed the adjusted compression design value. Calculations of f_c shall be based on the net section area (see 3.1.2) where the reduced section occurs in the critical part of the column length that is most subject to potential buckling. Where the reduced section does not occur in the critical part of the column length that is most subject to potential buckling, calculations of f_c shall be based on gross section area. In addition, f_c based on net section area shall not exceed the reference compression design value parallel to grain multiplied by all applicable adjustment factors except the column stability factor, C_P.

Figure 3F Simple Solid Column

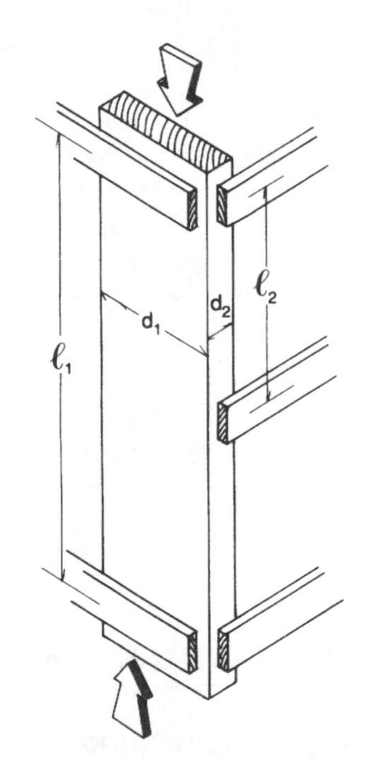

3.6.4 Compression Members Bearing End to End

For end grain bearing of wood on wood, and on metal plates or strips see 3.10.

3.6.5 Eccentric Loading or Combined Stresses

For compression members subject to eccentric loading or combined flexure and axial loading, see 3.9 and 15.4.

3.6.6 Column Bracing

Column bracing shall be installed where necessary to resist wind or other lateral forces (see Appendix A).

3.6.7 Lateral Support of Arches, Studs, and Compression Chords of Trusses

Guidelines for providing lateral support and determining ℓ_e/d in arches, studs, and compression chords of trusses are specified in Appendix A.11.

3.7 Solid Columns

3.7.1 Column Stability Factor, C_P

3.7.1.1 When a compression member is supported throughout its length to prevent lateral displacement in all directions, $C_P = 1.0$.

3.7.1.2 The effective column length, ℓ_e, for a solid column shall be determined in accordance with principles of engineering mechanics. One method for determining effective column length, when end-fixity conditions are known, is to multiply actual column length by the appropriate effective length factor specified in Appendix G, $\ell_e = (K_e)(\ell)$.

3.7.1.3 For solid columns with rectangular cross section, the slenderness ratio, ℓ_e/d, shall be taken as the larger of the ratios ℓ_{e1}/d_1 or ℓ_{e2}/d_2 (see Figure 3F) where each ratio has been adjusted by the appropriate buckling length coefficient, K_e, from Appendix G.

3.7.1.4 The slenderness ratio for solid columns, ℓ_e/d, shall not exceed 50, except that during construction ℓ_e/d shall not exceed 75.

3.7.1.5 The column stability factor shall be calculated as follows:

$$C_P = \frac{1+\left(F_{cE}/F_c^*\right)}{2c} - \sqrt{\left[\frac{1+\left(F_{cE}/F_c^*\right)}{2c}\right]^2 - \frac{F_{cE}/F_c^*}{c}} \quad (3.7\text{-}1)$$

where:

F_c^* = reference compression design value parallel to grain multiplied by all applicable adjustment factors except C_P (see 2.3), psi

$$F_{cE} = \frac{0.822\ E_{min}'}{(\ell_e/d)^2}$$

c = 0.8 for sawn lumber

c = 0.85 for round timber poles and piles

c = 0.9 for structural glued laminated timber, structural composite lumber, and cross-laminated timber

3.7.1.6 For especially severe service conditions and/or extraordinary hazard, use of lower adjusted design values may be necessary. See Appendix H for background information concerning column stability calculations and Appendix F for information concerning coefficient of variation in modulus of elasticity (COV_E).

3.7.2 Tapered Columns

For design of a column with rectangular cross section, tapered at one or both ends, the representative dimension, d, for each face of the column shall be derived as follows:

$$d = d_{min} + (d_{max} - d_{min})\left[a - 0.15\left(1 - \frac{d_{min}}{d_{max}}\right)\right] \quad (3.7\text{-}2)$$

where:

d = representative dimension for tapered column, in.

d_{min} = the minimum dimension for that face of the column, in.

d_{max} = the maximum dimension for that face of the column, in.

<u>Support Conditions</u>

Large end fixed, small end unsupported or simply supported	a = 0.70
Small end fixed, large end unsupported or simply supported	a = 0.30
Both ends simply supported:	
Tapered toward one end	a = 0.50
Tapered toward both ends	a = 0.70

For all other support conditions:

$$d = d_{min} + (d_{max} - d_{min})(1/3) \quad (3.7\text{-}3)$$

Calculations of f_c and C_P shall be based on the representative dimension, d. In addition, f_c at any cross section in the tapered column shall not exceed the reference compression design value parallel to grain multiplied by all applicable adjustment factors except the column stability factor, C_P.

3.7.3 Round Columns

The design of a column of round cross section shall be based on the design calculations for a square column of the same cross-sectional area and having the same degree of taper. Reference design values and special design provisions for round timber poles and piles are provided in Chapter 6.

3.8 Tension Members

3.8.1 Tension Parallel to Grain

The actual tension stress or force parallel to grain shall be based on the net section area (see 3.1.2) and shall not exceed the adjusted tension design value.

3.8.2 Tension Perpendicular to Grain

Designs that induce tension stress perpendicular to grain shall be avoided whenever possible (see References 16 and 19). When tension stress perpendicular to grain cannot be avoided, mechanical reinforcement sufficient to resist all such stresses shall be considered (see References 52 and 53 for additional information).

3.9 Combined Bending and Axial Loading

3.9.1 Bending and Axial Tension

Members subjected to a combination of bending and axial tension (see Figure 3G) shall be so proportioned that:

$$\frac{f_t}{F_t'} + \frac{f_b}{F_b^*} \leq 1.0 \quad (3.9\text{-}1)$$

and

$$\frac{f_b - f_t}{F_b^{**}} \leq 1.0 \quad (3.9\text{-}2)$$

where:

F_b^* = reference bending design value multiplied by all applicable adjustment factors except C_L, psi

F_b^{**} = reference bending design value multiplied by all applicable adjustment factors except C_V, psi

Figure 3G Combined Bending and Axial Tension

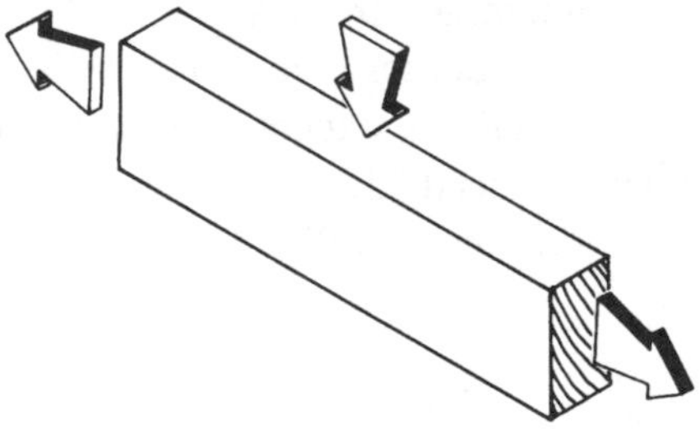

3.9.2 Bending and Axial Compression

Members subjected to a combination of bending about one or both principal axes and axial compression (see Figure 3H) shall be so proportioned that:

$$\left[\frac{f_c}{F_c'}\right]^2 + \frac{f_{b1}}{F_{b1}'\left[1-\left(f_c/F_{cE1}\right)\right]} + \frac{f_{b2}}{F_{b2}'\left[1-\left(f_c/F_{cE2}\right)-\left(f_{b1}/F_{bE}\right)^2\right]} \leq 1.0 \quad (3.9\text{-}3)$$

and

$$\frac{f_c}{F_{cE2}} + \left(\frac{f_{b1}}{F_{bE}}\right)^2 < 1.0 \quad (3.9\text{-}4)$$

where:

$$f_c < F_{cE1} = \frac{0.822\, E_{min}'}{(\ell_{e1}/d_1)^2}$$ for either uniaxial edgewise bending or biaxial bending

and

$$f_c < F_{cE2} = \frac{0.822\, E_{min}'}{(\ell_{e2}/d_2)^2}$$ for uniaxial flatwise bending or biaxial bending

and

$$f_{b1} < F_{bE} = \frac{1.20\, E_{min}'}{(R_B)^2}$$ for biaxial bending

f_{b1} = actual edgewise bending stress (bending load applied to narrow face of member), psi

f_{b2} = actual flatwise bending stress (bending load applied to wide face of member), psi

d_1 = wide face dimension (see Figure 3H), in.

d_2 = narrow face dimension (see Figure 3H), in.

Effective column lengths, ℓ_{e1} and ℓ_{e2}, shall be determined in accordance with 3.7.1.2. F_c', F_{cE1}, and F_{cE2} shall be determined in accordance with 2.3 and 3.7. F_{b1}', F_{b2}', and F_{bE} shall be determined in accordance with 2.3 and 3.3.3.

3.9.3 Eccentric Compression Loading

See 15.4 for members subjected to combined bending and axial compression due to eccentric loading, or eccentric loading in combination with other loads.

Figure 3H Combined Bending and Axial Compression

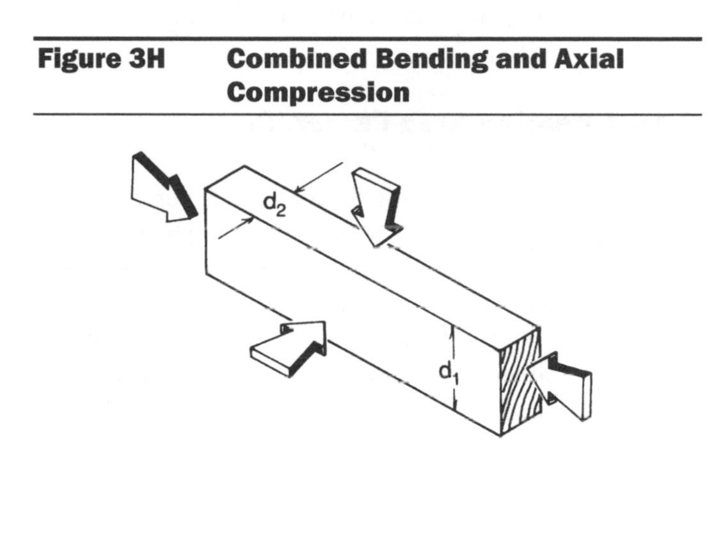

3.10 Design for Bearing

3.10.1 Bearing Parallel to Grain

3.10.1.1 The actual compressive bearing stress parallel to grain shall be based on the net bearing area and shall not exceed the reference compression design value parallel to grain multiplied by all applicable adjustment factors except the column stability factor, C_P.

3.10.1.2 F_c^*, the reference compression design values parallel to grain multiplied by all applicable adjustment factors except the column stability factor, applies to end-to-end bearing of compression members provided there is adequate lateral support and the end cuts are accurately squared and parallel.

3.10.1.3 When $f_c > (0.75)(F_c^*)$ bearing shall be on a metal plate or strap, or on other equivalently durable, rigid, homogeneous material with sufficient stiffness to distribute the applied load. Where a rigid insert is required for end-to-end bearing of compression members, it shall be equivalent to 20-gage metal plate or better, inserted with a snug fit between abutting ends.

3.10.2 Bearing Perpendicular to Grain

The actual compression stress perpendicular to grain shall be based on the net bearing area and shall not exceed the adjusted compression design value perpendicular to grain, $f_{c\perp} \leq F_{c\perp}'$. When calculating bearing area at the ends of bending members, no allowance shall be made for the fact that as the member bends, pressure upon the inner edge of the bearing is greater than at the member end.

3.10.3 Bearing at an Angle to Grain

The adjusted bearing design value at an angle to grain (see Figure 3I and Appendix J) shall be calculated as follows:

$$F_{\theta}' = \frac{F_c^* F_{c\perp}'}{F_c^* \sin^2\theta + F_{c\perp}' \cos^2\theta} \quad (3.10\text{-}1)$$

where:

θ = angle between direction of load and direction of grain (longitudinal axis of member), degrees

3.10.4 Bearing Area Factor, C_b

Reference compression design values perpendicular to grain, $F_{c\perp}$, apply to bearings of any length at the ends of a member, and to all bearings 6" or more in length at any other location. For bearings less than 6" in length and not nearer than 3" to the end of a member, the reference compression design value perpendicular to grain, $F_{c\perp}$, shall be permitted to be multiplied by the following bearing area factor, C_b:

$$C_b = \frac{\ell_b + 0.375}{\ell_b} \quad (3.10\text{-}2)$$

where:

ℓ_b = bearing length measured parallel to grain, in.

Equation 3.10-2 gives the following bearing area factors, C_b, for the indicated bearing length on such small areas as plates and washers:

Table 3.10.4 Bearing Area Factors, C_b

ℓ_b	0.5"	1"	1.5"	2"	3"	4"	6" or more
C_b	1.75	1.38	1.25	1.19	1.13	1.10	1.00

For round bearing areas such as washers, the bearing length, ℓ_b, shall be equal to the diameter.

Figure 3I Bearing at an Angle to Grain

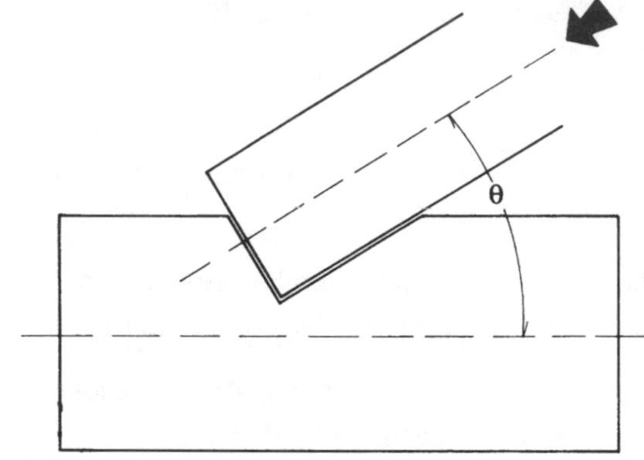

SAWN LUMBER

AMERICAN WOOD COUNCIL

4.1 General

4.1.1 Scope

Chapter 4 applies to engineering design with sawn lumber. Design procedures, reference design values, and other information herein apply only to lumber complying with the requirements specified below.

4.1.2 Identification of Lumber

4.1.2.1 When the reference design values specified herein are used, the lumber, including end-jointed or edge-glued lumber, shall be identified by the grade mark of, or certificate of inspection issued by, a lumber grading or inspection bureau or agency recognized as being competent (see Reference 31). A distinct grade mark of a recognized lumber grading or inspection bureau or agency, indicating that joint integrity is subject to qualification and quality control, shall be applied to glued lumber products.

4.1.2.2 Lumber shall be specified by commercial species and grade names, or by required levels of design values as listed in Tables 4A, 4B, 4C, 4D, 4E, and 4F (published in the Supplement to this Specification).

4.1.3 Definitions

4.1.3.1 Structural sawn lumber consists of lumber classifications known as "Dimension," "Beams and Stringers," "Posts and Timbers," and "Decking," with design values assigned to each grade.

4.1.3.2 "Dimension" refers to lumber from 2" to 4" (nominal) thick, and 2" (nominal) or more in width. Dimension lumber is further classified as Structural Light Framing, Light Framing, Studs, and Joists and Planks (see References 42, 43, 45, 46, 47, and 49 for additional information).

4.1.3.3 "Beams and Stringers" refers to lumber of rectangular cross section, 5" (nominal) or more thick, with width more than 2" greater than thickness, graded with respect to its strength in bending when loaded on the narrow face.

4.1.3.4 "Posts and Timbers" refers to lumber of square or approximately square cross section, 5" x 5" (nominal) and larger, with width not more than 2" greater than thickness, graded primarily for use as posts or columns carrying longitudinal load.

4.1.3.5 "Decking" refers to lumber from 2" to 4" (nominal) thick, tongued and grooved, or grooved for spline on the narrow face, and intended for use as a roof, floor, or wall membrane. Decking is graded for application in the flatwise direction, with the wide face of the decking in contact with the supporting members, as normally installed.

4.1.4 Moisture Service Condition of Lumber

The reference design values for lumber specified herein are applicable to lumber that will be used under dry service conditions such as in most covered structures, where the moisture content in use will be a maximum of 19%, regardless of the moisture content at the time of manufacture. For lumber used under conditions where the moisture content of the wood in service will exceed 19% for an extended period of time, the design values shall be multiplied by the wet service factors, C_M, specified in Tables 4A, 4B, 4C, 4D, 4E, and 4F.

4.1.5 Lumber Sizes

4.1.5.1 Lumber sizes referred to in this Specification are nominal sizes. Computations to determine the required sizes of members shall be based on the net dimensions (actual sizes) and not the nominal sizes. The dressed sizes specified in Reference 31 shall be accepted as the minimum net sizes associated with nominal dimensions (see Table 1A in the Supplement to this Specification).

4.1.5.2 For 4" (nominal) or thinner lumber, the net DRY dressed sizes shall be used in all computations of structural capacity regardless of the moisture content at the time of manufacture or use.

4.1.5.3 For 5" (nominal) and thicker lumber, the net GREEN dressed sizes shall be used in computations of structural capacity regardless of the moisture content at the time of manufacture or use.

4.1.5.4 Where a design is based on rough sizes or special sizes, the applicable moisture content and size used in design shall be clearly indicated in plans or specifications.

4.1.6 End-Jointed or Edge-Glued Lumber

Reference design values for sawn lumber are applicable to structural end-jointed or edge-glued lumber of the same species and grade. Such use shall include, but not be limited to light framing, studs, joists, planks, and decking. When finger jointed lumber is marked "STUD USE ONLY" or "VERTICAL USE ONLY" such lumber shall be limited to use where any bending or tension stresses are of short duration.

4.1.7 Resawn or Remanufactured Lumber

4.1.7.1 When structural lumber is resawn or remanufactured, it shall be regraded, and reference design values for the regraded material shall apply (see References 16, 42, 43, 45, 46, 47, and 49).

4.1.7.2 When sawn lumber is cross cut to shorter lengths, the requirements of 4.1.7.1 shall not apply, except for reference bending design values for those Beam and Stringer grades where grading provisions for the middle 1/3 of the length of the piece differ from grading provisions for the outer thirds.

4.2 Reference Design Values

4.2.1 Reference Design Values

Reference design values for visually graded lumber and for mechanically graded dimension lumber are specified in Tables 4A, 4B, 4C, 4D, 4E, and 4F (published in the Supplement to this Specification). The reference design values in Tables 4A, 4B, 4C, 4D, 4E, and 4F are taken from the published grading rules of the agencies cited in References 42, 43, 45, 46, 47, and 49.

4.2.2 Other Species and Grades

Reference design values for species and grades of lumber not otherwise provided herein shall be established in accordance with appropriate ASTM standards and other technically sound criteria (see References 16, 18, 19, and 31).

4.2.3 Basis for Reference Design Values

4.2.3.1 The reference design values in Tables 4A, 4B, 4C, 4D, 4E, and 4F are for the design of structures where an individual member, such as a beam, girder, post or other member, carries or is responsible for carrying its full design load. For repetitive member uses see 4.3.9.

4.2.3.2 Visually Graded Lumber. Reference design values for visually graded lumber in Tables 4A, 4B, 4C, 4D, 4E, and 4F are based on the provisions of ASTM Standards D 245 and D 1990.

4.2.3.3 Machine Stress Rated (MSR) Lumber and Machine Evaluated Lumber (MEL). Reference design values for machine stress rated lumber and machine evaluated lumber in Table 4C are determined by visual grading and nondestructive pretesting of individual pieces.

4.2.4 Modulus of Elasticity, E

4.2.4.1 Average Values. Reference design values for modulus of elasticity assigned to the visually graded species and grades of lumber listed in Tables 4A, 4B, 4C, 4D, 4E, and 4F are average values which conform to ASTM Standards D 245 and D 1990. Adjustments in modulus of elasticity have been taken to reflect increases for seasoning, increases for density where applicable, and, where required, reductions have been made to account for the effect of grade upon stiffness. Reference modulus of elasticity design values are based upon the species or species group average in accordance with ASTM Standards D 1990 and D 2555.

4.2.4.2 Special Uses. Average reference modulus of elasticity design values listed in Tables 4A, 4B, 4C, 4D, 4E, and 4F are to be used in design of repetitive member systems and in calculating the immediate deflection of single members which carry their full design load. In special applications where deflection is a critical factor, or where amount of deformation under long-term loading must be limited, the need for use of a reduced modulus of elasticity design value shall be determined. See Appendix F for provisions on design value adjustments for special end use requirements.

4.2.5 Bending, F_b

4.2.5.1 Dimension Grades. Adjusted bending design values for Dimension grades apply to members with the load applied to either the narrow or wide face.

4.2.5.2 Decking Grades. Adjusted bending design values for Decking grades apply only when the load is applied to the wide face.

4.2.5.3 Post and Timber Grades. Adjusted bending design values for Post and Timber grades apply to members with the load applied to either the narrow or wide face.

4.2.5.4 Beam and Stringer Grades. Adjusted bending design values for Beam and Stringer grades apply to members with the load applied to the narrow face. When Post and Timber sizes of lumber are graded to Beam and Stringer grade requirements, design values for the applicable Beam and Stringer grades shall be used. Such lumber shall be identified in accordance with 4.1.2.1 as conforming to Beam and Stringer grades.

4.2.5.5 Continuous or Cantilevered Beams. When Beams and Stringers are used as continuous or cantilevered beams, the design shall include a requirement that the grading provisions applicable to the middle 1/3 of the length (see References 42, 43, 45, 46, 47, and 49) shall be applied to at least the middle 2/3 of the length of pieces to be used as two span continuous beams, and to the entire length of pieces to be used over three or more spans or as cantilevered beams.

4.2.6 Compression Perpendicular to Grain, $F_{c\perp}$

For sawn lumber, the reference compression design values perpendicular to grain are based on a deformation limit that has been shown by experience to provide for adequate service in typical wood frame construction. The reference compression design values perpendicular to grain specified in Tables 4A, 4B, 4C, 4D, 4E, and 4F are species group average values associated with a deformation level of 0.04" for a steel plate on wood member loading condition. One method for limiting deformation in special applications where it is critical, is use of a reduced compression design value perpendicular to grain. The following equation shall be used to calculate the compression design value perpendicular to grain for a reduced deformation level of 0.02":

$$F_{c\perp 0.02} = 0.73\ F_{c\perp} \qquad (4.2\text{-}1)$$

where:

$F_{c\perp 0.02}$ = compression perpendicular to grain design value at 0.02" deformation limit, psi

$F_{c\perp}$ = reference compression perpendicular to grain design value at 0.04" deformation limit (as published in Tables 4A, 4B, 4C, 4D, 4E, and 4F), psi

4.3 Adjustment of Reference Design Values

4.3.1 General

Reference design values (F_b, F_t, F_v, $F_{c\perp}$, F_c, E, E_{min}) from Tables 4A, 4B, 4C, 4D, 4E, and 4F shall be multiplied by the adjustment factors specified in Table 4.3.1 to determine adjusted design values (F_b', F_t', F_v', $F_{c\perp}'$, F_c', E', E_{min}').

4.3.2 Load Duration Factor, C_D (ASD Only)

All reference design values except modulus of elasticity, E, modulus of elasticity for beam and column stability, E_{min}, and compression perpendicular to grain, $F_{c\perp}$, shall be multiplied by load duration factors, C_D, as specified in 2.3.2.

4.3.3 Wet Service Factor, C_M

Reference design values for structural sawn lumber are based on the moisture service conditions specified in 4.1.4. When the moisture content of structural members in use differs from these moisture service conditions, reference design values shall be multiplied by the wet service factors, C_M, specified in Tables 4A, 4B, 4C, 4D, 4E, and 4F.

4.3.4 Temperature Factor, C_t

When structural members will experience sustained exposure to elevated temperatures up to 150°F (see Appendix C), reference design values shall be multiplied by the temperature factors, C_t, specified in 2.3.3.

Table 4.3.1 Applicability of Adjustment Factors for Sawn Lumber

		ASD only	ASD and LRFD										LRFD only		
		Load Duration Factor	Wet Service Factor	Temperature Factor	Beam Stability Factor	Size Factor	Flat Use Factor	Incising Factor	Repetitive Member Factor	Column Stability Factor	Buckling Stiffness Factor	Bearing Area Factor	Format Conversion Factor	Resistance Factor	Time Effect Factor
													K_F	ϕ	
$F_b' = F_b$	x	C_D	C_M	C_t	C_L	C_F	C_{fu}	C_i	C_r	-	-	-	2.54	0.85	λ
$F_t' = F_t$	x	C_D	C_M	C_t	-	C_F	-	C_i	-	-	-	-	2.70	0.80	λ
$F_v' = F_v$	x	C_D	C_M	C_t	-	-	-	C_i	-	-	-	-	2.88	0.75	λ
$F_c' = F_c$	x	C_D	C_M	C_t	-	C_F	-	C_i	-	C_P	-	-	2.40	0.90	λ
$F_{c\perp}' = F_{c\perp}$	x	-	C_M	C_t	-	-	-	C_i	-	-	-	C_b	1.67	0.90	-
$E' = E$	x	-	C_M	C_t	-	-	-	C_i	-	-	-	-	-	-	-
$E_{min}' = E_{min}$	x	-	C_M	C_t	-	-	-	C_i	-	-	C_T	-	1.76	0.85	-

4.3.5 Beam Stability Factor, C_L

Reference bending design values, F_b, shall be multiplied by the beam stability factor, C_L, specified in 3.3.3.

4.3.6 Size Factor, C_F

4.3.6.1 Reference bending, tension, and compression parallel to grain design values for visually graded dimension lumber 2" to 4" thick shall be multiplied by the size factors specified in Tables 4A and 4B.

4.3.6.2 Where the depth of a rectangular sawn lumber bending member 5" or thicker exceeds 12", the reference bending design values, F_b, in Table 4D shall be multiplied by the following size factor:

$$C_F = (12 / d)^{1/9} \leq 1.0 \qquad (4.3\text{-}1)$$

4.3.6.3 For beams of circular cross section with a diameter greater than 13.5", or for 12" or larger square beams loaded in the plane of the diagonal, the size factor shall be determined in accordance with 4.3.6.2 on the basis of an equivalent conventionally loaded square beam of the same cross-sectional area.

4.3.6.4 Reference bending design values for all species of 2" thick or 3" thick Decking, except Redwood, shall be multiplied by the size factors specified in Table 4E.

4.3.7 Flat Use Factor, C_{fu}

4.3.7.1 When sawn lumber 2" to 4" thick is loaded on the wide face, multiplying the reference bending design value, F_b, by the flat use factors, C_{fu}, specified in Tables 4A, 4B, 4C, and 4F, shall be permitted.

4.3.7.2 When members classified as Beams and Stringers are loaded on the wide face, the reference bending design value, F_b, and the reference modulus of elasticity, (E or E_{min}), shall be multiplied by the flat use factors, C_{fu}, specified in Table 4D.

4.3.8 Incising Factor, C_i

Reference design values for dimension lumber shall be multiplied by the incising factor, C_i, in Table 4.3.8 when dimension lumber is incised parallel to grain a maximum depth of 0.4", a maximum length of 3/8", and a density of incisions up to $1100/ft^2$. As an alternative, incising factors for specific incising patterns and lumber sizes shall be obtained from the company providing the incising.

Table 4.3.8 Incising Factors, C_i

Design Value	C_i
E, E_{min}	0.95
F_b, F_t, F_c, F_v	0.80
$F_{c\perp}$	1.00

4.3.9 Repetitive Member Factor, C_r

Reference bending design values, F_b, in Tables 4A, 4B, 4C, and 4F for dimension lumber 2" to 4" thick shall be multiplied by the repetitive member factor, C_r = 1.15, where such members are used as joists, truss chords, rafters, studs, planks, decking, or similar members which are in contact or spaced not more than 24" on center, are not less than three in number and are joined by floor, roof or other load distributing elements adequate to support the design load. (A load distributing element is any adequate system that is designed or has been proven by experience to transmit the design load to adjacent members, spaced as described above, without displaying structural weakness or unacceptable deflection. Subflooring, flooring, sheathing, or other covering elements and nail gluing or tongue-and-groove joints, and through nailing generally meet these criteria.) Reference bending design values in Table 4E for visually graded Decking have already been multiplied by C_r = 1.15.

4.3.10 Column Stability Factor, C_P

Reference compression design values parallel to grain, F_c, shall be multiplied by the column stability factor, C_P, specified in 3.7.

4.3.11 Buckling Stiffness Factor, C_T

Reference modulus of elasticity for beam and column stability, E_{min}, shall be permitted to be multiplied by the buckling stiffness factor, C_T, as specified in 4.4.2.

4.3.12 Bearing Area Factor, C_b

Reference compression design values perpendicular to grain, $F_{c\perp}$, shall be permitted to be multiplied by the bearing area factor, C_b, as specified in 3.10.4.

4.3.13 Pressure-Preservative Treatment

Reference design values apply to sawn lumber pressure-treated by an approved process and preservative (see Reference 30). Load duration factors greater than 1.6 shall not apply to structural members pressure-treated with water-borne preservatives.

4.3.14 Format Conversion Factor, K_F (LRFD Only)

For LRFD, reference design values shall be multiplied by the format conversion factor, K_F, specified in Table 4.3.1.

4.3.15 Resistance Factor, ϕ (LRFD Only)

For LRFD, reference design values shall be multiplied by the resistance factor, ϕ, specified in Table 4.3.1.

4.3.16 Time Effect Factor, λ (LRFD Only)

For LRFD, reference design values shall be multiplied by the time effect factor, λ, specified in Appendix N.3.3.

4.4 Special Design Considerations

4.4.1 Stability of Bending Members

4.4.1.1 Sawn lumber bending members shall be designed in accordance with the lateral stability calculations in 3.3.3 or shall meet the lateral support requirements in 4.4.1.2 and 4.4.1.3.

4.4.1.2 As an alternative to 4.4.1.1, rectangular sawn lumber beams, rafters, joists, or other bending members, shall be designed in accordance with the following provisions to provide restraint against rotation or lateral displacement. If the depth to breadth, d/b, based on nominal dimensions is:

(a) $d/b \leq 2$; no lateral support shall be required.

(b) $2 < d/b \leq 4$; the ends shall be held in position, as by full depth solid blocking, bridging, hangers, nailing, or bolting to other framing members, or other acceptable means.

(c) $4 < d/b \leq 5$; the compression edge of the member shall be held in line for its entire length to prevent lateral displacement, as by adequate sheathing or subflooring, and ends at point of bearing shall be held in position to prevent rotation and/or lateral displacement.

(d) $5 < d/b \leq 6$; bridging, full depth solid blocking or diagonal cross bracing shall be installed at intervals not exceeding 8 feet, the compression edge of the member shall be held in line as by adequate sheathing or subflooring, and the ends at points of bearing shall be held in position to prevent rotation and/or lateral displacement.

(e) $6 < d/b \leq 7$; both edges of the member shall be held in line for their entire length and ends at points of bearing shall be held in position to prevent rotation and/or lateral displacement.

4.4.1.3 If a bending member is subjected to both flexure and axial compression, the depth to breadth ratio shall be no more than 5 to 1 if one edge is firmly held in line. If under all combinations of load, the unbraced edge of the member is in tension, the depth to breadth ratio shall be no more than 6 to 1.

4.4.2 Wood Trusses

4.4.2.1 Increased chord stiffness relative to axial loads where a 2" x 4" or smaller sawn lumber truss compression chord is subjected to combined flexure and axial compression under dry service condition and has 3/8" or thicker wood structural panel sheathing nailed to the narrow face of the chord in accordance with code required roof sheathing fastener schedules (see References 32, 33, and 34), shall be permitted to be accounted for by multiplying the reference modulus of elasticity design value for beam and column stability, E_{min}, by the buckling stiffness factor, C_T, in column stability calculations (see 3.7 and Appendix H). When $\ell_e < 96"$, C_T shall be calculated as follows:

$$C_T = 1 + \frac{K_M \ell_e}{K_T E} \tag{4.4-1}$$

where:

ℓ_e = effective column length of truss compression chord (see 3.7), in.

K_M = 2300 for wood seasoned to 19% moisture content or less at the time of wood structural panel sheathing attachment.

= 1200 for unseasoned or partially seasoned wood at the time of wood structural panel sheathing attachment.

K_T = 1 - 1.645(COV_E)

= 0.59 for visually graded lumber

= 0.75 for machine evaluated lumber (MEL)

= 0.82 for products with $COV_E \leq 0.11$ (see Appendix F.2)

When $\ell_e > 96"$, C_T shall be calculated based on $\ell_e = 96"$.

4.4.2.2 For additional information concerning metal plate connected wood trusses see Reference 9.

4

SAWN LUMBER

4.4.3 Notches

4.4.3.1 End notches, located at the ends of sawn lumber bending members for bearing over a support, shall be permitted, and shall not exceed 1/4 the beam depth (see Figure 4A).

4.4.3.2 Interior notches, located in the outer thirds of the span of a single span sawn lumber bending member, shall be permitted, and shall not exceed 1/6 the depth of the member. Interior notches on the tension side of 3-½" or greater thickness (4" nominal thickness) sawn lumber bending members are not permitted (see Figure 4A).

4.4.3.3 See 3.1.2 and 3.4.3 for effect of notches on strength.

Figure 4A Notch Limitations for Sawn Lumber Beams

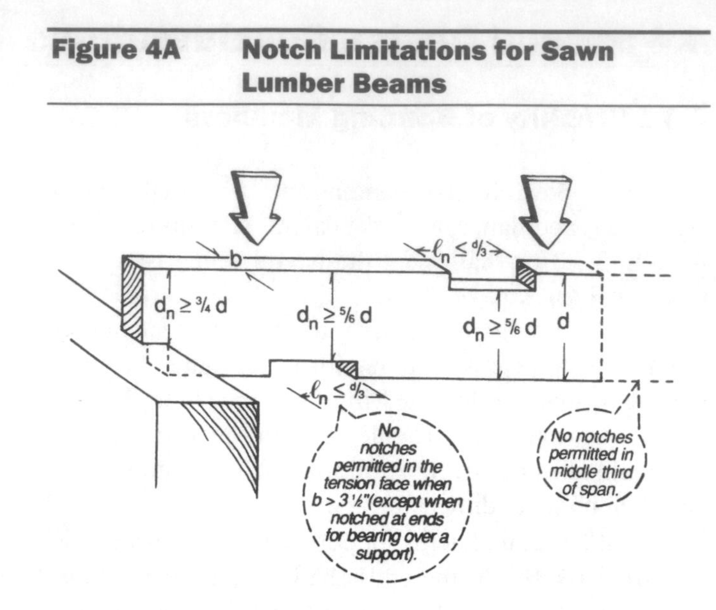

STRUCTURAL GLUED LAMINATED TIMBER

5.1 General

5.1.1 Scope

5.1.1.1 Chapter 5 applies to engineering design with structural glued laminated timber. Basic requirements are provided in this Specification; for additional detail, see Reference 52.

5.1.1.2 Design procedures, reference design values and other information provided herein apply only to structural glued laminated timber conforming to all pertinent provisions of the specifications referenced in the footnotes to Tables 5A, 5B, 5C, and 5D and produced in accordance with ANSI A190.1.

5.1.2 Definition

The term "structural glued laminated timber" refers to an engineered, stress rated product of a timber laminating plant, comprising assemblies of specially selected and prepared wood laminations bonded together with adhesives. The grain of all laminations is approximately parallel longitudinally. The separate laminations shall not exceed 2" in net thickness and are permitted to be comprised of:

- one piece
- pieces joined end-to-end to form any length
- pieces placed or glued edge-to-edge to make wider ones
- pieces bent to curved form during gluing.

5.1.3 Standard Sizes

5.1.3.1 Normal standard finished widths of structural glued laminated members shall be as shown in Table 5.1.3. This Specification is not intended to prohibit other finished widths where required to meet the size requirements of a design or to meet other special requirements.

5.1.3.2 The length and net dimensions of all members shall be specified. Additional dimensions necessary to define non-prismatic members shall be specified.

Table 5.1.3 Net Finished Widths of Structural Glued Laminated Timbers

Nominal Width of Laminations (in.)	3	4	6	8	10	12	14	16
Net Finished Width (in.)	Western Species							
	2-½	3-1/8	5-1/8	6-¾	8-¾	10-¾	12-¼	14-¼
	Southern Pine							
	2-½	3	5	6-¾	8-½	10-½	12	14

5.1.4 Service Conditions

5.1.4.1 Reference design values for dry service conditions shall apply when the moisture content in service is less than 16%, as in most covered structures.

5.1.4.2 Reference design values for glued laminated timber shall be multiplied by the wet service factors, C_M, specified in Tables 5A, 5B, 5C, and 5D when the moisture content in service is 16% or greater, as may occur in exterior or submerged construction, or humid environments.

5.2 Reference Design Values

5.2.1 Reference Design Values

Reference design values for softwood and hardwood structural glued laminated timber are specified in Tables 5A, 5B, 5C, and 5D (published in a separate Supplement to this Specification). The reference design values in Tables 5A, 5B, 5C, and 5D are a compilation of the reference design values provided in the specifications referenced in the footnotes to the tables.

5.2.2 Orientation of Member

Reference design values for structural glued laminated timber are dependent on the orientation of the laminations relative to the applied loads. Subscripts are used to indicate design values corresponding to a given orientation. The orientations of the cross-sectional axes for structural glued laminated timber are shown in Figure 5A. The x-x axis runs parallel to the wide face of the laminations. The y-y axis runs perpendicular to the wide faces of the laminations.

Figure 5A Axis Orientations

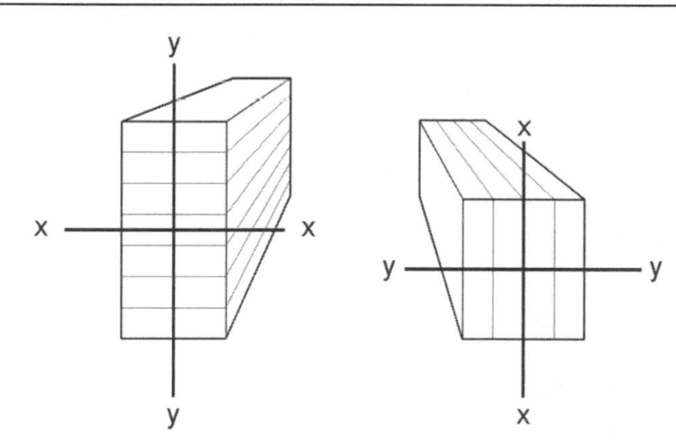

5.2.3 Balanced and Unbalanced Layups

Structural glued laminated timbers are permitted to be assembled with laminations of the same lumber grades placed symmetrically or asymmetrically about the neutral axis of the member. Symmetrical layups are referred to as "balanced" and have the same design values for positive and negative bending. Asymmetrical layups are referred to as "unbalanced" and have lower design values for negative bending than for positive bending. The top side of unbalanced members is required to be marked "TOP" by the manufacturer.

5.2.4 Bending, F_{bx}^+, F_{bx}^-, F_{by}

The reference bending design values, F_{bx}^+ and F_{bx}, shall apply to members with loads causing bending about the x-x axis. The reference bending design value for positive bending, F_{bx}^+, shall apply for bending stresses causing tension at the bottom of the beam. The reference bending design value for negative bending, F_{bx}^-, shall apply for bending stresses causing tension at the top of the beam.

The reference bending design value, F_{by}, shall apply to members with loads causing bending about the y-y axis.

5.2.5 Compression Perpendicular to Grain, $F_{c\perp x}$, $F_{c\perp y}$

The reference compression design value perpendicular to grain, $F_{c\perp x}$, shall apply to members with bearing loads on the wide faces of the laminations.

The reference compression design value perpendicular to grain, $F_{c\perp y}$, shall apply to members with bearing loads on the narrow edges of the laminations.

The reference compression design values perpendicular to grain are based on a deformation limit of 0.04" obtained from testing in accordance with ASTM D143. The compression perpendicular to grain stress associated with a 0.02" deformation limit shall be permitted to be calculated as 73% of the reference value (See also 4.2.6).

5.2.6 Shear Parallel to Grain, F_{vx}, F_{vy}

The reference shear design value parallel to grain, F_{vx} shall apply to members with shear loads causing bending about the x-x axis. The reference shear design value parallel to grain, F_{vy}, shall apply to members with shear loads causing bending about the y-y axis.

The reference shear design values parallel to grain shall apply to prismatic members except those subject to impact or repetitive cyclic loads. For non-prismatic members and for all members subject to impact or repetitive cyclic loads, the reference shear design values parallel to grain shall be multiplied by the shear reduction factor specified in 5.3.10. This reduction shall also apply to the design of connections transferring loads through mechanical fasteners (see 3.4.3.3, 11.1.2 and 11.2.2).

Prismatic members shall be defined as straight or cambered members with constant cross-section. Non-prismatic members include, but are not limited to: arches, tapered beams, curved beams, and notched members.

The reference shear design value parallel to grain, $\mathbf{F_{vy}}$, is tabulated for members with four or more laminations. For members with two or three laminations, the reference design value shall be multiplied by 0.84 or 0.95, respectively.

5.2.7 Modulus of Elasticity, E_x, $E_{x\ min}$, E_y, $E_{y\ min}$

The reference modulus of elasticity, $\mathbf{E_x}$, shall be used for determination of deflections due to bending about the x-x axis.

The reference modulus of elasticity, $\mathbf{E_{x\ min}}$, shall be used for beam and column stability calculations for members buckling about the x-x axis.

The reference modulus of elasticity, $\mathbf{E_y}$, shall be used for determination of deflections due to bending about the y-y axis.

The reference modulus of elasticity, $\mathbf{E_{y\ min}}$, shall be used for beam and column stability calculations for members buckling about the y-y axis.

For the calculation of extensional deformations, the axial modulus of elasticity shall be permitted to be estimated as $\mathbf{E_{axial}} = 1.05\mathbf{E_y}$.

5.2.8 Radial Tension, F_{rt}

For curved bending members, the following reference radial tension design values perpendicular to grain, $\mathbf{F_{rt}}$, shall apply:

Table 5.2.8 Radial Tension Design Values, F_{rt}, for Curved Members

Southern Pine	all loading conditions	$F_{rt} = (1/3)F_{vx}C_{vr}$
Douglas Fir-Larch, Douglas Fir South, Hem-Fir, Western Woods, and Canadian softwood species	wind or earthquake loading	$F_{rt} = (1/3)F_{vx}C_{vr}$
	other types of loading	$F_{rt} = 15$ psi

5.2.9 Radial Compression, F_{rc}

For curved bending members, the reference radial compression design value, $\mathbf{F_{rc}}$, shall be taken as the reference compression perpendicular to grain design value on the side face, $\mathbf{F_{c\perp y}}$.

5.2.10 Other Species and Grades

Reference design values for species and grades of structural glued laminated timber not otherwise provided herein shall be established in accordance with Reference 22, or shall be based on other substantiated information from an approved source.

5.3 Adjustment of Reference Design Values

5.3.1 General

Reference design values (F_b, F_t, F_v, $F_{c\perp}$, F_c, F_{rt}, E, E_{min}) provided in 5.2 and Tables 5A, 5B, 5C, and 5D shall be multiplied by the adjustment factors specified in Table 5.3.1 to determine adjusted design values (F_b', F_t', F_v', $F_{c\perp}'$, F_c', F_{rt}', E', E_{min}').

5.3.2 Load Duration Factor, C_D (ASD only)

All reference design values except modulus of elasticity, E, modulus of elasticity for beam and column stability, E_{min}, and compression perpendicular to grain, $F_{c\perp}$, shall be multiplied by load duration factors, C_D, as specified in 2.3.2.

5.3.3 Wet Service Factor, C_M

Reference design values for structural glued laminated timber are based on the moisture service conditions specified in 5.1.4. When the moisture content of structural members in use differs from these moisture service conditions, reference design values shall be multiplied by the wet service factors, C_M, specified in Tables 5A, 5B, 5C, and 5D.

Table 5.3.1 Applicability of Adjustment Factors for Structural Glued Laminated Timber

	ASD only	ASD and LRFD										LRFD only		
	Load Duration Factor	Wet Service Factor	Temperature Factor	Beam Stability Factor [1]	Volume Factor [1]	Flat Use Factor	Curvature Factor	Stress Interaction Factor	Shear Reduction Factor	Column Stability Factor	Bearing Area Factor	Format Conversion Factor K_F	Resistance Factor ϕ	Time Effect Factor
$F_b' = F_b$ x	C_D	C_M	C_t	C_L	C_V	C_{fu}	C_c	C_I	-	-	-	2.54	0.85	λ
$F_t' = F_t$ x	C_D	C_M	C_t	-	-	-	-	-	-	-	-	2.70	0.80	λ
$F_v' = F_v$ x	C_D	C_M	C_t	-	-	-	-	-	C_{vr}	-	-	2.88	0.75	λ
$F_{rt}' = F_{rt}$ x	C_D	C_M [2]	C_t [2]	-	-	-	-	-	-	-	-	2.88	0.75	λ
$F_c' = F_c$ x	C_D	C_M	C_t	-	-	-	-	-	-	C_P	-	2.40	0.90	λ
$F_{c\perp}' = F_{c\perp}$ x	-	C_M	C_t	-	-	-	-	-	-	-	C_b	1.67	0.90	-
$E' = E$ x	-	C_M	C_t	-	-	-	-	-	-	-	-	-	-	-
$E_{min}' = E_{min}$ x	-	C_M	C_t	-	-	-	-	-	-	-	-	1.76	0.85	-

1. The beam stability factor, C_L, shall not apply simultaneously with the volume factor, C_V, for structural glued laminated timber bending members (see 5.3.6). Therefore, the lesser of these adjustment factors shall apply.
2. For radial tension, F_{rt}, the same adjustment factors (C_M and C_t) for shear parallel to grain, F_v, shall be used.

5.3.4 Temperature Factor, C_t

When structural members will experience sustained exposure to elevated temperatures up to 150°F (see Appendix C), reference design values shall be multiplied by the temperature factors, C_t, specified in 2.3.3.

5.3.5 Beam Stability Factor, C_L

Reference bending design values, F_b, shall be multiplied by the beam stability factor, C_L, specified in 3.3.3. The beam stability factor, C_L, shall not apply simultaneously with the volume factor, C_V, for structural glued laminated timber bending members (see 5.3.6). Therefore, the lesser of these adjustment factors shall apply.

5.3.6 Volume Factor, C_V

When structural glued laminated timber members are loaded in bending about the x-x axis, the reference bending design values, $\mathbf{F_{bx}^+}$, and $\mathbf{F_{bx}^-}$, shall be multiplied by the following volume factor:

$$C_V = \left(\frac{21}{L}\right)^{1/x}\left(\frac{12}{d}\right)^{1/x}\left(\frac{5.125}{b}\right)^{1/x} \leq 1.0 \qquad (5.3\text{-}1)$$

where:

L = length of bending member between points of zero moment, ft

d = depth of bending member, in.

b = width (breadth) of bending member. For multiple piece width layups, b = width of widest piece used in the layup. Thus, b ≤ 10.75".

x = 20 for Southern Pine

x = 10 for all other species

The volume factor, C_V, shall not apply simultaneously with the beam stability factor, C_L (see 3.3.3). Therefore, the lesser of these adjustment factors shall apply.

5.3.7 Flat Use Factor, C_{fu}

When structural glued laminated timber is loaded in bending about the y-y axis and the member dimension parallel to the wide face of the laminations, d_y (see Figure 5B), is less than 12", the reference bending design value, F_{by}, shall be permitted to be multiplied by the flat use factor, C_{fu}, specified in Tables 5A, 5B, 5C, and 5D, or as calculated by the following formula:

$$C_{fu} = \left(\frac{12}{d_y}\right)^{1/9} \quad (5.3\text{-}2)$$

Figure 5B Depth, d_y, for Flat Use Factor

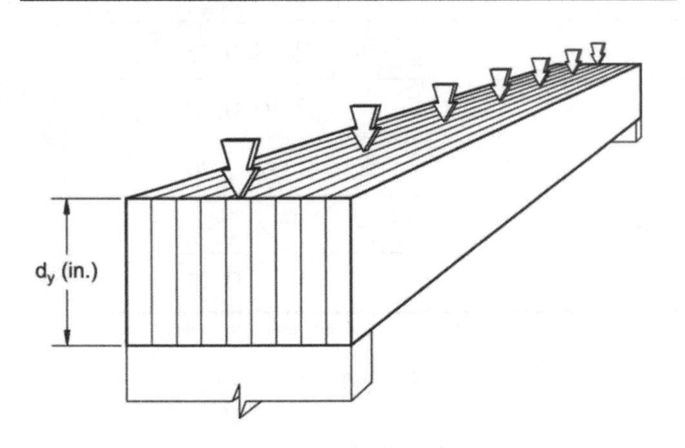

5.3.8 Curvature Factor, C_c

For curved portions of bending members, the reference bending design value shall be multiplied by the following curvature factor:

$$C_c = 1 - (2000)(t / R)^2 \quad (5.3\text{-}3)$$

where:

t = thickness of laminations, in.

R = radius of curvature of inside face of member, in.

$t/R \leq 1/100$ for hardwoods and Southern Pine

$t/R \leq 1/125$ for other softwoods

The curvature factor shall not apply to reference design values in the straight portion of a member, regardless of curvature elsewhere.

5.3.9 Stress Interaction Factor, C_I

For the tapered portion of bending members tapered on the compression face, the reference bending design value, F_{bx}, shall be multiplied by the following stress interaction factor:

$$C_I = \frac{1}{\sqrt{1+\left(F_b \tan\theta / F_v C_{vr}\right)^2 + \left(F_b \tan^2\theta / F_{c\perp}\right)^2}} \quad (5.3\text{-}4)$$

where:

θ = angle of taper, degrees

For members tapered on the compression face, the stress interaction factor, C_I, shall not apply simultaneously with the volume factor, C_V, therefore, the lesser of these adjustment factors shall apply.

For the tapered portion of bending members tapered on the tension face, the reference bending design value, F_{bx}, shall be multiplied by the following stress interaction factor:

$$C_I = \frac{1}{\sqrt{1+\left(F_b \tan\theta / F_v C_{vr}\right)^2 + \left(F_b \tan^2\theta / F_{rt}\right)^2}} \quad (5.3\text{-}5)$$

where:

θ = angle of taper, degrees

For members tapered on the tension face, the stress interaction factor, C_I, shall not apply simultaneously with the beam stability factor, C_L, therefore, the lesser of these adjustment factors shall apply.

Taper cuts on the tension face of structural glued laminated timber beams are not recommended.

5.3.10 Shear Reduction Factor, C_{vr}

The reference shear design values, F_{vx} and F_{vy}, shall be multiplied by the shear reduction factor, C_{vr} = 0.72 where any of the following conditions apply:

1. Design of non-prismatic members.
2. Design of members subject to impact or repetitive cyclic loading.
3. Design of members at notches (3.4.3.2).
4. Design of members at connections (3.4.3.3, 11.1.2, 11.2.2).

5.3.11 Column Stability Factor, C_P

Reference compression design values parallel to grain, F_c, shall be multiplied by the column stability factor, C_P, specified in 3.7.

5.3.12 Bearing Area Factor, C_b

Reference compression design values perpendicular to grain, $F_{c\perp}$, shall be permitted to be multiplied by the bearing area factor, C_b, as specified in 3.10.4.

5.3.13 Pressure-Preservative Treatment

Reference design values apply to structural glued laminated timber treated by an approved process and preservative (see Reference 30). Load duration factors greater than 1.6 shall not apply to structural members pressure-treated with water-borne preservatives.

5.3.14 Format Conversion Factor, K_F (LRFD only)

For LRFD, reference design values shall be multiplied by the format conversion factor, K_F, specified in Table 5.3.1.

5.3.15 Resistance Factor, ϕ (LRFD only)

For LRFD, reference design values shall be multiplied by the resistance factor, ϕ, specified in Table 5.3.1.

5.3.16 Time Effect Factor, λ (LRFD only)

For LRFD, reference design values shall be multiplied by the time effect factor, λ, specified in Appendix N.3.3.

5.4 Special Design Considerations

5.4.1 Curved Bending Members with Constant Cross Section

5.4.1.1 Curved bending members with constant rectangular cross section shall be designed for flexural strength in accordance with 3.3.

5.4.1.2 Curved bending members with constant rectangular cross section shall be designed for shear strength in accordance with 3.4, except that the provisions of 3.4.3.1 shall not apply. The shear reduction factor from 5.3.10 shall apply.

5.4.1.3 The radial stress induced by a bending moment in a curved bending member of constant rectangular cross section is:

$$f_r = \frac{3M}{2Rbd} \tag{5.4-1}$$

where:

M = bending moment, in.-lbs

R = radius of curvature at center line of member, in.

Where the bending moment is in the direction tending to decrease curvature (increase the radius), the radial stress shall not exceed the adjusted radial tension design value perpendicular to grain, $f_r \le F_{rt}'$, unless mechanical reinforcing sufficient to resist all radial stresses is used (see Reference 52). In no case shall f_r exceed $(1/3)F_v'$.

Where the bending moment is in the direction tending to increase curvature (decrease the radius), the radial stress shall not exceed the adjusted radial compression design, $f_r \le F_{rc}'$.

5.4.1.4 The deflection of curved bending members with constant cross section shall be determined in accordance with 3.5. Horizontal displacements at the supports shall also be considered.

5.4.2 Double-Tapered Curved Bending Members

5.4.2.1 The bending stress induced by a bending moment, M, at the peaked section of a double-tapered curved bending member (see Figure 5C) shall be calculated as follows:

$$f_b = K_\phi \frac{6M}{bd_c^2} \tag{5.4-2}$$

where:

K_ϕ = empirical bending stress shape factor

= $1 + 2.7 \tan \phi_T$.

ϕ_T = angle of roof slope, degrees

M = bending moment, in.-lbs

d_c = depth at peaked section of member, in.

The stress interaction factor from 5.3.9 shall apply for flexural design in the straight-tapered segments of double-tapered curved bending members.

5.4.2.2 Double-tapered curved members shall be designed for shear strength in accordance with 3.4, except that the provisions of 3.4.3.1 shall not apply. The shear reduction factor from 5.3.10 shall apply.

5.4.2.3 The radial stress induced by bending moment in a double-tapered curved member shall be calculated as follows:

$$f_r = K_{rs} C_{rs} \frac{6M}{bd_c^2} \tag{5.4-3}$$

where:

K_{rs} = empirical radial stress factor

= $0.29(d_c/R_m) + 0.32 \tan^{1.2}\phi_T$

C_{rs} = empirical load-shape radial stress reduction factor

= $0.27 \ln(\tan \phi_T) + 0.28 \ln(\ell/\ell_c) - 0.8d_c/R_m + 1 \leq 1.0$ for uniformly loaded members where $d_c/R_m \leq 0.3$

= 1.0 for members subject to constant moment

ℓ = span length, in.

ℓ_c = length between tangent points, in.

M = bending moment, in.-lbs

d_c = depth at peaked section of member, in.

R_m = radius of curvature at center line of member, in.

= $R + d_c/2$

R = radius of curvature of inside face of member, in.

Where the bending moment is in the direction tending to decrease curvature (increase the radius), the radial stress shall not exceed the adjusted radial tension design value perpendicular to grain, $f_r \leq F_{rt}'$, unless mechanical reinforcing sufficient to resist all radial stresses is used (see Reference 52). In no case shall f_r exceed $(1/3)F_{vx}'$.

Where the bending moment is in the direction tending to increase curvature (decrease the radius), the radial stress shall not exceed the adjusted radial compression design value, $f_r \leq F_{rc}'$.

5.4.2.4 The deflection of double-tapered curved members shall be determined in accordance with 3.5, except that the mid-span deflection of a symmetrical double-tapered curved beam subject to uniform loads shall be permitted to be calculated by the following empirical formula:

$$\Delta_c = \frac{5\omega\ell^4}{32E_x'b\left(d_{equiv}\right)^3} \tag{5.4-4}$$

where:

Δ_c = vertical deflection at midspan, in.

ω = uniformly distributed load, lbs/in.

d_{equiv} = $(d_e + d_c)(0.5 + 0.735 \tan \phi_T) - 1.41d_c \tan \phi_B$

d_e = depth at the ends of the member, in.

d_c = depth at the peaked section of the member, in.

ϕ_T = angle of roof slope, degrees

ϕ_B = soffit slope at the ends of the member, degrees

The horizontal deflection at the supports of symmetrical double-tapered curved beams shall be permitted to be estimated as:

$$\Delta_H = \frac{2h\Delta_c}{\ell} \tag{5.4-5}$$

where:

Δ_H = horizontal deflection at either support, in.

$h = h_a - d_c/2 - d_e/2$

$h_a = \ell/2 \tan \phi_T + d_e$

Figure 5C Double-Tapered Curved Bending Member

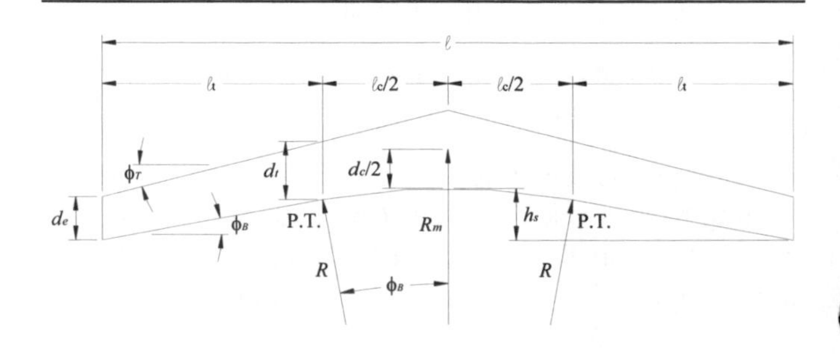

5.4.3 Lateral Stability for Tudor Arches

The ratio of tangent point depth to breadth (d/b) of tudor arches (see Figure 5D) shall not exceed 6, based on actual dimensions, when one edge of the arch is braced by decking fastened directly to the arch, or braced at frequent intervals as by girts or roof purlins. Where such lateral bracing is not present, d/b shall not exceed 5. Arches shall be designed for lateral stability in accordance with the provisions of 3.7 and 3.9.2.

Figure 5D Tudor Arch

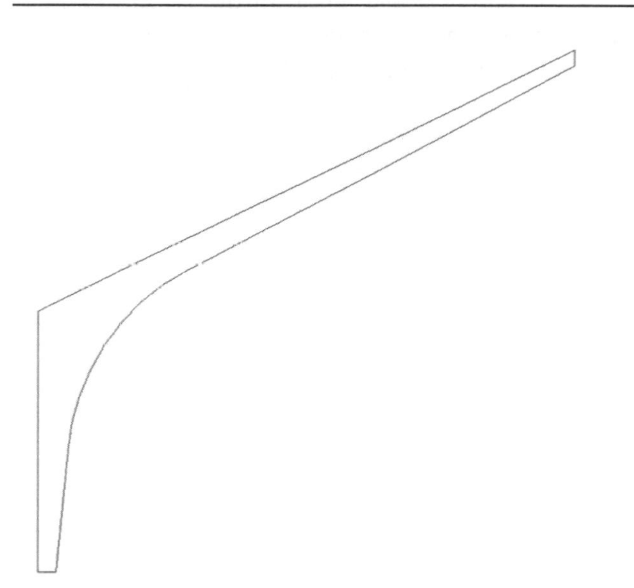

5.4.4 Tapered Straight Bending Members

5.4.4.1 Tapered straight beams (see Figure 5E) shall be designed for flexural strength in accordance with 3.3. The stress interaction factor from 5.3.9 shall apply. For field-tapered members, the reference bending design value, F_{bx}, and the reference modulus of elasticity, E_x, shall be reduced according to the manufacturer's recommendations to account for the removal of high grade material near the surface of the member.

5.4.4.2 Tapered straight beams shall be designed for shear strength in accordance with 3.4, except that the provisions of 3.4.3.1 shall not apply. The shear reduction factor from 5.3.10 shall apply.

5.4.4.3 The deflection of tapered straight beams shall be determined in accordance with 3.5, except that the maximum deflection of a tapered straight beam subject to uniform loads shall be permitted to be calculated as equivalent to the depth, d_{equiv}, of an equivalent prismatic member of the same width where:

$$d_{equiv} = C_{dt} d_e \qquad (5.4\text{-}6)$$

where:

d_e = depth at the small end of the member, in.

C_{dt} = empirical constant derived from relationship of equations for deflection of tapered straight beams and prismatic beams.

For symmetrical double-tapered beams:

$C_{dt} = 1 + 0.66C_y$ when $0 < C_y \leq 1$

$C_{dt} = 1 + 0.62C_y$ when $0 < C_y \leq 3$

For single-tapered beams:

$C_{dt} = 1 + 0.46C_y$ when $0 < C_y \leq 1.1$

$C_{dt} = 1 + 0.43C_y$ when $1.1 < C_y \leq 2$

For both single- and double-tapered beams:

$$C_y = \frac{d_c - d_e}{d_e}$$

Figure 5E Tapered Straight Bending Members

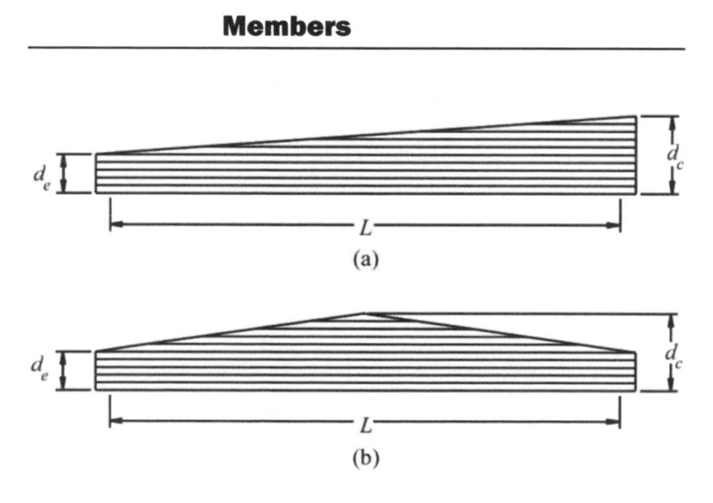

5.4.5 Notches

5.4.5.1 The tension side of structural glued laminated timber bending members shall not be notched, except at ends of members for bearing over a support, and notch depth shall not exceed the lesser of 1/10 the depth of the member or 3".

5.4.5.2 The compression side of structural glued laminated timber bending members shall not be notched, except at ends of members, and the notch depth on the compression side shall not exceed 2/5 the depth of the member. Compression side end-notches shall not extend into the middle 1/3 of the span.

> **Exception:** A taper cut on the compression edge at the end of a structural glued laminated timber bending member shall not exceed 2/3 the depth of the member and the length shall not exceed three times the depth of the member, 3d. For tapered beams where the taper extends into the middle 1/3 of the span, design shall be in accordance with 5.4.4.

5.4.5.3 Notches shall not be permitted on both the tension and compression face at the same cross-section.

5.4.5.4 See 3.1.2 and 3.4.3 for the effect of notches on strength. The shear reduction factor from 5.3.10 shall apply for the evaluation of members at notches.

ROUND TIMBER POLES AND PILES

AMERICAN WOOD COUNCIL

6.1 General

6.1.1 Scope

6.1.1.1 Chapter 6 applies to engineering design with round timber poles and piles. Design procedures and reference design values herein pertain to the load carrying capacity of poles and piles as structural wood members.

6.1.1.2 This Specification does not apply to the load supporting capacity of the soil.

6.1.2 Specifications

6.1.2.1 The procedures and reference design values herein apply only to timber piles conforming to applicable provisions of ASTM Standard D 25 and only to poles conforming to applicable provisions of ASTM Standard D 3200.

6.1.2.2 Specifications for round timber poles and piles shall include the standard for preservative treatment, pile length, and nominal tip circumference or nominal circumference 3 feet from the butt. Specifications for piles shall state whether piles are to be used as foundation piles, land and fresh water piles, or marine piles.

6.1.3 Standard Sizes

6.1.3.1 Standard sizes for round timber piles are given in ASTM Standard D 25.

6.1.3.2 Standard sizes for round timber poles are given in ASTM Standard D 3200.

6.1.4 Preservative Treatment

6.1.4.1 Reference design values apply to untreated, air dried timber poles and piles, and shall be adjusted in accordance with 6.3.5 when conditioned and treated by an approved process (see Reference 30). Load duration factors greater than 1.6 shall not apply to structural members pressure-treated with water-borne preservatives.

6.1.4.2 Untreated, timber poles and piles shall not be used unless the cutoff is below the lowest ground water level expected during the life of the structure, but in no case less than 3 feet below the existing ground water level unless approved by the authority having jurisdiction.

6.2 Reference Design Values

6.2.1 Reference Design Values

6.2.1.1 Reference design values for round timber piles are specified in Table 6A (published in the Supplement to this Specification). Reference design values in Table 6A are based on the provisions of ASTM Standard D 2899.

6.2.1.2 Reference design values for round timber poles are specified in Table 6B (published in the Supplement to this Specification). Reference design values in Table 6B are based on provisions of ASTM Standard D 3200.

6.2.2 Other Species or Grades

Reference design values for piles of other species or grades shall be determined in accordance with ASTM Standard D 2899.

6.3 Adjustment of Reference Design Values

6.3.1 General

Reference design values (F_c, F_b, F_v, $F_{c\perp}$, E, E_{min}) from Table 6A and 6B shall be multiplied by the adjustment factors specified in Table 6.3.1 to determine adjusted design values (F_c', F_b', F_v', $F_{c\perp}'$, E', E_{min}').

6.3.2 Load Duration Factor, C_D (ASD Only)

All reference design values except modulus of elasticity, E, modulus of elasticity for column stability, E_{min}, and compression perpendicular to grain, $F_{c\perp}$, shall be multiplied by load duration factors, C_D, as specified in 2.3.2. Load duration factors greater than 1.6 shall not apply to timber poles or piles pressure-treated with wa-

Table 6.3.1 Applicability of Adjustment Factors for Round Timber Poles and Piles

		ASD only	ASD and LRFD							LRFD only		
		Load Duration Factor	Temperature Factor	Condition Treatment Factor	Size Factor	Column Stability Factor	Critical Section Factor	Bearing Area Factor	Load Sharing Factor	Format Conversion Factor	Resistance Factor	Time Effect Factor
										K_F	ϕ	
$F_c' = F_c$	x	C_D	C_t	C_{ct}	-	C_P	C_{cs}	-	C_{ls}	2.40	0.90	λ
$F_b' = F_b$	x	C_D	C_t	C_{ct}	C_F	-	-	-	C_{ls}	2.54	0.85	λ
$F_v' = F_v$	x	C_D	C_t	C_{ct}	-	-	-	-	-	2.88	0.75	λ
$F_{c\perp}' = F_{c\perp}$	x	-	C_t	C_{ct}	-	-	-	C_b	-	1.67	0.90	-
$E' = E$	x	-	C_t	-	-	-	-	-	-	-	-	-
$E_{min}' = E_{min}$	x	-	C_t	-	-	-	-	-	-	1.76	0.85	-

ter-borne preservatives, (see Reference 30), nor to structural members pressure-treated with fire retardant chemicals (see Table 2.3.2).

6.3.3 Wet Service Factor, C_M

Reference design values apply to wet or dry service conditions ($C_M = 1.0$).

6.3.4 Temperature Factor, C_t

Reference design values shall be multiplied by temperature factors, C_t, as specified in 2.3.3.

6.3.5 Condition Treatment Factor, C_{ct}

Reference design values are based on air dried conditioning. If kiln-drying, steam-conditioning, or boultonizing is used prior to treatment (see reference 20) then the reference design values shall be multiplied by the condition treatment factors, C_{ct}, in Table 6.3.5.

Table 6.3.5 Condition Treatment Factor, C_{ct}

Air Dried	Kiln Dried	Boulton Drying	Steaming (Normal)	Steaming (Marine)
1.0	0.90	0.95	0.80	0.74

6.3.6 Beam Stability Factor, C_L

Reference bending design values, F_b, for round timber poles or piles shall not be adjusted for beam stability.

6.3.7 Size Factor, C_F

Where pole or pile circumference exceeds 43" (diameter exceeds 13.5") at the critical section in bending, the reference bending design value, F_b, shall be multiplied by the size factor, C_F, specified in 4.3.6.2 and 4.3.6.3.

6.3.8 Column Stability Factor, C_P

Reference compression design values parallel to grain, F_c, shall be multiplied by the column stability factor, C_P, specified in 3.7 for the portion of a timber pole or pile standing unbraced in air, water, or material not capable of providing lateral support.

6.3.9 Critical Section Factor, C_{cs}

Reference compression design values parallel to grain, F_c, for round timber piles and poles are based on the strength at the tip of the pile. Reference compression design values parallel to grain, F_c, in Table 6A and Table 6B shall be permitted to be multiplied by the critical section factor. The critical section factor, C_{cs}, shall be determined as follows:

$$C_{cs} = 1.0 + 0.004L_c \qquad (6.3\text{-}1)$$

where:

L_c = length from tip of pile to critical section, ft

The increase for location of critical section shall not exceed 10% for any pile or pole ($C_{cs} \leq 1.10$). The critical section factors, C_{cs}, are independent of tapered column provisions in 3.7.2 and both shall be permitted to be used in design calculations.

6.3.10 Bearing Area Factor, C_b

Reference compression design values perpendicular to grain, $F_{c\perp}$, for timber poles or piles shall be permitted to be multiplied by the bearing area factor, C_b, specified in 3.10.4.

6.3.11 Load Sharing Factor (Pile Group Factor), C_{ls}

For piles, reference design values are based on single piles. If multiple piles are connected by concrete caps or equivalent force distributing elements so that the pile group deforms as a single element when subjected to the load effects imposed on the element, reference bending design values, F_b, and reference compression design values parallel to the grain, F_c, shall be permitted to be multiplied by the load sharing factors, C_{ls}, in Table 6.3.11.

Table 6.3.11 Load Sharing Factor, C_{ls}, per ASTM D 2899

Reference Design Value	Number of Piles in Group	C_{ls}
	2	1.06
F_c	3	1.09
	4 or more	1.11
	2	1.05
F_b	3	1.07
	4 or more	1.08

6.3.12 Format Conversion Factor, K_F (LRFD Only)

For LRFD, reference design values shall be multiplied by the format conversion factor, K_F, specified in Table 6.3.1.

6.3.13 Resistance Factor, ϕ (LRFD Only)

For LRFD, reference design values shall be multiplied by the resistance factor, ϕ, specified in Table 6.3.1.

6.3.14 Time Effect Factor, λ (LRFD Only)

For LRFD, reference design values shall be multiplied by the time effect factor, λ, specified in Appendix N.3.3.

PREFABRICATED WOOD I-JOISTS

AMERICAN WOOD COUNCIL

7.1 General

7.1.1 Scope

Chapter 7 applies to engineering design with prefabricated wood I-joists. Basic requirements are provided in this Specification. Design procedures and other information provided herein apply only to prefabricated wood I-joists conforming to all pertinent provisions of ASTM D 5055.

7.1.2 Definition

The term "prefabricated wood I-joist" refers to a structural member manufactured using sawn or structural composite lumber flanges and wood structural panel webs bonded together with exterior exposure adhesives, forming an "I" cross-sectional shape.

7.1.3 Identification

When the design procedures and other information provided herein are used, the prefabricated wood I-joists shall be identified with the manufacturer's name and the quality assurance agency's name.

7.1.4 Service Conditions

Reference design values reflect dry service conditions, where the moisture content of sawn lumber in service is less than 16%, as in most covered structures. Prefabricated wood I-joists shall not be used in higher moisture service conditions unless specifically permitted by the prefabricated wood I-joist manufacturer.

7.2 Reference Design Values

Reference design values for prefabricated wood I-joists shall be obtained from the prefabricated wood I-joist manufacturer's literature or code evaluation reports.

7.3 Adjustment of Reference Design Values

7.3.1 General

Reference design values (M_r, V_r, R_r, EI, $(EI)_{min}$, K) shall be multiplied by the adjustment factors specified in Table 7.3.1 to determine adjusted design values (M_r', V_r', R_r', EI', $(EI)_{min}'$, K').

7.3.2 Load Duration Factor, C_D (ASD Only)

All reference design values except stiffness, EI, $(EI)_{min}$, and K, shall be multiplied by load duration factors, C_D, as specified in 2.3.2.

7.3.3 Wet Service Factor, C_M

Reference design values for prefabricated wood I-joists are applicable to dry service conditions as specified in 7.1.4 where $C_M = 1.0$. When the service conditions differ from the specified conditions, adjustments for high moisture shall be in accordance with information provided by the prefabricated wood I-joist manufacturer.

7.3.4 Temperature Factor, C_t

When structural members will experience sustained exposure to elevated temperatures up to 150°F (see Appendix C), reference design values shall be multiplied by the temperature factors, C_t, specified in 2.3.3. For M_r, V_r, R_r, EI, $(EI)_{min}$, and K use C_t for F_b, F_v, F_v, E, E_{min}, and F_v, respectively.

Table 7.3.1 Applicability of Adjustment Factors for Prefabricated Wood I-Joists

		ASD only	ASD and LRFD				LRFD only		
		Load Duration Factor	Wet Service Factor	Temperature Factor	Beam Stability Factor	Repetitive Member Factor	Format Conversion Factor	Resistance Factor	Time Effect Factor
							K_F	ϕ	
$M_r' = M_r$	x	C_D	C_M	C_t	C_L	C_r	K_F	0.85	λ
$V_r' = V_r$	x	C_D	C_M	C_t	-	-	K_F	0.75	λ
$R_r' = R_r$	x	C_D	C_M	C_t	-	-	K_F	0.75	λ
$EI' = EI$	x	-	C_M	C_t	-	-	-	-	-
$(EI)_{min}' = (EI)_{min}$	x	-	C_M	C_t	-	-	K_F	0.85	-
$K' = K$	x	-	C_M	C_t	-	-	-	-	-

7.3.5 Beam Stability Factor, C_L

7.3.5.1 Lateral stability of prefabricated wood I-joists shall be considered.

7.3.5.2 When the compression flange of a prefabricated wood I-joist is supported throughout its length to prevent lateral displacement, and the ends at points of bearing have lateral support to prevent rotation, C_L=1.0.

7.3.5.3 When the compression flange of a prefabricated wood I-joist is not supported throughout its length to prevent lateral displacement, one acceptable method is to design the prefabricated wood I-joist compression flange as a column in accordance with the procedure of 3.7.1 using the section properties of the compression flange only. The compression flange shall be evaluated as a column continuously restrained from buckling in the plane of the web. C_P of the compression flange shall be used as C_L of the prefabricated wood I-joist. Prefabricated wood I-joists shall be provided with lateral support at points of bearing to prevent rotation.

7.3.6 Repetitive Member Factor, C_r

For prefabricated wood I-joists with structural composite lumber flanges or sawn lumber flanges, reference moment design resistances shall be multiplied by the repetitive member factor, C_r = 1.0.

7.3.7 Pressure-Preservative Treatment

Adjustments to reference design values to account for the effects of pressure-preservative treatment shall be in accordance with information provided by the prefabricated wood I-joist manufacturer.

7.3.8 Format Conversion Factor, K_F (LRFD Only)

For LRFD, reference design values shall be multiplied by the format conversion factor, K_F, provided by the prefabricated wood I-joist manufacturer.

7.3.9 Resistance Factor, ϕ (LRFD Only)

For LRFD, reference design values shall be multiplied by the resistance factor, ϕ, specified in Table 7.3.1.

7.3.10 Time Effect Factor, λ (LRFD Only)

For LRFD, reference design values shall be multiplied by the time effect factor, λ, specified in Appendix N.3.3.

7.4 Special Design Considerations

7.4.1 Bearing

Reference bearing design values, as a function of bearing length, for prefabricated wood I-joists with and without web stiffeners shall be obtained from the prefabricated wood I-joist manufacturer's literature or code evaluation reports.

7.4.2 Load Application

Prefabricated wood I-joists act primarily to resist loads applied to the top flange. Web stiffener requirements, if any, at concentrated loads applied to the top flange and design values to resist concentrated loads applied to the web or bottom flange shall be obtained from the prefabricated wood I-joist manufacturer's literature or code evaluation reports.

7.4.3 Web Holes

The effects of web holes on strength shall be accounted for in the design. Determination of critical shear at a web hole shall consider load combinations of 1.4.4 and partial span loadings defined as live or snow loads applied from each adjacent bearing to the opposite edge of a rectangular hole (centerline of a circular hole). The effects of web holes on deflection are negligible when the number of holes is limited to 3 or less per span. Reference design values for prefabricated wood I-joists with round or rectangular holes shall be obtained from the prefabricated wood I-joist manufacturer's literature or code evaluation reports.

7.4.4 Notches

Notched flanges at or between bearings significantly reduces prefabricated wood I-joist capacity and is beyond the scope of this document. See the manufacturer for more information.

7.4.5 Deflection

Both bending and shear deformations shall be considered in deflection calculations, in accordance with the prefabricated wood I-joist manufacturer's literature or code evaluation reports.

7.4.6 Vertical Load Transfer

Prefabricated wood I-joists supporting bearing walls located directly above the prefabricated wood I-joist support require rim joists, blocking panels, or other means to directly transfer vertical loads from the bearing wall to the supporting structure below.

7.4.7 Shear

Provisions of 3.4.3.1 for calculating shear force, V, shall not be used for design of prefabricated wood I-joist bending members.

STRUCTURAL COMPOSITE LUMBER

AMERICAN WOOD COUNCIL

8.1 General

8.1.1 Scope

Chapter 8 applies to engineering design with structural composite lumber. Basic requirements are provided in this Specification. Design procedures and other information provided herein apply only to structural composite lumber conforming to all pertinent provisions of ASTM D5456.

8.1.2 Definitions

8.1.2.1 The term "laminated veneer lumber" refers to a composite of wood veneer sheet elements with wood fiber primarily oriented along the length of the member. Veneer thickness shall not exceed 0.25".

8.1.2.2 The term "parallel strand lumber" refers to a composite of wood strand elements with wood fibers primarily oriented along the length of the member. The least dimension of the strands shall not exceed 0.25" and the average length shall be a minimum of 150 times the least dimension.

8.1.2.3 The term "laminated strand lumber", refers to a composite of wood strand elements with wood fibers primarily oriented along the length of the member. The least dimension of the strands shall not exceed 0.10" and the average length shall be a minimum of 150 times the least dimension.

8.1.2.4 The term "oriented strand lumber", refers to a composite of wood strand elements with wood fibers primarily oriented along the length of the member. The least dimension of the strands shall not exceed 0.10" and the average length shall be a minimum of 75 times the least dimension.

8.1.2.5 The term "structural composite lumber" refers to either laminated veneer lumber, parallel strand lumber, laminated strand lumber, or oriented strand lumber. These materials are structural members bonded with an exterior adhesive.

8.1.3 Identification

When the design procedures and other information provided herein are used, the structural composite lumber shall be identified with the manufacturer's name and the quality assurance agency's name.

8.1.4 Service Conditions

Reference design values reflect dry service conditions, where the moisture content of sawn lumber in service is less than 16%, as in most covered structures. Structural composite lumber shall not be used in higher moisture service conditions unless specifically permitted by the structural composite lumber manufacturer.

8.2 Reference Design Values

Reference design values for structural composite lumber shall be obtained from the structural composite lumber manufacturer's literature or code evaluation report. In special applications where deflection is a critical factor, or where deformation under long-term loading must be limited, the need for use of a reduced modulus of elasticity shall be determined. See Appendix F for provisions on adjusted values for special end use requirements.

8.3 Adjustment of Reference Design Values

8.3.1 General

Reference design values (F_b, F_t, F_v, $F_{c\perp}$, F_c, E, E_{min}) shall be multiplied by the adjustment factors specified in Table 8.3.1 to determine adjusted design values (F_b', F_t', F_v', $F_{c\perp}'$, F_c', E', E_{min}').

Table 8.3.1 Applicability of Adjustment Factors for Structural Composite Lumber

		ASD only	ASD and LRFD							LRFD only		
		Load Duration Factor	Wet Service Factor	Temperature Factor	Beam Stability Factor	Volume Factor	Repetitive Member Factor	Column Stability Factor	Bearing Area Factor	Format Conversion Factor	Resistance Factor	Time Effect Factor
										K_F	ϕ	
$F_b' = F_b$	x	C_D	C_M	C_t	C_L[1]	C_V[1]	C_r	-	-	2.54	0.85	λ
$F_t' = F_t$	x	C_D	C_M	C_t	-	C_V	-	-	-	2.70	0.80	λ
$F_v' = F_v$	x	C_D	C_M	C_t	-	-	-	-	-	2.88	0.75	λ
$F_c' = F_c$	x	C_D	C_M	C_t	-	-	-	C_P	-	2.40	0.90	λ
$F_{c\perp}' = F_{c\perp}$	x	-	C_M	C_t	-	-	-	-	C_b	1.67	0.90	-
$E' = E$	x	-	C_M	C_t	-	-	-	-	-	-	-	-
$E_{min}' = E_{min}$	x	-	C_M	C_t	-	-	-	-	-	1.76	0.85	-

1. See 8.3.6.1 for information on simultaneous application of the volume factor, C_V, and the beam stability factor, C_L, to the reference bending design value, F_b

8.3.2 Load Duration Factor, C_D (ASD Only)

All reference design values except modulus of elasticity, E, modulus of elasticity for beam and column stability, E_{min}, and compression perpendicular to grain, $F_{c\perp}$, shall be multiplied by load duration factors, C_D, as specified in 2.3.2.

8.3.3 Wet Service Factor, C_M

Reference design values for structural composite lumber are applicable to dry service conditions as specified in 8.1.4 where $C_M = 1.0$. When the service conditions differ from the specified conditions, adjustments for high moisture shall be in accordance with information provided by the structural composite lumber manufacturer.

8.3.4 Temperature Factor, C_t

When structural members will experience sustained exposure to elevated temperatures up to 150°F (see Appendix C), reference design values shall be multiplied by the temperature factors, C_t, specified in 2.3.3.

8.3.5 Beam Stability Factor, C_L

Structural composite lumber bending members shall be laterally supported in accordance with 3.3.3.

8.3.6 Volume Factor, C_V

8.3.6.1 Reference bending design values, F_b, for structural composite lumber shall be multiplied by the volume factor, C_V, which shall be obtained from the structural composite lumber manufacturer's literature or code evaluation reports. When $C_V \leq 1.0$, the volume factor, C_V, shall not apply simultaneously with the beam stability factor, C_L (see 3.3.3) and therefore, the lesser value of these adjustment factors shall apply. When $C_V > 1.0$, the volume factor, C_V, shall apply simultaneously with the beam stability factor, C_L (see 3.3.3).

8.3.6.2 Reference tension design values, F_t, for structural composite lumber shall be multiplied by the volume factor, C_V, which shall be obtained from the structural composite lumber manufacturer's literature or code evaluation reports.

8.3.7 Repetitive Member Factor, C_r

Reference bending design values, F_b, shall be multiplied by the repetitive member factor, C_r = 1.04, where such members are used as joists, studs, or similar members which are in contact or spaced not more than 24" on center, are not less than 3 in number and are joined by floor, roof, or other load distributing elements adequate to support the design load. (A load distributing element is any adequate system that is designed or has been proven by experience to transmit the design load to adjacent members, spaced as described above, without displaying structural weakness or unacceptable deflection. Subflooring, flooring, sheathing, or other covering elements and nail gluing or tongue-and-groove joints, and through nailing generally meet these criteria.)

8.3.8 Column Stability Factor, C_P

Reference compression design values parallel to grain, F_c, shall be multiplied by the column stability factor, C_P, specified in 3.7.

8.3.9 Bearing Area Factor, C_b

Reference compression design values perpendicular to grain, $F_{c\perp}$, shall be permitted to be multiplied by the bearing area factor, C_b, as specified in 3.10.4.

8.3.10 Pressure-Preservative Treatment

Adjustments to reference design values to account for the effects of pressure-preservative treatment shall be in accordance with information provided by the structural composite lumber manufacturer.

8.3.11 Format Conversion Factor, K_F (LRFD Only)

For LRFD, reference design values shall be multiplied by the format conversion factor, K_F, specified in Table 8.3.1.

8.3.12 Resistance Factor, ϕ (LRFD Only)

For LRFD, reference design values shall be multiplied by the resistance factor, ϕ, specified in Table 8.3.1.

8.3.13 Time Effect Factor, λ (LRFD Only)

For LRFD, reference design values shall be multiplied by the time effect factor, λ, specified in Appendix N.3.3.

8.4 Special Design Considerations

8.4.1 Notches

8.4.1.1 The tension side of structural composite bending members shall not be notched, except at ends of members for bearing over a support, and notch depth shall not exceed 1/10 the depth of the member. The compression side of structural composite bending members shall not be notched, except at ends of members, and the notch depth on the compression side shall not exceed 2/5 the depth of the member. Compression side end-notches shall not extend into the middle third of the span.

8.4.1.2 See 3.1.2 and 3.4.3 for effect of notches on strength.

WOOD STRUCTURAL PANELS

9.1 General

9.1.1 Scope

Chapter 9 applies to engineering design with the following wood structural panels: plywood, oriented strand board, and composite panels. Basic requirements are provided in this Specification. Design procedures and other information provided herein apply only to wood structural panels complying with the requirements specified in this Chapter.

9.1.2 Identification

9.1.2.1 When design procedures and other information herein are used, the wood structural panel shall be identified for grade and glue type by the trademarks of an approved testing and grading agency.

9.1.2.2 Wood structural panels shall be specified by span rating, nominal thickness, exposure rating, and grade.

9.1.3 Definitions

9.1.3.1 The term "wood structural panel" refers to a wood-based panel product bonded with a waterproof adhesive. Included under this designation are plywood, oriented strand board (OSB) and composite panels. These panel products meet the requirements of USDOC PS 1 or PS 2 and are intended for structural use in residential, commercial, and industrial applications.

9.1.3.2 The term "composite panel" refers to a wood structural panel comprised of wood veneer and reconstituted wood-based material and bonded with waterproof adhesive.

9.1.3.3 The term "oriented strand board" refers to a mat-formed wood structural panel comprised of thin rectangular wood strands arranged in cross-aligned layers with surface layers normally arranged in the long panel direction and bonded with waterproof adhesive.

9.1.3.4 The term "plywood" refers to a wood structural panel comprised of plies of wood veneer arranged in cross-aligned layers. The plies are bonded with an adhesive that cures on application of heat and pressure.

9.1.4 Service Conditions

9.1.4.1 Reference design values reflect dry service conditions, where the moisture content in service is less than 16%, as in most covered structures.

9.2 Reference Design Values

9.2.1 Panel Stiffness and Strength

9.2.1.1 Reference panel stiffness and strength design values (the product of material and section properties) shall be obtained from an approved source.

9.2.1.2 Due to the orthotropic nature of panels, reference design values shall be provided for the primary and secondary strength axes. The appropriate reference design values shall be applied when designing for each panel orientation. When forces act at an angle to the principal axes of the panel, the capacity of the panel at the angle shall be calculated by adjusting the reference design values for the principal axes using principles of engineering mechanics.

9.2.2 Strength and Elastic Properties

Where required, strength and elastic parameters shall be calculated from reference strength and stiffness design values, respectively, on the basis of tabulated design section properties.

9.2.3 Design Thickness

Nominal thickness shall be used in design calculations. The relationships between span ratings and nominal thicknesses are provided with associated reference design values.

9.2.4 Design Section Properties

Design section properties shall be assigned on the basis of span rating or design thickness and are provided on a per-foot-of-panel-width basis.

9.3 Adjustment of Reference Design Values

9.3.1 General

Reference design values shall be multiplied by the adjustment factors specified in Table 9.3.1 to determine adjusted design values.

9.3.2 Load Duration Factor, C_D (ASD Only)

All reference strength design values (F_bS, F_tA, F_vt_v, $F_s(Ib/Q)$, F_cA) shall be multiplied by load duration factors, C_D, as specified in 2.3.2.

9.3.3 Wet Service Factor, C_M, and Temperature Factor, C_t

Reference design values for wood structural panels are applicable to dry service conditions as specified in 9.1.4 where C_M = 1.0 and C_t = 1.0. When the service conditions differ from the specified conditions, adjustments for high moisture and/or high temperature shall be based on information from an approved source.

Table 9.3.1 Applicability of Adjustment Factors for Wood Structural Panels

		ASD only	ASD and LRFD			LRFD only		
		Load Duration Factor	Wet Service Factor	Temperature Factor	Panel Size Factor	Format Conversion Factor	Resistance Factor	Time Effect Factor
						K_F	ϕ	
$F_bS' = F_bS$	x	C_D	C_M	C_t	C_s	2.54	0.85	λ
$F_tA' = F_tA$	x	C_D	C_M	C_t	C_s	2.70	0.80	λ
$F_vt_v' = F_vt_v$	x	C_D	C_M	C_t	-	2.88	0.75	λ
$F_s(Ib/Q)' = F_s(Ib/Q)$	x	C_D	C_M	C_t	-	2.88	0.75	λ
$F_cA' = F_cA$	x	C_D	C_M	C_t	-	2.40	0.90	λ
$F_{c\perp}' = F_{c\perp}$	x	-	C_M	C_t	-	1.67	0.90	-
$EI' = EI$	x	-	C_M	C_t	-	-	-	-
$EA' = EA$	x	-	C_M	C_t	-	-	-	-
$G_vt_v' = G_vt_v$	x	-	C_M	C_t	-	-	-	-

9.3.4 Panel Size Factor, C_s

Reference bending and tension design values (F_bS and F_tA) for wood structural panels are applicable to panels that are 24" or greater in width (i.e., dimension perpendicular to the applied stress). For panels less than 24" in width, reference bending and tension design values shall be multiplied by the panel size factor, C_s, specified in Table 9.3.4.

Table 9.3.4 Panel Size Factor, C_s

Panel Strip Width, w	C_s
$w \leq 8"$	0.5
$8" < w < 24"$	$(8 + w) / 32$
$w \geq 24"$	1.0

9.3.5 Format Conversion Factor, K_F (LRFD Only)

For LRFD, reference design values shall be multiplied by the format conversion factor, K_F, specified in Table 9.3.1.

9.3.6 Resistance Factor, ϕ (LRFD Only)

For LRFD, reference design values shall be multiplied by the resistance factor, ϕ, specified in Table 9.3.1.

9.3.7 Time Effect Factor, λ (LRFD Only)

For LRFD, reference design values shall be multiplied by the time effect factor, λ, specified in Appendix N.3.3.

9.4 Design Considerations

9.4.1 Flatwise Bending

Wood structural panels shall be designed for flexure by checking bending moment, shear, and deflection. Adjusted planar shear shall be used as the shear resistance in checking the shear for panels in flatwise bending. Appropriate beam equations shall be used with the design spans as defined below.

(a) Bending moment-distance between center-line of supports.

(b) Shear-clear span.

(c) Deflection-clear span plus the support width factor. For 2" nominal and 4" nominal framing, the support width factor is equal to 0.25" and 0.625", respectively.

9.4.2 Tension in the Plane of the Panel

When wood structural panels are loaded in axial tension, the orientation of the primary strength axis of the panel with respect to the direction of loading, shall be considered in determining adjusted tensile capacity.

9.4.3 Compression in the Plane of the Panel

When wood structural panels are loaded in axial compression, the orientation of the primary strength axis of the panel with respect to the direction of loading, shall be considered in determining the adjusted compressive capacity. In addition, panels shall be designed to prevent buckling.

9.4.4 Planar (Rolling) Shear

The adjusted planar (rolling) shear shall be used in design when the shear force is applied in the plane of wood structural panels.

9.4.5 Through-the-Thickness Shear

The adjusted through-the-thickness shear shall be used in design when the shear force is applied through-the-thickness of wood structural panels.

9.4.6 Bearing

The adjusted bearing design value of wood structural panels shall be used in design when the load is applied perpendicular to the panel face.

CROSS-LAMINATED TIMBER

AMERICAN WOOD COUNCIL

10.1 General

10.1.1 Application

10.1.1.1 Chapter 10 applies to engineering design with performance-rated cross-laminated timber.

10.1.1.2 Design procedures, reference design values and other information provided herein apply only to performance-rated cross-laminated timber produced in accordance with ANSI/APA PRG-320.

10.1.2 Definition

Cross-Laminated Timber (CLT) – a prefabricated engineered wood product consisting of at least three layers of solid-sawn lumber or structural composite lumber where the adjacent layers are cross-oriented and bonded with structural adhesive to form a solid wood element.

10.1.3 Standard Dimensions

10.1.3.1 The net thickness of a lamination for all layers at the time of gluing shall not be less than 5/8 inch or more than 2 inches.

10.1.3.2 The thickness of cross-laminated timber shall not exceed 20 inches.

10.1.4 Specification

All required reference design values shall be specified in accordance with Section 10.2.

10.1.5 Service Conditions

Reference design values reflect dry service conditions, where the moisture content in service is less than 16%, as in most covered structures. Cross-laminated timber shall not be used in higher moisture service conditions unless specifically permitted by the cross-laminated timber manufacturer.

10.2 Reference Design Values

10.2.1 Reference Design Values

Reference design values for cross-laminated timber shall be obtained from the cross-laminated timber manufacturer's literature or code evaluation report.

10.2.2 Design Section Properties

Reference design values shall be used with design section properties provided by the cross-laminated timber manufacturer based on the actual layup used in the manufacturing process.

10.3 Adjustment of Reference Design Values

10.3.1 General

Reference design values: $F_b(S_{eff})$, $F_t(A_{parallel})$, $F_v(t_v)$, $F_s(Ib/Q)_{eff}$, $F_c(A_{parallel})$, $F_{c\perp}(A)$, $(EI)_{app}$, and $(EI)_{app\text{-}min}$ provided in 10.2 shall be multiplied by the adjustment factors specified in Table 10.3.1 to determine adjusted design values: $F_b(S_{eff})'$, $F_t(A_{parallel})'$, $F_v(t_v)'$, $F_s(Ib/Q)_{eff}'$, $F_c(A_{parallel})'$, $F_{c\perp}(A)'$, $(EI)_{app}'$, and $(EI)_{app\text{-}min}'$.

10.3.2 Load Duration Factor, C_D (ASD only)

All reference design values except stiffness, $(EI)_{app}$, $(EI)_{app\text{-}min}$, rolling shear, $F_s(Ib/Q)_{eff}$, and compression perpendicular to grain, $F_{c\perp}(A)$, shall be multiplied by load duration factors, C_D, as specified in 2.3.2.

Table 10.3.1 Applicability of Adjustment Factors for Cross-Laminated Timber

		ASD only	ASD and LRFD						LRFD only		
		Load Duration Factor	Wet Service Factor	Temperature Factor	Beam Stability Factor	Column Stability Factor	Bearing Area Factor	Format Conversion Factor	Resistance Factor	Time Effect Factor
$F_b(S_{eff})' = F_b(S_{eff})$	x	C_D	C_M	C_t	C_L	-	-	2.54	0.85	λ
$F_t(A_{parallel})' = F_t(A_{parallel})$	x	C_D	C_M	C_t	-	-	-	2.70	0.80	λ
$F_v(t_v)' = F_v(t_v)$	x	C_D	C_M	C_t	-	-	-	2.88	0.75	λ
$F_s(Ib/Q)_{eff}' = F_s(Ib/Q)_{eff}$	x	-	C_M	C_t	-	-	-	2.00	0.75	-
$F_c(A_{parallel})' = F_c(A_{parallel})$	x	C_D	C_M	C_t	-	C_P	-	2.40	0.90	λ
$F_{c\perp}(A)' = F_{c\perp}(A)$	x	-	C_M	C_t	-	-	C_b	1.67	0.90	-
$(EI)_{app}' = (EI)_{app}$	x	-	C_M	C_t	-	-	-	-	-	-
$(EI)_{app\text{-}min}' = (EI)_{app\text{-}min}$	x	-	C_M	C_t	-	-	-	1.76	0.85	-

10.3.3 Wet Service Factor, C_M

Reference design values for cross-laminated timber are applicable to dry service conditions as specified in 10.1.5 where $C_M = 1.0$. When the service conditions differ from the specified conditions, adjustments for high moisture shall be in accordance with information provided by the cross-laminated timber manufacturer.

10.3.4 Temperature Factor, C_t

When structural members will experience sustained exposure to elevated temperatures up to 150°F (see Appendix C), reference design values shall be multiplied by the temperature factors, C_t, specified in 2.3.3.

10.3.5 Curvature Factor, C_c

The design of curved cross-laminated timber is beyond the scope of this standard.

10.3.6 Beam Stability Factor, C_L

Reference bending design values, $F_b(S_{eff})$, shall be multiplied by the beam stability factor, C_L, specified in 3.3.3.

10.3.7 Column Stability Factor, C_P

For cross-laminated timber loaded in-plane as a compression member, reference compression design values parallel to grain, $F_c(A_{parallel})$, shall be multiplied by the column stability factor, C_P, specified in 3.7.

10.3.8 Bearing Area Factor, C_b

Reference compression design values perpendicular to grain, $F_{c\perp}(A)$, shall be permitted to be multiplied by the bearing area factor, C_b, as specified in 3.10.4.

10.3.9 Pressure-Preservative Treatment

Reference design values apply to cross-laminated timber treated by an approved process and preservative (see Reference 30). Load duration factors greater than

1.6 shall not apply to structural members pressure-treated with water-borne preservatives.

10.3.10 Format Conversion Factor, K_F (LRFD only)

For LRFD, reference design values shall be multiplied by the format conversion factor, K_F, specified in Table 10.3.1

10.3.11 Resistance Factor, ϕ (LRFD only)

For LRFD, reference design values shall be multiplied by the resistance factor, ϕ, specified in Table 10.3.1.

10.3.12 Time Effect Factor, λ (LRFD only)

For LRFD, reference design values shall be multiplied by the time effect factor, λ, specified in Appendix N.3.3.

10.4 Special Design Considerations

10.4.1 Deflection

10.4.1.1 Where reference design values for bending stiffness have not been adjusted to include the effects of shear deformation, the shear component of the total deflection of a cross-laminated timber element shall be determined in accordance with principles of engineering mechanics. One method of designing for shear deformation is to reduce the effective bending stiffness, EI_{eff}, for the effects of shear deformation which is a function of loading and support conditions, beam geometry, span and the effective shear stiffness, GA_{eff}. For the cases addressed in Table 10.4.1.1, the apparent bending stiffness, $(EI)_{app}$, adjusted for shear deformation shall be calculated as follows:

$$(EI)_{app} = \frac{EI_{eff}}{1 + \frac{K_s EI_{eff}}{GA_{eff} L^2}} \quad (10.4\text{-}1)$$

where:

EI_{eff} = Effective bending stiffness of the CLT section, lbs-in.^{2}/ft of panel width

K_s = Shear deformation adjustment factor

GA_{eff} = Effective shear stiffness of the CLT section, lbs/ft of panel width

L = Span of the CLT section, in.

Table 10.4.1.1 Shear Deformation Adjustment Factors, K_s

Loading	End Fixity	K_s
Uniformly Distributed	Pinned	11.5
	Fixed	57.6
Line Load at midspan	Pinned	14.4
	Fixed	57.6
Line Load at quarter points	Pinned	10.5
Constant Moment	Pinned	0
Uniformly Distributed	Cantilevered	4.8
Line Load at free-end	Cantilevered	3.6
Column Buckling	Pinned	11.8
	Fixed	47.4

MECHANICAL CONNECTIONS

AMERICAN WOOD COUNCIL

11.1 General

11.1.1 Scope

11.1.1.1 Chapter 11 applies to the engineering design of connections using bolts, lag screws, split ring connectors, shear plate connectors, drift bolts, drift pins, wood screws, nails, spikes, timber rivets, spike grids, or other fasteners in sawn lumber, structural glued laminated timber, timber poles, timber piles, structural composite lumber, prefabricated wood I-joists, wood structural panels, and cross-laminated timber. Except where specifically limited herein, the provisions of Chapter 11 shall apply to all fastener types covered in Chapters 12, 13, and 14.

11.1.1.2 The requirements of 3.1.3, 3.1.4, and 3.1.5 shall be accounted for in the design of connections.

11.1.1.3 Connection design provisions in Chapters 11, 12, 13, and 14 shall not preclude the use of connections where it is demonstrated by analysis based on generally recognized theory, full-scale or prototype loading tests, studies of model analogues or extensive experience in use that the connections will perform satisfactorily in their intended end uses (see 1.1.1.5).

11.1.2 Stresses in Members at Connections

Structural members shall be checked for load carrying capacity at connections in accordance with all applicable provisions of this standard including 3.1.2, 3.1.3, and 3.4.3.3. Local stresses in connections using multiple fasteners shall be checked in accordance with principles of engineering mechanics. One method for determining these stresses is provided in Appendix E.

11.1.3 Eccentric Connections

Eccentric connections that induce tension stress perpendicular to grain in the wood shall not be used unless appropriate engineering procedures or tests are employed in the design of such connections to insure that all applied loads will be safely carried by the members and connections. Connections similar to those in Figure 11A are examples of connections requiring appropriate engineering procedures or tests.

11.1.4 Mixed Fastener Connections

Methods of analysis and test data for establishing reference design values for connections made with more than one type of fastener have not been developed. Reference design values and design value adjustments for mixed fastener connections shall be based on tests or other analysis (see 1.1.1.3).

11.1.5 Connection Fabrication

Reference lateral design values for connections in Chapters 12, 13, and 14 are based on:

(a) the assumption that the faces of the members are brought into contact when the fasteners are installed, and

(b) allowance for member shrinkage due to seasonal variations in moisture content (see 11.3.3).

Figure 11A Eccentric Connections

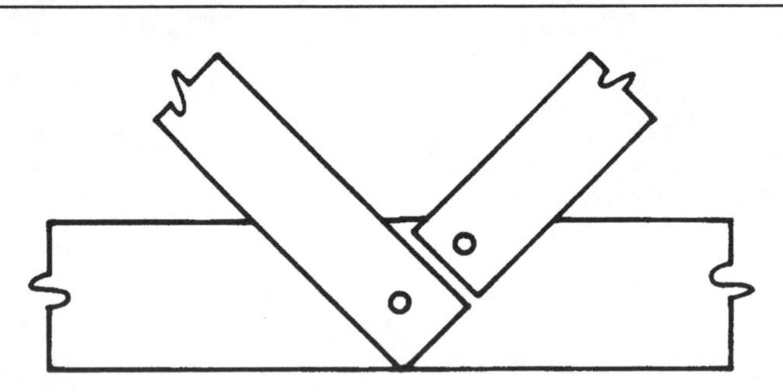

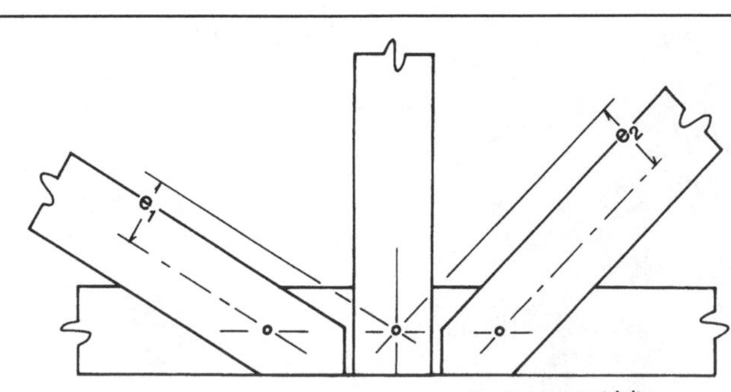

11.2 Reference Design Values

11.2.1 Single Fastener Connections

11.2.1.1 Chapters 12, 13, and 14 contain tabulated reference design values and design provisions for calculating reference design values for various types of single fastener connections. Reference design values for connections in a given species apply to all grades of that species unless otherwise indicated. Dowel-type fastener connection reference design values for one species of wood are also applicable to other species having the same or higher dowel bearing strength, F_e.

11.2.1.2 Design provisions and reference design values for dowel-type fastener connections such as bolts, lag screws, wood screws, nails, spikes, drift bolts, and drift pins are provided in Chapter 12.

11.2.1.3 Design provisions and reference design values for split ring and shear plate connections are provided in Chapter 13.

11.2.1.4 Design provisions and reference design values for timber rivet connections are provided in Chapter 14.

11.2.1.5 Wood to wood connections involving spike grids for load transfer shall be designed in accordance with principles of engineering mechanics (see Reference 50 for additional information).

11.2.2 Multiple Fastener Connections

Where a connection contains two or more fasteners of the same type and similar size, each of which exhibits the same yield mode (see Appendix I), the total adjusted design value for the connection shall be the sum of the adjusted design values for each individual fastener. Local stresses in connections using multiple fasteners shall be evaluated in accordance with principles of engineering mechanics (see 11.1.2).

11.2.3 Design of Metal Parts

Metal plates, hangers, fasteners, and other metal parts shall be designed in accordance with applicable metal design procedures to resist failure in tension, shear, bearing (metal on metal), bending, and buckling (see References 39, 40, and 41). When the capacity of a connection is controlled by metal strength rather than wood strength, metal strength shall not be multiplied by the adjustment factors in this Specification. In addition, metal strength shall not be increased by wind and earthquake factors if design loads have already been reduced by load combination factors (see Reference 5 for additional information).

11.2.4 Design of Concrete or Masonry Parts

Concrete footers, walls, and other concrete or masonry parts shall be designed in accordance with accepted practices (see References 1 and 2). When the capacity of a connection is controlled by concrete or masonry strength rather than wood strength, concrete or masonry strength shall not be multiplied by the adjustment factors in this Specification. In addition, concrete or masonry strength shall not be increased by wind and earthquake factors if design loads have already been reduced by load combination factors (see Reference 5 for additional information).

11.3 Adjustment of Reference Design Values

11.3.1 Applicability of Adjustment Factors

Reference design values (Z, W, W_H) shall be multiplied by all applicable adjustment factors to determine adjusted design values (Z', W', W'_H). Table 11.3.1 specifies the adjustment factors which apply to reference lateral design values (Z) and reference withdrawal design values (W) for each fastener type, and reference fastener head pull-through design values (W_H) for fasteners with round heads. The actual load applied to a connection shall not exceed the adjusted design value (Z', W', W'_H) for the connection.

Table 11.3.1 Applicability of Adjustment Factors for Connections

		ASD Only	ASD and LRFD									LRFD Only		
		Load Duration Factor [1]	Wet Service Factor	Temperature Factor	Group Action Factor	Geometry Factor [3]	Penetration Depth Factor [3]	End Grain Factor [3]	Metal Side Plate Factor [3]	Diaphragm Factor [3]	Toe-Nail Factor [3]	Format Conversion Factor K_F	Resistance Factor ϕ	Time Effect Factor
Lateral Loads														
Dowel-type Fasteners (e.g. bolts, lag screws, wood screws, nails, spikes, drift bolts, & drift pins)	$Z' = Z$ x	C_D	C_M	C_t	C_g	C_Δ	-	C_{eg}	-	C_{di}	C_{tn}	3.32	0.65	λ
Split Ring and Shear Plate Connectors	$P' = P$ x	C_D	C_M	C_t	C_g	C_Δ	C_d	-	C_{st}	-	-	3.32	0.65	λ
	$Q' = Q$ x	C_D	C_M	C_t	C_g	C_Δ	C_d	-	-	-	-	3.32	0.65	λ
Timber Rivets	$P' = P$ x	C_D	C_M	C_t	-	-	-	-	C_{st}^{4}	-	-	3.32	0.65	λ
	$Q' = Q$ x	C_D	C_M	C_t	-	C_Δ^{5}	-	-	C_{st}^{4}	-	-	3.32	0.65	λ
Spike Grids	$Z' = Z$ x	C_D	C_M	C_t	-	C_Δ	-	-	-	-	-	3.32	0.65	λ
Withdrawal Loads														
Nails, spikes, lag screws, wood screws, & drift pins	$W' = W$ x	C_D	C_M^{2}	C_t	-	-	-	C_{eg}	-	-	C_{tn}	3.32	0.65	λ
Pull-Through														
Fasteners with Round Heads	$W_H' = W_H$ x	C_D	C_M	C_t	-	-	-	-	-	-	-	3.32	0.65	λ

1. The load duration factor, C_D, shall not exceed 1.6 for connections (see 11.3.2).
2. The wet service factor, C_M, shall not apply to toe-nails loaded in withdrawal (see 12.5.4.1).
3. Specific information concerning geometry factors C_Δ, penetration depth factors C_d, end grain factors, C_{eg}, metal side plate factors, C_{st}, diaphragm factors, C_{di}, and toe-nail factors, C_{tn}, is provided in Chapters 12, 13, and 14.
4. The metal side plate factor, C_{st}, is only applied when rivet capacity (P_r, Q_r) controls (see Chapter 14).
5. The geometry factor, C_Δ, is only applied when wood capacity, Q_w, controls (see Chapter 14).

11.3.2 Load Duration Factor, C_D (ASD Only)

Reference design values shall be multiplied by the load duration factors, $C_D \leq 1.6$, specified in 2.3.2 and Appendix B, except when the capacity of the connection is controlled by metal strength or strength of concrete/masonry (see 11.2.3, 11.2.4, and Appendix B.3). The impact load duration factor shall not apply to connections.

11.3.3 Wet Service Factor, C_M

Reference design values are for connections in wood seasoned to a moisture content of 19% or less and used under continuously dry conditions, as in most covered structures. For connections in wood that is unseasoned or partially seasoned, or when connections are exposed to wet service conditions in use, reference design values shall be multiplied by the wet service factors, C_M, specified in Table 11.3.3.

11.3.4 Temperature Factor, C_t

Reference design values shall be multiplied by the temperature factors, C_t, in Table 11.3.4 for connections that will experience sustained exposure to elevated temperatures up to 150°F (see Appendix C).

Table 11.3.3 Wet Service Factors, C_M, for Connections

Fastener Type	Moisture Content		C_M
	At Time of Fabrication	In-Service	
Lateral Loads			
Split Ring and Shear Plate Connectors[1]	≤ 19%	≤ 19%	1.0
	> 19%	≤ 19%	0.8
	any	> 19%	0.7
Dowel-type Fasteners (e.g. bolts, lag screws, wood screws, nails, spikes, drift bolts, & drift pins)	≤ 19%	≤ 19%	1.0
	> 19%	≤ 19%	0.4[2]
	any	> 19%	0.7
Timber Rivets	≤ 19%	≤ 19%	1.0
	≤ 19%	> 19%	0.8
Withdrawal Loads			
Lag Screws & Wood Screws	any	≤ 19%	1.0
	any	> 19%	0.7
Nails & Spikes[3]	≤ 19%	≤ 19%	1.0
	> 19%	≤ 19%	0.25[3]
	≤ 19%	> 19%	0.25[3]
	> 19%	> 19%	1.0
Pull-Through Loads			
Fasteners with Round Heads	any	≤ 19%	1.0
	any	> 19%	0.7

1. For split ring or shear plate connectors, moisture content limitations apply to a depth of 3/4" below the surface of the wood.
2. C_M = 0.7 for dowel-type fasteners with diameter, D, less than 1/4".
   C_M = 1.0 for dowel-type fastener connections with:
   1) one fastener only, or
   2) two or more fasteners placed in a single row parallel to grain, or
   3) fasteners placed in two or more rows parallel to grain with separate splice plates for each row.
3. For Roof Sheathing Ring Shank (RSRS) and Post-Frame Ring Shank (PF) nails, C_M=1.0.

Table 11.3.4 Temperature Factors, C_t, for Connections

In-Service Moisture Conditions[1]	C_t		
	T≤100°F	100°F<T≤125°F	125°F<T≤150°F
Dry	1.0	0.8	0.7
Wet	1.0	0.7	0.5

1. Wet and dry service conditions for connections are specified in 11.3.3.

11.3.5 Fire Retardant Treatment

Adjusted design values for connections in lumber and structural glued laminated timber pressure-treated with fire retardant chemicals shall be obtained from the company providing the treatment and redrying service (see 2.3.4). The impact load duration factor shall not apply to connections in wood pressure-treated with fire retardant chemicals (see Table 2.3.2).

11.3.6 Group Action Factors, C_g

11.3.6.1 Reference lateral design values for split ring connectors, shear plate connectors, or dowel-type fasteners with $D \leq 1"$ in a row shall be multiplied by the following group action factor, C_g:

$$C_g = \left[\frac{m(1-m^{2n})}{n\left[\left(1+R_{EA}m^n\right)(1+m)-1+m^{2n}\right]} \right] \left[\frac{1+R_{EA}}{1-m} \right] \quad (11.3\text{-}1)$$

where:

C_g = 1.0 for dowel type fasteners with $D < 1/4"$

n = number of fasteners in a row

R_{EA} = the lesser of $\frac{E_sA_s}{E_mA_m}$ or $\frac{E_mA_m}{E_sA_s}$

E_m = modulus of elasticity of main member, psi

E_s = modulus of elasticity of side members, psi

A_m = gross cross-sectional area of main member, in.^{2}

A_s = sum of gross cross-sectional areas of side members, in.^{2}

$m = u - \sqrt{u^2 - 1}$

$u = 1 + \gamma \frac{s}{2} \left[\frac{1}{E_mA_m} + \frac{1}{E_sA_s} \right]$

s = center to center spacing between adjacent fasteners in a row, in.

γ = load/slip modulus for a connection, lbs/in.

= 500,000 lbs/in. for 4" split ring or shear plate connectors

= 400,000 lbs/in. for 2-1/2" split ring or 2-5/8" shear plate connectors

= $(180{,}000)(D^{1.5})$ for dowel-type fasteners in wood-to-wood connections

= $(270{,}000)(D^{1.5})$ for dowel-type fasteners in wood-to-metal connections

D = diameter of dowel-type fastener, in.

Group action factors for various connection geometries are provided in Tables 11.3.6A, 11.3.6B, 11.3.6C, and 11.3.6D.

11.3.6.2 For determining group action factors, a row of fasteners is defined as any of the following:

(a) Two or more split rings or shear plate connector units, as defined in 13.1.1, aligned with the direction of load.

(b) Two or more dowel-type fasteners of the same diameter loaded in single or multiple shear and aligned with the direction of load.

Where fasteners in adjacent rows are staggered and the distance between adjacent rows is less than 1/4 the distance between the closest fasteners in adjacent rows measured parallel to the rows, the adjacent rows shall be considered as one row for purposes of determining group action factors. For groups of fasteners having an even number of rows, this principle shall apply to each pair of rows. For groups of fasteners having an odd number of rows, the most conservative interpretation shall apply (see Figure 11B).

11.3.6.3 Gross section areas shall be used, with no reductions for net section, when calculating A_m and A_s for determining group action factors. When a member is loaded perpendicular to grain its equivalent cross-sectional area shall be the product of the thickness of the member and the overall width of the fastener group (see Figure 11B). Where only one row of fasteners is used, the width of the fastener group shall be the minimum parallel to grain spacing of the fasteners.

Figure 11B Group Action for Staggered Fasteners

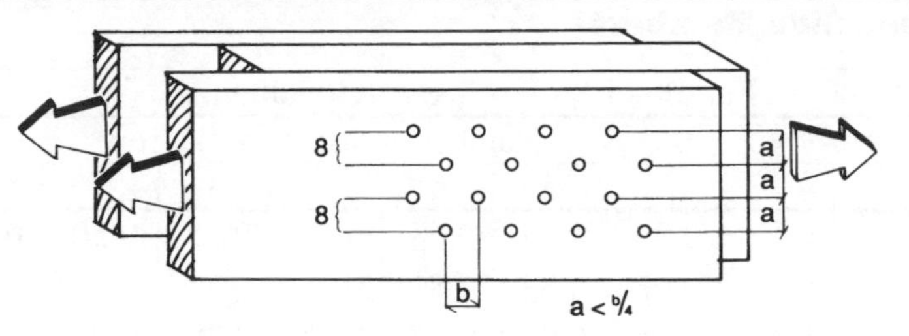

Consider as 2 rows of 8 fasteners

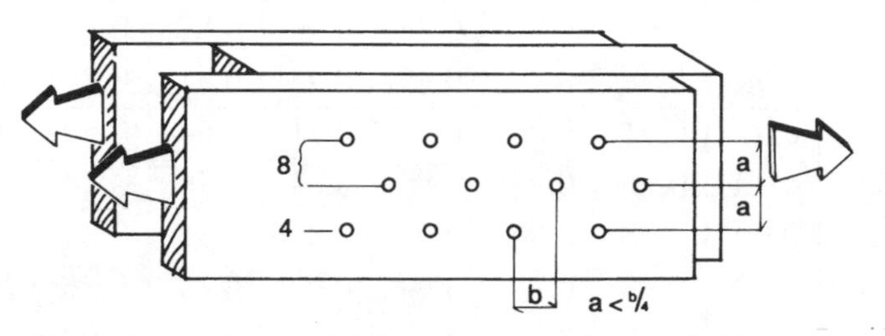

Consider as 1 row of 8 fasteners and 1 row of 4 fasteners

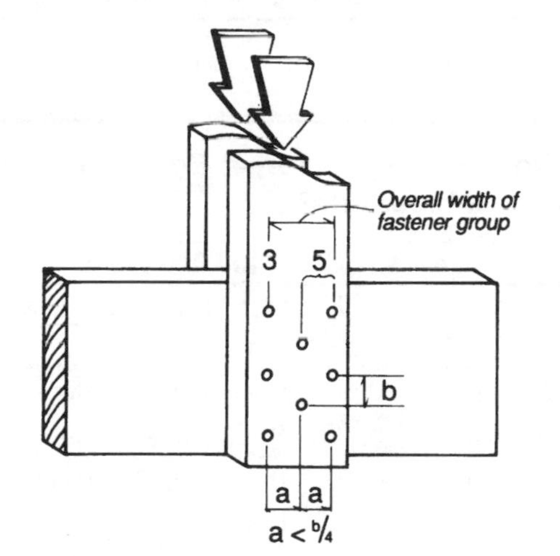

Consider as 1 row of 5 fasteners and 1 row of 3 fasteners

11.3.7 Format Conversion Factor, K_F (LRFD Only)

For LRFD, reference design values shall be multiplied by the format conversion factor, K_F, specified in Table 11.3.1.

11.3.8 Resistance Factor, ϕ (LRFD Only)

For LRFD, reference design values shall be multiplied by the resistance factor, ϕ, specified in Table 11.3.1.

11.3.9 Time Effect Factor, λ (LRFD Only)

For LRFD, reference design values shall be multiplied by the time effect factor, λ, specified in Appendix N.3.3.

Table 11.3.6A Group Action Factors, C_g, for Bolt or Lag Screw Connections with Wood Side Members[2]

For D = 1", s = 4", E = 1,400,000 psi												
A_s/A_m[1]	A_s[1] in.^{2}	Number of fasteners in a row										
		2	3	4	5	6	7	8	9	10	11	12
0.5	5	0.98	0.92	0.84	0.75	0.68	0.61	0.55	0.50	0.45	0.41	0.38
	12	0.99	0.96	0.92	0.87	0.81	0.76	0.70	0.65	0.61	0.57	0.53
	20	0.99	0.98	0.95	0.91	0.87	0.83	0.78	0.74	0.70	0.66	0.62
	28	1.00	0.98	0.96	0.93	0.90	0.87	0.83	0.79	0.76	0.72	0.69
	40	1.00	0.99	0.97	0.95	0.93	0.90	0.87	0.84	0.81	0.78	0.75
	64	1.00	0.99	0.98	0.97	0.95	0.93	0.91	0.89	0.87	0.84	0.82
1	5	1.00	0.97	0.91	0.85	0.78	0.71	0.64	0.59	0.54	0.49	0.45
	12	1.00	0.99	0.96	0.93	0.88	0.84	0.79	0.74	0.70	0.65	0.61
	20	1.00	0.99	0.98	0.95	0.92	0.89	0.86	0.82	0.78	0.75	0.71
	28	1.00	0.99	0.98	0.97	0.94	0.92	0.89	0.86	0.83	0.80	0.77
	40	1.00	1.00	0.99	0.98	0.96	0.94	0.92	0.90	0.87	0.85	0.82
	64	1.00	1.00	0.99	0.98	0.97	0.96	0.95	0.93	0.91	0.90	0.88

1. Where $A_s/A_m > 1.0$, use A_m/A_s and use A_m instead of A_s.
2. Tabulated group action factors (C_g) are conservative for D < 1", s < 4", or E > 1,400,000 psi.

Table 11.3.6B Group Action Factors, C_g, for 4" Split Ring or Shear Plate Connectors with Wood Side Members[2]

s = 9", E = 1,400,000 psi												
A_s/A_m[1]	A_s[1] in.^{2}	Number of fasteners in a row										
		2	3	4	5	6	7	8	9	10	11	12
0.5	5	0.90	0.73	0.59	0.48	0.41	0.35	0.31	0.27	0.25	0.22	0.20
	12	0.95	0.83	0.71	0.60	0.52	0.45	0.40	0.36	0.32	0.29	0.27
	20	0.97	0.88	0.78	0.69	0.60	0.53	0.47	0.43	0.39	0.35	0.32
	28	0.97	0.91	0.82	0.74	0.66	0.59	0.53	0.48	0.44	0.40	0.37
	40	0.98	0.93	0.86	0.79	0.72	0.65	0.59	0.54	0.49	0.45	0.42
	64	0.99	0.95	0.91	0.85	0.79	0.73	0.67	0.62	0.58	0.54	0.50
1	5	1.00	0.87	0.72	0.59	0.50	0.43	0.38	0.34	0.30	0.28	0.25
	12	1.00	0.93	0.83	0.72	0.63	0.55	0.48	0.43	0.39	0.36	0.33
	20	1.00	0.95	0.88	0.79	0.71	0.63	0.57	0.51	0.46	0.42	0.39
	28	1.00	0.97	0.91	0.83	0.76	0.69	0.62	0.57	0.52	0.47	0.44
	40	1.00	0.98	0.93	0.87	0.81	0.75	0.69	0.63	0.58	0.54	0.50
	64	1.00	0.98	0.95	0.91	0.87	0.82	0.77	0.72	0.67	0.62	0.58

1. Where $A_s/A_m > 1.0$, use A_m/A_s and use A_m instead of A_s.
2. Tabulated group action factors (C_g) are conservative for 2-1/2" split ring connectors, 2-5/8" shear plate connectors, s < 9", or E > 1,400,000 psi.

Table 11.3.6C Group Action Factors, C_g, for Bolt or Lag Screw Connections with Steel Side Plates[1]

For D = 1", s = 4", E_{wood} = 1,400,000 psi, E_{steel} = 30,000,000 psi

A_m/A_s	A_m in.^{2}	Number of fasteners in a row										
		2	3	4	5	6	7	8	9	10	11	12
12	5	0.97	0.89	0.80	0.70	0.62	0.55	0.49	0.44	0.40	0.37	0.34
	8	0.98	0.93	0.85	0.77	0.70	0.63	0.57	0.52	0.47	0.43	0.40
	16	0.99	0.96	0.92	0.86	0.80	0.75	0.69	0.64	0.60	0.55	0.52
	24	0.99	0.97	0.94	0.90	0.85	0.81	0.76	0.71	0.67	0.63	0.59
	40	1.00	0.98	0.96	0.94	0.90	0.87	0.83	0.79	0.76	0.72	0.69
	64	1.00	0.99	0.98	0.96	0.94	0.91	0.88	0.86	0.83	0.80	0.77
	120	1.00	0.99	0.99	0.98	0.96	0.95	0.93	0.91	0.90	0.87	0.85
	200	1.00	1.00	0.99	0.99	0.98	0.97	0.96	0.95	0.93	0.92	0.90
18	5	0.99	0.93	0.85	0.76	0.68	0.61	0.54	0.49	0.44	0.41	0.37
	8	0.99	0.95	0.90	0.83	0.75	0.69	0.62	0.57	0.52	0.48	0.44
	16	1.00	0.98	0.94	0.90	0.85	0.79	0.74	0.69	0.65	0.60	0.56
	24	1.00	0.98	0.96	0.93	0.89	0.85	0.80	0.76	0.72	0.68	0.64
	40	1.00	0.99	0.97	0.95	0.93	0.90	0.87	0.83	0.80	0.77	0.73
	64	1.00	0.99	0.98	0.97	0.95	0.93	0.91	0.89	0.86	0.83	0.81
	120	1.00	1.00	0.99	0.98	0.97	0.96	0.95	0.93	0.92	0.90	0.88
	200	1.00	1.00	0.99	0.99	0.98	0.98	0.97	0.96	0.95	0.94	0.92
24	40	1.00	0.99	0.97	0.95	0.93	0.89	0.86	0.83	0.79	0.76	0.72
	64	1.00	0.99	0.98	0.97	0.95	0.93	0.91	0.88	0.85	0.83	0.80
	120	1.00	1.00	0.99	0.98	0.97	0.96	0.95	0.93	0.91	0.90	0.88
	200	1.00	1.00	0.99	0.99	0.98	0.98	0.97	0.96	0.95	0.93	0.92
30	40	1.00	0.98	0.96	0.93	0.89	0.85	0.81	0.77	0.73	0.69	0.65
	64	1.00	0.99	0.97	0.95	0.93	0.90	0.87	0.83	0.80	0.77	0.73
	120	1.00	0.99	0.99	0.97	0.96	0.94	0.92	0.90	0.88	0.85	0.83
	200	1.00	1.00	0.99	0.98	0.97	0.96	0.95	0.94	0.92	0.90	0.89
35	40	0.99	0.97	0.94	0.91	0.86	0.82	0.77	0.73	0.68	0.64	0.60
	64	1.00	0.98	0.96	0.94	0.91	0.87	0.84	0.80	0.76	0.73	0.69
	120	1.00	0.99	0.98	0.97	0.95	0.92	0.90	0.88	0.85	0.82	0.79
	200	1.00	0.99	0.99	0.98	0.97	0.95	0.94	0.92	0.90	0.88	0.86
42	40	0.99	0.97	0.93	0.88	0.83	0.78	0.73	0.68	0.63	0.59	0.55
	64	0.99	0.98	0.95	0.92	0.88	0.84	0.80	0.76	0.72	0.68	0.64
	120	1.00	0.99	0.97	0.95	0.93	0.90	0.88	0.85	0.81	0.78	0.75
	200	1.00	0.99	0.98	0.97	0.96	0.94	0.92	0.90	0.88	0.85	0.83
50	40	0.99	0.96	0.91	0.85	0.79	0.74	0.68	0.63	0.58	0.54	0.51
	64	0.99	0.97	0.94	0.90	0.85	0.81	0.76	0.72	0.67	0.63	0.59
	120	1.00	0.98	0.97	0.94	0.91	0.88	0.85	0.81	0.78	0.74	0.71
	200	1.00	0.99	0.98	0.96	0.95	0.92	0.90	0.87	0.85	0.82	0.79

1. Tabulated group action factors (C_g) are conservative for D < 1" or s < 4".

Table 11.3.6D Group Action Factors, C_g, for 4" Shear Plate Connectors with Steel Side Plates[1]

$s = 9"$, $E_{wood} = 1,400,000$ psi, $E_{steel} = 30,000,000$ psi												
A_m/A_s	A_m in.^{2}	Number of fasteners in a row										
		2	3	4	5	6	7	8	9	10	11	12
12	5	0.91	0.75	0.60	0.50	0.42	0.36	0.31	0.28	0.25	0.23	0.21
	8	0.94	0.80	0.67	0.56	0.47	0.41	0.36	0.32	0.29	0.26	0.24
	16	0.96	0.87	0.76	0.66	0.58	0.51	0.45	0.40	0.37	0.33	0.31
	24	0.97	0.90	0.82	0.73	0.64	0.57	0.51	0.46	0.42	0.39	0.35
	40	0.98	0.94	0.87	0.80	0.73	0.66	0.60	0.55	0.50	0.46	0.43
	64	0.99	0.96	0.91	0.86	0.80	0.74	0.69	0.63	0.59	0.55	0.51
	120	0.99	0.98	0.95	0.91	0.87	0.83	0.79	0.74	0.70	0.66	0.63
	200	1.00	0.99	0.97	0.95	0.92	0.89	0.85	0.82	0.79	0.75	0.72
18	5	0.97	0.83	0.68	0.56	0.47	0.41	0.36	0.32	0.28	0.26	0.24
	8	0.98	0.87	0.74	0.62	0.53	0.46	0.40	0.36	0.32	0.30	0.27
	16	0.99	0.92	0.82	0.73	0.64	0.56	0.50	0.45	0.41	0.37	0.34
	24	0.99	0.94	0.87	0.78	0.70	0.63	0.57	0.51	0.47	0.43	0.39
	40	0.99	0.96	0.91	0.85	0.78	0.72	0.66	0.60	0.55	0.51	0.47
	64	1.00	0.97	0.94	0.89	0.84	0.79	0.74	0.69	0.64	0.60	0.56
	120	1.00	0.99	0.97	0.94	0.90	0.87	0.83	0.79	0.75	0.71	0.67
	200	1.00	0.99	0.98	0.96	0.94	0.91	0.89	0.86	0.82	0.79	0.76
24	40	1.00	0.96	0.91	0.84	0.77	0.71	0.65	0.59	0.54	0.50	0.46
	64	1.00	0.98	0.94	0.89	0.84	0.78	0.73	0.68	0.63	0.58	0.54
	120	1.00	0.99	0.96	0.94	0.90	0.86	0.82	0.78	0.74	0.70	0.66
	200	1.00	0.99	0.98	0.96	0.94	0.91	0.88	0.85	0.82	0.78	0.75
30	40	0.99	0.93	0.86	0.78	0.70	0.63	0.57	0.52	0.47	0.43	0.40
	64	0.99	0.96	0.90	0.84	0.78	0.71	0.66	0.60	0.56	0.51	0.48
	120	0.99	0.98	0.94	0.90	0.86	0.81	0.76	0.71	0.67	0.63	0.59
	200	1.00	0.98	0.96	0.94	0.91	0.87	0.83	0.79	0.76	0.72	0.68
35	40	0.98	0.91	0.83	0.74	0.66	0.59	0.53	0.48	0.43	0.40	0.36
	64	0.99	0.94	0.88	0.81	0.73	0.67	0.61	0.56	0.51	0.47	0.43
	120	0.99	0.97	0.93	0.88	0.82	0.77	0.72	0.67	0.62	0.58	0.54
	200	1.00	0.98	0.95	0.92	0.88	0.84	0.80	0.76	0.71	0.68	0.64
42	40	0.97	0.88	0.79	0.69	0.61	0.54	0.48	0.43	0.39	0.36	0.33
	64	0.98	0.92	0.84	0.76	0.69	0.62	0.56	0.51	0.46	0.42	0.39
	120	0.99	0.95	0.90	0.85	0.78	0.72	0.67	0.62	0.57	0.53	0.49
	200	0.99	0.97	0.94	0.90	0.85	0.80	0.76	0.71	0.67	0.62	0.59
50	40	0.95	0.86	0.75	0.65	0.56	0.49	0.44	0.39	0.35	0.32	0.30
	64	0.97	0.90	0.81	0.72	0.64	0.57	0.51	0.46	0.42	0.38	0.35
	120	0.98	0.94	0.88	0.81	0.74	0.68	0.62	0.57	0.52	0.48	0.45
	200	0.99	0.96	0.92	0.87	0.82	0.77	0.71	0.66	0.62	0.58	0.54

1. Tabulated group action factors (C_g) are conservative for 2-5/8" shear plate connectors or $s < 9"$.

DOWEL-TYPE FASTENERS

(BOLTS, LAG SCREWS, WOOD SCREWS, NAILS/SPIKES, DRIFT BOLTS, AND DRIFT PINS)

AMERICAN WOOD COUNCIL

12.1 General

12.1.1 Scope

Chapter 12 applies to the engineering design of connections using bolts, lag screws, wood screws, nails, spikes, drift bolts, drift pins, or other dowel-type fasteners in sawn lumber, structural glued laminated timber, timber poles, timber piles, structural composite lumber, prefabricated wood I-joists, wood structural panels, and cross-laminated timber.

12.1.2 Terminology

12.1.2.1 "Edge distance" is the distance from the edge of a member to the center of the nearest fastener, measured perpendicular to grain. When a member is loaded perpendicular to grain, the loaded edge shall be defined as the edge in the direction toward which the fastener is acting. The unloaded edge shall be defined as the edge opposite the loaded edge (see Figure 12G).

12.1.2.2 "End distance" is the distance measured parallel to grain from the square-cut end of a member to the center of the nearest bolt (see Figure 12G).

12.1.2.3 "Spacing" is the distance between centers of fasteners measured along a line joining their centers (see Figure 12G).

12.1.2.4 A "row of fasteners" is defined as two or more fasteners aligned with the direction of load (see Figure 12G).

12.1.2.5 End distance, edge distance, and spacing requirements herein are based on wood properties. Wood-to-metal and wood-to-concrete connections are subject to placement provisions as shown in 12.5.1, however, applicable end and edge distance and spacing requirements for metal and concrete, also apply (see 11.2.3 and 11.2.4).

12.1.3 Bolts

12.1.3.1 Installation requirements apply to bolts meeting requirements of ANSI/ASME Standard B18.2.1. See Appendix Table L1 for standard hex bolt dimensions.

12.1.3.2 Holes shall be a minimum of 1/32" to a maximum of 1/16" larger than the bolt diameter. Holes shall be accurately aligned in main members and side plates. Bolts shall not be forcibly driven.

12.1.3.3 A standard cut washer (Appendix Table L6), or metal plate or metal strap of equal or greater dimensions shall be provided between the wood and the bolt head and between the wood and the nut.

12.1.3.4 Edge distances, end distances, and fastener spacings shall not be less than the requirements in Tables 12.5.1A through 12.5.1D.

12.1.4 Lag Screws

12.1.4.1 Installation requirements apply to lag screws meeting requirements of ANSI/ASME Standard B18.2.1. See Appendix Table L2 for standard hex lag screw dimensions.

12.1.4.2 Lead holes for lag screws loaded laterally and in withdrawal shall be bored as follows to avoid splitting of the wood member during connection fabrication:

(a) The clearance hole for the shank shall have the same diameter as the shank, and the same depth of penetration as the length of unthreaded shank.

(b) The lead hole for the threaded portion shall have a diameter equal to 65% to 85% of the shank diameter in wood with $G > 0.6$, 60% to 75% in wood with $0.5 < G \leq 0.6$, and 40% to 70% in wood with $G \leq 0.5$ (see Table 12.3.3A) and a length equal to at least the length of the threaded portion. The larger percentile in each range shall apply to lag screws of greater diameters.

12.1.4.3 Lead holes or clearance holes shall not be required for 3/8" and smaller diameter lag screws loaded primarily in withdrawal in wood with $G \leq 0.5$ (see Table 12.3.3A), provided that edge distances, end distances, and spacing are sufficient to prevent unusual splitting.

12.1.4.4 The threaded portion of the lag screw shall be inserted in its lead hole by turning with a wrench, not by driving with a hammer.

12.1.4.5 No reduction to reference design values is anticipated if soap or other lubricant is used on the lag screw or in the lead holes to facilitate insertion and to prevent damage to the lag screw.

12.1.4.6 The minimum length of lag screw penetration, p_{min}, not including the length of the tapered tip, E, of the lag screw into the main member of single shear connections and the side members of double shear connections shall be 4D.

12.1.4.7 Edge distances, end distances, and fastener spacings shall not be less than the requirements in Tables 12.5.1A through 12.5.1E.

12.1.5 Wood Screws

12.1.5.1 Installation requirements apply to wood screws meeting requirements of ANSI/ASME Standard B18.6.1. See Appendix Table L3 for standard wood screw dimensions.

12.1.5.2 Lead holes for wood screws loaded in withdrawal shall have a diameter equal to approximately 90% of the wood screw root diameter in wood with $G > 0.6$, and approximately 70% of the wood screw root diameter in wood with $0.5 < G \leq 0.6$. Wood with $G \leq 0.5$ (see Table 12.3.3A) is not required to have a lead hole for insertion of wood screws.

12.1.5.3 Lead holes for wood screws loaded laterally shall be bored as follows:

(a) For wood with $G > 0.6$ (see Table 12.3.3A), the part of the lead hole receiving the shank shall have about the same diameter as the shank, and that receiving the threaded portion shall have about the same diameter as the screw at the root of the thread (see Reference 8).

(b) For $G \leq 0.6$ (see Table 12.3.3A), the part of the lead hole receiving the shank shall be about 7/8 the diameter of the shank and that receiving the threaded portion shall be about 7/8 the diameter of the screw at the root of the thread (see Reference 8).

12.1.5.4 The wood screw shall be inserted in its lead hole by turning with a screw driver or other tool, not by driving with a hammer.

12.1.5.5 No reduction to reference design values is anticipated if soap or other lubricant is used on the wood screw or in the lead holes to facilitate insertion and to prevent damage to the wood screw.

12.1.5.6 The minimum length of wood screw penetration, p_{min}, including the length of the tapered tip where part of the penetration into the main member for single shear connections and the side members for double shear connections shall be 6D.

12.1.5.7 Edge distances, end distances, and fastener spacings shall be sufficient to prevent splitting of the wood.

12.1.6 Nails and Spikes

12.1.6.1 Installation requirements apply to common steel wire nails and spikes, box nails, sinker nails, Roof Sheathing Ring Shank nails, and Post-Frame Ring Shank nails meeting requirements in ASTM F1667. Nails and spikes used in engineered construction shall meet the Supplementary Requirements of ASTM F1667 S1 Nail Bending Yield Strength. Nail specifications for engineered construction shall include the minimum lengths, head diameters, and shank diameters for the nails and spikes to be used. See Appendix Table L4 for standard common, box, and sinker nail dimensions, Appendix Table L5 for standard Post-Frame Ring Shank nail dimensions, and Appendix Table L6 for Roof Sheathing Ring Shank nail dimensions.

12.1.6.2 Reference design values herein apply to nailed and spiked connections either with or without bored holes. When a bored hole is desired to prevent splitting of wood, the diameter of the bored hole shall not exceed 90% of the nail or spike diameter for wood with $G > 0.6$, nor 75% of the nail or spike diameter for wood with $G \leq 0.6$ (see Table 12.3.3A).

12.1.6.3 Toe-nails shall be driven at an angle of approximately 30° with the member and started approximately 1/3 the length of the nail from the member end (see Figure 12A).

Figure 12A Toe-Nail Connection

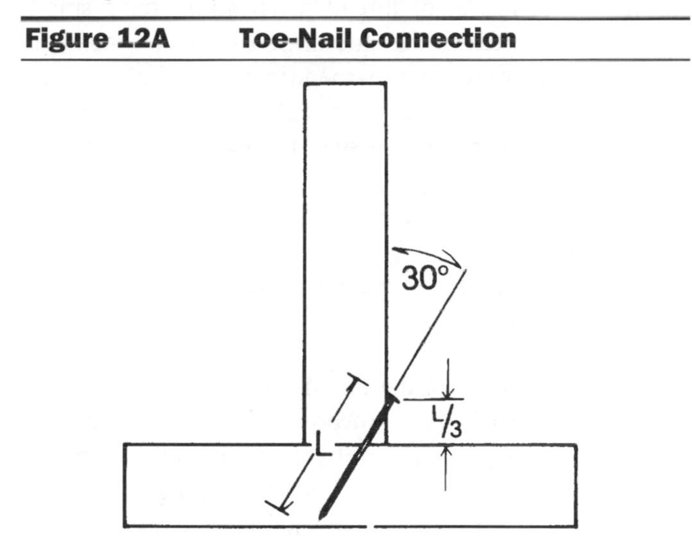

12.1.6.4 The minimum length of nail or spike penetration, p_{min}, including the length of the tapered tip where part of the penetration into the main member for single shear connections and the side members of double shear connections shall be 6D.

> **Exception:** The minimum length of penetration, p_{min}, need not be 6D for symmetric double shear connections where nails with diameter of 0.148" or smaller extend at least three diameters beyond the side member and are clinched, and side members are at least 3/8" thick.

12.1.6.5 Edge distances, end distances, and fastener spacings shall be sufficient to prevent splitting of the wood.

12.1.7 Drift Bolts and Drift Pins

12.1.7.1 Lead holes shall be drilled 0" to 1/32" smaller than the actual pin diameter.

12.1.7.2 Additional penetration of pin into members shall be provided in lieu of the washer, head, and nut on a common bolt (see Reference 53 for additional information).

12.1.7.3 Edge distances, end distances, and fastener spacings shall not be less than the requirements in Tables 12.5.1A through 12.5.1D.

12.1.8 Other Dowel-Type Fasteners

Where fastener type or installation requirements vary from those specified in 12.1.3, 12.1.4, 12.1.5, 12.1.6, and 12.1.7, provisions of 12.2 and 12.3 shall be permitted to be used in the determination of reference withdrawal and lateral design values, respectively, provided allowance is made to account for such variation (see 11.1.1.3). Edge distances, end distances, and spacings shall be sufficient to prevent splitting of the wood.

12.2 Reference Withdrawal and Pull-Through Design Values

12.2.1 Lag Screws

12.2.1.1 The lag screw reference withdrawal design value, W, in lbs/in. of thread penetration, for a single lag screw inserted in the side grain of a wood member, with the lag screw axis perpendicular to the wood fibers, shall be determined from Table 12.2A or Equation 12.2-1, within the range of specific gravities, G, and lag screw diameters, D, given in Table 12.2A. Reference withdrawal design values, W, shall be multiplied by all applicable adjustment factors (see Table 11.3.1) to obtain adjusted withdrawal design values, W'.

$$W = 1800\, G^{3/2} D^{3/4} \qquad (12.2\text{-}1)$$

12.2.1.2 For calculation of the fastener reference withdrawal design value in pounds, the unit reference withdrawal design value in lbs/in. of thread penetration from 12.2.1.1 shall be multiplied by the length of thread penetration, p_t, into a wood member, excluding the length of the tapered tip.

12.2.1.3 Where lag screws are loaded in withdrawal from end grain, reference withdrawal design values, W, shall be multiplied by the end grain factor, $C_{eg} = 0.75$.

12.2.1.4 Where lag screws are loaded in withdrawal, the tensile strength of the lag screw at the net section (root diameter, D_r) shall not be exceeded (see 11.2.3 and Appendix Table L2).

12.2.1.5 Where lag screws are loaded in withdrawal from the narrow edge of cross-laminated timber, the reference withdrawal value, W, shall be multiplied by the end grain factor, $C_{eg}=0.75$, regardless of grain orientation.

12.2.2 Wood Screws

12.2.2.1 The wood screw reference withdrawal design value, W, in lbs/in. of thread penetration, for a single wood screw (cut thread or rolled thread) inserted in the side grain of a wood member, with the wood screw axis perpendicular to the wood fibers, shall be determined from Table 12.2B or Equation 12.2-2, within the range of specific gravities, G, and screw diameters, D, given in Table 12.2B. Reference withdrawal design values, W, shall be multiplied by all applicable adjustment factors (see Table 11.3.1) to obtain adjusted withdrawal design values, W'.

$$W = 2850\, G^2 D \qquad (12.2\text{-}2)$$

12.2.2.2 For calculation of the fastener reference withdrawal design value in pounds, the unit reference withdrawal design value in lbs/in. of thread penetration from 12.2.2.1 shall be multiplied by the length of thread penetration, p_t, into the wood member.

12.2.2.3 Wood screws shall not be loaded in withdrawal from end grain of wood ($C_{eg}=0.0$).

12.2.2.4 Wood screws shall not be loaded in withdrawal from end-grain of laminations in cross-laminated timber ($C_{eg}=0.0$).

12.2.2.5 Where wood screws are loaded in withdrawal, the adjusted tensile strength of the wood screw at the net section (root diameter, D_r) shall not be exceeded (see 11.2.3 and Appendix Table L3).

12.2.3 Nails and Spikes

12.2.3.1 Smooth shank nails or spikes

(a) The nail or spike reference withdrawal design value, W, in lbs/in. of penetration, for a smooth shank (bright or galvanized) carbon steel nail or spike driven into the side grain of a wood member, with the nail or spike axis perpendicular to the wood fibers, shall be determined from Table 12.2C or Equation 12.2-3, within the range of specific gravities, G, and nail or spike diameters, D, given in Table 12.2C. Reference withdrawal design values, W, shall be multiplied by all applicable

Table 12.2A Lag Screw Reference Withdrawal Values, W[1]

Tabulated withdrawal design values (W) are in pounds per inch of thread penetration into side grain of wood member. Length of thread penetration in main member shall not include the length of the tapered tip (see 12.2.1.1).

Specific Gravity, G[2]	Lag Screw Diameter, D										
	1/4"	5/16"	3/8"	7/16"	1/2"	5/8"	3/4"	7/8"	1"	1-1/8"	1-1/4"
0.73	397	469	538	604	668	789	905	1016	1123	1226	1327
0.71	381	450	516	579	640	757	868	974	1077	1176	1273
0.68	357	422	484	543	600	709	813	913	1009	1103	1193
0.67	349	413	473	531	587	694	796	893	987	1078	1167
0.58	281	332	381	428	473	559	641	719	795	869	940
0.55	260	307	352	395	437	516	592	664	734	802	868
0.51	232	274	314	353	390	461	528	593	656	716	775
0.50	225	266	305	342	378	447	513	576	636	695	752
0.49	218	258	296	332	367	434	498	559	617	674	730
0.47	205	242	278	312	345	408	467	525	580	634	686
0.46	199	235	269	302	334	395	453	508	562	613	664
0.44	186	220	252	283	312	369	423	475	525	574	621
0.43	179	212	243	273	302	357	409	459	508	554	600
0.42	173	205	235	264	291	344	395	443	490	535	579
0.41	167	198	226	254	281	332	381	428	473	516	559
0.40	161	190	218	245	271	320	367	412	455	497	538
0.39	155	183	210	236	261	308	353	397	438	479	518
0.38	149	176	202	227	251	296	340	381	422	461	498
0.37	143	169	194	218	241	285	326	367	405	443	479
0.36	137	163	186	209	231	273	313	352	389	425	460
0.35	132	156	179	200	222	262	300	337	373	407	441
0.31	110	130	149	167	185	218	250	281	311	339	367

1. Tabulated withdrawal design values, W, for lag screw connections shall be multiplied by all applicable adjustment factors (see Table 11.3.1).
2. Specific gravity, G, shall be determined in accordance with Table 12.3.3A.

adjustment factors (see Table 11.3.1) to obtain adjusted withdrawal design values, W'.

$$W = 1380\ G^{5/2}\ D \qquad (12.2\text{-}3)$$

(b) The nail or spike reference withdrawal design value, W, in lbs/in. of penetration, for a smooth shank stainless steel nail or spike driven into the side grain of a wood member, with the nail or spike axis perpendicular to the wood fibers, shall be determined from Table 12.2D or Equation 12.2-4, within the range of specific gravities, G, and nail or spike diameters, D, given in Table 12.2D. Reference withdrawal design values, W, shall be multiplied by all applicable adjustment factors (see Table 11.3.1) to obtain adjusted withdrawal design values, W'.

$$W = 465\ G^{3/2}\ D \qquad (12.2\text{-}4)$$

(c) For calculation of the fastener reference withdrawal design value in pounds, the unit reference withdrawal design value in lbs/in. of fastener penetration from 12.2.3.1a or 12.2.3.1b shall be multiplied by the length of fastener penetration, p_t, into the wood member.

12.2.3.2 Deformed shank nails

(a) The reference withdrawal design value, in lbs/in. of ring shank penetration, for a Roof Sheathing Ring Shank nail or Post-Frame Ring Shank nail driven in the side grain of the main member, with the nail axis perpendicular to the wood fibers, shall be determined from Table 12.2E or Equation 12.2-5, within the range of specific gravities and nail diameters given in Table 12.2E. Reference withdrawal design values, W, shall be multiplied by all applicable adjustment factors (see Table 11.3.1) to obtain adjusted withdrawal design values, W'.

$$W = 1800\ G^{2}\ D \qquad (12.2\text{-}5)$$

Table 12.2B Cut Thread or Rolled Thread Wood Screw Reference Withdrawal Design Values, W[1]

Tabulated withdrawal design values, W, are in pounds per inch of thread penetration into side grain of wood member (see 12.2.2.1).

Specific Gravity, G[2]	Wood Screw Number										
	6	7	8	9	10	12	14	16	18	20	24
0.73	209	229	249	268	288	327	367	406	446	485	564
0.71	198	216	235	254	272	310	347	384	421	459	533
0.68	181	199	216	233	250	284	318	352	387	421	489
0.67	176	193	209	226	243	276	309	342	375	409	475
0.58	132	144	157	169	182	207	232	256	281	306	356
0.55	119	130	141	152	163	186	208	231	253	275	320
0.51	102	112	121	131	141	160	179	198	217	237	275
0.50	98	107	117	126	135	154	172	191	209	228	264
0.49	94	103	112	121	130	147	165	183	201	219	254
0.47	87	95	103	111	119	136	152	168	185	201	234
0.46	83	91	99	107	114	130	146	161	177	193	224
0.44	76	83	90	97	105	119	133	148	162	176	205
0.43	73	79	86	93	100	114	127	141	155	168	196
0.42	69	76	82	89	95	108	121	134	147	161	187
0.41	66	72	78	85	91	103	116	128	141	153	178
0.40	63	69	75	81	86	98	110	122	134	146	169
0.39	60	65	71	77	82	93	105	116	127	138	161
0.38	57	62	67	73	78	89	99	110	121	131	153
0.37	54	59	64	69	74	84	94	104	114	125	145
0.36	51	56	60	65	70	80	89	99	108	118	137
0.35	48	53	57	62	66	75	84	93	102	111	130
0.31	38	41	45	48	52	59	66	73	80	87	102

1. Tabulated withdrawal design values, W, for wood screw connections shall be multiplied by all applicable adjustment factors (see Table 11.3.1).
2. Specific gravity, G, shall be determined in accordance with Table 12.3.3A.

(b) For Roof Sheathing Ring Shank nails (Appendix Table L6) or Post-Frame Ring Shank nails (Appendix Table L5) that are uncoated carbon steel, reference withdrawal design values determined from Table 12.2E or Equation 12.2-5 shall be permitted to be multiplied by 1.25.

(c) For calculation of the fastener reference withdrawal design value in pounds, the unit reference withdrawal design value in lbs/in. of ring shank penetration from 12.2.3.2a or 12.2.3.2b shall be multiplied by the length of ring shank penetration, p_t, into the wood member.

(d) For other deformed shank nails, reference withdrawal design values shall be permitted to be calculated in accordance with 12.2.3.1.

12.2.3.3 Nails and spikes shall not be loaded in withdrawal from end grain of wood (C_{eg}=0.0).

12.2.3.4 Nails and spikes shall not be loaded in withdrawal from end-grain of laminations in cross-laminated timber (C_{eg}=0.0).

12.2.4 Drift Bolts and Drift Pins

Reference withdrawal design values, W, for connections using drift bolt and drift pin connections shall be determined in accordance with 11.1.1.3.

12.2.5 Fastener Head Pull-Through

12.2.5.1 For fasteners with round heads, the reference pull-through design value, W_H, in pounds for wood side members shall be determined from Table 12.2F or Equation 12.2-6, within the range of fastener head diameters, D_H, and net side member thicknesses, t_{ns}, given in Table 12.2F. Reference pull-through design values, W_H, shall be multiplied by all applicable adjustment factors (see Table 11.3.1) to obtain adjusted pull-through design values, W'_H.

Table 12.2C Smooth Shank (Bright or Galvanized) Carbon Steel Nail and Spike Reference Withdrawal Design Values, W[1,3]

Tabulated withdrawal design values, W, are in pounds per inch of fastener penetration into side grain of wood member (see 12.2.3.1)

Specific Gravity[2], G	Smooth Shank (Bright or Galvanized) Carbon Steel Nail and Spike Diameter, D																	
	0.092"	0.099"	0.113"	0.120"	0.128"	0.131"	0.135"	0.148"	0.162"	0.177"	0.192"	0.207"	0.225"	0.244"	0.263"	0.283"	0.312"	0.375"
0.73	58	62	71	75	80	82	85	93	102	111	121	130	141	153	165	178	196	236
0.71	54	58	66	70	75	77	79	87	95	104	113	121	132	143	154	166	183	220
0.68	48	52	59	63	67	69	71	78	85	93	101	109	118	128	138	149	164	197
0.67	47	50	57	61	65	66	68	75	82	90	97	105	114	124	133	144	158	190
0.58	33	35	40	42	45	46	48	52	57	63	68	73	80	86	93	100	110	133
0.55	28	31	35	37	40	41	42	46	50	55	59	64	70	76	81	88	97	116
0.51	24	25	29	31	33	34	35	38	42	45	49	53	58	63	67	73	80	96
0.50	22	24	28	29	31	32	33	36	40	43	47	50	55	60	64	69	76	91
0.49	21	23	26	28	30	30	31	34	38	41	45	48	52	57	61	66	72	87
0.47	19	21	24	25	27	27	28	31	34	37	40	43	47	51	55	59	65	78
0.46	18	20	22	24	25	26	27	29	32	35	38	41	45	48	52	56	62	74
0.44	16	18	20	21	23	23	24	26	29	31	34	37	40	43	47	50	55	66
0.43	15	17	19	20	21	22	23	25	27	30	32	35	38	41	44	47	52	63
0.42	15	16	18	19	20	21	21	23	26	28	30	33	35	38	41	45	49	59
0.41	14	15	17	18	19	19	20	22	24	26	29	31	33	36	39	42	46	56
0.40	13	14	16	17	18	18	19	21	23	25	27	29	31	34	37	40	44	52
0.39	12	13	15	16	17	17	18	19	21	23	25	27	29	32	34	37	41	49
0.38	11	12	14	15	16	16	17	18	20	22	24	25	28	30	32	35	38	46
0.37	11	11	13	14	15	15	16	17	19	20	22	24	26	28	30	33	36	43
0.36	10	11	12	13	14	14	14	16	17	19	21	22	24	26	28	30	33	40
0.35	9	10	11	12	13	13	14	15	16	18	19	21	23	24	26	28	31	38
0.31	7	7	8	9	9	10	10	11	12	13	14	15	17	18	19	21	23	28

1. Tabulated withdrawal design values, W, for nail or spike connections shall be multiplied by all applicable adjustment factors (see Table 11.3.1).
2. Specific gravity shall be determined in accordance with Table 12.3.3A.
3. Tabulated withdrawal design values for smooth shank nails are permitted to be used for deformed shank nails of equivalent diameter, D.

Table 12.2D Smooth Shank Stainless Steel Nail and Spike Reference Withdrawal Design Values, W[1,3]

Tabulated withdrawal design values, W, are in pounds per inch of fastener penetration into side grain of wood member (see 12.2.3.1)

Specific Gravity[2], G	Smooth Shank Stainless Steel Nail and Spike Diameter, D																	
	0.092"	0.099"	0.113"	0.120"	0.128"	0.131"	0.135"	0.148"	0.162"	0.177"	0.192"	0.207"	0.225"	0.244"	0.263"	0.283"	0.312"	0.375"
0.73	27	29	33	35	37	38	39	43	47	51	56	60	65	71	76	82	90	109
0.71	26	28	31	33	36	36	38	41	45	49	53	58	63	68	73	79	87	104
0.68	24	26	29	31	33	34	35	39	42	46	50	54	59	64	69	74	81	98
0.67	23	25	29	31	33	33	34	38	41	45	49	53	57	62	67	72	80	96
0.58	19	20	23	25	26	27	28	30	33	36	39	43	46	50	54	58	64	77
0.55	17	19	21	23	24	25	26	28	31	34	36	39	43	46	50	54	59	71
0.51	16	17	19	20	22	22	23	25	27	30	33	35	38	41	45	48	53	64
0.50	15	16	19	20	21	22	22	24	27	29	32	34	37	40	43	47	51	62
0.49	15	16	18	19	20	21	22	24	26	28	31	33	36	39	42	45	50	60
0.47	14	15	17	18	19	20	20	22	24	27	29	31	34	37	39	42	47	56
0.46	13	14	16	17	19	19	20	21	24	26	28	30	33	35	38	41	45	54
0.44	12	13	15	16	17	18	18	20	22	24	26	28	31	33	36	38	42	51
0.43	12	13	15	16	17	17	18	19	21	23	25	27	30	32	34	37	41	49
0.42	12	13	14	15	16	17	17	19	21	22	24	26	28	31	33	36	39	47
0.41	11	12	14	15	16	16	16	18	20	22	23	25	27	30	32	35	38	46
0.40	11	12	13	14	15	15	16	17	19	21	23	24	26	29	31	33	37	44
0.39	10	11	13	14	14	15	15	17	18	20	22	23	25	28	30	32	35	42
0.38	10	11	12	13	14	14	15	16	18	19	21	23	25	27	29	31	34	41
0.37	10	10	12	13	13	14	14	15	17	19	20	22	24	26	28	30	33	39
0.36	9	10	11	12	13	13	14	15	16	18	19	21	23	25	26	28	31	38
0.35	9	10	11	12	12	13	13	14	16	17	18	20	22	23	25	27	30	36
0.31	7	8	9	10	10	11	11	12	13	14	15	17	18	20	21	23	25	30

1. Tabulated withdrawal design values, W, for nail or spike connections shall be multiplied by all applicable adjustment factors (see Table 11.3.1).

2. Specific gravity shall be determined in accordance with Table 12.3.3A.

3. Tabulated withdrawal design values for smooth shank stainless steel nails are permitted to be used for deformed shank stainless steel nails of equivalent diameter, D.

Table 12.2E Roof Sheathing Ring Shank Nail and Post-Frame Ring Shank Nail Reference Withdrawal Design Values, W[1,2]

Tabulated withdrawal design values, W, are in pounds per inch of ring shank penetration into side grain of wood main member (see Appendix Table L5 and Table L6).

Specific Gravity[3], G	Roof Sheathing Ring Shank Nail Diameter, D (in.)			Post-Frame Ring Shank Nail Diameter, D (in.)				
	0.113	0.120	0.131	0.135	0.148	0.177	0.200	0.207
0.73	108	115	126	129	142	170	192	199
0.71	103	109	119	122	134	161	181	188
0.68	94	100	109	112	123	147	166	172
0.67	91	97	106	109	120	143	162	167
0.58	68	73	79	82	90	107	121	125
0.55	62	65	71	74	81	96	109	113
0.51	53	56	61	63	69	83	94	97
0.50	51	54	59	61	67	80	90	93
0.49	49	52	57	58	64	76	86	89
0.47	45	48	52	54	59	70	80	82
0.46	43	46	50	51	56	67	76	79
0.44	39	42	46	47	52	62	70	72
0.43	38	40	44	45	49	59	67	69
0.42	36	38	42	43	47	56	64	66
0.41	34	36	40	41	45	54	61	63
0.40	33	35	38	39	43	51	58	60
0.39	31	33	36	37	41	48	55	57
0.38	29	31	34	35	38	46	52	54
0.37	28	30	32	33	36	44	49	51
0.36	26	28	31	31	35	41	47	48
0.35	25	26	29	30	33	39	44	46
0.31	20	21	23	23	26	31	35	36

1. Tabulated withdrawal design values, W, for Roof Sheathing Ring Shank (RSRS) nails and Post-Frame Ring Shank (PF) nails shall be multiplied by all applicable adjustment factors (see Table 11.3.1).
2. Tabulated reference withdrawal design values, W, are only applicable to Roof Sheathing Ring Shank (RSRS) nails or Post-Frame Ring Shank (PF) nails meeting requirements of ASTM F1667.
3. Specific gravity shall be determined in accordance with Table 12.3.3A.

$W_H = 690\ \pi\ D_H\ G^2\ t_{ns}$ for $t_{ns} \leq 2.5\ D_H$ (12.2-6a)

$W_H = 1725\ \pi\ D_H^2\ G^2$ for $t_{ns} > 2.5\ D_H$ (12.2-6b)

Where:

πD_H = perimeter for fasteners with round heads

D_H = fastener head diameter, in.

G = specific gravity of side member

Pull-through for other materials shall be determined in accordance with 11.1.1.3.

Table 12.2F Head Pull-Through, W_H[1]

Tabulated pull-through design values, W_H, are in pounds.

Side Member Specific Gravity[2], G	Head Diameter, D_H (in.)	Net Side Member Thickness, t_{ns} (in.)											
		5/16	3/8	7/16	15/32	1/2	19/32	5/8	23/32	3/4	1	1-1/8	1-1/2
0.50	0.234	40	48	55	59	63	74	74	74	74	74	74	74
	0.250	42	51	59	64	68	80	85	85	85	85	85	85
	0.266	45	54	63	68	72	86	90	96	96	96	96	96
	0.281	48	57	67	71	76	90	95	107	107	107	107	107
	0.297	50	60	70	75	80	96	101	116	120	120	120	120
	0.312	53	63	74	79	85	100	106	122	127	132	132	132
	0.344	58	70	82	87	93	111	117	134	140	160	160	160
	0.375	64	76	89	95	102	121	127	146	152	191	191	191
	0.406	69	83	96	103	110	131	138	158	165	220	223	223
	0.438	74	89	104	111	119	141	148	171	178	237	260	260
	0.469	79	95	111	119	127	151	159	183	191	254	286	298
	0.500	85	102	119	127	135	161	169	195	203	271	305	339
0.42	0.234	28	34	39	42	45	52	52	52	52	52	52	52
	0.250	30	36	42	45	48	57	60	60	60	60	60	60
	0.266	32	38	44	48	51	60	64	68	68	68	68	68
	0.281	34	40	47	50	54	64	67	75	75	75	75	75
	0.297	35	43	50	53	57	67	71	82	84	84	84	84
	0.312	37	45	52	56	60	71	75	86	89	93	93	93
	0.344	41	49	58	62	66	78	82	95	99	113	113	113
	0.375	45	54	63	67	72	85	90	103	108	134	134	134
	0.406	49	58	68	73	78	92	97	112	116	155	158	158
	0.438	52	63	73	79	84	99	105	120	126	167	183	183
	0.469	56	67	78	84	90	106	112	129	135	179	202	210
	0.500	60	72	84	90	96	114	119	137	143	191	215	239

1. Tabulated pull-through design values, W_H, shall be multiplied by all adjustment factors as applicable per Table 11.3.1.
2. Specific gravity, G, shall be determined in accordance with Table 12.3.3A for lumber and Table 12.3.3B for panels.

12.3 Reference Lateral Design Values

12.3.1 Yield Limit Equations

Reference lateral design values, Z, for single shear and symmetric double shear connections using dowel-type fasteners shall be the minimum computed yield mode value using equations in Tables 12.3.1A and 12.3.1B (see Figures 12B, 12C, and Appendix I) where:

(a) the faces of the connected members are in contact;

(b) the load acts perpendicular to the axis of the dowel;

(c) edge distances, end distances, and spacing are not less than the requirements in 12.5; and

(d) for lag screws, wood screws, and nails and spikes, the length of fastener penetration, p, into the main member of a single shear connection or the side member of a double shear connection is greater than or equal to p_{min} (see 12.1).

12.3.2 Common Connection Conditions

Reference lateral design values, Z, for connections with bolts (see Tables 12A through 12I), lag screws (see Tables 12J and 12K), wood screws (see Tables 12L and 12M), nails and spikes (see Tables 12N through 12R), and post-frame ring shank nails (see Tables 12S and 12T), are calculated for common connection conditions in accordance with yield mode equations in Tables 12.3.1A and 12.3.1B. Tabulated reference lateral design values, Z, shall be multiplied by applicable Table footnotes to determine an adjusted lateral design value, Z'.

Table 12.3.1A Yield Limit Equations

Yield Mode	Single Shear		Double Shear	
I_m	$Z=\frac{D\,\ell_m\,F_{em}}{R_d}$	(12.3-1)	$Z=\frac{D\,\ell_m\,F_{em}}{R_d}$	(12.3-7)
I_s	$Z=\frac{D\,\ell_s\,F_{es}}{R_d}$	(12.3-2)	$Z=\frac{2\,D\,\ell_s\,F_{es}}{R_d}$	(12.3-8)
II	$Z=\frac{k_1\,D\,\ell_s\,F_{es}}{R_d}$	(12.3-3)		
III_m	$Z=\frac{k_2\,D\,\ell_m\,F_{em}}{(1+2R_e)\,R_d}$	(12.3-4)		
III_s	$Z=\frac{k_3\,D\,\ell_s\,F_{em}}{(2+R_e)\,R_d}$	(12.3-5)	$Z=\frac{2\,k_3\,D\,\ell_s\,F_{em}}{(2+R_e)\,R_d}$	(12.3-9)
IV	$Z=\frac{D^2}{R_d}\sqrt{\frac{2\,F_{em}\,F_{yb}}{3\,(1+R_e)}}$	(12.3-6)	$Z=\frac{2\,D^2}{R_d}\sqrt{\frac{2\,F_{em}\,F_{yb}}{3\,(1+R_e)}}$	(12.3-10)

Notes:

$$k_1=\frac{\sqrt{R_e+2R_e^{2}(1+R_t+R_t^{2})+R_t^{2}R_e^{3}}-R_e(1+R_t)}{(1+R_e)}$$

$$k_2=-1+\sqrt{2(1+R_e)+\frac{2F_{yb}(1+2R_e)D^2}{3F_{em}\ell_m^{2}}}$$

$$k_3=-1+\sqrt{\frac{2(1+R_e)}{R_e}+\frac{2F_{yb}(2+R_e)D^2}{3F_{em}\ell_s^{2}}}$$

D = diameter, in. (see 12.3.7)

F_{yb} = dowel bending yield strength, psi

R_d = reduction term (see Table 12.3.1B)

R_e = F_{em}/F_{es}

R_t = ℓ_m/ℓ_s

ℓ_m = main member dowel bearing length, in.

ℓ_s = side member dowel bearing length, in.

F_{em} = main member dowel bearing strength, psi (see Table 12.3.3)

F_{es} = side member dowel bearing strength, psi (see Table 12.3.3)

DOWEL-TYPE FASTENERS

12

Table 12.3.1B Reduction Term, R_d

Fastener Size	Yield Mode	Reduction Term, R_d
$0.25" \le D \le 1"$	I_m, I_s	$4\ K_\theta$
	II	$3.6\ K_\theta$
	III_m, III_s, IV	$3.2\ K_\theta$
$D < 0.25"$	I_m, I_s, II, III_m, III_s, IV	K_D [1]

Notes:
K_θ = $1 + 0.25(\theta/90)$
θ = maximum angle between the direction of load and the direction of grain ($0^\circ \le \theta \le 90^\circ$) for any member in a connection
D = diameter, in. (see 12.3.7)
K_D = 2.2 for $D \le 0.17"$
K_D = $10D + 0.5$ for $0.17" < D < 0.25"$

1. For threaded fasteners where nominal diameter (see Appendix L) is greater than or equal to 0.25" and root diameter is less than 0.25", $R_d = K_D\ K_\theta$.

12.3.3 Dowel Bearing Strength

12.3.3.1 Dowel bearing strengths, F_e, for wood members other than wood structural panels and structural composite lumber shall be determined from Table 12.3.3.

12.3.3.2 Dowel bearing strengths, F_e, for dowel-type fasteners with $D \le 1/4"$ in wood structural panels shall be determined from Table 12.3.3B.

12.3.3.3 Dowel bearing strengths, F_e, for structural composite lumber shall be determined from the manufacturer's literature or code evaluation report.

12.3.3.4 Where dowel-type fasteners with $D \ge 1/4"$ are inserted into the end grain of the main member, with the fastener axis parallel to the wood fibers, $F_{e\perp}$ shall be used in the determination of the dowel bearing strength of the main member, F_{em}.

12.3.3.5 Dowel bearing strengths, F_e, for dowel-type fasteners installed into the panel face of cross-laminated timber shall be based on the direction of loading with respect to the grain orientation of the cross-laminated timber ply at the shear plane.

12.3.3.6 Where dowel-type fasteners are installed in the narrow edge of cross-laminated timber panels, the dowel bearing strength shall be $F_{e\perp}$ for $D \ge 1/4"$ and F_e for $D < 1/4"$.

12.3.4 Dowel Bearing Strength at an Angle to Grain

Where a member in a connection is loaded at an angle to grain, the dowel bearing strength, $F_{e\theta}$, for the member shall be determined as follows (see Appendix J):

$$F_{e\theta} = \frac{F_{e\|}F_{e\perp}}{F_{e\|}\sin^2\theta + F_{e\perp}\cos^2\theta} \quad (12.3\text{-}11)$$

where:

θ = angle between the direction of load and the direction of grain (longitudinal axis of member)

12.3.5 Dowel Bearing Length

12.3.5.1 Dowel bearing length in the side member(s) and main member, ℓ_s and ℓ_m, shall be determined based on the length of dowel bearing perpendicular to the application of load.

12.3.5.2 For cross-laminated timber where the direction of loading relative to the grain orientation at the shear plane is parallel to grain, the dowel bearing length in the perpendicular plies shall be reduced by multiplying the bearing length of those plies by the ratio of dowel bearing strength perpendicular to grain to dowel bearing strength parallel to grain ($F_{e\perp} / F_{e\|}$).

Figure 12B Single Shear Bolted Connections

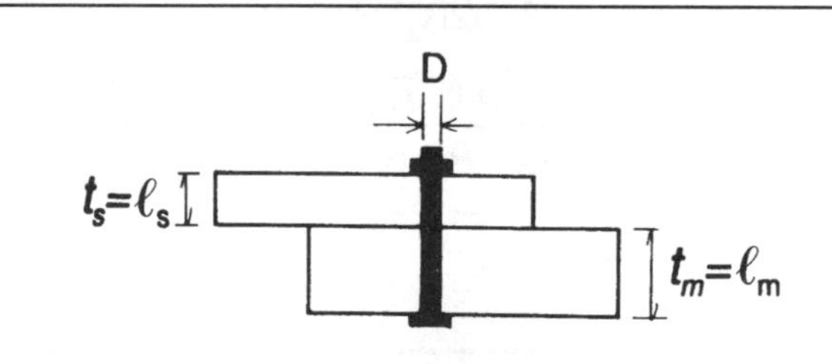

Figure 12C Double Shear Bolted Connections

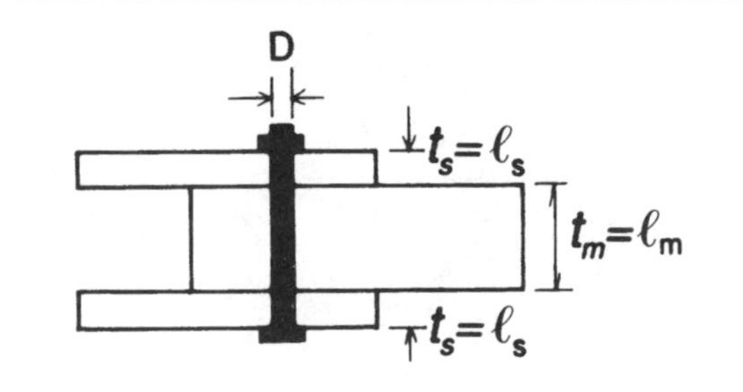

12.3.5.3 For lag screws, wood screws, nails, spikes, and similar dowel-type fasteners, the dowel bearing length, ℓ_s or ℓ_m, shall not exceed the length of fastener penetration, p, into the wood member. Where p includes the length of a tapered tip, E, the dowel bearing length, ℓ_s or ℓ_m, shall not exceed p - E/2.

(a) For lag screws, E is permitted to be taken from Appendix L, Table L2.

(b) For wood screws, nails, and spikes, E is permitted to be taken as 2D.

12.3.6 Dowel Bending Yield Strength

12.3.6.1 The reference lateral design values, Z, for bolts, lag screws, wood screws, and nails are based on dowel bending yield strengths, F_{yb}, provided in Tables 12A through 12T.

12.3.6.2 Dowel bending yield strengths, F_{yb}, used in the determination of reference lateral design values, Z, shall be based on yield strength derived using the methods provided in ASTM F 1575 or the tensile yield strength derived using the procedures of ASTM F 606.

12.3.7 Dowel Diameter

12.3.7.1 Where used in Tables 12.3.1A and 12.3.1B, the fastener diameter shall be taken as:

(a) D for smooth shank nails and deformed shank nails in accordance with ASTM F1667,

(b) D for unthreaded full-body diameter fasteners, and

(c) D_r for reduced body diameter fasteners or threaded fasteners except as provided in 12.3.7.2.

12.3.7.2 For threaded full-body fasteners (see Appendix L), D shall be permitted to be used in lieu of D_r where the bearing length of the threads does not exceed ¼ of the full bearing length in the member holding the threads. Alternatively, a more detailed analysis accounting for the moment and bearing resistance of the threaded portion of the fastener shall be permitted (see Appendix I).

Table 12.3.3 Dowel Bearing Strengths, F_e, for Dowel-Type Fasteners in Wood Members

Specific[1] Gravity, G	Dowel bearing strength in pounds per square inch (psi)[2]										
	F_e	$F_{e\|}$	$F_{e\perp}$								
	D<1/4"	1/4" ≤ D ≤ 1"	D=1/4"	D=5/16"	D=3/8"	D=7/16"	D=1/2"	D=5/8"	D=3/4"	D=7/8"	D=1"
0.73	9300	8200	7750	6900	6300	5850	5450	4900	4450	4150	3850
0.72	9050	8050	7600	6800	6200	5750	5350	4800	4350	4050	3800
0.71	8850	7950	7400	6650	6050	5600	5250	4700	4300	3950	3700
0.70	8600	7850	7250	6500	5950	5500	5150	4600	4200	3900	3650
0.69	8400	7750	7100	6350	5800	5400	5050	4500	4100	3800	3550
0.68	8150	7600	6950	6250	5700	5250	4950	4400	4050	3750	3500
0.67	7950	7500	6850	6100	5550	5150	4850	4300	3950	3650	3400
0.66	7750	7400	6700	5950	5450	5050	4700	4200	3850	3550	3350
0.65	7500	7300	6550	5850	5350	4950	4600	4150	3750	3500	3250
0.64	7300	7150	6400	5700	5200	4850	4500	4050	3700	3400	3200
0.63	7100	7050	6250	5600	5100	4700	4400	3950	3600	3350	3100
0.62	6900	6950	6100	5450	5000	4600	4300	3850	3500	3250	3050
0.61	6700	6850	5950	5350	4850	4500	4200	3750	3450	3200	3000
0.60	6500	6700	5800	5200	4750	4400	4100	3700	3350	3100	2900
0.59	6300	6600	5700	5100	4650	4300	4000	3600	3300	3050	2850
0.58	6100	6500	5550	4950	4500	4200	3900	3500	3200	2950	2750
0.57	5900	6400	5400	4850	4400	4100	3800	3400	3100	2900	2700
0.56	5700	6250	5250	4700	4300	4000	3700	3350	3050	2800	2650
0.55	5550	6150	5150	4600	4200	3900	3650	3250	2950	2750	2550
0.54	5350	6050	5000	4450	4100	3750	3550	3150	2900	2650	2500
0.53	5150	5950	4850	4350	3950	3650	3450	3050	2800	2600	2450
0.52	5000	5800	4750	4250	3850	3550	3350	3000	2750	2550	2350
0.51	4800	5700	4600	4100	3750	3450	3250	2900	2650	2450	2300
0.50	4650	5600	4450	4000	3650	3400	3150	2800	2600	2400	2250
0.49	4450	5500	4350	3900	3550	3300	3050	2750	2500	2300	2150
0.48	4300	5400	4200	3750	3450	3200	3000	2650	2450	2250	2100
0.47	4150	5250	4100	3650	3350	3100	2900	2600	2350	2200	2050
0.46	4000	5150	3950	3550	3250	3000	2800	2500	2300	2100	2000
0.45	3800	5050	3850	3450	3150	2900	2700	2400	2200	2050	1900
0.44	3650	4950	3700	3300	3050	2800	2600	2350	2150	2000	1850
0.43	3500	4800	3600	3200	2950	2700	2550	2250	2050	1900	1800
0.42	3350	4700	3450	3100	2850	2600	2450	2200	2000	1850	1750
0.41	3200	4600	3350	3000	2750	2550	2350	2100	1950	1800	1650
0.40	3100	4500	3250	2900	2650	2450	2300	2050	1850	1750	1600
0.39	2950	4350	3100	2800	2550	2350	2200	1950	1800	1650	1550
0.38	2800	4250	3000	2700	2450	2250	2100	1900	1750	1600	1500
0.37	2650	4150	2900	2600	2350	2200	2050	1850	1650	1550	1450
0.36	2550	4050	2750	2500	2250	2100	1950	1750	1600	1500	1400
0.35	2400	3900	2650	2400	2150	2000	1900	1700	1550	1400	1350
0.34	2300	3800	2550	2300	2100	1950	1800	1600	1450	1350	1300
0.33	2150	3700	2450	2200	2000	1850	1750	1550	1400	1300	1200
0.32	2050	3600	2350	2100	1900	1750	1650	1500	1350	1250	1150
0.31	1900	3450	2250	2000	1800	1700	1600	1400	1300	1200	1100

1. Specific gravity, G, shall be determined in accordance with Table 12.3.3A.

2. $F_{e\|} = 11200G$; $F_{e\perp} = (6100G^{1.45}) / (D)^{0.5}$; F_e for D < 1/4" = $16600\ G^{1.84}$; Tabulated values are rounded to the nearest 50 psi.

Table 12.3.3A Assigned Specific Gravities

Species Combination	Specific[1] Gravity, G
Alaska Cedar	0.47
Alaska Hemlock	0.46
Alaska Spruce	0.41
Alaska Yellow Cedar	0.46
Aspen	0.39
Balsam Fir	0.36
Beech-Birch-Hickory	0.71
Coast Sitka Spruce	0.39
Cottonwood	0.41
Douglas Fir-Larch	0.50
Douglas Fir-Larch (North)	0.49
Douglas Fir-South	0.46
Eastern Hemlock	0.41
Eastern Hemlock-Balsam Fir	0.36
Eastern Hemlock-Tamarack	0.41
Eastern Hemlock-Tamarack (North)	0.47
Eastern Softwoods	0.36
Eastern Spruce	0.41
Eastern White Pine	0.36
Engelmann Spruce-Lodgepole Pine	0.38
Hem-Fir	0.43
Hem Fir (North)	0.46
Mixed Maple	0.55
Mixed Oak	0.68
Mixed Southern Pine	0.51
Mountain Hemlock	0.47
Northern Pine	0.42
Northern Red Oak	0.68
Northern Species	0.35
Northern White Cedar	0.31
Ponderosa Pine	0.43
Red Maple	0.58
Red Oak	0.67
Red Pine	0.44
Redwood	0.37
Sitka Spruce	0.43
Southern Pine	0.55
Spruce-Pine-Fir	0.42
Spruce-Pine-Fir (South)	0.36
Western Cedars	0.36
Western Cedars (North)	0.35
Western Hemlock	0.47
Western Hemlock (North)	0.46
Western Juniper	0.42
Western White Pine	0.40
Western Woods	0.36
White Oak	0.73
Yellow Poplar	0.43

Species Combinations of MSR and MEL Lumber	Specific[1] Gravity, G
Douglas Fir-Larch	
E=1,900,000 psi and lower grades of MSR	0.50
E=2,000,000 psi grades of MSR	0.51
E=2,100,000 psi grades of MSR	0.52
E=2,200,000 psi grades of MSR	0.53
E=2,300,000 psi grades of MSR	0.54
E=2,400,000 psi grades of MSR	0.55
Douglas Fir-Larch (North)	
E=1,900,000 psi and lower grades of MSR and MEL	0.49
E=2,000,000 psi to 2,200,000 psi grades of MSR and MEL	0.53
E=2,300,000 psi and higher grades of MSR and MEL	0.57
Douglas Fir-Larch (South)	
E=1,000,000 psi and higher grades of MSR	0.46
Engelmann Spruce-Lodgepole Pine	
E=1,400,000 psi and lower grades of MSR	0.38
E=1,500,000 psi and higher grades of MSR	0.46
Hem-Fir	
E=1,500,000 psi and lower grades of MSR	0.43
E=1,600,000 psi grades of MSR	0.44
E=1,700,000 psi grades of MSR	0.45
E=1,800,000 psi grades of MSR	0.46
E=1,900,000 psi grades of MSR	0.47
E=2,000,000 psi grades of MSR	0.48
E=2,100,000 psi grades of MSR	0.49
E=2,200,000 psi grades of MSR	0.50
E=2,300,000 psi grades of MSR	0.51
E=2,400,000 psi grades of MSR	0.52
Hem-Fir (North)	
E=1,000,000 psi and higher grades of MSR and MEL	0.46
Southern Pine	
E=1,700,000 psi and lower grades of MSR and MEL	0.55
E=1,800,000 psi and higher grades of MSR and MEL	0.57
Spruce-Pine-Fir	
E=1,700,000 psi and lower grades of MSR and MEL	0.42
E=1,800,000 psi and 1,900,000 grades of MSR and MEL	0.46
E=2,000,000 psi and higher grades of MSR and MEL	0.50
Spruce-Pine-Fir (South)	
E=1,100,000 psi and lower grades of MSR	0.36
E=1,200,000 psi to1,900,000 psi grades of MSR	0.42
E=2,000,000 psi and higher grades of MSR	0.50
Western Cedars	
E=1,000,000 psi and higher grades of MSR	0.36
Western Woods	
E=1,000,000 psi and higher grades of MSR	0.36

1. Specific gravity, G, based on weight and volume when oven-dry. Different specific gravities, G, are possible for different grades of MSR and MEL lumber (see Table 4C, Footnote 2).

Table 12.3.3B Dowel Bearing Strengths for Wood Structural Panels

Wood Structural Panel	Specific[1] Gravity, G	Dowel Bearing Strength, F_e, in pounds per square inch (psi) for D≤1/4"
Plywood		
Structural 1, Marine	0.50	4650
Other Grades[1]	0.42	3350
Oriented Strand Board		
All Grades	0.50	4650

1. Use G = 0.42 when species of the plies is not known. When species of the plies is known, specific gravity listed for the actual species and the corresponding dowel bearing strength may be used, or the weighted average may be used for mixed species.

12.3.8 Asymmetric Three Member Connections, Double Shear

Reference lateral design values, Z, for asymmetric three member connections shall be the minimum computed yield mode value for symmetric double shear connections using the smaller dowel bearing length in the side member as ℓ_s and the minimum dowel diameter, D, occurring in either of the connection shear planes.

12.3.9 Multiple Shear Connections

For a connection with four or more members (see Figure 12D), each shear plane shall be evaluated as a single shear connection. The reference lateral design value, Z, for the connection shall be the lowest reference lateral design value for any single shear plane, multiplied by the number of shear planes.

Figure 12D Multiple Shear Bolted Connections

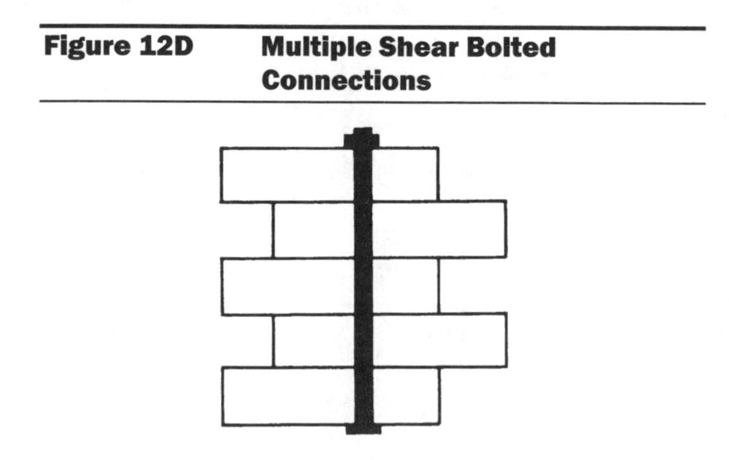

12.3.10 Load at an Angle to Fastener Axis

12.3.10.1 When the applied load in a single shear (two member) connection is at an angle (other than 90°) with the fastener axis, the fastener lengths in the two members shall be designated ℓ_s and ℓ_m (see Figure 12E). The component of the load acting at 90° with the fastener axis shall not exceed the adjusted lateral design value, Z', for a connection in which two members at 90° with the fastener axis have thicknesses $t_s = \ell_s$ and $t_m = \ell_m$. Ample bearing area shall be provided to resist the load component acting parallel to the fastener axis.

12.3.10.2 For toe-nailed connections, the minimum of t_s or L/3 shall be used for ℓ_s (see Figure 12A).

12.3.11 Drift Bolts and Drift Pins

Adjusted lateral design values, Z', for drift bolts and drift pins driven in the side grain of wood shall not exceed 75% of the adjusted lateral design values for common bolts of the same diameter and length in main member.

Figure 12E Shear Area for Bolted Connections

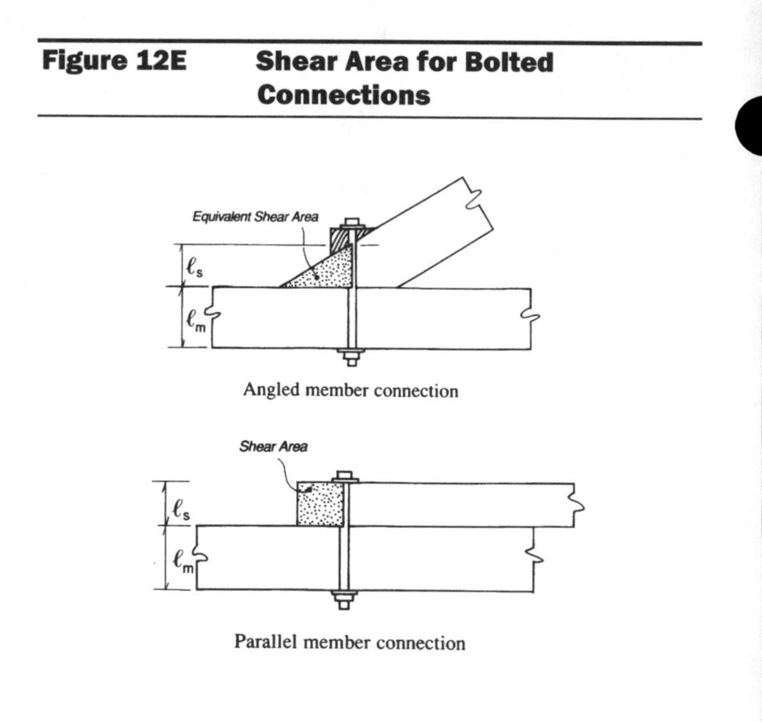

12.4 Combined Lateral and Withdrawal Loads

12.4.1 Lag Screws and Wood Screws

Where a lag screw or wood screw is subjected to combined lateral and withdrawal loading, as when the fastener is inserted perpendicular to the fiber and the load acts at an angle, α, to the wood surface (see Figure 12F), the adjusted design value, Z_α', shall be determined as follows (see Appendix J):

$$Z_\alpha' = \frac{(W'p)Z'}{(W'p)\cos^2\alpha + Z'\sin^2\alpha} \quad (12.4\text{-}1)$$

where:

α = angle between the wood surface and the direction of applied load, degrees

p = length of thread penetration into the main member, in.

12.4.2 Nails and Spikes

Where a nail or spike is subjected to combined lateral and withdrawal loading, as when the nail or spike is inserted perpendicular to the fiber and the load acts at an angle, α, to the wood surface, the adjusted design value, Z_α', shall be determined as follows:

$$Z_\alpha' = \frac{(W'p)Z'}{(W'p)\cos\alpha + Z'\sin\alpha} \quad (12.4\text{-}2)$$

where:

α = angle between the wood surface and the direction of applied load, degrees

p = length of fastener penetration into the main member, in.

Figure 12F Combined Lateral and Withdrawal Loading

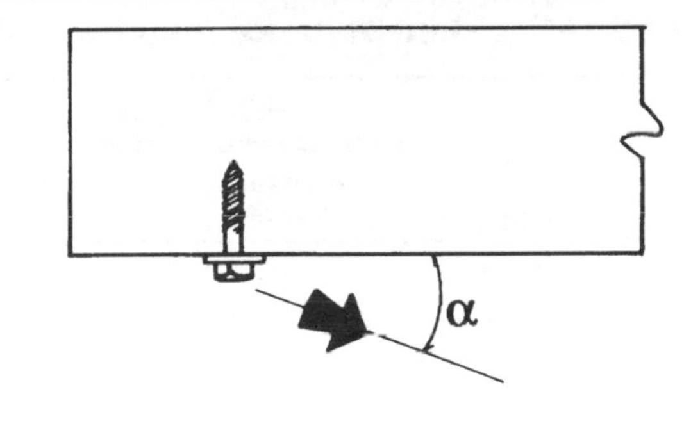

12.5 Adjustment of Reference Design Values

12.5.1 Geometry Factor, C_Δ

12.5.1.1 For dowel-type fasteners where D < 1/4", $C_\Delta = 1.0$.

12.5.1.2 Where D ≥ 1/4" and the end distance or spacing provided for dowel-type fasteners is less than the minimum required for $C_\Delta = 1.0$ for any condition in (a), (b), or (c), reference lateral design values, Z, shall be multiplied by the smallest applicable geometry factor, C_Δ, determined in (a), (b), or (c). The smallest geometry factor for any fastener in a group shall apply to all fasteners in the group. For multiple shear connections or for asymmetric three member connections, the smallest geometry factor, C_Δ, for any shear plane shall apply to all fasteners in the connection.

(a) Where dowel-type fasteners are used and the actual end distance for parallel or perpendicular to grain loading is greater than or equal to the minimum end distance (see Table 12.5.1A) for $C_\Delta = 0.5$, but less than the minimum end distance for $C_\Delta = 1.0$, the geometry factor, C_Δ, shall be determined as follows:

$$C_\Delta = \frac{\text{actual end distance}}{\text{minimum end distance for } C_\Delta = 1.0}$$

DOWEL-TYPE FASTENERS

12

Figure 12G Bolted Connection Geometry

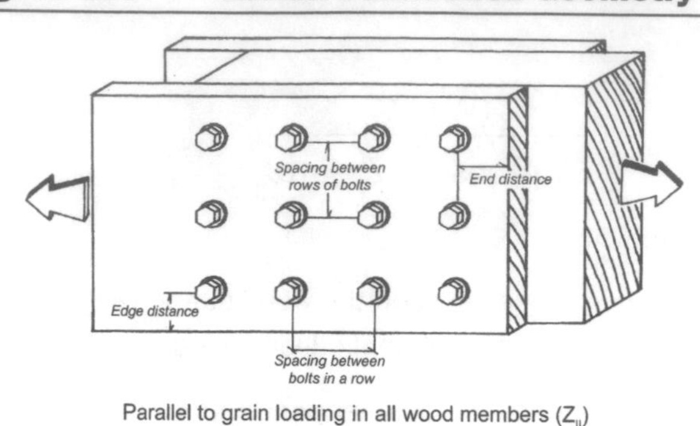

Parallel to grain loading in all wood members ($Z_{||}$)

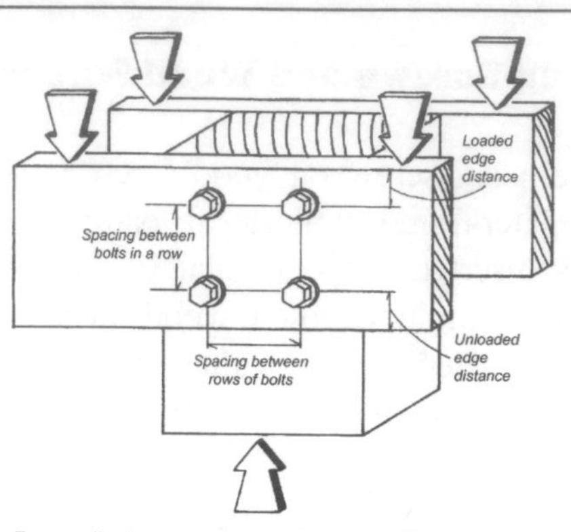

Perpendicular to grain loading in the side member and parallel to grain loading in the main member ($Z_{s\perp}$)

Table 12.5.1A End Distance Requirements

Direction of Loading	End Distances	
	Minimum end distance for $C_\Delta = 0.5$	Minimum end distance for $C_\Delta = 1.0$
Perpendicular to Grain	2D	4D
Parallel to Grain, Compression: (fastener bearing away from member end)	2D	4D
Parallel to Grain, Tension: (fastener bearing toward member end)		
for softwoods	3.5D	7D
for hardwoods	2.5D	5D

(b) For loading at an angle to the fastener, where dowel-type fasteners are used, the minimum shear area for $C_\Delta = 1.0$ shall be equivalent to the shear area for a parallel member connection with minimum end distance for $C_\Delta = 1.0$ (see Table 12.5.1A and Figure 12E). The minimum shear area for $C_\Delta = 0.5$ shall be equivalent to ½ the minimum shear area for $C_\Delta = 1.0$. Where the actual shear area is greater than or equal to the minimum shear area for $C_\Delta = 0.5$, but less than the minimum shear area for $C_\Delta = 1.0$, the geometry factor, C_Δ, shall be determined as follows:

$$C_\Delta = \frac{\text{actual shear area}}{\text{minimum shear area for } C_\Delta = 1.0}$$

(c) Where the actual spacing between dowel-type fasteners in a row for parallel or perpendicular to grain loading is greater than or equal to the minimum spacing (see Table 12.5.1B), but less than the minimum spacing for $C_\Delta = 1.0$, the geometry factor, C_Δ, shall be determined as follows:

$$C_\Delta = \frac{\text{actual spacing}}{\text{minimum spacing for } C_\Delta = 1.0}$$

12.5.1.3 Where D ≥ 1/4", edge distance and spacing between rows of fasteners shall be in accordance with Table 12.5.1C and Table 12.5.1D and applicable requirements of 12.1. The perpendicular to grain distance between the outermost fasteners shall not exceed 5" (see Figure 12H) unless special detailing is provided to accommodate cross-grain shrinkage of the wood member. For structural glued laminated timber members, the perpendicular to grain distance between the outermost fasteners shall not exceed the limits in Table 12.5.1F, unless special detailing is provided to accommodate cross-grain shrinkage of the member.

12.5.1.4 Where fasteners are installed in the narrow edge of cross-laminated timber panels and D ≥ 1/4", end distances, edge distances, and fastener spacing in a row shall not be less than the minimum values in Table 12.5.1G.

Table 12.5.1B Spacing Requirements for Fasteners in a Row

Direction of Loading	Spacing	
	Minimum spacing	Minimum spacing for $C_\Delta = 1.0$
Parallel to Grain	3D	4D
Perpendicular to Grain	3D	Required spacing for attached members

12.5.2 End Grain Factor, C_{eg}

12.5.2.1 Where lag screws are loaded in withdrawal from end grain, the reference withdrawal design values, W, shall be multiplied by the end grain factor, $C_{eg} = 0.75$.

12.5.2.2 Where dowel-type fasteners are inserted in the end grain of the main member, with the fastener axis parallel to the wood fibers, reference lateral design values, Z, shall be multiplied by the end grain factor, $C_{eg} = 0.67$.

12.5.2.3 Where dowel-type fasteners with D≥1/4" are loaded laterally in the narrow edge of cross-laminated timber, the reference lateral design value, Z, shall be multiplied by the end grain factor, C_{eg}=0.67, regardless of grain orientation.

Table 12.5.1C Edge Distance Requirements[1,2]

Direction of Loading	Minimum Edge Distance
Parallel to Grain:	
where $\ell/D \leq 6$	1.5D
where $\ell/D > 6$	1.5D or ½ the spacing between rows, whichever is greater
Perpendicular to Grain:[2]	
loaded edge	4D
unloaded edge	1.5D

1. The ℓ/D ratio used to determine the minimum spacing between rows shall be the lesser of:
   (a) length of fastener in wood main member/D = ℓ_m/D
   (b) total length of fastener in wood side member(s)/D = ℓ_s/D
2. Heavy or medium concentrated loads shall not be suspended below the neutral axis of a single sawn lumber or structural glued laminated timber beam except where mechanical or equivalent reinforcement is provided to resist tension stresses perpendicular to grain (see 3.8.2 and 11.1.3).

Table 12.5.1D Spacing Requirements Between Rows[1]

Direction of Loading	Minimum Spacing
Parallel to Grain	1.5D
Perpendicular to Grain:	
where $\ell/D \leq 2$	2.5D
where $2 < \ell/D < 6$	$(5\ell + 10D) / 8$
where $\ell/D \geq 6$	5D

1. The ℓ/D ratio used to determine the minimum spacing between rows shall be the lesser of:
   (a) length of fastener in wood main member/D = ℓ_m/D
   (b) total length of fastener in wood side member(s)/D = ℓ_s/D

12.5.3 Diaphragm Factor, C_{di}

Where nails or spikes are used in diaphragm construction, reference lateral design values, Z, are permitted to be multiplied by the diaphragm factor, C_{di} = 1.1.

12.5.4 Toe-Nail Factor, C_{tn}

12.5.4.1 Reference withdrawal design values, W, for toe-nailed connections shall be multiplied by the toe-nail factor, $C_{tn} = 0.67$. The wet service factor, C_M, shall not apply.

12.5.4.2 Reference lateral design values, Z, for toe-nailed connections shall be multiplied by the toe-nail factor, $C_{tn} = 0.83$.

Table 12.5.1E Edge and End Distance and Spacing Requirements for Lag Screws Loaded in Withdrawal and Not Loaded Laterally

Orientation	Minimum Distance/Spacing
Edge Distance	1.5D
End Distance	4D
Spacing	4D

Table 12.5.1F Perpendicular to Grain Distance Requirements for Outermost Fasteners in Structural Glued Laminated Timber Members

Fastener Type	Moisture Content		Maximum Distance Between Outer Rows
	At Time of Fabrication	In-Service	
All Fasteners	>16%	<16%	5"
	Any	>16%	5"
Bolts	<16%	<16%	10"
Lag Screws	<16%	<16%	6"
Drift Pins	<16%	<16%	6"

DOWEL-TYPE FASTENERS

12

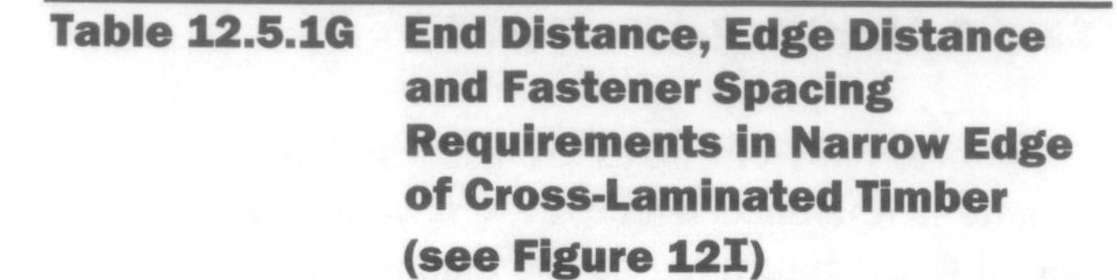

Table 12.5.1G End Distance, Edge Distance and Fastener Spacing Requirements in Narrow Edge of Cross-Laminated Timber (see Figure 12I)

Direction of Loading	Minimum End Distance	Minimum Edge Distance	Minimum Spacing for Fasteners in a Row
Perpendicular to Plane of CLT	4D	3D	4D
Parallel to Plane of CLT, Compression: (fastener bearing away from member end)	4D		
Parallel to Plane of CLT, Tension: (fastener bearing toward member end)	7D		

Figure 12H Spacing Between Outer Rows of Bolts

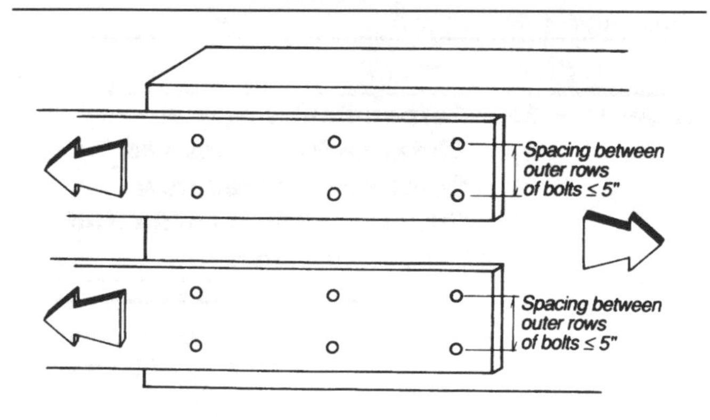

Figure 12I End Distance, Edge Distance and Fastener Spacing Requirements in Narrow Edge of Cross-Laminated Timber

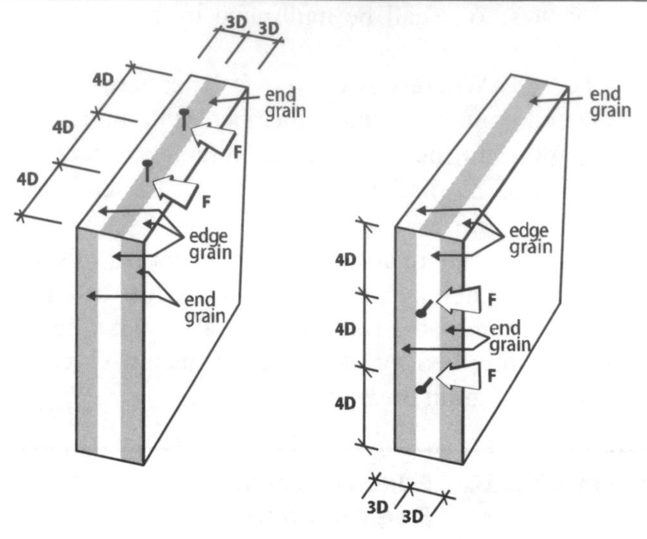

Direction of loading perpendicular to the plane of CLT

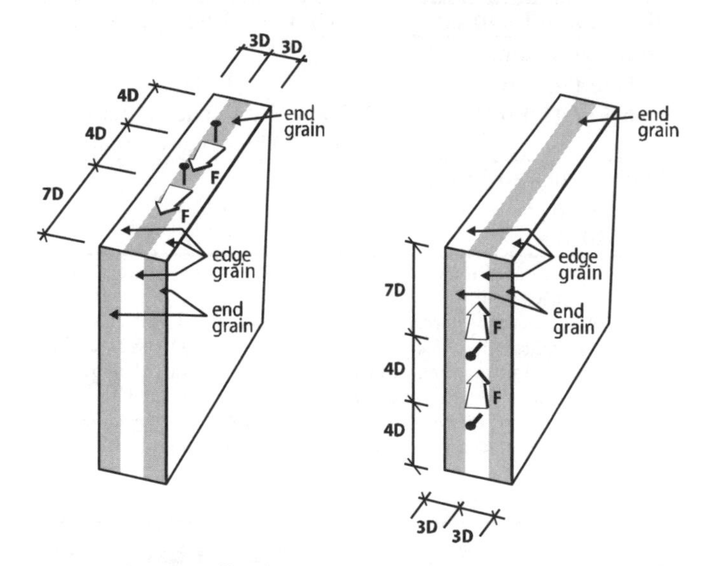

Direction of loading parallel to the plane of CLT

12.6 Multiple Fasteners

12.6.1 Symmetrically Staggered Fasteners

Where a connection contains multiple fasteners, fasteners shall be staggered symmetrically in members loaded perpendicular to grain whenever possible (see 11.3.6.2 for special design provisions where bolts, lag screws, or drift pins are staggered).

12.6.2 Fasteners Loaded at an Angle to Grain

When a multiple fastener connection is loaded at an angle to grain, the gravity axis of each member shall pass through the center of resistance of the group of fasteners to insure uniform stress in the main member and a uniform distribution of load to all fasteners.

12.6.3 Local Stresses in Connections

Local stresses in connections using multiple fasteners shall be evaluated in accordance with principles of engineering mechanics (see 11.1.2).

Table 12A BOLTS: Reference Lateral Design Values, Z, for Single Shear (two member) Connections[1,2]

for sawn lumber or SCL with both members of identical specific gravity

Thickness Main Member t_m in.	Thickness Side Member t_s in.	Bolt Diameter D in.	G=0.67 Red Oak $Z_{\parallel}$ lbs.	$Z_{s\perp}$ lbs.	$Z_{m\perp}$ lbs.	$Z_{\perp}$ lbs.	G=0.55 Mixed Maple Southern Pine $Z_{\parallel}$ lbs.	$Z_{s\perp}$ lbs.	$Z_{m\perp}$ lbs.	$Z_{\perp}$ lbs.	G=0.50 Douglas Fir-Larch $Z_{\parallel}$ lbs.	$Z_{s\perp}$ lbs.	$Z_{m\perp}$ lbs.	$Z_{\perp}$ lbs.	G=0.49 Douglas Fir-Larch(N) $Z_{\parallel}$ lbs.	$Z_{s\perp}$ lbs.	$Z_{m\perp}$ lbs.	$Z_{\perp}$ lbs.	G=0.46 Douglas Fir(S) Hem-Fir(N) $Z_{\parallel}$ lbs.	$Z_{s\perp}$ lbs.	$Z_{m\perp}$ lbs.	$Z_{\perp}$ lbs.
1-1/2	1-1/2	1/2	650	420	420	330	530	330	330	250	480	300	300	220	470	290	290	210	440	270	270	190
		5/8	810	500	500	370	660	400	400	280	600	360	360	240	590	350	350	240	560	320	320	220
		3/4	970	580	580	410	800	460	460	310	720	420	420	270	710	400	400	260	670	380	380	240
		7/8	1130	660	660	440	930	520	520	330	850	470	470	290	830	460	460	280	780	420	420	250
		1	1290	740	740	470	1060	580	580	350	970	530	530	310	950	510	510	300	890	480	480	280
1-3/4	1-3/4	1/2	760	490	490	390	620	390	390	290	560	350	350	250	550	340	340	250	520	320	320	230
		5/8	940	590	590	430	770	470	470	330	700	420	420	280	690	410	410	280	650	380	380	250
		3/4	1130	680	680	480	930	540	540	360	850	480	480	310	830	470	470	300	780	440	440	280
		7/8	1320	770	770	510	1080	610	610	390	990	550	550	340	970	530	530	320	910	500	500	300
		1	1510	860	860	550	1240	680	680	410	1130	610	610	360	1110	600	600	350	1040	560	560	320
2-1/2	1-1/2	1/2	770	480	540	440	660	400	420	350	610	370	370	310	610	360	360	300	580	340	330	270
		5/8	1070	660	630	520	930	560	490	390	850	520	430	340	830	520	420	330	780	470	390	300
		3/4	1360	890	720	570	1120	660	560	430	1020	590	500	380	1000	560	480	360	940	520	450	330
		7/8	1590	960	800	620	1300	720	620	470	1190	630	550	410	1170	600	540	390	1090	550	500	360
		1	1820	1020	870	660	1490	770	680	490	1360	680	610	440	1330	650	590	420	1250	600	550	390
3-1/2	1-1/2	1/2	770	480	560	440	660	400	470	360	610	370	430	330	610	360	420	320	580	340	400	310
		5/8	1070	660	760	590	940	560	620	500	880	520	540	460	870	520	530	450	830	470	490	410
		3/4	1450	890	900	770	1270	660	690	580	1200	590	610	510	1190	560	590	490	1140	520	550	450
		7/8	1890	960	990	830	1680	720	770	630	1590	630	680	550	1570	600	650	530	1470	550	600	480
		1	2410	1020	1080	890	2010	770	830	670	1830	680	740	590	1790	650	710	560	1680	600	660	520
	1-3/4	1/2	830	510	590	480	720	420	510	390	670	380	470	350	660	380	460	340	620	360	440	320
		5/8	1160	680	820	620	1000	580	640	520	930	530	560	460	920	530	550	450	880	500	510	410
		3/4	1530	900	940	780	1330	770	720	580	1250	680	640	520	1240	660	620	500	1190	600	580	460
		7/8	1970	1120	1040	840	1730	840	810	640	1620	740	710	550	1590	700	690	530	1490	640	640	490
		1	2480	1190	1130	900	2030	890	880	670	1850	790	780	590	1820	750	760	570	1700	700	700	530
	3-1/2	1/2	830	590	590	530	750	520	520	460	720	490	490	430	710	480	480	420	690	460	460	410
		5/8	1290	880	880	780	1170	780	780	650	1120	700	700	560	1110	690	690	550	1070	650	650	500
		3/4	1860	1190	1190	950	1690	960	960	710	1610	870	870	630	1600	850	850	600	1540	800	800	560
		7/8	2540	1410	1410	1030	2170	1160	1160	780	1970	1060	1060	680	1940	1040	1040	650	1810	980	980	590
		1	3020	1670	1670	1100	2480	1360	1360	820	2260	1230	1230	720	2210	1190	1190	690	2070	1110	1110	640
5-1/4	1-1/2	5/8	1070	660	760	590	940	560	640	500	880	520	590	460	870	520	590	450	830	470	560	430
		3/4	1450	890	990	780	1270	660	850	660	1200	590	790	590	1190	560	780	560	1140	520	740	520
		7/8	1890	960	1260	960	1680	720	1060	720	1590	630	940	630	1570	600	900	600	1520	550	830	550
		1	2410	1020	1500	1020	2150	770	1140	770	2050	680	1010	680	2030	650	970	650	1930	600	910	600
	1-3/4	5/8	1160	680	820	620	1000	580	690	520	930	530	630	470	920	530	630	470	880	500	590	440
		3/4	1530	900	1050	800	1330	770	890	680	1250	680	830	630	1240	660	810	620	1190	600	780	590
		7/8	1970	1120	1320	1020	1730	840	1090	840	1640	740	960	740	1620	700	920	700	1550	640	850	640
		1	2480	1190	1530	1190	2200	890	1170	890	2080	790	1040	790	2060	750	1000	750	1990	700	930	700
	3-1/2	5/8	1290	880	880	780	1170	780	780	680	1120	700	730	630	1110	690	720	620	1070	650	690	580
		3/4	1860	1190	1240	1080	1690	960	1090	850	1610	870	1030	780	1600	850	1010	750	1540	800	970	710
		7/8	2540	1410	1640	1260	2300	1160	1380	1000	2190	1060	1230	870	2170	1040	1190	840	2060	980	1100	770
		1	3310	1670	1940	1420	2870	1390	1520	1060	2660	1290	1360	940	2630	1260	1320	900	2500	1210	1230	830
5-1/2	1-1/2	5/8	1070	660	760	590	940	560	640	500	880	520	590	460	870	520	590	450	830	470	560	430
		3/4	1450	890	990	780	1270	660	850	660	1200	590	790	590	1190	560	780	560	1140	520	740	520
		7/8	1890	960	1260	960	1680	720	1090	720	1590	630	980	630	1570	600	940	600	1520	550	860	550
		1	2410	1020	1560	1020	2150	770	1190	770	2050	680	1060	680	2030	650	1010	650	1930	600	940	600
	3-1/2	5/8	1290	880	880	780	1170	780	780	680	1120	700	730	630	1110	690	720	620	1070	650	690	580
		3/4	1860	1190	1240	1080	1690	960	1090	850	1610	870	1030	780	1600	850	1010	750	1540	800	970	710
		7/8	2540	1410	1640	1260	2300	1160	1410	1020	2190	1060	1260	910	2170	1040	1220	870	2060	980	1130	790
		1	3310	1670	1980	1470	2870	1390	1550	1100	2660	1290	1390	970	2630	1260	1340	930	2500	1210	1250	860
7-1/2	1-1/2	5/8	1070	660	760	590	940	560	640	500	880	520	590	460	870	520	590	450	830	470	560	430
		3/4	1450	890	990	780	1270	660	850	660	1200	590	790	590	1190	560	780	560	1140	520	740	520
		7/8	1890	960	1260	960	1680	720	1090	720	1590	630	1010	630	1570	600	990	600	1520	550	950	550
		1	2410	1020	1560	1020	2150	770	1350	770	2050	680	1270	680	2030	650	1240	650	1930	600	1190	600
	3-1/2	5/8	1290	880	880	780	1170	780	780	680	1120	700	730	630	1110	690	720	620	1070	650	690	580
		3/4	1860	1190	1240	1080	1690	960	1090	850	1610	870	1030	780	1600	850	1010	750	1540	800	970	710
		7/8	2540	1410	1640	1260	2300	1160	1450	1020	2190	1060	1360	930	2170	1040	1340	900	2060	980	1280	850
		1	3310	1670	2090	1470	2870	1390	1830	1210	2660	1290	1630	1110	2630	1260	1570	1080	2500	1210	1470	1030

1. Tabulated lateral design values, Z, for bolted connections shall be multiplied by all applicable adjustment factors (see Table 11.3.1).
2. Tabulated lateral design values, Z, are for "full-body diameter" bolts (see Appendix Table L1) with bolt bending yield strength, F_{yb}, of 45,000 psi.

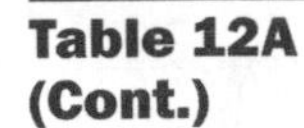

Table 12A (Cont.) **BOLTS: Reference Lateral Design Values, Z, for Single Shear (two member) Connections[1,2]**

for sawn lumber or SCL with both members of identical specific gravity

Thickness Main Member t_m in.	Thickness Side Member t_s in.	Bolt Diameter D in.	G=0.43 Hem-Fir $Z_{\parallel}$ lbs.	$Z_{s\perp}$ lbs.	$Z_{m\perp}$ lbs.	$Z_{\perp}$ lbs.	G=0.42 Spruce-Pine-Fir $Z_{\parallel}$ lbs.	$Z_{s\perp}$ lbs.	$Z_{m\perp}$ lbs.	$Z_{\perp}$ lbs.	G=0.37 Redwood $Z_{\parallel}$ lbs.	$Z_{s\perp}$ lbs.	$Z_{m\perp}$ lbs.	$Z_{\perp}$ lbs.	G=0.36 Eastern Softwoods, Spruce-Pine-Fir(S), Western Cedars, Western Woods $Z_{\parallel}$ lbs.	$Z_{s\perp}$ lbs.	$Z_{m\perp}$ lbs.	$Z_{\perp}$ lbs.	G=0.35 Northern Species $Z_{\parallel}$ lbs.	$Z_{s\perp}$ lbs.	$Z_{m\perp}$ lbs.	$Z_{\perp}$ lbs.
1-1/2	1-1/2	1/2	410	250	250	180	410	240	240	170	360	210	210	140	350	200	200	130	340	200	200	130
		5/8	520	300	300	190	510	290	290	190	450	250	250	160	440	240	240	150	420	240	240	150
		3/4	620	350	350	210	610	340	340	210	540	290	290	170	520	280	280	170	500	270	270	160
		7/8	720	390	390	230	710	380	380	220	630	330	330	190	610	320	320	180	590	310	310	170
		1	830	440	440	250	810	430	430	240	720	370	370	200	700	360	360	190	670	350	350	190
1-3/4	1-3/4	1/2	480	290	290	210	470	280	280	200	420	250	250	170	410	240	240	160	390	230	230	150
		5/8	600	350	350	230	590	340	340	220	520	290	290	190	510	280	280	180	490	270	270	170
		3/4	720	400	400	250	710	390	390	240	630	340	340	200	610	330	330	190	590	320	320	190
		7/8	850	460	460	270	830	450	450	260	730	390	390	220	710	380	380	210	690	360	360	200
		1	970	510	510	290	950	500	500	280	840	430	430	230	820	420	420	230	790	410	410	220
2-1/2	1-1/2	1/2	550	320	310	250	540	320	300	240	500	290	250	200	490	280	240	190	470	280	240	180
		5/8	730	420	360	270	710	410	350	270	630	350	300	220	610	330	290	210	590	320	280	210
		3/4	870	460	410	300	850	450	400	290	750	370	340	240	740	360	330	230	710	350	320	230
		7/8	1020	500	450	320	1000	490	440	310	880	410	380	260	860	390	370	250	830	370	350	240
		1	1160	540	500	350	1140	530	490	340	1010	440	420	280	980	420	410	270	940	410	390	260
3-1/2	1-1/2	1/2	550	320	380	290	540	320	370	280	500	290	320	250	490	280	300	250	480	280	290	240
		5/8	790	420	440	370	780	410	430	360	720	350	370	300	710	330	350	290	700	320	340	280
		3/4	1100	460	500	400	1080	450	480	390	1010	370	410	320	990	360	400	310	950	350	380	300
		7/8	1370	500	550	430	1340	490	540	420	1180	410	460	350	1160	390	440	340	1110	370	420	320
		1	1570	540	600	470	1530	530	590	460	1350	440	500	380	1320	420	480	370	1270	410	470	350
	1-3/4	1/2	590	340	400	300	580	330	390	290	530	300	330	260	520	290	320	250	510	280	310	250
		5/8	840	480	460	370	820	470	450	360	760	400	390	310	740	380	370	290	730	370	360	280
		3/4	1130	540	520	410	1120	530	510	400	1030	430	430	330	1000	420	420	320	970	410	410	310
		7/8	1390	580	580	440	1360	570	570	430	1200	470	480	360	1170	460	470	350	1130	430	440	320
		1	1590	630	640	480	1550	610	630	460	1370	510	530	380	1340	490	520	370	1290	470	500	360
	3-1/2	1/2	660	440	440	390	660	430	430	380	620	400	400	330	610	390	390	310	600	380	380	310
		5/8	1040	600	600	450	1020	590	590	440	960	520	520	370	950	500	500	350	930	490	490	340
		3/4	1450	740	740	500	1420	730	730	480	1250	650	650	400	1220	630	630	390	1180	620	620	370
		7/8	1690	910	910	540	1660	890	890	520	1460	770	770	440	1430	750	750	420	1370	720	720	390
		1	1930	1030	1030	580	1890	1000	1000	560	1670	870	870	470	1630	840	840	450	1570	810	810	430
5-1/4	1-1/2	5/8	790	420	530	410	780	410	520	400	720	350	470	350	710	330	460	330	700	320	450	320
		3/4	1100	460	690	460	1080	450	670	450	1010	370	560	370	990	360	540	360	970	350	530	350
		7/8	1460	500	750	500	1440	490	730	490	1350	410	620	410	1330	390	600	390	1280	370	560	370
		1	1800	540	820	540	1760	530	800	530	1560	440	670	440	1520	420	650	420	1460	410	630	410
	1-3/4	5/8	840	480	560	410	820	470	550	410	760	400	500	370	740	380	480	360	730	370	470	350
		3/4	1130	540	700	540	1120	530	680	530	1040	430	570	430	1020	420	560	420	1000	410	540	410
		7/8	1490	580	770	580	1470	570	750	570	1370	470	640	470	1350	460	620	460	1320	430	580	430
		1	1910	630	850	630	1890	610	820	610	1760	510	690	510	1740	490	670	490	1700	470	650	470
	3-1/2	5/8	1040	600	660	530	1020	590	650	520	960	520	610	460	950	500	590	440	930	490	580	430
		3/4	1490	740	900	640	1480	730	880	620	1390	650	750	520	1370	630	730	500	1330	620	710	480
		7/8	1950	920	1010	690	1920	910	990	670	1740	820	850	560	1710	800	830	550	1660	770	780	510
		1	2370	1140	1130	750	2330	1120	1100	730	2120	1020	940	600	2080	980	910	580	2030	950	880	560
5-1/2	1-1/2	5/8	790	420	530	410	780	410	520	400	720	350	470	350	710	330	460	330	700	320	450	320
		3/4	1100	460	700	460	1080	450	690	450	1010	370	580	370	990	360	570	360	970	350	550	350
		7/8	1460	500	780	500	1440	490	760	490	1350	410	650	410	1330	390	630	390	1280	370	590	370
		1	1800	540	860	540	1760	530	830	530	1560	440	700	440	1520	420	680	420	1460	410	650	410
	3-1/2	5/8	1040	600	660	530	1020	590	650	520	960	520	610	460	950	500	590	440	930	490	580	430
		3/4	1490	740	920	650	1480	730	900	640	1390	650	770	530	1370	630	750	520	1330	620	720	500
		7/8	1950	920	1030	720	1920	910	1010	700	1740	820	870	590	1710	800	840	570	1660	770	800	530
		1	2370	1140	1150	780	2330	1120	1120	760	2120	1020	960	630	2080	980	930	600	2030	950	890	580
7-1/2	1-1/2	5/8	790	420	530	410	780	410	520	400	720	350	470	350	710	330	460	330	700	320	450	320
		3/4	1100	460	700	460	1080	450	690	450	1010	370	630	370	990	360	620	360	970	350	600	350
		7/8	1460	500	900	500	1440	490	890	490	1350	410	810	410	1330	390	800	390	1280	370	770	370
		1	1800	540	1130	540	1760	530	1110	530	1560	440	920	440	1520	420	890	420	1460	410	860	410
	3-1/2	5/8	1040	600	660	530	1020	590	650	520	960	520	610	460	950	500	590	440	930	490	580	430
		3/4	1490	740	920	650	1480	730	910	640	1390	650	840	560	1370	630	820	550	1330	620	810	540
		7/8	1950	920	1210	790	1920	910	1180	780	1740	820	1010	700	1710	800	980	680	1660	770	920	650
		1	2370	1140	1340	970	2330	1120	1300	950	2120	1020	1100	820	2080	980	1070	790	2030	950	1030	760

1. Tabulated lateral design values, Z, for bolted connections shall be multiplied by all applicable adjustment factors (see Table 11.3.1).
2. Tabulated lateral design values, Z, are for "full-body diameter" bolts (see Appendix Table L1) with bolt bending yield strength, F_{yb}, of 45,000 psi.

Table 12B BOLTS: Reference Lateral Design Values, Z, for Single Shear (two member) Connections[1,2]

for sawn lumber or SCL main member with 1/4" ASTM A 36 steel side plate

Thickness: Main Member t_m in.	Thickness: Side Member t_s in.	Bolt Diameter D in.	G=0.67 Red Oak $Z_{\parallel}$ lbs.	$Z_{\perp}$ lbs.	G=0.55 Mixed Maple Southern Pine $Z_{\parallel}$ lbs.	$Z_{\perp}$ lbs.	G=0.50 Douglas Fir-Larch $Z_{\parallel}$ lbs.	$Z_{\perp}$ lbs.	G=0.49 Douglas Fir-Larch(N) $Z_{\parallel}$ lbs.	$Z_{\perp}$ lbs.	G=0.46 Douglas Fir(S) Hem-Fir(N) $Z_{\parallel}$ lbs.	$Z_{\perp}$ lbs.	G=0.43 Hem-Fir $Z_{\parallel}$ lbs.	$Z_{\perp}$ lbs.	G=0.42 Spruce-Pine-Fir $Z_{\parallel}$ lbs.	$Z_{\perp}$ lbs.	G=0.37 Redwood $Z_{\parallel}$ lbs.	$Z_{\perp}$ lbs.	G=0.36 Eastern Softwoods Spruce-Pine-Fir(S) Western Cedars Western Woods $Z_{\parallel}$ lbs.	$Z_{\perp}$ lbs.	G=0.35 Northern Species $Z_{\parallel}$ lbs.	$Z_{\perp}$ lbs.
1-1/2	1/4	1/2	730	420	620	350	580	310	580	310	550	290	520	280	510	270	470	240	460	240	450	230
		5/8	910	480	780	400	730	360	720	360	690	340	650	320	640	320	590	290	580	280	560	270
		3/4	1090	550	940	450	870	420	860	410	820	390	780	360	770	360	710	320	690	320	680	310
		7/8	1270	600	1090	510	1020	470	1010	450	960	430	910	410	900	400	820	370	810	360	790	350
		1	1460	660	1250	550	1170	510	1150	500	1100	480	1040	450	1030	450	940	400	930	400	900	390
1-3/4	1/4	1/2	810	460	690	370	640	340	630	330	600	310	570	290	560	280	510	250	500	250	490	240
		5/8	1020	520	870	430	800	390	790	380	750	360	710	340	700	330	640	300	630	290	610	280
		3/4	1220	590	1040	480	960	440	950	430	900	410	860	380	840	370	770	330	750	330	730	320
		7/8	1420	650	1210	540	1130	490	1110	480	1050	450	1000	420	980	420	890	380	880	370	850	360
		1	1630	710	1380	580	1290	540	1270	520	1200	500	1140	470	1120	460	1020	410	1000	410	980	400
2-1/2	1/4	1/2	930	600	860	470	830	410	820	400	780	380	740	350	720	340	650	300	640	290	620	280
		5/8	1370	670	1150	530	1050	470	1040	470	980	430	920	400	910	390	810	340	800	330	770	320
		3/4	1640	750	1370	590	1270	530	1250	520	1180	490	1110	450	1090	440	980	380	960	370	930	360
		7/8	1910	820	1600	650	1480	590	1450	570	1370	530	1290	490	1270	480	1140	420	1120	410	1080	400
		1	2190	880	1830	700	1690	640	1660	620	1570	580	1480	540	1450	530	1300	460	1280	450	1240	440
3-1/2	1/4	1/2	930	620	860	550	830	510	820	510	800	480	770	450	770	430	720	370	720	360	710	350
		5/8	1370	860	1260	690	1210	610	1200	600	1160	550	1130	500	1120	490	1060	420	1050	410	1020	400
		3/4	1900	990	1740	760	1670	680	1660	660	1580	610	1480	560	1450	540	1290	460	1260	450	1220	440
		7/8	2530	1070	2170	840	1990	740	1950	710	1840	660	1720	610	1690	590	1510	510	1480	500	1430	470
		1	2980	1150	2480	890	2270	800	2230	770	2100	730	1970	660	1930	650	1720	560	1690	540	1630	530
5-1/4	1/4	5/8	1370	860	1260	760	1210	710	1200	700	1160	670	1130	640	1120	630	1060	580	1050	560	1030	540
		3/4	1900	1140	1740	1000	1670	940	1660	930	1610	860	1560	770	1550	760	1460	640	1450	620	1420	600
		7/8	2530	1460	2320	1190	2220	1050	2200	1010	2140	920	2070	840	2050	820	1940	700	1920	680	1890	640
		1	3260	1660	2980	1270	2860	1130	2840	1080	2750	1010	2670	920	2640	890	2490	750	2450	730	2360	710
5-1/2	1/4	5/8	1370	860	1260	760	1210	710	1200	700	1160	670	1130	640	1120	630	1060	580	1050	570	1030	560
		3/4	1900	1140	1740	1000	1670	940	1660	930	1610	890	1560	810	1550	790	1460	660	1450	640	1420	620
		7/8	2530	1460	2320	1240	2220	1090	2200	1050	2140	960	2070	880	2050	860	1940	730	1920	710	1890	660
		1	3260	1730	2980	1320	2860	1170	2840	1130	2750	1050	2670	950	2640	930	2490	780	2470	760	2420	740
7-1/2	1/4	5/8	1370	860	1260	760	1210	710	1200	700	1160	670	1130	640	1120	630	1060	580	1050	570	1030	560
		3/4	1900	1140	1740	1000	1670	940	1660	930	1610	890	1560	850	1550	840	1460	760	1450	750	1420	740
		7/8	2530	1460	2320	1280	2220	1210	2200	1180	2140	1130	2070	1080	2050	1070	1940	960	1920	930	1890	870
		1	3260	1820	2980	1590	2860	1500	2840	1470	2750	1400	2670	1270	2640	1230	2490	1030	2470	1000	2420	960
9-1/2	1/4	3/4	1900	1140	1740	1000	1670	940	1660	930	1610	890	1560	850	1550	840	1460	760	1450	750	1420	740
		7/8	2530	1460	2320	1280	2220	1210	2200	1180	2140	1130	2070	1080	2050	1070	1940	980	1920	970	1890	930
		1	3260	1820	2980	1590	2860	1500	2840	1470	2750	1420	2670	1350	2640	1330	2490	1220	2470	1200	2420	1180
11-1/2	1/4	7/8	2530	1460	2320	1280	2220	1210	2200	1180	2140	1130	2070	1080	2050	1070	1940	980	1920	970	1890	930
		1	3260	1820	2980	1590	2860	1500	2840	1470	2750	1420	2670	1350	2640	1330	2490	1220	2470	1200	2420	1180
13-1/2	1/4	1	3260	1820	2980	1590	2860	1500	2840	1470	2750	1420	2670	1350	2640	1330	2490	1220	2470	1200	2420	1180

1. Tabulated lateral design values, Z, for bolted connections shall be multiplied by all applicable adjustment factors (see Table 11.3.1).
2. Tabulated lateral design values, Z, are for "full-body diameter" bolts (see Appendix Table L1) with bolt bending yield strength, F_{yb}, of 45,000 psi and dowel bearing strength, F_e, of 87,000 psi for ASTM A36 steel.

Table 12C BOLTS: Reference Lateral Design Values, Z, for Single Shear (two member) Connections[1,2]

for structural glued laminated timber main member with sawn lumber side member of identical specific gravity

Thickness		Bolt Diameter	G=0.55 Southern Pine				G=0.50 Douglas Fir-Larch				G=0.46 Douglas Fir(S)				G=0.43 Hem-Fir				G=0.42 Spruce-Pine-Fir				G=0.36 Spruce-Pine-Fir(S) Western Woods			
Main Member t_m in.	Side Member t_s in.	D in.	$Z_{\parallel}$ lbs.	$Z_{s\perp}$ lbs.	$Z_{m\perp}$ lbs.	$Z_{\perp}$ lbs.	$Z_{\parallel}$ lbs.	$Z_{s\perp}$ lbs.	$Z_{m\perp}$ lbs.	$Z_{\perp}$ lbs.	$Z_{\parallel}$ lbs.	$Z_{s\perp}$ lbs.	$Z_{m\perp}$ lbs.	$Z_{\perp}$ lbs.	$Z_{\parallel}$ lbs.	$Z_{s\perp}$ lbs.	$Z_{m\perp}$ lbs.	$Z_{\perp}$ lbs.	$Z_{\parallel}$ lbs.	$Z_{s\perp}$ lbs.	$Z_{m\perp}$ lbs.	$Z_{\perp}$ lbs.	$Z_{\parallel}$ lbs.	$Z_{s\perp}$ lbs.	$Z_{m\perp}$ lbs.	$Z_{\perp}$ lbs.
2-1/2	1-1/2	1/2	-	-	-	-	610	370	370	310	580	340	330	270	550	320	310	250	540	320	300	240	490	280	240	190
		5/8	-	-	-	-	850	520	430	340	780	470	390	300	730	420	360	270	710	410	350	270	610	330	290	210
		3/4	-	-	-	-	1020	590	500	380	940	520	450	330	870	460	410	300	850	450	400	290	740	360	330	230
		7/8	-	-	-	-	1190	630	550	410	1090	550	500	360	1020	500	450	320	1000	490	440	310	860	390	370	250
		1	-	-	-	-	1360	680	610	440	1250	600	550	390	1160	540	500	350	1140	530	490	340	980	420	410	270
3	1-1/2	1/2	660	400	470	360	-	-	-	-	-	-	-	-	-	-	-	-	-	-	-	-	-	-	-	-
		5/8	940	560	550	460	-	-	-	-	-	-	-	-	-	-	-	-	-	-	-	-	-	-	-	-
		3/4	1270	660	620	500	-	-	-	-	-	-	-	-	-	-	-	-	-	-	-	-	-	-	-	-
		7/8	1520	720	690	540	-	-	-	-	-	-	-	-	-	-	-	-	-	-	-	-	-	-	-	-
		1	1740	770	750	580	-	-	-	-	-	-	-	-	-	-	-	-	-	-	-	-	-	-	-	-
3-1/8	1-1/2	1/2	-	-	-	-	610	370	430	330	580	340	390	310	550	320	360	290	540	320	340	280	490	280	280	230
		5/8	-	-	-	-	880	520	500	410	830	470	450	370	790	420	410	330	780	410	400	320	710	330	330	260
		3/4	-	-	-	-	1200	590	570	460	1130	520	510	410	1060	460	460	360	1040	450	450	350	890	360	370	280
		7/8	-	-	-	-	1440	630	630	490	1320	550	560	430	1230	500	510	390	1210	490	500	380	1040	390	410	310
		1	-	-	-	-	1640	680	690	530	1510	600	620	470	1410	540	560	420	1380	530	550	410	1190	420	450	330
5	1-1/2	5/8	940	560	640	500	-	-	-	-	-	-	-	-	-	-	-	-	-	-	-	-	-	-	-	-
		3/4	1270	660	850	660	-	-	-	-	-	-	-	-	-	-	-	-	-	-	-	-	-	-	-	-
		7/8	1680	720	1020	720	-	-	-	-	-	-	-	-	-	-	-	-	-	-	-	-	-	-	-	-
		1	2150	770	1100	770	-	-	-	-	-	-	-	-	-	-	-	-	-	-	-	-	-	-	-	-
5-1/8	1-1/2	5/8	-	-	-	-	880	520	590	460	830	470	560	430	790	420	530	410	780	410	520	400	710	330	460	330
		3/4	-	-	-	-	1200	590	790	590	1140	520	740	520	1100	460	670	460	1080	450	660	450	990	360	530	360
		7/8	-	-	-	-	1590	630	920	630	1520	550	810	550	1460	500	740	500	1440	490	720	490	1330	390	590	390
		1	-	-	-	-	2050	680	990	680	1930	600	890	600	1800	540	810	540	1760	530	780	530	1520	420	640	420
6-3/4	1-1/2	5/8	940	560	640	500	880	520	590	460	830	470	560	430	790	420	530	410	780	410	520	400	710	330	460	330
		3/4	1270	660	850	660	1200	590	790	590	1140	520	740	520	1100	460	700	460	1080	450	690	450	990	360	620	360
		7/8	1680	720	1090	720	1590	630	1010	630	1520	550	950	550	1460	500	900	500	1440	490	890	490	1330	390	750	390
		1	2150	770	1350	770	2050	680	1270	680	1930	600	1140	600	1800	540	1030	540	1760	530	1000	530	1520	420	810	420

1. Tabulated lateral design values, Z, for bolted connections shall be multiplied by all applicable adjustment factors (see Table 11.3.1).
2. Tabulated lateral design values, Z, are for "full-body diameter" bolts (see Appendix Table L1) with bolt bending yield strength, F_{yb}, of 45,000 psi.

Table 12D BOLTS: Reference Lateral Design Values, Z, for Single Shear (two member) Connections[1,2]

for structural glued laminated timber main member with 1/4" ASTM A 36 steel side plate

Thickness: Main Member t_m in.	Thickness: Side Member t_s in.	Bolt Diameter D in.	G=0.55 Southern Pine $Z_{\parallel}$ lbs.	G=0.55 Southern Pine $Z_{\perp}$ lbs.	G=0.50 Douglas Fir-Larch $Z_{\parallel}$ lbs.	G=0.50 Douglas Fir-Larch $Z_{\perp}$ lbs.	G=0.46 Douglas Fir(S) Hem-Fir(N) $Z_{\parallel}$ lbs.	G=0.46 Douglas Fir(S) Hem-Fir(N) $Z_{\perp}$ lbs.	G=0.43 Hem-Fir $Z_{\parallel}$ lbs.	G=0.43 Hem-Fir $Z_{\perp}$ lbs.	G=0.42 Spruce-Pine-Fir $Z_{\parallel}$ lbs.	G=0.42 Spruce-Pine-Fir $Z_{\perp}$ lbs.	G=0.36 Spruce-Pine-Fir(S) Western Woods $Z_{\parallel}$ lbs.	G=0.36 Spruce-Pine-Fir(S) Western Woods $Z_{\perp}$ lbs.
2-1/2	1/4	1/2	-	-	830	410	780	380	740	350	720	340	640	290
		5/8	-	-	1050	470	980	430	920	400	910	390	800	330
		3/4	-	-	1270	530	1180	490	1110	450	1090	440	960	370
		7/8	-	-	1480	590	1370	530	1290	490	1270	480	1120	410
		1	-	-	1690	640	1570	580	1480	540	1450	530	1280	450
3	1/4	1/2	860	540	-	-	-	-	-	-	-	-	-	-
		5/8	1260	610	-	-	-	-	-	-	-	-	-	-
		3/4	1610	670	-	-	-	-	-	-	-	-	-	-
		7/8	1880	740	-	-	-	-	-	-	-	-	-	-
		1	2150	790	-	-	-	-	-	-	-	-	-	-
3-1/8	1/4	1/2	-	-	830	490	800	440	770	410	770	400	720	330
		5/8	-	-	1210	550	1160	500	1110	460	1090	450	960	380
		3/4	-	-	1540	620	1420	560	1340	510	1310	500	1150	420
		7/8	-	-	1790	680	1660	610	1560	560	1530	550	1340	470
		1	-	-	2050	740	1900	670	1780	610	1750	600	1530	510
5	1/4	5/8	1260	760	-	-	-	-	-	-	-	-	-	-
		3/4	1740	1000	-	-	-	-	-	-	-	-	-	-
		7/8	2320	1140	-	-	-	-	-	-	-	-	-	-
		1	2980	1210	-	-	-	-	-	-	-	-	-	-
5-1/8	1/4	5/8	-	-	1210	710	1160	670	1130	640	1120	630	1050	550
		3/4	-	-	1670	940	1610	840	1560	760	1550	740	1450	610
		7/8	-	-	2220	1020	2140	900	2070	830	2050	810	1920	670
		1	-	-	2860	1100	2750	990	2670	900	2640	880	2390	720
6-3/4	1/4	5/8	1260	760	1210	710	1160	670	1130	640	1120	630	1050	570
		3/4	1740	1000	1670	940	1610	890	1560	850	1550	840	1450	750
		7/8	2320	1280	2220	1210	2140	1130	2070	1060	2050	1030	1920	850
		1	2980	1590	2860	1420	2750	1270	2670	1150	2640	1120	2470	910
8-1/2	1/4	3/4	1740	1000	-	-	-	-	-	-	-	-	-	-
		7/8	2320	1280	-	-	-	-	-	-	-	-	-	-
		1	2980	1590	-	-	-	-	-	-	-	-	-	-
8-3/4	1/4	3/4	-	-	1670	940	1610	890	1560	850	1550	840	1450	750
		7/8	-	-	2220	1210	2140	1130	2070	1080	2050	1070	1920	970
		1	-	-	2860	1500	2750	1420	2670	1350	2640	1330	2470	1150
10-1/2	1/4	7/8	2320	1280	-	-	-	-	-	-	-	-	-	-
		1	2980	1590	-	-	-	-	-	-	-	-	-	-
10-3/4	1/4	7/8	-	-	2220	1210	2140	1130	2070	1080	2050	1070	1920	970
		1	-	-	2860	1500	2750	1420	2670	1350	2640	1330	2470	1200
12-1/4	1/4	7/8	-	-	2220	1210	2140	1130	2070	1080	2050	1070	1920	970
		1	-	-	2860	1500	2750	1420	2670	1350	2640	1330	2470	1200
14-1/4	1/4	1	-	-	2860	1500	2750	1420	2670	1350	2640	1330	2470	1200

1. Tabulated lateral design values, Z, for bolted connections shall be multiplied by all applicable adjustment factors (see Table 11.3.1).
2. Tabulated lateral design values, Z, are for "full-body diameter" bolts (see Appendix Table L1) with bolt bending yield strength, F_{yb}, of 45,000 psi and dowel bearing strength, F_e, of 87,000 psi for ASTM A36 steel.

Table 12E BOLTS: Reference Lateral Design Values, Z, for Single Shear (two member) Connections[1,2,3,4]

for sawn lumber or SCL to concrete

Embedment Depth in Concrete t_m (in.)	Side Member Thickness t_s (in.)	Bolt Diameter D (in.)	G=0.67 Red Oak $Z_{\parallel}$ (lbs.)	G=0.67 Red Oak $Z_{\perp}$ (lbs.)	G=0.55 Mixed Maple Southern Pine $Z_{\parallel}$ (lbs.)	G=0.55 Mixed Maple Southern Pine $Z_{\perp}$ (lbs.)	G=0.50 Douglas Fir-Larch $Z_{\parallel}$ (lbs.)	G=0.50 Douglas Fir-Larch $Z_{\perp}$ (lbs.)	G=0.49 Douglas Fir-Larch(N) $Z_{\parallel}$ (lbs.)	G=0.49 Douglas Fir-Larch(N) $Z_{\perp}$ (lbs.)	G=0.46 Douglas Fir(S) Hem-Fir(N) $Z_{\parallel}$ (lbs.)	G=0.46 Douglas Fir(S) Hem-Fir(N) $Z_{\perp}$ (lbs.)
6.0 and greater	1-1/2	1/2	770	480	680	410	650	380	640	380	620	360
		5/8	1070	660	970	580	930	530	920	520	890	470
		3/4	1450	890	1330	660	1270	590	1260	560	1230	520
		7/8	1890	960	1750	720	1690	630	1680	600	1640	550
		1	2410	1020	2250	770	2100	680	2060	650	1930	600
	1-3/4	1/2	830	510	740	430	700	400	690	390	670	370
		5/8	1160	680	1030	600	980	550	970	550	940	530
		3/4	1530	900	1390	770	1330	680	1310	660	1270	600
		7/8	1970	1120	1800	840	1730	740	1720	700	1680	640
		1	2480	1190	2290	890	2210	790	2200	750	2150	700
	2-1/2	1/2	830	590	790	520	770	470	760	460	750	440
		5/8	1290	800	1230	670	1180	610	1170	610	1120	570
		3/4	1840	1000	1630	850	1540	800	1520	780	1460	750
		7/8	2290	1240	2050	1080	1940	1020	1920	1000	1860	920
		1	2800	1520	2530	1280	2410	1130	2390	1080	2310	1000
	3-1/2	1/2	830	590	790	540	770	510	760	500	750	490
		5/8	1290	880	1230	810	1200	730	1190	720	1170	670
		3/4	1860	1190	1770	980	1720	900	1720	880	1680	830
		7/8	2540	1410	2410	1190	2320	1100	2290	1070	2200	1020
		1	3310	1670	2970	1420	2800	1330	2770	1300	2660	1260

Embedment Depth in Concrete t_m (in.)	Side Member Thickness t_s (in.)	Bolt Diameter D (in.)	G=0.43 Hem-Fir $Z_{\parallel}$ (lbs.)	G=0.43 Hem-Fir $Z_{\perp}$ (lbs.)	G=0.42 Spruce-Pine-Fir $Z_{\parallel}$ (lbs.)	G=0.42 Spruce-Pine-Fir $Z_{\perp}$ (lbs.)	G=0.37 Redwood $Z_{\parallel}$ (lbs.)	G=0.37 Redwood $Z_{\perp}$ (lbs.)	G=0.36 Eastern Softwoods Spruce-Pine-Fir(S) Western Cedars Western Woods $Z_{\parallel}$ (lbs.)	G=0.36 Eastern Softwoods Spruce-Pine-Fir(S) Western Cedars Western Woods $Z_{\perp}$ (lbs.)	G=0.35 Northern Species $Z_{\parallel}$ (lbs.)	G=0.35 Northern Species $Z_{\perp}$ (lbs.)
6.0 and greater	1-1/2	1/2	590	340	590	340	550	310	540	290	530	290
		5/8	860	420	850	410	810	350	800	330	780	320
		3/4	1200	460	1190	450	1130	370	1120	360	1100	350
		7/8	1580	500	1540	490	1360	410	1330	390	1280	370
		1	1800	540	1760	530	1560	440	1520	420	1460	410
	1-3/4	1/2	640	360	630	350	580	320	580	310	560	310
		5/8	910	490	900	480	840	400	830	380	810	370
		3/4	1230	540	1220	530	1160	430	1140	420	1120	410
		7/8	1630	580	1610	570	1540	470	1520	460	1490	430
		1	2090	630	2060	610	1820	510	1770	490	1710	470
	2-1/2	1/2	730	410	730	400	700	360	690	340	680	340
		5/8	1070	540	1060	530	980	480	960	470	940	460
		3/4	1400	710	1380	700	1290	620	1270	600	1240	580
		7/8	1790	830	1770	810	1660	680	1640	660	1600	610
		1	2230	900	2210	880	2080	730	2060	700	2030	680
	3-1/2	1/2	730	470	730	470	700	430	690	410	690	400
		5/8	1140	620	1140	610	1090	550	1080	530	1070	520
		3/4	1650	780	1640	770	1540	680	1510	670	1470	660
		7/8	2100	960	2070	950	1910	870	1880	850	1840	820
		1	2550	1190	2520	1180	2340	1020	2310	980	2260	950

1. Tabulated lateral design values, Z, for bolted connections shall be multiplied by all applicable adjustment factors (see Table 11.3.1).
2. Tabulated lateral design values, Z, are for "full-body diameter" bolts (see Appendix Table L1) with bolt bending yield strength, F_{yb}, of 45,000 psi.
3. Tabulated lateral design values, Z, are based on dowel bearing strength, F_e, of 7,500 psi for concrete with minimum f_c'=2,500 psi.
4. Six inch anchor embedment assumed.

Table 12F BOLTS: Reference Lateral Design Values, Z, for Double Shear (three member) Connections[1,2]

for sawn lumber or SCL with all members of identical specific gravity

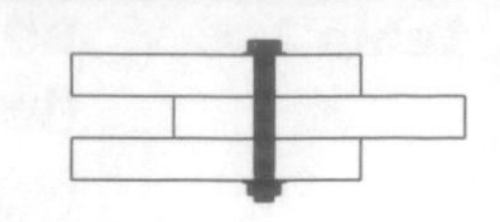

Thickness: Main Member t_m in.	Thickness: Side Member t_s in.	Bolt Diameter D in.	G=0.67 Red Oak $Z_{\parallel}$ lbs.	$Z_{s\perp}$ lbs.	$Z_{m\perp}$ lbs.	G=0.55 Mixed Maple Southern Pine $Z_{\parallel}$ lbs.	$Z_{s\perp}$ lbs.	$Z_{m\perp}$ lbs.	G=0.50 Douglas Fir-Larch $Z_{\parallel}$ lbs.	$Z_{s\perp}$ lbs.	$Z_{m\perp}$ lbs.	G=0.49 Douglas Fir-Larch(N) $Z_{\parallel}$ lbs.	$Z_{s\perp}$ lbs.	$Z_{m\perp}$ lbs.	G=0.46 Douglas Fir(S) Hem-Fir(N) $Z_{\parallel}$ lbs.	$Z_{s\perp}$ lbs.	$Z_{m\perp}$ lbs.
1-1/2	1-1/2	1/2	1410	960	730	1150	800	550	1050	730	470	1030	720	460	970	680	420
		5/8	1760	1310	810	1440	1130	610	1310	1040	530	1290	1030	520	1210	940	470
		3/4	2110	1690	890	1730	1330	660	1580	1170	590	1550	1130	560	1450	1040	520
		7/8	2460	1920	960	2020	1440	720	1840	1260	630	1800	1210	600	1690	1100	550
		1	2810	2040	1020	2310	1530	770	2100	1350	680	2060	1290	650	1930	1200	600
1-3/4	1-3/4	1/2	1640	1030	850	1350	850	640	1230	770	550	1200	750	530	1130	710	490
		5/8	2050	1370	940	1680	1160	710	1530	1070	610	1500	1060	600	1410	1000	550
		3/4	2460	1810	1040	2020	1550	770	1840	1370	680	1800	1310	660	1690	1210	600
		7/8	2870	2240	1120	2350	1680	840	2140	1470	740	2110	1410	700	1970	1290	640
		1	3280	2380	1190	2690	1790	890	2450	1580	790	2410	1510	750	2250	1400	700
2-1/2	1-1/2	1/2	1530	960	1120	1320	800	910	1230	730	790	1210	720	760	1160	680	700
		5/8	2150	1310	1340	1870	1130	1020	1760	1040	880	1740	1030	860	1660	940	780
		3/4	2890	1770	1480	2550	1330	1110	2400	1170	980	2380	1130	940	2280	1040	860
		7/8	3780	1920	1600	3360	1440	1200	3060	1260	1050	3010	1210	1010	2820	1100	920
		1	4690	2040	1700	3840	1530	1280	3500	1350	1130	3440	1290	1080	3220	1200	1000
3-1/2	1-1/2	1/2	1530	960	1120	1320	800	940	1230	730	860	1210	720	850	1160	680	810
		5/8	2150	1310	1510	1870	1130	1290	1760	1040	1190	1740	1030	1170	1660	940	1090
		3/4	2890	1770	1980	2550	1330	1550	2400	1170	1370	2380	1130	1310	2280	1040	1210
		7/8	3780	1920	2240	3360	1440	1680	3180	1260	1470	3150	1210	1410	3030	1100	1290
		1	4820	2040	2380	4310	1530	1790	4090	1350	1580	4050	1290	1510	3860	1200	1400
	1-3/4	1/2	1660	1030	1180	1430	850	1030	1330	770	940	1310	750	920	1250	710	870
		5/8	2310	1370	1630	1990	1160	1380	1860	1070	1230	1840	1060	1200	1760	1000	1090
		3/4	3060	1810	2070	2670	1550	1550	2510	1370	1370	2480	1310	1310	2370	1210	1210
		7/8	3940	2240	2240	3470	1680	1680	3270	1470	1470	3240	1410	1410	3110	1290	1290
		1	4960	2380	2380	4400	1790	1790	4170	1580	1580	4120	1510	1510	3970	1400	1400
	3-1/2	1/2	1660	1180	1180	1500	1040	1040	1430	970	970	1420	960	960	1370	920	920
		5/8	2590	1770	1770	2340	1560	1420	2240	1410	1230	2220	1390	1200	2150	1290	1090
		3/4	3730	2380	2070	3380	1910	1550	3220	1750	1370	3190	1700	1310	3090	1610	1210
		7/8	5080	2820	2240	4600	2330	1680	4290	2130	1470	4210	2070	1410	3940	1960	1290
		1	6560	3340	2380	5380	2780	1790	4900	2580	1580	4810	2520	1510	4510	2410	1400
5-1/4	1-1/2	5/8	2150	1310	1510	1870	1130	1290	1760	1040	1190	1740	1030	1170	1660	940	1110
		3/4	2890	1770	1980	2550	1330	1690	2400	1170	1580	2380	1130	1550	2280	1040	1480
		7/8	3780	1920	2520	3360	1440	2170	3180	1260	2030	3150	1210	1990	3030	1100	1900
		1	4820	2040	3120	4310	1530	2680	4090	1350	2360	4050	1290	2260	3860	1200	2100
	1-3/4	5/8	2310	1370	1630	1990	1160	1380	1860	1070	1270	1840	1060	1250	1760	1000	1180
		3/4	3060	1810	2110	2670	1550	1790	2510	1370	1660	2480	1310	1630	2370	1210	1550
		7/8	3940	2240	2640	3470	1680	2260	3270	1470	2100	3240	1410	2060	3110	1290	1930
		1	4960	2380	3240	4400	1790	2680	4170	1580	2360	4120	1510	2260	3970	1400	2100
	3-1/2	5/8	2590	1770	1770	2340	1560	1560	2240	1410	1460	2220	1390	1450	2150	1290	1390
		3/4	3730	2380	2480	3380	1910	2180	3220	1750	2050	3190	1700	1970	3090	1610	1810
		7/8	5080	2820	3290	4600	2330	2530	4390	2130	2210	4350	2070	2110	4130	1960	1930
		1	6630	3340	3570	5740	2780	2680	5330	2580	2360	5250	2520	2260	4990	2410	2100
5-1/2	1-1/2	5/8	2150	1310	1510	1870	1130	1290	1760	1040	1190	1740	1030	1170	1660	940	1110
		3/4	2890	1770	1980	2550	1330	1690	2400	1170	1580	2380	1130	1550	2280	1040	1480
		7/8	3780	1920	2520	3360	1440	2170	3180	1260	2030	3150	1210	1990	3030	1100	1900
		1	4820	2040	3120	4310	1530	2700	4090	1350	2480	4050	1290	2370	3860	1200	2200
	3-1/2	5/8	2590	1770	1770	2340	1560	1560	2240	1410	1460	2220	1390	1450	2150	1290	1390
		3/4	3730	2380	2480	3380	1910	2180	3220	1750	2050	3190	1700	2020	3090	1610	1900
		7/8	5080	2820	3290	4600	2330	2650	4390	2130	2310	4350	2070	2210	4130	1960	2020
		1	6630	3340	3740	5740	2780	2810	5330	2580	2480	5250	2520	2370	4990	2410	2200
7-1/2	1-1/2	5/8	2150	1310	1510	1870	1130	1290	1760	1040	1190	1740	1030	1170	1660	940	1110
		3/4	2890	1770	1980	2550	1330	1690	2400	1170	1580	2380	1130	1550	2280	1040	1480
		7/8	3780	1920	2520	3360	1440	2170	3180	1260	2030	3150	1210	1990	3030	1100	1900
		1	4820	2040	3120	4310	1530	2700	4090	1350	2530	4050	1290	2480	3860	1200	2390
	3-1/2	5/8	2590	1770	1770	2340	1560	1560	2240	1410	1460	2220	1390	1450	2150	1290	1390
		3/4	3730	2380	2480	3380	1910	2180	3220	1750	2050	3190	1700	2020	3090	1610	1940
		7/8	5080	2820	3290	4600	2330	2890	4390	2130	2720	4350	2070	2670	4130	1960	2560
		1	6630	3340	4190	5740	2780	3680	5330	2580	3380	5250	2520	3230	4990	2410	3000

1. Tabulated lateral design values, Z, for bolted connections shall be multiplied by all applicable adjustment factors (see Table 11.3.1).
2. Tabulated lateral design values, Z, are for "full-body diameter" bolts (see Appendix Table L1) with bolt bending yield strength, F_{yb}, of 45,000 psi.

BOLTS

Table 12F (Cont.) BOLTS: Reference Lateral Design Values, Z, for Double Shear (three member) Connections[1,2]

for sawn lumber or SCL with all members of identical specific gravity

Thickness Main Member	Thickness Side Member	Bolt Diameter	G=0.43 Hem-Fir			G=0.42 Spruce-Pine-Fir			G=0.37 Redwood			G=0.36 Eastern Softwoods Spruce-Pine-Fir(S) Western Cedars Western Woods			G=0.35 Northern Species		
t_m	t_s	D	$Z_{\parallel}$	$Z_{s\perp}$	$Z_{m\perp}$	$Z_{\parallel}$	$Z_{s\perp}$	$Z_{m\perp}$	$Z_{\parallel}$	$Z_{s\perp}$	$Z_{m\perp}$	$Z_{\parallel}$	$Z_{s\perp}$	$Z_{m\perp}$	$Z_{\parallel}$	$Z_{s\perp}$	$Z_{m\perp}$
in.	in.	in.	lbs.	lbs.	lbs.	lbs.	lbs.	lbs.	lbs.	lbs.	lbs.	lbs.	lbs.	lbs.	lbs.	lbs.	lbs.
1-1/2	1-1/2	1/2	900	650	380	880	640	370	780	580	310	760	560	290	730	550	290
		5/8	1130	840	420	1100	830	410	970	690	350	950	660	330	910	640	320
		3/4	1350	920	460	1320	900	450	1170	740	370	1140	720	360	1100	700	350
		7/8	1580	1000	500	1540	970	490	1360	810	410	1330	790	390	1280	740	370
		1	1800	1080	540	1760	1050	530	1560	870	440	1520	840	420	1460	810	410
1-3/4	1-3/4	1/2	1050	670	450	1030	660	430	910	590	360	890	580	340	850	570	330
		5/8	1310	950	490	1290	940	480	1130	810	400	1110	770	380	1070	740	370
		3/4	1580	1080	540	1540	1050	530	1360	870	430	1330	840	420	1280	810	410
		7/8	1840	1160	580	1800	1130	570	1590	950	470	1550	920	460	1490	860	430
		1	2100	1260	630	2060	1230	610	1820	1020	510	1770	980	490	1710	950	470
2-1/2	1-1/2	1/2	1100	650	640	1080	640	610	990	580	510	980	560	490	950	550	480
		5/8	1590	840	700	1570	830	690	1450	690	580	1430	660	550	1390	640	530
		3/4	2190	920	770	2160	900	750	1950	740	620	1900	720	600	1830	700	580
		7/8	2630	1000	830	2570	970	810	2270	810	680	2210	790	660	2130	740	610
		1	3000	1080	900	2940	1050	880	2590	870	730	2530	840	700	2440	810	680
3-1/2	1-1/2	1/2	1100	650	760	1080	640	740	990	580	670	980	560	660	950	550	640
		5/8	1590	840	980	1570	830	960	1450	690	810	1430	660	770	1390	640	740
		3/4	2190	920	1080	2160	900	1050	2010	740	870	1990	720	840	1940	700	810
		7/8	2920	1000	1160	2880	970	1130	2690	810	950	2660	790	920	2560	740	860
		1	3600	1080	1260	3530	1050	1230	3110	870	1020	3040	840	980	2930	810	950
	1-3/4	1/2	1180	670	820	1160	660	800	1060	590	720	1040	580	680	1010	570	670
		5/8	1670	950	980	1650	940	960	1510	810	810	1490	770	770	1450	740	740
		3/4	2270	1080	1080	2240	1050	1050	2070	870	870	2040	840	840	1990	810	810
		7/8	2980	1160	1160	2950	1130	1130	2740	950	950	2700	920	920	2640	860	860
		1	3820	1260	1260	3770	1230	1230	3520	1020	1020	3480	980	980	3410	950	950
	3-1/2	1/2	1330	880	880	1310	870	860	1230	800	720	1220	780	680	1200	760	670
		5/8	2070	1190	980	2050	1170	960	1930	1030	810	1900	1000	770	1870	970	740
		3/4	2980	1490	1080	2950	1460	1050	2720	1290	870	2660	1270	840	2560	1240	810
		7/8	3680	1840	1160	3600	1810	1130	3180	1640	950	3100	1610	920	2990	1550	860
		1	4200	2280	1260	4110	2240	1230	3630	2030	1020	3540	1960	980	3410	1890	950
5-1/4	1-1/2	5/8	1590	840	1050	1570	830	1040	1450	690	940	1430	660	920	1390	640	900
		3/4	2190	920	1400	2160	900	1380	2010	740	1250	1990	720	1230	1940	700	1210
		7/8	2920	1000	1750	2880	970	1700	2690	810	1420	2660	790	1380	2560	740	1290
		1	3600	1080	1890	3530	1050	1840	3110	870	1520	3040	840	1470	2930	810	1420
	1-3/4	5/8	1670	950	1110	1650	940	1100	1510	810	990	1490	770	970	1450	740	940
		3/4	2270	1080	1460	2240	1050	1440	2070	870	1300	2040	840	1260	1990	810	1220
		7/8	2980	1160	1750	2950	1130	1700	2740	950	1420	2700	920	1380	2640	860	1290
		1	3820	1260	1890	3770	1230	1840	3520	1020	1520	3480	980	1470	3410	950	1420
	3-1/2	5/8	2070	1190	1320	2050	1170	1310	1930	1030	1210	1900	1000	1150	1870	970	1120
		3/4	2980	1490	1610	2950	1460	1580	2770	1290	1300	2740	1270	1260	2660	1240	1220
		7/8	3900	1840	1750	3840	1810	1700	3480	1640	1420	3410	1610	1380	3320	1550	1290
		1	4730	2280	1890	4660	2240	1840	4240	2030	1520	4170	1960	1470	4050	1890	1420
5-1/2	1-1/2	5/8	1590	840	1050	1570	830	1040	1450	690	940	1430	660	920	1390	640	900
		3/4	2190	920	1400	2160	900	1380	2010	740	1250	1990	720	1230	1940	700	1210
		7/8	2920	1000	1800	2880	970	1780	2690	810	1490	2660	790	1440	2560	740	1350
		1	3600	1080	1980	3530	1050	1930	3110	870	1600	3040	840	1540	2930	810	1490
	3-1/2	5/8	2070	1190	1320	2050	1170	1310	1930	1030	1210	1900	1000	1180	1870	970	1160
		3/4	2980	1490	1690	2950	1460	1650	2770	1290	1360	2740	1270	1320	2660	1240	1280
		7/8	3900	1840	1830	3840	1810	1780	3480	1640	1490	3410	1610	1440	3320	1550	1350
		1	4730	2280	1980	4660	2240	1930	4240	2030	1600	4170	1960	1540	4050	1890	1490
7-1/2	1-1/2	5/8	1590	840	1050	1570	830	1040	1450	690	940	1430	660	920	1390	640	900
		3/4	2190	920	1400	2160	900	1380	2010	740	1250	1990	720	1230	1940	700	1210
		7/8	2920	1000	1800	2880	970	1780	2690	810	1630	2660	790	1600	2560	740	1550
		1	3600	1080	2270	3530	1050	2240	3110	870	2040	3040	840	2010	2930	810	1970
	3-1/2	5/8	2070	1190	1320	2050	1170	1310	1930	1030	1210	1900	1000	1180	1870	970	1160
		3/4	2980	1490	1850	2950	1460	1820	2770	1290	1670	2740	1270	1650	2660	1240	1620
		7/8	3900	1840	2450	3840	1810	2420	3480	1640	2030	3410	1610	1970	3320	1550	1840
		1	4730	2280	2700	4660	2240	2630	4240	2030	2180	4170	1960	2100	4050	1890	2030

1. Tabulated lateral design values, Z, for bolted connections shall be multiplied by all applicable adjustment factors (see Table 11.3.1).
2. Tabulated lateral design values, Z, are for "full-body diameter" bolts (see Appendix Table L1) with bolt bending yield strength, F_{yb}, of 45,000 psi.

DOWEL-TYPE FASTENERS 12

BOLTS

Table 12G BOLTS: Reference Lateral Design Values, Z, for Double Shear (three member) Connections[1,2]

for sawn lumber or SCL main member with 1/4" ASTM A 36 steel side plates

Thickness: Main Member t_m in.	Thickness: Side Member t_s in.	Bolt Diameter D in.	G=0.67 Red Oak $Z_{\parallel}$ lbs.	G=0.67 Red Oak $Z_{\perp}$ lbs.	G=0.55 Mixed Maple Southern Pine $Z_{\parallel}$ lbs.	G=0.55 Mixed Maple Southern Pine $Z_{\perp}$ lbs.	G=0.50 Douglas Fir-Larch $Z_{\parallel}$ lbs.	G=0.50 Douglas Fir-Larch $Z_{\perp}$ lbs.	G=0.49 Douglas Fir-Larch (N) $Z_{\parallel}$ lbs.	G=0.49 Douglas Fir-Larch (N) $Z_{\perp}$ lbs.	G=0.46 Douglas Fir(S) Hem-Fir(N) $Z_{\parallel}$ lbs.	G=0.46 Douglas Fir(S) Hem-Fir(N) $Z_{\perp}$ lbs.	G=0.43 Hem-Fir $Z_{\parallel}$ lbs.	G=0.43 Hem-Fir $Z_{\perp}$ lbs.	G=0.42 Spruce-Pine-Fir $Z_{\parallel}$ lbs.	G=0.42 Spruce-Pine-Fir $Z_{\perp}$ lbs.	G=0.37 Redwood $Z_{\parallel}$ lbs.	G=0.37 Redwood $Z_{\perp}$ lbs.	G=0.36 Eastern Softwoods Spruce-Pine-Fir(S) Western Cedars Western Woods $Z_{\parallel}$ lbs.	G=0.36 Eastern Softwoods Spruce-Pine-Fir(S) Western Cedars Western Woods $Z_{\perp}$ lbs.	G=0.35 Northern Species $Z_{\parallel}$ lbs.	G=0.35 Northern Species $Z_{\perp}$ lbs.
1-1/2	1/4	1/2	1410	730	1150	550	1050	470	1030	460	970	420	900	380	880	370	780	310	760	290	730	290
		5/8	1760	810	1440	610	1310	530	1290	520	1210	470	1130	420	1100	410	970	350	950	330	910	320
		3/4	2110	890	1730	660	1580	590	1550	560	1450	520	1350	460	1320	450	1170	370	1140	360	1100	350
		7/8	2460	960	2020	720	1840	630	1800	600	1690	550	1580	500	1540	490	1360	410	1330	390	1280	370
		1	2810	1020	2310	770	2100	680	2060	650	1930	600	1800	540	1760	530	1560	440	1520	420	1460	410
1-3/4	1/4	1/2	1640	850	1350	640	1230	550	1200	530	1130	490	1050	450	1030	430	910	360	890	340	850	330
		5/8	2050	940	1680	710	1530	610	1500	600	1410	550	1310	490	1290	480	1130	400	1110	380	1070	370
		3/4	2460	1040	2020	770	1840	680	1800	660	1690	600	1580	540	1540	530	1360	430	1330	420	1280	410
		7/8	2870	1120	2350	840	2140	740	2110	700	1970	640	1840	580	1800	570	1590	470	1550	460	1490	430
		1	3280	1190	2690	890	2450	790	2410	750	2250	700	2100	630	2060	610	1820	510	1770	490	1710	470
2-1/2	1/4	1/2	1870	1210	1720	910	1650	790	1640	760	1590	700	1500	640	1470	610	1300	510	1270	490	1220	480
		5/8	2740	1340	2400	1020	2190	880	2150	860	2010	780	1880	700	1840	690	1620	580	1580	550	1520	530
		3/4	3520	1480	2880	1110	2630	980	2580	940	2410	860	2250	770	2200	750	1950	620	1900	600	1830	580
		7/8	4100	1600	3360	1200	3060	1050	3010	1010	2820	920	2630	830	2570	810	2270	680	2210	660	2130	610
		1	4690	1700	3840	1280	3500	1130	3440	1080	3220	1000	3000	900	2940	880	2590	730	2530	700	2440	680
3-1/2	1/4	1/2	1870	1240	1720	1100	1650	1030	1640	1010	1590	970	1540	890	1530	860	1450	720	1430	680	1410	670
		5/8	2740	1720	2510	1420	2410	1230	2390	1200	2330	1090	2260	980	2230	960	2110	810	2090	770	2060	740
		3/4	3800	2070	3480	1550	3340	1370	3320	1310	3220	1210	3120	1080	3080	1050	2720	870	2660	840	2560	810
		7/8	5060	2240	4630	1680	4290	1470	4210	1410	3940	1290	3680	1160	3600	1130	3180	950	3100	920	2990	860
		1	6520	2380	5380	1790	4900	1580	4810	1510	4510	1400	4200	1260	4110	1230	3630	1020	3540	980	3410	950
5-1/4	1/4	5/8	2740	1720	2510	1510	2410	1420	2390	1400	2330	1340	2260	1280	2230	1270	2110	1170	2090	1140	2060	1120
		3/4	3800	2290	3480	2000	3340	1890	3320	1850	3220	1780	3120	1610	3090	1580	2920	1300	2890	1260	2840	1220
		7/8	5060	2930	4630	2530	4440	2210	4410	2110	4280	1930	4150	1750	4110	1700	3880	1420	3840	1380	3770	1290
		1	6520	3570	5960	2680	5720	2360	5670	2260	5510	2100	5330	1890	5280	1840	4990	1520	4930	1470	4850	1420
5-1/2	1/4	5/8	2740	1720	2510	1510	2410	1420	2390	1400	2330	1340	2260	1280	2230	1270	2110	1170	2090	1140	2060	1120
		3/4	3800	2290	3480	2000	3340	1890	3320	1850	3220	1780	3120	1690	3090	1650	2920	1360	2890	1320	2840	1280
		7/8	5060	2930	4630	2570	4440	2310	4410	2210	4280	2020	4150	1830	4110	1780	3880	1490	3840	1440	3770	1350
		1	6520	3640	5960	2810	5720	2480	5670	2370	5510	2200	5330	1980	5280	1930	4990	1600	4930	1540	4850	1490
7-1/2	1/4	5/8	2740	1720	2510	1510	2410	1420	2390	1400	2330	1340	2260	1280	2230	1270	2110	1170	2090	1140	2060	1120
		3/4	3800	2290	3480	2000	3340	1890	3320	1850	3220	1780	3120	1690	3090	1670	2920	1530	2890	1500	2840	1480
		7/8	5060	2930	4630	2570	4440	2410	4410	2360	4280	2260	4150	2160	4110	2130	3880	1960	3840	1930	3770	1840
		1	6520	3640	5960	3180	5720	3000	5670	2940	5510	2840	5330	2700	5280	2630	4990	2180	4930	2100	4850	2030
9-1/2	1/4	3/4	3800	2290	3480	2000	3340	1890	3320	1850	3220	1780	3120	1690	3090	1670	2920	1530	2890	1500	2840	1480
		7/8	5060	2930	4630	2570	4440	2410	4410	2360	4280	2260	4150	2160	4110	2130	3880	1960	3840	1930	3770	1870
		1	6520	3640	5960	3180	5720	3000	5670	2940	5510	2840	5330	2700	5280	2660	4990	2440	4930	2400	4850	2350
11-1/2	1/4	7/8	5060	2930	4630	2570	4440	2410	4410	2360	4280	2260	4150	2160	4110	2130	3880	1960	3840	1930	3770	1870
		1	6520	3640	5960	3180	5720	3000	5670	2940	5510	2840	5330	2700	5280	2660	4990	2440	4930	2400	4850	2350
13-1/2	1/4	1	6520	3640	5960	3180	5720	3000	5670	2940	5510	2840	5330	2700	5280	2660	4990	2440	4930	2400	4850	2350

1. Tabulated lateral design values, Z, for bolted connections shall be multiplied by all applicable adjustment factors (see Table 11.3.1).
2. Tabulated lateral design values, Z, are for "full-body diameter" bolts (see Appendix Table L1) with bolt bending yield strength, F_{yb}, of 45,000 psi and dowel bearing strength, F_e, of 87,000 psi for ASTM A36 steel.

Table 12H BOLTS: Reference Lateral Design Values, Z, for Double Shear (three member) Connections[1,2]

for structural glued laminated timber main member with sawn lumber side members of identical specific gravity

Thickness			G=0.55 Southern Pine			G=0.50 Douglas Fir-Larch			G=0.46 Douglas Fir(S) Hem-Fir(N)			G=0.43 Hem-Fir			G=0.42 Spruce-Pine-Fir			G=0.36 Spruce-Pine-Fir(S) Western Woods		
Main Member	Side Member	Bolt Diameter																		
t_m in.	t_s in.	D in.	$Z_{\parallel}$ lbs.	$Z_{s\perp}$ lbs.	$Z_{m\perp}$ lbs.	$Z_{\parallel}$ lbs.	$Z_{s\perp}$ lbs.	$Z_{m\perp}$ lbs.	$Z_{\parallel}$ lbs.	$Z_{s\perp}$ lbs.	$Z_{m\perp}$ lbs.	$Z_{\parallel}$ lbs.	$Z_{s\perp}$ lbs.	$Z_{m\perp}$ lbs.	$Z_{\parallel}$ lbs.	$Z_{s\perp}$ lbs.	$Z_{m\perp}$ lbs.	$Z_{\parallel}$ lbs.	$Z_{s\perp}$ lbs.	$Z_{m\perp}$ lbs.
2-1/2	1-1/2	1/2	-	-	-	1230	730	790	1160	680	700	1100	650	640	1080	640	610	980	560	490
		5/8	-	-	-	1760	1040	880	1660	940	780	1590	840	700	1570	830	690	1430	660	550
		3/4	-	-	-	2400	1170	980	2280	1040	860	2190	920	770	2160	900	750	1900	720	600
		7/8	-	-	-	3060	1260	1050	2820	1100	920	2630	1000	830	2570	970	810	2210	790	660
		1	-	-	-	3500	1350	1130	3220	1200	1000	3000	1080	900	2940	1050	880	2530	840	700
3	1-1/2	1/2	1320	800	940	-	-	-	-	-	-	-	-	-	-	-	-	-	-	-
		5/8	1870	1130	1220	-	-	-	-	-	-	-	-	-	-	-	-	-	-	-
		3/4	2550	1330	1330	-	-	-	-	-	-	-	-	-	-	-	-	-	-	-
		7/8	3360	1440	1440	-	-	-	-	-	-	-	-	-	-	-	-	-	-	-
		1	4310	1530	1530	-	-	-	-	-	-	-	-	-	-	-	-	-	-	-
3-1/8	1-1/2	1/2	-	-	-	1230	730	860	1160	680	810	1100	650	760	1080	640	740	980	560	610
		5/8	-	-	-	1760	1040	1090	1660	940	980	1590	840	880	1570	830	860	1430	660	680
		3/4	-	-	-	2400	1170	1220	2280	1040	1080	2190	920	960	2160	900	940	1990	720	750
		7/8	-	-	-	3180	1260	1310	3030	1100	1150	2920	1000	1040	2880	970	1010	2660	790	820
		1	-	-	-	4090	1350	1410	3860	1200	1250	3600	1080	1130	3530	1050	1090	3040	840	880
5	1-1/2	5/8	1870	1130	1290	-	-	-	-	-	-	-	-	-	-	-	-	-	-	-
		3/4	2550	1330	1690	-	-	-	-	-	-	-	-	-	-	-	-	-	-	-
		7/8	3360	1440	2170	-	-	-	-	-	-	-	-	-	-	-	-	-	-	-
		1	4310	1530	2550	-	-	-	-	-	-	-	-	-	-	-	-	-	-	-
5-1/8	1-1/2	5/8	-	-	-	1760	1040	1190	1660	940	1110	1590	840	1050	1570	830	1040	1430	660	920
		3/4	-	-	-	2400	1170	1580	2280	1040	1480	2190	920	1400	2160	900	1380	1990	720	1230
		7/8	-	-	-	3180	1260	2030	3030	1100	1880	2920	1000	1700	2880	970	1660	2660	790	1350
		1	-	-	-	4090	1350	2310	3860	1200	2050	3600	1080	1850	3530	1050	1790	3040	840	1440
6-3/4	1-1/2	5/8	1870	1130	1290	1760	1040	1190	1660	940	1110	1590	840	1050	1570	830	1040	1430	660	920
		3/4	2550	1330	1690	2400	1170	1580	2280	1040	1480	2190	920	1400	2160	900	1380	1990	720	1230
		7/8	3360	1440	2170	3180	1260	2030	3030	1100	1900	2920	1000	1800	2880	970	1780	2660	790	1600
		1	4310	1530	2700	4090	1350	2530	3860	1200	2390	3600	1080	2270	3530	1050	2240	3040	840	1890

1. Tabulated lateral design values, Z, for bolted connections shall be multiplied by all applicable adjustment factors (see Table 11.3.1).
2. Tabulated lateral design values, Z, are for "full-body diameter" bolts (see Appendix Table L1) with bolt bending yield strength, F_{yb}, of 45,000 psi.

Table 12I BOLTS: Reference Lateral Design Values, Z, for Double Shear (three member) Connections[1,2]

for structural glued laminated timber main member with 1/4" ASTM A 36 steel side plates

Thickness			G=0.55 Southern Pine		G=0.50 Douglas Fir-Larch		G=0.46 Douglas Fir(S) Hem-Fir(N)		G=0.43 Hem-Fir		G=0.42 Spruce-Pine-Fir		G=0.36 Spruce-Pine-Fir(S) Western Woods	
Main Member	Side Member	Bolt Diameter												
t_m in.	t_s in.	D in.	$Z_{\parallel}$ lbs.	$Z_{\perp}$ lbs.	$Z_{\parallel}$ lbs.	$Z_{\perp}$ lbs.	$Z_{\parallel}$ lbs.	$Z_{\perp}$ lbs.	$Z_{\parallel}$ lbs.	$Z_{\perp}$ lbs.	$Z_{\parallel}$ lbs.	$Z_{\perp}$ lbs.	$Z_{\parallel}$ lbs.	$Z_{\perp}$ lbs.
2-1/2	1/4	1/2	-	-	1650	790	1590	700	1500	640	1470	610	1270	490
		5/8	-	-	2190	880	2010	780	1880	700	1840	690	1580	550
		3/4	-	-	2630	980	2410	860	2250	770	2200	750	1900	600
		7/8	-	-	3060	1050	2820	920	2630	830	2570	810	2210	660
		1	-	-	3500	1130	3220	1000	3000	900	2940	880	2530	700
3	1/4	1/2	1720	1100	-	-	-	-	-	-	-	-	-	-
		5/8	2510	1220	-	-	-	-	-	-	-	-	-	-
		3/4	3460	1330	-	-	-	-	-	-	-	-	-	-
		7/8	4040	1440	-	-	-	-	-	-	-	-	-	-
		1	4610	1530	-	-	-	-	-	-	-	-	-	-
3-1/8	1/4	1/2	-	-	1650	980	1590	880	1540	800	1530	770	1430	610
		5/8	-	-	2410	1090	2330	980	2260	880	2230	860	1980	680
		3/4	-	-	3280	1220	3020	1080	2810	960	2750	940	2370	750
		7/8	-	-	3830	1310	3520	1150	3280	1040	3210	1010	2770	820
		1	-	-	4380	1410	4020	1250	3750	1130	3670	1090	3160	880
5	1/4	5/8	2510	1510	-	-	-	-	-	-	-	-	-	-
		3/4	3480	2000	-	-	-	-	-	-	-	-	-	-
		7/8	4630	2410	-	-	-	-	-	-	-	-	-	-
		1	5960	2550	-	-	-	-	-	-	-	-	-	-
5-1/8	1/4	5/8	-	-	2410	1420	2330	1340	2260	1280	2230	1270	2090	1120
		3/4	-	-	3340	1890	3220	1770	3120	1580	3090	1540	2890	1230
		7/8	-	-	4440	2150	4280	1880	4150	1700	4110	1660	3840	1350
		1	-	-	5720	2310	5510	2050	5330	1850	5280	1790	4930	1440
6-3/4	1/4	5/8	2510	1510	2410	1420	2330	1340	2260	1280	2230	1270	2090	1140
		3/4	3480	2000	3340	1890	3220	1780	3120	1690	3090	1670	2890	1500
		7/8	4630	2570	4440	2410	4280	2260	4150	2160	4110	2130	3840	1770
		1	5960	3180	5720	3000	5510	2700	5330	2430	5280	2360	4930	1890
8-1/2	1/4	3/4	3480	2000	-	-	-	-	-	-	-	-	-	-
		7/8	4630	2570	-	-	-	-	-	-	-	-	-	-
		1	5960	3180	-	-	-	-	-	-	-	-	-	-
8-3/4	1/4	3/4	-	-	3340	1890	3220	1780	3120	1690	3090	1670	2890	1500
		7/8	-	-	4440	2410	4280	2260	4150	2160	4110	2130	3840	1930
		1	-	-	5720	3000	5510	2840	5330	2700	5280	2660	4930	2400
10-1/2	1/4	7/8	4630	2570	-	-	-	-	-	-	-	-	-	-
		1	5960	3180	-	-	-	-	-	-	-	-	-	-
10-3/4	1/4	7/8	-	-	4440	2410	4280	2260	4150	2160	4110	2130	3840	1930
		1	-	-	5720	3000	5510	2840	5330	2700	5280	2660	4930	2400
12-1/4	1/4	7/8	-	-	4440	2410	4280	2260	4150	2160	4110	2130	3840	1930
		1	-	-	5720	3000	5510	2840	5330	2700	5280	2660	4930	2400
14-1/4	1/4	1	-	-	5720	3000	5510	2840	5330	2700	5280	2660	4930	2400

1. Tabulated lateral design values, Z, for bolted connections shall be multiplied by all applicable adjustment factors (see Table 11.3.1).
2. Tabulated lateral design values, Z, are for "full-body diameter" bolts (see Appendix Table L1) with bolt bending yield strength, F_{yb}, of 45,000 psi and dowel bearing strength, F_e, of 87,000 psi for ASTM A36 steel.

This page left blank intentionally.

Table 12J LAG SCREWS: Reference Lateral Design Values, Z, for Single Shear (two member) Connections[1,2,3,4]

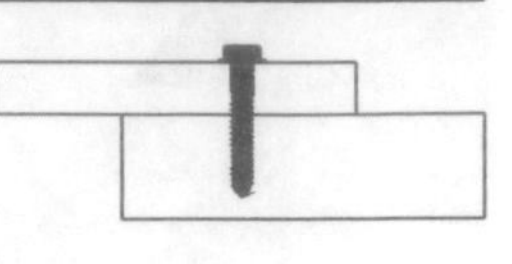

for sawn lumber or SCL with both members of identical specific gravity (tabulated lateral design values are calculated based on an assumed length of lag screw penetration, p, into the main member equal to 8D)

Side Member Thickness	Lag Screw Diameter	G=0.67 Red Oak				G=0.55 Mixed Maple Southern Pine				G=0.50 Douglas Fir-Larch				G=0.49 Douglas Fir-Larch(N)				G=0.46 Douglas Fir(S) Hem-Fir(N)			
t_s	D	$Z_{\parallel}$	$Z_{s\perp}$	$Z_{m\perp}$	$Z_{\perp}$	$Z_{\parallel}$	$Z_{s\perp}$	$Z_{m\perp}$	$Z_{\perp}$	$Z_{\parallel}$	$Z_{s\perp}$	$Z_{m\perp}$	$Z_{\perp}$	$Z_{\parallel}$	$Z_{s\perp}$	$Z_{m\perp}$	$Z_{\perp}$	$Z_{\parallel}$	$Z_{s\perp}$	$Z_{m\perp}$	$Z_{\perp}$
in.	in.	lbs.	lbs.	lbs.	lbs.	lbs.	lbs.	lbs.	lbs.	lbs.	lbs.	lbs.	lbs.	lbs.	lbs.	lbs.	lbs.	lbs.	lbs.	lbs.	lbs.
1/2	1/4	150	110	110	110	130	90	100	90	120	90	90	80	120	90	90	80	110	80	90	80
	5/16	170	130	130	120	150	110	120	100	150	100	110	100	140	100	110	90	140	100	100	90
	3/8	180	130	130	120	160	110	110	100	150	100	110	90	150	90	110	90	140	90	100	90
5/8	1/4	160	120	130	120	140	100	110	100	130	90	100	90	130	90	100	90	120	90	90	80
	5/16	190	140	140	130	160	110	120	110	150	110	110	100	150	100	110	100	150	100	110	90
	3/8	190	130	140	120	170	110	120	100	160	100	110	100	160	100	110	90	150	100	110	90
3/4	1/4	180	140	140	130	150	110	120	110	140	100	110	100	140	100	110	90	130	90	100	90
	5/16	210	150	160	140	180	120	130	120	170	110	120	100	160	110	120	100	160	100	110	100
	3/8	210	140	160	130	180	120	130	110	170	110	120	100	170	110	120	100	160	100	110	90
1	1/4	180	140	140	140	160	120	120	120	150	120	120	110	150	110	110	110	150	110	110	100
	5/16	230	170	170	160	210	140	150	130	190	130	140	120	190	120	140	120	180	120	130	110
	3/8	230	160	170	160	210	130	150	120	200	120	140	110	190	120	140	110	180	110	130	100
1-1/4	1/4	180	140	140	140	160	120	120	120	150	120	120	110	150	110	110	110	150	110	110	100
	5/16	230	170	170	160	210	150	150	140	200	140	140	130	200	140	140	130	190	130	140	120
	3/8	230	170	170	160	210	150	150	140	200	140	140	130	200	130	140	120	190	120	140	120
1-1/2	1/4	180	140	140	140	160	120	120	120	150	120	120	110	150	110	110	110	150	110	110	100
	5/16	230	170	170	160	210	150	150	140	200	140	140	130	200	140	140	130	190	140	140	130
	3/8	230	170	170	160	210	150	150	140	200	140	140	130	200	140	140	130	190	140	140	120
	7/16	360	260	260	240	320	220	230	200	310	200	210	180	310	190	210	180	300	180	200	160
	1/2	460	310	320	280	410	250	290	230	390	220	270	200	390	220	260	200	370	210	250	190
	5/8	700	410	500	370	600	340	420	310	560	310	380	280	550	310	380	270	530	290	360	260
	3/4	950	550	660	490	830	470	560	410	770	440	510	380	760	430	510	370	730	400	480	360
	7/8	1240	720	830	630	1080	560	710	540	1020	490	660	490	1010	470	650	470	970	430	610	430
	1	1550	800	1010	780	1360	600	870	600	1290	530	810	530	1280	500	790	500	1230	470	760	470
1-3/4	1/4	180	140	140	140	160	120	120	120	150	120	120	110	150	110	110	110	150	110	110	100
	5/16	230	170	170	160	210	150	150	140	200	140	140	130	200	140	140	130	190	140	140	130
	3/8	230	170	170	160	210	150	150	140	200	140	140	130	200	140	140	130	190	140	140	120
	7/16	360	260	260	240	320	230	230	210	310	210	210	190	310	210	210	190	300	200	200	180
	1/2	460	320	320	290	410	270	290	250	390	240	270	220	390	240	260	220	380	220	250	200
	5/8	740	440	500	400	660	360	440	320	610	330	420	290	600	320	410	290	570	300	390	270
	3/4	1030	580	720	520	890	480	600	430	830	450	550	390	820	440	540	380	780	420	510	360
	7/8	1320	740	890	650	1150	630	750	550	1070	570	700	510	1060	550	680	490	1010	500	650	470
	1	1630	910	1070	790	1420	700	910	670	1340	610	850	610	1320	590	830	590	1270	550	790	550
2-1/2	1/4	180	140	140	140	160	120	120	120	150	120	120	110	150	110	110	110	150	110	110	100
	5/16	230	170	170	160	210	150	150	140	200	140	140	130	200	140	140	130	190	140	140	130
	3/8	230	170	170	160	210	150	150	140	200	140	140	130	200	140	140	130	190	140	140	120
	7/16	360	260	260	240	320	230	230	210	310	210	210	190	310	210	210	190	300	200	200	180
	1/2	460	320	320	290	410	290	290	250	390	270	270	240	390	260	260	230	380	250	250	220
	5/8	740	500	500	450	670	430	440	390	640	390	420	350	630	380	410	340	610	360	390	320
	3/4	1110	680	740	610	1010	550	650	490	960	500	610	450	950	490	600	430	920	460	580	410
	7/8	1550	830	1000	740	1370	690	880	600	1280	630	830	550	1260	620	810	530	1190	580	770	500
	1	1940	980	1270	860	1660	830	1080	720	1550	770	990	660	1520	750	970	640	1450	720	920	620
3-1/2	1/4	180	140	140	140	160	120	120	120	150	120	120	110	150	110	110	110	150	110	110	100
	5/16	230	170	170	160	210	150	150	140	200	140	140	130	200	140	140	130	190	140	140	130
	3/8	230	170	170	160	210	150	150	140	200	140	140	130	200	140	140	130	190	140	140	120
	7/16	360	260	260	240	320	230	230	210	310	210	210	190	310	210	210	190	300	200	200	180
	1/2	460	320	320	290	410	290	290	250	390	270	270	240	390	260	260	230	380	250	250	220
	5/8	740	500	500	450	670	440	440	390	640	420	420	360	630	410	410	360	610	390	390	340
	3/4	1110	740	740	650	1010	650	650	560	960	600	610	520	950	580	600	510	920	550	580	490
	7/8	1550	990	1000	860	1400	800	880	710	1340	720	830	640	1320	700	810	620	1280	660	780	570
	1	2020	1140	1270	1010	1830	930	1120	810	1740	850	1060	740	1730	830	1040	720	1670	790	1000	680

1. Tabulated lateral design values, Z, shall be multiplied by all applicable adjustment factors (see Table 11.3.1).
2. Tabulated lateral design values, Z, are for "reduced body diameter" lag screws (see Appendix Table L2) inserted in side grain with screw axis perpendicular to wood fibers; screw penetration, p, into the main member equal to 8D; screw bending yield strengths, F_{yb}, of 70,000 psi for D = 1/4", 60,000 psi for D = 5/16", and 45,000 psi for D $\geq$3/8".
3. Where the lag screw penetration, p, is less than 8D but not less than 4D, tabulated lateral design values, Z, shall be multiplied by p/8D or lateral design values shall be calculated using the provisions of 12.3 for the reduced penetration.
4. The length of lag screw penetration, p, not including the length of the tapered tip, E (see Appendix Table L2), of the lag screw into the main member shall not be less than 4D. See 12.1.4.6 for minimum length of penetration, p_{min}.

Table 12J (Cont.) LAG SCREWS: Reference Lateral Design Values (Z) for Single Shear (two member) Connections[1,2,3,4]

for sawn lumber or SCL with both members of identical specific gravity (tabulated lateral design values are calculated based on an assumed length of lag screw penetration, p, into the main member equal to 8D)

Side Member Thickness	Lag Screw Diameter	G=0.43 Hem-Fir				G=0.42 Spruce-Pine-Fir				G=0.37 Redwood				G=0.36 Eastern Softwoods Spruce-Pine-Fir(S) Western Cedars Western Woods				G=0.35 Northern Species			
t_s	D	$Z_{\parallel}$	$Z_{s\perp}$	$Z_{m\perp}$	$Z_{\perp}$	$Z_{\parallel}$	$Z_{s\perp}$	$Z_{m\perp}$	$Z_{\perp}$	$Z_{\parallel}$	$Z_{s\perp}$	$Z_{m\perp}$	$Z_{\perp}$	$Z_{\parallel}$	$Z_{s\perp}$	$Z_{m\perp}$	$Z_{\perp}$	$Z_{\parallel}$	$Z_{s\perp}$	$Z_{m\perp}$	$Z_{\perp}$
in.	in.	lbs.	lbs.	lbs.	lbs.	lbs.	lbs.	lbs.	lbs.	lbs.	lbs.	lbs.	lbs.	lbs.	lbs.	lbs.	lbs.	lbs.	lbs.	lbs.	lbs.
1/2	1/4	110	80	80	70	110	80	80	70	100	70	70	60	100	70	70	60	90	70	70	60
	5/16	130	90	100	80	130	90	90	80	120	80	90	80	120	80	90	70	120	80	80	70
	3/8	140	80	100	80	130	80	90	80	120	60	90	60	120	60	80	60	120	60	80	60
5/8	1/4	120	80	90	80	110	80	90	70	110	70	80	70	100	70	80	60	100	70	70	60
	5/16	140	90	100	90	140	90	100	90	130	80	90	80	130	80	90	80	120	80	90	70
	3/8	140	90	100	80	140	90	100	80	130	80	90	70	130	70	90	70	120	70	90	70
3/4	1/4	130	90	100	80	120	80	90	80	110	80	80	70	110	70	80	70	110	70	80	70
	5/16	150	100	110	90	150	100	110	90	130	90	100	80	130	90	90	80	130	80	90	80
	3/8	150	100	110	90	150	90	110	90	140	90	100	80	130	80	90	70	130	80	90	70
1	1/4	140	100	110	90	140	100	100	90	130	90	100	80	130	80	90	80	130	80	90	70
	5/16	170	110	130	100	170	110	120	100	150	90	110	90	150	90	110	80	150	90	100	80
	3/8	170	100	120	100	170	100	120	90	150	90	110	80	150	90	110	80	150	90	100	80
1-1/4	1/4	140	110	110	100	140	100	100	100	130	100	100	90	130	90	90	90	130	90	90	80
	5/16	180	120	130	110	180	120	130	110	170	100	120	100	170	100	120	90	160	100	110	90
	3/8	190	120	130	110	180	110	130	100	170	100	120	90	170	100	120	90	170	90	110	80
1-1/2	1/4	140	110	110	100	140	100	100	100	130	100	100	90	130	90	90	90	130	90	90	80
	5/16	180	130	130	120	180	130	130	120	170	110	120	110	170	110	120	100	160	110	110	100
	3/8	190	130	130	120	180	130	130	110	170	110	120	100	170	110	120	100	170	100	110	90
	7/16	290	170	190	150	280	160	190	150	260	140	180	130	260	140	170	130	250	140	170	120
	1/2	350	190	240	180	350	190	240	170	310	170	210	150	310	160	210	150	300	160	200	140
	5/8	500	280	340	240	490	270	330	240	450	250	300	210	440	240	290	210	430	240	280	200
	3/4	700	360	450	330	690	350	440	330	630	290	400	290	620	280	390	280	610	270	380	270
	7/8	930	390	580	390	910	380	570	380	850	320	520	320	840	310	510	310	820	290	490	290
	1	1180	420	720	420	1160	410	710	410	1080	340	640	340	1070	330	630	330	1050	320	620	320
1-3/4	1/4	140	110	110	100	140	100	100	100	130	100	100	90	130	90	90	90	130	90	90	80
	5/16	180	130	130	120	180	130	130	120	170	120	120	110	170	120	120	110	160	110	110	100
	3/8	190	130	130	120	180	130	130	110	170	120	120	100	170	120	120	100	170	110	110	100
	7/16	290	180	190	160	280	180	190	160	270	160	180	140	260	150	170	140	260	140	170	130
	1/2	360	210	240	190	360	200	240	180	340	180	220	160	340	170	220	150	330	170	210	150
	5/8	540	290	360	250	530	280	360	250	480	250	320	220	480	250	310	210	460	240	300	210
	3/4	740	400	480	340	730	390	470	340	670	330	420	300	660	320	420	300	640	310	410	290
	7/8	970	450	610	440	950	440	600	440	880	370	540	370	870	360	530	360	850	330	520	330
	1	1210	490	750	490	1200	480	740	480	1110	400	670	400	1090	380	650	380	1070	370	640	370
2-1/2	1/4	140	110	110	100	140	100	100	100	130	100	100	90	130	90	90	90	130	90	90	80
	5/16	180	130	130	120	180	130	130	120	170	120	120	110	170	120	120	110	160	110	110	100
	3/8	190	130	130	120	180	130	130	110	170	120	120	100	170	120	120	100	170	110	110	100
	7/16	290	190	190	170	280	190	190	170	270	180	180	150	260	170	170	150	260	170	170	150
	1/2	360	240	240	210	360	240	240	210	340	220	220	190	340	210	220	190	330	200	210	180
	5/8	590	330	380	290	580	320	370	290	550	290	340	250	540	280	340	240	530	270	330	240
	3/4	890	430	550	380	880	420	540	370	800	380	500	320	780	370	490	320	760	360	480	310
	7/8	1130	550	730	470	1110	540	710	460	1010	490	640	420	990	480	620	410	970	470	600	390
	1	1380	680	870	580	1360	670	850	570	1240	570	760	510	1220	550	750	500	1190	530	730	490
3-1/2	1/4	140	110	110	100	140	100	100	100	130	100	100	90	130	90	90	90	130	90	90	80
	5/16	180	130	130	120	180	130	130	120	170	120	120	110	170	120	120	110	160	110	110	100
	3/8	190	130	130	120	180	130	130	110	170	120	120	100	170	120	120	100	170	110	110	100
	7/16	290	190	190	170	280	190	190	170	270	180	180	150	260	170	170	150	260	170	170	150
	1/2	360	240	240	210	360	240	240	210	340	220	220	190	340	220	220	190	330	210	210	180
	5/8	590	380	380	320	580	370	370	320	550	340	340	290	540	330	340	280	530	320	330	280
	3/4	890	500	550	440	880	490	540	430	830	430	500	370	820	420	490	370	800	410	480	360
	7/8	1240	610	750	530	1220	600	740	520	1150	530	680	460	1140	520	670	450	1110	500	650	430
	1	1610	740	950	630	1600	720	940	620	1480	650	860	550	1450	630	850	540	1410	620	830	520

1. Tabulated lateral design values, Z, shall be multiplied by all applicable adjustment factors (see Table 11.3.1).
2. Tabulated lateral design values, Z, are for "reduced body diameter" lag screws (see Appendix Table L2) inserted in side grain with screw axis perpendicular to wood fibers; screw penetration, p, into the main member equal to 8D; screw bending yield strengths, F_{yb}, of 70,000 psi for D = 1/4", 60,000 psi for D = 5/16", and 45,000 psi for D $\geq$3/8".
3. Where the lag screw penetration, p, is less than 8D but not less than 4D, tabulated lateral design values, Z, shall be multiplied by p/8D or lateral design values shall be calculated using the provisions of 12.3 for the reduced penetration.
4. The length of lag screw penetration, p, not including the length of the tapered tip, E (see Appendix Table L2), of the lag screw into the main member shall not be less than 4D. See 12.1.4.6 for minimum length of penetration, p_{min}.

Table 12K LAG SCREWS: Reference Lateral Design Values, Z, for Single Shear (two member) Connections[1,2,3,4]

for sawn lumber or SCL with ASTM A653, Grade 33 steel side plate (for t_s<1/4") or ASTM A 36 steel side plate (for t_s=1/4")
(tabulated lateral design values are calculated based on an assumed length of lag screw penetration, p, into the main member equal to 8D)

Side Member Thickness	Lag Screw Diameter	G=0.67 Red Oak		G=0.55 Mixed Maple Southern Pine		G=0.5 Douglas Fir-Larch		G=0.49 Douglas Fir-Larch (N)		G=0.46 Douglas Fir(S) Hem-Fir(N)		G=0.43 Hem-Fir		G=0.42 Spruce-Pine-Fir		G=0.37 Redwood		G=0.36 Eastern Softwoods Spruce-Pine-Fir(S) Western Cedars Western Woods		G=0.35 Northern Species	
t_s	D	$Z_{\parallel}$	$Z_{\perp}$	$Z_{\parallel}$	$Z_{\perp}$	$Z_{\parallel}$	$Z_{\perp}$	$Z_{\parallel}$	$Z_{\perp}$	$Z_{\parallel}$	$Z_{\perp}$	$Z_{\parallel}$	$Z_{\perp}$	$Z_{\parallel}$	$Z_{\perp}$	$Z_{\parallel}$	$Z_{\perp}$	$Z_{\parallel}$	$Z_{\perp}$	$Z_{\parallel}$	$Z_{\perp}$
in.	in.	lbs.	lbs.	lbs.	lbs.	lbs.	lbs.	lbs.	lbs.	lbs.	lbs.	lbs.	lbs.	lbs.	lbs.	lbs.	lbs.	lbs.	lbs.	lbs.	lbs.
0.075	1/4	170	130	160	120	150	110	150	110	150	100	140	100	140	100	130	90	130	90	130	90
(14 gage)	5/16	220	160	200	140	190	130	190	130	190	130	180	120	180	120	170	110	170	110	160	100
	3/8	220	160	200	140	200	130	190	130	190	120	180	120	180	120	170	110	170	100	170	100
0.105	1/4	180	140	170	130	160	120	160	120	160	110	150	110	150	110	140	100	140	100	140	90
(12 gage)	5/16	230	170	210	150	200	140	200	140	190	130	190	130	190	120	180	110	170	110	170	110
	3/8	230	160	210	140	200	140	200	130	200	130	190	120	190	120	180	110	180	110	170	110
0.120	1/4	190	150	180	130	170	120	170	120	160	120	160	110	160	110	150	100	150	100	140	100
(11 gage)	5/16	230	170	210	150	210	140	200	140	200	140	190	130	190	130	180	120	180	120	180	110
	3/8	240	170	220	150	210	140	210	140	200	130	200	130	190	120	180	110	180	110	180	110
0.134	1/4	200	150	180	140	180	130	170	130	170	120	160	120	160	110	150	110	150	100	150	100
(10 gage)	5/16	240	180	220	160	210	150	210	140	200	140	200	130	200	130	190	120	180	120	180	120
	3/8	240	170	220	150	220	140	210	140	210	140	200	130	200	130	190	120	190	120	180	110
0.179	1/4	220	170	210	150	200	150	200	140	190	140	190	130	190	130	180	120	170	120	170	120
(7 gage)	5/16	260	190	240	170	230	160	230	160	230	150	220	150	220	150	210	130	200	130	200	130
	3/8	270	190	250	170	240	160	240	160	230	150	220	140	220	140	210	130	210	130	200	130
0.239	1/4	240	180	220	160	210	150	210	150	200	140	190	140	190	130	180	120	180	120	180	120
(3 gage)	5/16	300	220	280	190	270	180	260	180	260	170	250	160	250	160	230	150	230	150	230	140
	3/8	310	220	280	190	270	180	270	180	260	170	250	160	250	160	240	140	230	140	230	140
	7/16	420	290	390	260	380	240	370	240	360	230	350	220	350	220	330	200	330	200	320	190
	1/2	510	340	470	300	460	290	450	280	440	270	430	260	420	260	400	240	400	230	390	230
	5/8	770	490	710	430	680	400	680	400	660	380	640	370	630	360	600	330	590	330	580	320
	3/4	1110	670	1020	590	980	560	970	550	950	530	920	500	910	500	860	450	850	450	840	440
	7/8	1510	880	1390	780	1330	730	1320	710	1280	690	1250	650	1230	650	1170	590	1160	590	1140	570
	1	1940	1100	1780	960	1710	910	1700	890	1650	860	1600	820	1590	810	1500	740	1480	730	1460	710
1/4	1/4	240	180	220	160	210	150	210	150	200	140	200	140	190	130	180	120	180	120	180	120
	5/16	310	220	280	200	270	180	270	180	260	170	250	170	250	160	230	150	230	150	230	140
	3/8	320	220	290	190	280	180	270	180	270	170	260	160	250	160	240	150	240	140	230	140
	7/16	480	320	440	280	420	270	420	260	410	250	390	240	390	230	370	220	360	210	360	210
	1/2	580	390	540	340	520	320	510	320	500	310	480	290	480	290	460	270	450	260	440	260
	5/8	850	530	780	470	750	440	740	440	720	420	700	400	690	400	660	370	650	360	640	350
	3/4	1200	730	1100	640	1060	600	1050	590	1020	570	990	540	980	530	930	490	920	480	900	470
	7/8	1600	930	1470	820	1410	770	1400	750	1360	720	1320	690	1310	680	1240	630	1220	620	1200	600
	1	2040	1150	1870	1000	1800	950	1780	930	1730	900	1680	850	1660	840	1570	770	1550	760	1530	740

1. Tabulated lateral design values, Z, shall be multiplied by all applicable adjustment factors (see Table 11.3.1).
2. Tabulated lateral design values, Z, are for "reduced body diameter" lag screws (see Appendix Table L2) inserted in side grain with screw axis perpendicular to wood fibers; screw penetration, p, into the main member equal to 8D; dowel bearing strengths, F_e, of 61,850 psi for ASTM A653, Grade 33 steel and 87,000 psi for ASTM A36 steel and screw bending yield strengths, F_{yb}, of 70,000 psi for D = 1/4", 60,000 psi for D = 5/16", and 45,000 psi for D $\geq$3/8".
3. Where the lag screw penetration, p, is less than 8D but not less than 4D, tabulated lateral design values, Z, shall be multiplied by p/8D or lateral design values shall be calculated using the provisions of 12.3 for the reduced penetration.
4. The length of lag screw penetration, p, not including the length of the tapered tip, E (see Appendix Table L2), of the lag screw into the main member shall not be less than 4D. See 12.1.4.6 for minimum length of penetration, p_{min}.

Table 12L WOOD SCREWS: Reference Lateral Design Values, Z, for Single Shear (two member) Connections[1,2,3]

for sawn lumber or SCL with both members of identical specific gravity (tabulated lateral design values are calculated based on an assumed length of wood screw penetration, p, into the main member equal to 10D)

Side Member Thickness t_s in.	Wood Screw Diameter D in.	Wood Screw Number	G=0.67 Red Oak lbs.	G=0.55 Mixed Maple Southern Pine lbs.	G=0.5 Douglas Fir-Larch lbs.	G=0.49 Douglas Fir-Larch(N) lbs.	G=0.46 Douglas Fir(S) Hem-Fir(N) lbs.	G=0.43 Hem-Fir lbs.	G=0.42 Spruce-Pine-Fir lbs.	G=0.37 Redwood lbs.	G=0.36 Eastern Softwoods Spruce-Pine-Fir(S) Western Cedars Western Woods lbs.	G=0.35 Northern Species lbs.
1/2	0.138	6	88	67	59	57	53	49	47	41	40	38
	0.151	7	96	74	65	63	59	54	52	45	44	42
	0.164	8	107	82	73	71	66	61	59	51	50	48
	0.177	9	121	94	83	81	76	70	68	59	58	56
	0.190	10	130	101	90	87	82	75	73	64	63	60
	0.216	12	156	123	110	107	100	93	91	79	78	75
	0.242	14	168	133	120	117	110	102	99	87	86	83
5/8	0.138	6	94	76	66	64	59	53	52	44	43	41
	0.151	7	104	83	72	70	64	58	56	48	47	45
	0.164	8	120	92	80	77	72	65	63	54	53	51
	0.177	9	136	103	91	88	81	74	72	62	61	58
	0.190	10	146	111	97	94	88	80	78	67	65	63
	0.216	12	173	133	117	114	106	97	95	82	80	77
	0.242	14	184	142	126	123	115	106	103	89	87	84
3/4	0.138	6	94	79	72	71	65	58	57	47	46	44
	0.151	7	104	87	80	77	71	64	62	52	50	48
	0.164	8	120	101	88	85	78	71	69	58	56	54
	0.177	9	142	114	99	96	88	80	78	66	64	61
	0.190	10	153	122	107	103	95	86	83	71	69	66
	0.216	12	192	144	126	122	113	103	100	86	84	80
	0.242	14	203	154	135	131	122	111	108	93	91	87
1	0.138	6	94	79	72	71	67	63	61	55	54	51
	0.151	7	104	87	80	78	74	69	68	60	59	56
	0.164	8	120	101	92	90	85	80	78	67	65	62
	0.177	9	142	118	108	106	100	94	90	75	73	70
	0.190	10	153	128	117	114	108	101	97	81	78	75
	0.216	12	193	161	147	143	131	118	114	96	93	89
	0.242	14	213	178	157	152	139	126	122	102	100	95
1-1/4	0.138	6	94	79	72	71	67	63	61	55	54	52
	0.151	7	104	87	80	78	74	69	68	60	59	57
	0.164	8	120	101	92	90	85	80	78	70	68	66
	0.177	9	142	118	108	106	100	94	92	82	80	78
	0.190	10	153	128	117	114	108	101	99	88	87	84
	0.216	12	193	161	147	144	137	128	125	108	105	100
	0.242	14	213	178	163	159	151	141	138	115	111	106
1-1/2	0.138	6	94	79	72	71	67	63	61	55	54	52
	0.151	7	104	87	80	78	74	69	68	60	59	57
	0.164	8	120	101	92	90	85	80	78	70	68	66
	0.177	9	142	118	108	106	100	94	92	82	80	78
	0.190	10	153	128	117	114	108	101	99	88	87	84
	0.216	12	193	161	147	144	137	128	125	111	109	106
	0.242	14	213	178	163	159	151	141	138	123	120	117
1-3/4	0.138	6	94	79	72	71	67	63	61	55	54	52
	0.151	7	104	87	80	78	74	69	68	60	59	57
	0.164	8	120	101	92	90	85	80	78	70	68	66
	0.177	9	142	118	108	106	100	94	92	82	80	78
	0.190	10	153	128	117	114	108	101	99	88	87	84
	0.216	12	193	161	147	144	137	128	125	111	109	106
	0.242	14	213	178	163	159	151	141	138	123	120	117

1. Tabulated lateral design values, Z, shall be multiplied by all applicable adjustment factors (see Table 11.3.1).
2. Tabulated lateral design values, Z, are for rolled thread wood screws (see Appendix Table L3) inserted in side grain with screw axis perpendicular to wood fibers; screw penetration, p, into the main member equal to 10D; and screw bending yield strengths, F_{yb}, of 100,000 psi for $0.099" \leq D \leq 0.142"$, 90,000 psi for $0.142" < D \leq 0.177"$, 80,000 psi for $0.177" < D \leq 0.236"$, and 70,000 psi for $0.236" < D \leq 0.273"$.
3. Where the wood screw penetration, p, is less than 10D but not less than 6D, tabulated lateral design values, Z, shall be multiplied by p/10D or lateral design values shall be calculated using the provisions of 12.3 for the reduced penetration.

WOOD SCREWS

Table 12M WOOD SCREWS: Reference Lateral Design Values, Z, for Single Shear (two member) Connections[1,2,3]

for sawn lumber or SCL with ASTM 653, Grade 33 steel side plate
(tabulated lateral design values are calculated based on an assumed length of wood screw penetration, p, into the main member equal to 10D)

Side Member Thickness t_s in.	Wood Screw Diameter D in.	Wood Screw Number	G=0.67 Red Oak lbs.	G=0.55 Mixed Maple Southern Pine lbs.	G=0.5 Douglas Fir-Larch lbs.	G=0.49 Douglas Fir-Larch(N) lbs.	G=0.46 Douglas Fir(S) Hem-Fir(N) lbs.	G=0.43 Hem-Fir lbs.	G=0.42 Spruce-Pine-Fir lbs.	G=0.37 Redwood lbs.	G=0.36 Eastern Softwoods Spruce-Pine-Fir(S) Western Cedars Western Woods lbs.	G=0.35 Northern Species lbs.
0.036 (20 gage)	0.138	6	89	76	70	69	66	62	60	54	53	52
	0.151	7	99	84	78	76	72	68	67	60	59	57
	0.164	8	113	97	89	87	83	78	77	69	67	66
0.048 (18 gage)	0.138	6	90	77	71	70	67	63	61	55	54	53
	0.151	7	100	85	79	77	74	69	68	61	60	58
	0.164	8	114	98	90	89	84	79	78	70	69	67
0.060 (16 gage)	0.138	6	92	79	73	72	68	64	63	57	56	54
	0.151	7	101	87	81	79	75	71	70	63	61	60
	0.164	8	116	100	92	90	86	81	79	71	70	68
	0.177	9	136	116	107	105	100	94	93	83	82	79
	0.190	10	146	125	116	114	108	102	100	90	88	86
0.075 (14 gage)	0.138	6	95	82	76	75	71	67	66	59	58	57
	0.151	7	105	90	84	82	78	74	72	65	64	62
	0.164	8	119	103	95	93	89	84	82	74	73	71
	0.177	9	139	119	110	108	103	97	95	86	84	82
	0.190	10	150	128	119	117	111	105	103	92	91	88
	0.216	12	186	159	147	145	138	130	127	114	112	109
	0.242	14	204	175	162	158	151	142	139	125	123	120
0.105 (12 gage)	0.138	6	104	90	84	82	79	74	73	66	65	63
	0.151	7	114	99	92	90	86	81	80	72	71	69
	0.164	8	129	111	103	102	97	92	90	81	80	77
	0.177	9	148	128	119	116	111	105	103	93	91	89
	0.190	10	160	138	128	125	120	113	111	100	98	96
	0.216	12	196	168	156	153	146	138	135	122	120	116
	0.242	14	213	183	170	167	159	150	147	132	130	126
0.120 (11 gage)	0.138	6	110	95	89	87	83	79	77	70	68	67
	0.151	7	120	104	97	95	91	86	84	76	75	73
	0.164	8	135	117	109	107	102	96	94	85	84	82
	0.177	9	154	133	124	121	116	110	107	97	95	93
	0.190	10	166	144	133	131	125	118	116	104	103	100
	0.216	12	202	174	162	159	152	143	140	126	124	121
	0.242	14	219	189	175	172	164	155	152	137	134	131
0.134 (10 gage)	0.138	6	116	100	93	92	88	83	81	73	72	70
	0.151	7	126	110	102	100	96	91	89	80	79	77
	0.164	8	141	122	114	112	107	101	99	89	88	86
	0.177	9	160	139	129	127	121	114	112	101	100	97
	0.190	10	173	149	139	136	130	123	121	109	107	104
	0.216	12	209	180	167	164	157	148	145	131	129	126
	0.242	14	226	195	181	177	169	160	157	141	139	135
0.179 (7 gage)	0.138	6	126	107	99	97	92	86	84	76	74	72
	0.151	7	139	118	109	107	102	95	93	84	82	80
	0.164	8	160	136	126	123	117	110	108	96	95	92
	0.177	9	184	160	148	145	138	129	127	113	111	108
	0.190	10	198	172	159	156	149	140	137	122	120	117
	0.216	12	234	203	189	186	178	168	165	149	146	143
	0.242	14	251	217	202	198	190	179	176	159	156	152
0.239 (3 gage)	0.138	6	126	107	99	97	92	86	84	76	74	72
	0.151	7	139	118	109	107	102	95	93	84	82	80
	0.164	8	160	136	126	123	117	110	108	96	95	92
	0.177	9	188	160	148	145	138	129	127	113	111	108
	0.190	10	204	173	159	156	149	140	137	122	120	117
	0.216	12	256	218	201	197	187	176	172	154	151	147
	0.242	14	283	241	222	217	207	194	190	170	167	162

1. Tabulated lateral design values, Z, shall be multiplied by all applicable adjustment factors (see Table 11.3.1).
2. Tabulated lateral design values, Z, are for rolled thread wood screws (see Appendix L) inserted in side grain with screw axis perpendicular to wood fibers; screw penetration, p, into the main member equal to 10D; dowel bearing strength, F_e, of 61,850 psi for ASTM A653, Grade 33 steel and screw bending yield strengths, F_{yb}, of 100,000 psi for 0.099" $\leq$ D $\leq$ 0.142", 90,000 psi for 0.142" < D $\leq$ 0.177", 80,000 psi for 0.177" < D $\leq$ 0.236", 70,000 psi for 0.236" < D $\leq$ 0.273".
3. Where the wood screw penetration, p, is less than 10D but not less than 6D, tabulated lateral design values, Z, shall be multiplied by p/10D or lateral design values shall be calculated using the provisions of 12.3 for the reduced penetration.

Table 12N COMMON, BOX, or SINKER STEEL WIRE NAILS: Reference Lateral Design Values, Z, for Single Shear (two member) Connections[1,2,3]

for sawn lumber or SCL with both members of identical specific gravity (tabulated lateral design values are calculated based on an assumed length of nail penetration, p, into the main member equal to 10D)

Side Member Thickness t_s in.	Nail Diameter D in.	Common Wire Nail	Box Nail	Sinker Nail	G=0.67 Red Oak	G=0.55 Mixed Maple Southern Pine	G=0.5 Douglas Fir-Larch	G=0.49 Douglas Fir-Larch (N)	G=0.46 Douglas Fir(S) Hem-Fir(N)	G=0.43 Hem-Fir	G=0.42 Spruce-Pine-Fir	G=0.37 Redwood	G=0.36 Eastern Softwoods Spruce-Pine-Fir(S) Western Cedars Western Woods	G=0.35 Northern Species
		Pennyweight			lbs.	lbs.	lbs.	lbs.	lbs.	lbs.	lbs.	lbs.	lbs.	lbs.
3/4	0.099		6d	7d	73	61	55	54	51	48	47	39	38	36
	0.113	6d	8d	8d	94	79	72	71	65	58	57	47	46	44
	0.120			10d	107	89	80	77	71	64	62	52	50	48
	0.128		10d		121	101	87	84	78	70	68	57	56	54
	0.131	8d			127	104	90	87	80	73	70	60	58	56
	0.135		16d	12d	135	108	94	91	84	76	74	63	61	58
	0.148	10d	20d	16d	154	121	105	102	94	85	83	70	69	66
	0.162	16d	40d		183	138	121	117	108	99	96	82	80	77
	0.177			20d	200	153	134	130	121	111	107	92	90	87
	0.192	20d		30d	206	157	138	134	125	114	111	96	93	90
	0.207	30d		40d	216	166	147	143	133	122	119	103	101	97
	0.225	40d			229	178	158	154	144	132	129	112	110	106
	0.244	50d		60d	234	182	162	158	147	136	132	115	113	109
1	0.099		6d	7d	73	61	55	54	51	48	47	42	41	40
	0.113	*6d*[4]	8d	8d	94	79	72	71	67	63	61	55	54	51
	0.120			10d	107	89	81	80	76	71	69	60	59	56
	0.128		10d		121	101	93	91	86	80	79	66	64	61
	0.131	8d			127	106	97	95	90	84	82	68	66	63
	0.135		16d	12d	135	113	103	101	96	89	86	71	69	66
	0.148	10d	20d	16d	154	128	118	115	109	99	96	80	77	74
	0.162	16d	40d		184	154	141	137	125	113	109	91	89	85
	0.177			20d	213	178	155	150	138	125	121	102	99	95
	0.192	20d		30d	222	183	159	154	142	128	124	105	102	98
	0.207	30d		40d	243	192	167	162	149	135	131	111	109	104
	0.225	40d			268	202	177	171	159	144	140	120	117	112
	0.244	50d		60d	274	207	181	175	162	148	143	123	120	115
1-1/4	0.099		*6d*[4]	*7d*[4]	73	61	55	54	51	48	47	42	41	40
	0.113	*6d*[4]	8d	8d[4]	94	79	72	71	67	63	61	55	54	52
	0.120			10d	107	89	81	80	76	71	69	62	60	59
	0.128		10d		121	101	93	91	86	80	79	70	69	67
	0.131	*8d*[4]			127	106	97	95	90	84	82	73	72	70
	0.135		16d	12d	135	113	103	101	96	89	88	78	76	74
	0.148	10d	20d	16d	154	128	118	115	109	102	100	89	87	84
	0.162	16d	40d		184	154	141	138	131	122	120	103	100	95
	0.177			20d	213	178	163	159	151	141	136	113	110	105
	0.192	20d		30d	222	185	170	166	157	145	140	116	113	108
	0.207	30d		40d	243	203	186	182	169	152	147	123	119	114
	0.225	40d			268	224	200	193	177	160	155	130	127	121
	0.244	50d		60d	276	230	204	197	181	163	158	133	129	124
1-1/2	0.099			*7d*[4]	73	61	55	54	51	48	47	42	41	40
	0.113		*8d*[4]	*8d*[4]	94	79	72	71	67	63	61	55	54	52
	0.120			10d	107	89	81	80	76	71	69	62	60	59
	0.128		10d		121	101	93	91	86	80	79	70	69	67
	0.131	*8d*[4]			127	106	97	95	90	84	82	73	72	70
	0.135		16d	12d	135	113	103	101	96	89	88	78	76	74
	0.148	10d	20d	16d	154	128	118	115	109	102	100	89	87	84
	0.162	16d	40d		184	154	141	138	131	122	120	106	104	101
	0.177			20d	213	178	163	159	151	141	138	123	121	117
	0.192	20d		30d	222	185	170	166	157	147	144	128	126	120
	0.207	30d		40d	243	203	186	182	172	161	158	135	131	125
	0.225	40d			268	224	205	201	190	178	172	143	138	132
	0.244	50d		60d	276	230	211	206	196	181	175	146	141	135
1-3/4	0.113		*8d*[4]		94	79	72	71	67	63	61	55	54	52
	0.120			10d[4]	107	89	81	80	76	71	69	62	60	59
	0.128		10d[4]		121	101	93	91	86	80	79	70	69	67
	0.135		16d	12d	135	113	103	101	96	89	88	78	76	74
	0.148	10d[4]	20d	16d	154	128	118	115	109	102	100	89	87	84
	0.162	16d	40d		184	154	141	138	131	122	120	106	104	101
	0.177			20d	213	178	163	159	151	141	138	123	121	117
	0.192	20d		30d	222	185	170	166	157	147	144	128	126	122
	0.207	30d		40d	243	203	186	182	172	161	158	140	137	133
	0.225	40d			268	224	205	201	190	178	174	155	151	144
	0.244	50d		60d	276	230	211	206	196	183	179	159	154	147

1. Tabulated lateral design values, Z, shall be multiplied by all applicable adjustment factors (see Table 11.3.1).
2. Tabulated lateral design values, Z, are for common, box, or sinker steel wire nails (see Appendix Table L4) inserted in side grain with nail axis perpendicular to wood fibers; nail penetration, p, into the main member equal to 10D; and nail bending yield strengths, F_{yb}, of 100,000 psi for 0.099" $\leq$ D $\leq$ 0.142", 90,000 psi for 0.142" < D $\leq$ 0.177", 80,000 psi for 0.177" < D $\leq$ 0.236", and 70,000 psi for 0.236" < D $\leq$ 0.273".
3. Where the nail or spike penetration, p, is less than 10D but not less than 6D, tabulated lateral design values, Z, shall be multiplied by p/10D or lateral design values shall be calculated using the provisions of 12.3 for the reduced penetration.
4. Nail length is insufficient to provide 10D penetration. Tabulated lateral design values, Z, shall be adjusted per footnote 3.

NAILS

Table 12P COMMON, BOX, or SINKER STEEL WIRE NAILS: Reference Lateral Design Values, Z, for Single Shear (two member) Connections[1,2,3]

for sawn lumber or SCL with ASTM 653, Grade 33 steel side plate
(tabulated lateral design values are calculated based on an assumed length of nail penetration, p, into the main member equal to 10D)

Side Member Thickness t_s in.	Nail Diameter D in.	Common Wire Nail (Pennyweight)	Box Nail (Pennyweight)	Sinker Nail (Pennyweight)	G=0.67 Red Oak lbs.	G=0.55 Mixed Maple Southern Pine lbs.	G=0.5 Douglas Fir-Larch lbs.	G=0.49 Douglas Fir-Larch (N) lbs.	G=0.46 Douglas Fir(S) Hem-Fir(N) lbs.	G=0.43 Hem-Fir lbs.	G=0.42 Spruce-Pine-Fir lbs.	G=0.37 Redwood lbs.	G=0.36 Eastern Softwoods Spruce-Pine-Fir(S) Western Cedars Western Woods lbs.	G=0.35 Northern Species lbs.
0.036 (20 gage)	0.099		6d	7d	69	59	54	53	51	48	47	42	41	40
	0.113	6d	8d	8d	89	76	70	69	66	62	60	54	53	52
	0.120			10d	100	86	79	77	74	69	68	61	60	58
	0.128		10d		114	97	90	88	84	79	77	69	68	66
	0.131	8d			120	102	94	92	88	82	81	72	71	69
	0.135		16d	12d	127	108	100	98	93	87	86	77	75	73
	0.148	10d	20d	16d	145	123	114	111	106	100	98	87	86	83
0.048 (18 gage)	0.099		6d	7d	70	60	55	54	52	49	48	43	42	41
	0.113	6d	8d	8d	90	77	71	70	67	63	61	55	54	53
	0.120			10d	101	87	80	78	75	70	69	62	61	59
	0.128		10d		115	98	91	89	85	80	78	70	69	67
	0.131	8d			120	103	95	93	89	83	82	73	72	70
	0.135		16d	12d	128	109	101	99	94	88	87	78	76	74
	0.148	10d	20d	16d	145	124	115	112	107	101	99	88	87	84
	0.162	16d	40d		174	148	137	134	128	120	118	105	104	101
	0.177			20d	201	171	158	155	147	138	136	122	119	116
	0.192	20d		30d	209	178	164	161	153	144	141	126	124	121
	0.207	30d		40d	229	195	179	176	167	157	154	138	136	132
0.060 (16 gage)	0.099		6d	7d	72	62	57	56	54	51	50	45	44	43
	0.113	6d	8d	8d	92	79	73	72	68	64	63	57	56	54
	0.120			10d	103	88	82	80	76	72	71	63	62	61
	0.128		10d		117	100	92	91	86	81	80	72	70	68
	0.131	8d			122	104	97	95	90	85	83	75	73	71
	0.135		16d	12d	129	111	102	100	96	90	88	79	78	76
	0.148	10d	20d	16d	147	126	116	114	109	102	100	90	88	86
	0.162	16d	40d		175	150	138	135	129	121	119	107	105	102
	0.177			20d	202	172	159	156	149	140	137	123	121	117
	0.192	20d		30d	210	179	165	162	154	145	142	128	125	122
	0.207	30d		40d	229	195	180	177	168	158	155	139	137	133
	0.225	40d			253	215	199	195	185	174	171	153	150	146
	0.244	50d		60d	260	221	204	200	191	179	176	157	155	150
0.075 (14 gage)	0.099		6d	7d	75	65	60	59	56	53	52	47	46	45
	0.113	6d	8d	8d	95	82	76	75	71	67	66	59	58	57
	0.120			10d	106	91	85	83	79	75	73	66	65	63
	0.128		10d		120	103	95	93	89	84	82	74	73	71
	0.131	8d			125	107	99	97	93	88	86	77	76	74
	0.135		16d	12d	132	113	105	103	98	93	91	82	80	78
	0.148	10d	20d	16d	150	129	119	117	111	105	103	92	91	88
	0.162	16d	40d		178	152	141	138	132	124	122	109	107	104
	0.177			20d	204	175	162	158	151	142	139	125	123	120
	0.192	20d		30d	212	182	168	165	157	148	145	130	128	124
	0.207	30d		40d	231	198	183	179	171	161	157	141	139	135
	0.225	40d			254	217	201	197	187	176	173	155	152	148
	0.244	50d		60d	261	223	206	202	193	181	178	159	156	152
0.105 (12 gage)	0.099		6d	7d	84	73	68	67	64	60	59	53	53	51
	0.113	6d	8d	8d	104	90	84	82	79	74	73	66	65	63
	0.120			10d	115	100	93	91	87	82	80	73	71	69
	0.128		10d		129	111	103	101	97	91	90	81	79	77
	0.131	8d			134	116	107	105	101	95	93	84	82	80
	0.135		16d	12d	141	122	113	111	106	100	98	88	87	84
	0.148	10d	20d	16d	159	137	127	125	119	113	110	99	98	95
	0.162	16d	40d		187	161	149	146	140	132	129	116	114	111
	0.177			20d	213	183	169	166	159	149	147	132	130	126
	0.192	20d		30d	220	189	175	172	164	155	152	137	134	131
	0.207	30d		40d	238	205	190	186	177	167	164	147	145	141
	0.225	40d			260	223	207	203	193	182	179	161	158	153
	0.244	50d		60d	268	230	212	208	199	187	183	165	162	158

1. Tabulated lateral design values, Z, shall be multiplied by all applicable adjustment factors (see Table 11.3.1).
2. Tabulated lateral design values, Z, are for common, box, or sinker steel wire nails (see Appendix Table L4) inserted in side grain with nail axis perpendicular to wood fibers; nail penetration, p, into the main member equal to 10D; dowel bearing strength, F_e, of 61,850 psi for ASTM A653, Grade 33 steel and nail bending yield strengths, F_{yb}, of 100,000 psi for 0.099" $\leq D \leq$ 0.142", 90,000 psi for 0.142" $< D \leq$ 0.177", 80,000 psi for 0.177" $< D \leq$ 0.236", 70,000 psi for 0.236" $< D \leq$ 0.273".
3. Where the nail or spike penetration, p, is less than 10D but not less than 6D, tabulated lateral design values, Z, shall be multiplied by p/10D or lateral design values shall be calculated using the provisions of 12.3 for the reduced penetration.

Table 12P (Cont.) **COMMON, BOX, or SINKER STEEL WIRE NAILS: Reference Lateral Design Values, Z, for Single Shear (two member) Connections[1,2,3]**

for sawn lumber or SCL with ASTM 653, Grade 33 steel side plate (tabulated lateral design values are calculated based on an assumed length of nail penetration, p, into the main member equal to 10D)

Side Member Thickness	Nail Diameter	Common Wire Nail	Box Nail	Sinker Nail	G=0.67 Red Oak	G=0.55 Mixed Maple Southern Pine	G=0.5 Douglas Fir-Larch	G=0.49 Douglas Fir-Larch (N)	G=0.46 Douglas Fir(S) Hem-Fir(N)	G=0.43 Hem-Fir	G=0.42 Spruce-Pine-Fir	G=0.37 Redwood	G=0.36 Eastern Softwoods Spruce-Pine-Fir(S) Western Cedars Western Woods	G=0.35 Northern Species
t_s	D													
in.	in.	Pennyweight			lbs.	lbs.	lbs.	lbs.	lbs.	lbs.	lbs.	lbs.	lbs.	lbs.
0.120	0.099		6d	7d	90	78	72	71	68	64	63	57	56	53
(11 gage)	0.113	6d	8d	8d	110	95	89	87	83	79	77	70	68	66
	0.120			10d	121	105	97	96	91	86	85	76	75	73
	0.128		10d		134	116	108	106	101	96	94	85	83	81
	0.131	8d			140	121	112	110	105	99	97	88	86	84
	0.135		16d	12d	147	127	118	116	110	104	102	92	91	88
	0.148	10d	20d	16d	165	143	133	130	124	117	115	104	102	99
	0.162	16d	40d		193	166	154	152	145	137	134	121	119	115
	0.177			20d	218	188	174	171	163	154	151	136	134	130
	0.192	20d		30d	226	195	181	177	169	159	156	141	138	135
	0.207	30d		40d	244	210	194	191	182	172	168	151	149	145
	0.225	40d			265	228	211	207	198	186	183	164	161	157
	0.244	50d		60d	272	234	217	213	203	191	187	169	166	161
0.134	0.099		6d	7d	95	82	76	74	71	66	65	58	56	54
(10 gage)	0.113	6d	8d	8d	116	100	93	92	88	83	81	73	72	69
	0.120			10d	127	110	102	100	96	91	89	80	79	76
	0.128		10d		140	122	113	111	106	100	98	89	87	85
	0.131	8d			146	126	117	115	110	104	102	92	90	88
	0.135		16d	12d	153	132	123	121	115	109	107	96	95	92
	0.148	10d	20d	16d	172	148	138	135	129	122	120	108	106	104
	0.162	16d	40d		199	172	160	157	150	142	139	125	123	120
	0.177			20d	224	194	180	176	169	159	156	141	138	135
	0.192	20d		30d	232	200	186	182	174	164	161	145	143	139
	0.207	30d		40d	249	215	199	196	187	176	173	156	153	149
	0.225	40d			270	233	216	212	202	191	187	168	165	161
	0.244	50d		60d	277	239	221	217	207	195	192	173	170	165
0.179	0.099		6d	7d	97	82	76	74	71	66	65	58	56	54
(7 gage)	0.113	6d	8d	8d	126	107	99	97	92	86	84	76	74	70
	0.120			10d	142	121	111	109	104	97	95	85	83	79
	0.128		10d		161	137	126	124	118	111	108	97	94	90
	0.131	8d			168	144	132	130	123	116	114	102	99	94
	0.135		16d	12d	175	152	141	138	131	123	121	108	105	100
	0.148	10d	20d	16d	195	170	158	155	148	140	137	123	121	117
	0.162	16d	40d		224	194	180	177	169	160	157	142	140	136
	0.177			20d	249	215	200	197	188	178	174	157	155	151
	0.192	20d		30d	256	222	206	203	194	183	179	162	159	155
	0.207	30d		40d	272	236	219	215	205	194	190	172	169	164
	0.225	40d			292	252	234	230	220	207	203	184	180	176
	0.244	50d		60d	299	258	240	235	225	212	208	188	185	180
0.239	0.099		6d	7d	97	82	76	74	71	66	65	58	56	54
(3 gage)	0.113	6d	8d	8d	126	107	99	97	92	86	84	76	74	70
	0.120			10d	142	121	111	109	104	97	95	85	83	79
	0.128		10d		161	137	126	124	118	111	108	97	94	90
	0.131	8d			169	144	132	130	123	116	114	102	99	94
	0.135		16d	12d	180	153	141	138	131	123	121	108	105	100
	0.148	10d	20d	16d	205	174	160	157	149	140	137	123	121	117
	0.162	16d	40d		245	209	192	188	179	168	165	147	145	140
	0.177			20d	284	241	222	218	207	195	191	170	167	162
	0.192	20d		30d	295	251	231	227	216	202	198	177	174	169
	0.207	30d		40d	310	270	251	246	236	222	217	194	191	185
	0.225	40d			328	285	265	260	249	235	231	209	205	200
	0.244	50d		60d	336	291	271	266	254	240	236	213	210	204

1. Tabulated lateral design values, Z, shall be multiplied by all applicable adjustment factors (see Table 11.3.1).
2. Tabulated lateral design values, Z, are for common, box, or sinker steel wire nails (see Appendix Table L4) inserted in side grain with nail axis perpendicular to wood fibers; nail penetration, p, into the main member equal to 10D; dowel bearing strength, F_e, of 61,850 psi for ASTM A653, Grade 33 steel and nail bending yield strengths, F_{yb}, of 100,000 psi for 0.099" $\leq D \leq$ 0.142", 90,000 psi for 0.142" $< D \leq$ 0.177", 80,000 psi for 0.177" $< D \leq$ 0.236", 70,000 psi for 0.236" $< D \leq$ 0.273".
3. Where the nail or spike penetration, p, is less than 10D but not less than 6D, tabulated lateral design values, Z, shall be multiplied by p/10D or lateral design values shall be calculated using the provisions of 12.3 for the reduced penetration.

Table 12Q COMMON, BOX, SINKER, or ROOF SHEATHING RING SHANK (RSRS) STEEL WIRE NAILS: Reference Lateral Design Values, Z, for Single Shear (two member) Connections[1,2,3]

for sawn lumber or SCL with wood structural panel side members with an effective G=0.50 (tabulated lateral design values are calculated based on an assumed length of nail penetration, p, into the main member equal to 10D)

Side Member Thickness t_s	Nail Diameter D	Common Wire Nail	Box Nail	Sinker Nail	RSRS (Dash No.)	G=0.67 Red Oak	G=0.55 Mixed Maple Southern Pine	G=0.5 Douglas Fir-Larch	G=0.49 Douglas Fir-Larch (N)	G=0.46 Douglas Fir(S) Hem-Fir(N)	G=0.43 Hem-Fir	G=0.42 Spruce-Pine-Fir	G=0.37 Redwood	G=0.36 Eastern Softwoods Spruce-Pine-Fir(S) Western Cedars Western Woods	G=0.35 Northern Species
in.	in.	Pennyweight				lbs.	lbs.	lbs.	lbs.	lbs.	lbs.	lbs.	lbs.	lbs.	lbs.
3/8	0.099		6d	7d		47	45	43	43	42	40	40	38	37	37
	0.113	6d	8d	8d	01	60	56	54	54	52	51	50	47	47	46
	0.120			10d	02	67	62	60	60	58	56	56	52	52	51
	0.128		10d			75	70	68	67	65	63	63	59	58	57
	0.131	8d			03	78	73	71	70	68	66	65	61	61	60
	0.135		16d	12d		83	78	75	74	72	70	69	65	64	63
	0.148	10d	20d	16d		94	88	85	84	82	79	78	73	72	71
7/16	0.099		6d	7d		50	47	45	45	44	43	42	40	40	39
	0.113	6d	8d	8d	01	62	58	56	56	55	53	52	49	49	48
	0.120			10d	02	69	65	63	62	60	59	58	55	54	53
	0.128		10d			77	72	70	69	68	66	65	61	60	59
	0.131	8d			03	80	75	73	72	70	68	67	63	63	62
	0.135		16d	12d		85	80	77	76	74	72	71	67	66	65
	0.148	10d	20d	16d		96	90	87	86	84	81	80	76	75	73
	0.162	16d	40d			114	106	102	101	99	96	95	89	88	86
15/32	0.099		6d	7d		51	48	47	46	45	44	44	41	41	40
	0.113	6d	8d	8d	01	64	60	58	57	56	54	54	51	50	49
	0.120			10d	02	70	66	64	63	62	60	59	56	55	54
	0.128		10d			78	74	71	71	69	67	66	62	62	61
	0.131	8d			03	82	77	74	73	72	70	69	65	64	63
	0.135		16d	12d		86	81	78	77	76	73	72	68	67	66
	0.148	10d	20d	16d		97	91	88	87	85	83	82	77	76	75
	0.162	16d	40d			115	108	104	103	100	97	96	90	89	88
19/32	0.099		6d	7d		58	55	53	53	51	50	50	47	46	46
	0.113	6d	8d	8d	01	70	66	64	64	62	61	60	57	56	55
	0.120			10d	02	77	73	70	70	68	66	66	62	61	60
	0.128		10d			85	80	78	77	75	73	72	68	68	67
	0.131	8d			03	88	83	80	80	78	76	75	71	70	69
	0.135		16d	12d		93	87	84	84	82	79	79	74	73	72
	0.148	10d	20d	16d		104	98	95	94	92	89	88	83	82	81
	0.162	16d	40d			121	114	110	109	107	103	102	96	95	94
	0.177			20d		137	128	124	123	120	116	115	108	107	105
	0.192	20d		30d		142	133	128	127	124	120	119	112	111	109
23/32	0.099		6d	7d		62	58	55	55	53	51	51	47	47	46
	0.113	6d	8d	8d	01	78	74	72	71	69	67	66	62	61	60
	0.120			10d	02	85	80	78	77	76	73	73	69	68	67
	0.128		10d			93	88	85	85	83	80	80	75	75	74
	0.131	8d			03	96	91	88	87	86	83	82	78	77	76
	0.135		16d	12d		101	95	92	91	89	87	86	81	81	79
	0.148	10d	20d	16d		113	106	103	102	100	97	96	91	90	89
	0.162	16d	40d			130	122	118	117	115	111	110	104	103	102
	0.177			20d		145	137	132	131	128	124	123	116	115	113
	0.192	20d		30d		150	141	136	135	132	128	127	120	118	116
1	0.099[5]		6d	7d		62	58	55	55	53	51	51	47	47	46
	0.113[5]	6d[4]	8d	8d	01	81	75	72	71	69	67	66	62	61	60
	0.120[5]			10d	02	92	85	81	81	78	76	75	69	69	67
	0.128		10d			104	97	93	92	89	86	85	79	78	77
	0.131	8d			03	109	101	97	96	93	90	89	83	82	80
	0.135		16d	12d		116	108	103	102	99	96	94	88	87	85
	0.148	10d	20d	16d		132	123	118	116	113	109	108	100	99	97
	0.162	16d	40d			154	146	141	139	135	131	129	120	119	116
	0.177			20d		169	160	155	154	151	146	145	137	136	134
	0.192	20d		30d		174	164	159	158	155	150	149	141	140	138
1-1/8	0.128[5]		10d			104	97	93	92	89	86	85	79	78	77
	0.131[5]	8d			03	109	101	97	96	93	90	89	83	82	80
	0.135[5]		16d	12d		116	108	103	102	99	96	94	88	87	85
	0.148[5]	10d	20d	16d		132	123	118	116	113	109	108	100	99	97
	0.162	16d	40d			158	147	141	139	135	131	129	120	119	116
	0.177			20d		181	170	163	161	157	151	149	139	137	135
	0.192	20d		30d		186	176	170	168	163	157	155	145	143	140
1-1/4	0.148	10d	20d	16d		132	123	118	116	113	109	108	100	99	97
	0.162	16d	40d			158	147	141	139	135	131	129	120	119	116
	0.177			20d		183	170	163	161	157	151	149	139	137	135
	0.192	20d		30d		191	177	170	168	163	157	155	145	143	140

1. Tabulated lateral design values, Z, shall be multiplied by all applicable adjustment factors (see Table 11.3.1).
2. Tabulated lateral design values, Z, are for common, box, or sinker steel wire nails (see Appendix Table L4) and for roof sheathing ring shank nails (see Appendix Table L6) inserted in side grain with nail axis perpendicular to wood fibers; nail penetration, p, into the main member equal to 10D and nail bending yield strengths, F_{yb}, of 100,000 psi for 0.099" $\leq D \leq$ 0.142", 90,000 psi for 0.142" $< D \leq$ 0.177", 80,000 psi for 0.177" $< D \leq$ 0.236", and 70,000 psi for 0.236" $< D \leq$ 0.273".
3. Where the nail or spike penetration, p, is less than 10D but not less than 6D, tabulated lateral design values, Z, shall be multiplied by p/10D or lateral design values shall be calculated using the provisions of 12.3 for the reduced penetration.
4. Nail length is insufficient to provide 10D penetration. Tabulated lateral design values, Z, shall be adjusted per footnote 3.
5. Tabulated lateral design values, Z, shall be permitted to apply for greater side member thickness when adjusted per footnote 3.

Table 12R COMMON, BOX, SINKER, or ROOF SHEATHING RING SHANK (RSRS) STEEL WIRE NAILS: Reference Lateral Design Values, Z, for Single Shear (two member) Connections[1,2,3]

with wood structural panel side members with an effective G=0.42
(tabulated lateral design values are calculated based on an assumed nail penetration, p, into the main member equal to 10D)

Side Member Thickness t_s in.	Nail Diameter D in.	Common Wire Nail (Pennyweight)	Box Nail (Pennyweight)	Sinker Nail (Pennyweight)	RSRS (Dash No.)	G=0.67 Red Oak lbs.	G=0.55 Mixed Maple Southern Pine lbs.	G=0.5 Douglas Fir-Larch lbs.	G=0.49 Douglas Fir-Larch (N) lbs.	G=0.46 Douglas Fir(S) Hem-Fir(N) lbs.	G=0.43 Hem-Fir lbs.	G=0.42 Spruce-Pine-Fir lbs.	G=0.37 Redwood lbs.	G=0.36 Eastern Softwoods Spruce-Pine-Fir(S) Western Cedars Western Woods lbs.	G=0.35 Northern Species lbs.
3/8	0.099		6d	7d		41	39	37	37	36	35	35	33	33	32
	0.113	6d	8d	8d	01	52	49	48	47	46	45	45	42	42	41
	0.120			10d	02	58	55	53	53	52	50	50	47	47	46
	0.128		10d			66	62	60	60	59	57	56	53	53	52
	0.131	8d			03	69	65	63	63	61	59	59	56	55	54
	0.135		16d	12d		73	69	67	66	65	63	62	59	58	57
	0.148	10d	20d	16d		84	79	76	76	74	72	71	67	66	65
7/16	0.099		6d	7d		42	40	39	38	38	37	36	35	34	34
	0.113	6d	8d	8d	01	53	50	49	48	48	46	46	43	43	42
	0.120			10d	02	59	56	54	54	53	51	51	48	48	47
	0.128		10d			67	63	61	61	60	58	57	54	54	53
	0.131	8d			03	70	66	64	64	62	60	60	57	56	55
	0.135		16d	12d		74	70	68	67	66	64	63	60	59	58
	0.148	10d	20d	16d		84	80	77	76	75	73	72	68	67	66
	0.162	16d	40d			100	95	92	91	89	86	85	81	80	78
15/32	0.099		6d	7d		43	41	40	39	39	38	37	35	35	35
	0.113	6d	8d	8d	01	54	51	50	49	48	47	47	44	44	43
	0.120			10d	02	60	57	55	55	54	52	52	49	49	48
	0.128		10d			68	64	62	62	60	59	58	55	55	54
	0.131	8d			03	70	67	65	64	63	61	61	57	57	56
	0.135		16d	12d		75	71	68	68	66	65	64	61	60	59
	0.148	10d	20d	16d		85	80	78	77	75	73	72	69	68	67
	0.162	16d	40d			101	95	92	91	89	87	86	81	80	79
19/32	0.099		6d	7d		47	45	44	43	43	41	41	39	39	38
	0.113	6d	8d	8d	01	58	55	54	53	52	51	50	48	48	47
	0.120			10d	02	64	61	59	59	58	56	56	53	52	52
	0.128		10d			71	68	66	65	64	62	62	59	58	57
	0.131	8d			03	74	70	68	68	67	65	64	61	61	60
	0.135		16d	12d		78	74	72	71	70	68	68	64	64	63
	0.148	10d	20d	16d		88	84	81	81	79	77	76	72	72	71
	0.162	16d	40d			103	98	95	94	93	90	89	85	84	83
	0.177			20d		118	112	108	108	105	102	101	96	95	94
	0.192	20d		30d		123	116	112	112	109	106	105	100	99	97
23/32	0.099		6d	7d		52	50	48	48	47	46	46	44	43	43
	0.113	6d	8d	8d	01	63	60	58	58	57	56	55	53	52	52
	0.120			10d	02	69	66	64	64	62	61	60	58	57	56
	0.128		10d			76	73	71	70	69	67	67	63	63	62
	0.131	8d			03	79	75	73	73	71	70	69	66	65	64
	0.135		16d	12d		83	79	77	76	75	73	72	69	68	67
	0.148	10d	20d	16d		93	89	86	86	84	82	81	77	77	76
	0.162	16d	40d			108	103	100	99	98	95	94	90	89	87
	0.177			20d		122	116	113	112	110	107	106	101	100	98
	0.192	20d		30d		127	120	117	116	114	111	110	104	103	102
1	0.099[5]		6d	7d		56	53	51	50	49	48	47	44	44	43
	0.113[5]	6d[4]	8d	8d	01	73	68	66	66	64	62	61	58	57	56
	0.120[5]			10d	02	82	77	75	74	72	70	69	65	64	63
	0.128		10d			91	87	85	84	82	80	79	74	73	72
	0.131	8d			03	93	89	87	87	85	83	82	77	77	75
	0.135		16d	12d		97	93	91	90	89	87	86	82	81	80
	0.148	10d	20d	16d		109	104	101	101	99	97	96	91	91	90
	0.162	16d	40d			124	118	115	115	113	110	109	104	103	102
	0.177			20d		137	131	128	127	125	122	121	115	114	112
	0.192	20d		30d		141	135	131	131	128	125	124	118	117	116
1-1/8	0.128[5]		10d			93	88	85	84	82	80	79	74	73	72
	0.131[5]	8d			03	98	92	89	88	86	83	82	77	77	75
	0.135[5]		16d	12d		104	98	94	94	91	88	88	82	81	80
	0.148[5]	10d	20d	16d		117	111	108	107	104	101	100	94	93	91
	0.162	16d	40d			132	127	123	123	120	118	117	111	110	109
	0.177			20d		146	139	136	135	132	129	128	122	121	120
	0.192	20d		30d		150	143	139	138	136	133	132	126	125	123
1-1/4	0.148	10d	20d	16d		118	111	108	107	104	101	100	94	93	91
	0.162	16d	40d			141	134	129	128	125	121	120	112	111	109
	0.177			20d		155	148	144	143	141	138	136	130	129	126
	0.192	20d		30d		159	152	148	147	144	141	140	134	133	131

1. Tabulated lateral design values, Z, shall be multiplied by all applicable adjustment factors (see Table 11.3.1).
2. Tabulated lateral design values, Z, are for common, box, or sinker steel wire nails (see Appendix Table L4) and for roof sheathing ring shank nails (see Appendix Table L6) inserted in side grain with nail axis perpendicular to wood fibers; nail penetration, p, into the main member equal to 10D and nail bending yield strengths, F_{yb}, of 100,000 psi for 0.099" $\leq D \leq$ 0.142", 90,000 psi for 0.142" $< D \leq$ 0.177", 80,000 psi for 0.177" $< D \leq$ 0.236", and 70,000 psi for 0.236" $< D \leq$ 0.273".
3. Where the nail or spike penetration, p, is less than 10D but not less than 6D, tabulated lateral design values, Z, shall be multiplied by p/10D or lateral design values shall be calculated using the provisions of 12.3 for the reduced penetration.
4. Nail length is insufficient to provide 10D penetration. Tabulated lateral design values, Z, shall be adjusted per footnote 3.
5. Tabulated lateral design values, Z, shall be permitted to apply for greater side member thickness when adjusted per footnote 3.

Table 12S POST FRAME RING SHANK NAILS: Reference Lateral Design Values, Z, for Single Shear (two member) Connections[1,2,3]

for sawn lumber or SCL with both members of identical specific gravity (tabulated lateral design values are calculated based on an assumed length of nail penetration, p, into the main member equal to 10D)

Side Member Thickness	Nail Diameter	Nail Length	G=0.67 Red Oak	G=0.55 Mixed Maple Southern Pine	G=0.5 Douglas Fir-Larch	G=0.49 Douglas Fir-Larch (N)	G=0.46 Douglas Fir(S) Hem-Fir(N)	G=0.43 Hem-Fir	G=0.42 Spruce-Pine-Fir	G=0.37 Redwood	G=0.36 Eastern Softwoods Spruce-Pine-Fir (S) Western Cedars Western Woods	G=0.35 Northern Species
t_s	D	L										
in.	in.	in.	lb	lb	lb	lb	lb	lb	lb	lb	lb	lb
1/2	0.135	3, 3.5	115	89	79	77	72	66	65	56	55	53
	0.148	3 - 4.5	129	101	90	87	82	75	73	64	63	61
	0.177	3 - 8	167	133	119	116	109	102	99	87	86	83
	0.200	3.5 - 8	179	143	129	126	119	110	108	95	93	91
	0.207	4 - 8	185	148	134	131	123	115	112	99	97	94
3/4	0.135	3, 3.5	135	108	94	91	84	76	74	63	61	58
	0.148	3 - 4.5	154	121	105	102	94	85	83	70	69	66
	0.177	3 - 8	200	153	134	130	121	111	107	92	90	87
	0.200	3.5 - 8	212	162	143	139	129	118	115	100	97	94
	0.207	4 - 8	216	166	147	143	133	122	119	103	101	97
1	0.135	3, 3.5	135	113	103	101	96	89	86	71	69	66
	0.148	3 - 4.5	154	128	118	115	109	99	96	80	77	74
	0.177	3 - 8	213	178	155	150	138	125	121	102	99	95
	0.200	3.5 - 8	233	188	164	158	146	132	128	108	105	101
	0.207	4 - 8	243	192	167	162	149	135	131	111	109	104
1 1/4	0.135	3, 3.5	135	113	103	101	96	89	88	78	76	74
	0.148	3 - 4.5	154	128	118	115	109	102	100	89	87	84
	0.177	3 - 8	213	178	163	159	151	141	136	113	110	105
	0.200	3.5 - 8	233	195	178	174	165	149	144	120	116	111
	0.207	4 - 8	243	203	186	182	169	152	147	123	119	114
1 1/2	0.135	3, 3.5	135	113	103	101	96	89	88	78	76	74
	0.148	3 - 4.5	154	128	118	115	109	102	100	89	87	84
	0.177	3 - 8	213	178	163	159	151	141	138	123	121	117
	0.200	3.5 - 8	233	195	178	174	165	155	151	133	129	123
	0.207	4 - 8	243	203	186	182	172	161	158	135	131	125
1 3/4	0.135	3, 3.5	135	113	103	101	96	89	88	78	76	74
	0.148	3 - 4.5	154	128	118	115	109	102	100	89	87	84
	0.177	3[4], 3.5[4], 4 - 8	213	178	163	159	151	141	138	123	121	117
	0.200	3.5[4], 4 - 8	233	195	178	174	165	155	151	135	132	128
	0.207	4 - 8	243	203	186	182	172	161	158	140	137	133
2 1/2	0.135	3.5[4]	135	113	103	101	96	89	88	78	76	74
	0.148	3.5[4], 4, 4.5	154	128	118	115	109	102	100	89	87	84
	0.177	4[4], 4.5, 5, 6, 8	213	178	163	159	151	141	138	123	121	117
	0.200	4[4], 4.5, 5, 6, 8	233	195	178	174	165	155	151	135	132	128
	0.207	4[4], 4.5[4], 5, 6, 8	243	203	186	182	172	161	158	140	137	133
3 1/2	0.148	4.5[4]	154	128	118	115	109	102	100	89	87	84
	0.177	5[4], 6, 8	213	178	163	159	151	141	138	123	121	117
	0.200	5[4], 6, 8	233	195	178	174	165	155	151	135	132	128
	0.207	5[4], 6, 8	243	203	186	182	172	161	158	140	137	133

1. Tabulated lateral design values, Z, shall be multiplied by all applicable adjustment factors (see Table 11.3.1).
2. Tabulated lateral design values, Z, are for post frame ring shank nails (see Appendix Table L5) inserted in side grain with nail axis perpendicular to wood fibers; nail penetration, p, into the main member equal to 10D; and nail bending yield strengths, F_{yb}, of 100,000 psi for 0.120" $<$ D $\leq$0.142", 90,000 psi for 0.142" $<$ D $\leq$0.192", and 80,000 psi for 0.192" $<$ D $\leq$0.207".
3. Where the post-frame ring shank nail penetration, p, is less than 10D but not less than 6D, tabulated lateral design values, Z, shall be multiplied by p/10D or lateral design values shall be calculated using the provisions of 12.3 for the reduced penetration.
4. Nail length is insufficient to provide 10D penetration. Tabulated lateral design values, Z, shall be adjusted per footnote 3.

Table 12T POST FRAME RING SHANK NAILS: Reference Lateral Design Values, Z, for Single Shear (two member) Connections[1,2,3]

for sawn lumber or SCL with ASTM A653, Grade 33 steel side plates (tabulated lateral design values are calculated based on an assumed nail penetration, p, into the main member equal to 10D)

Side Member Thickness t_s in.	Nail Diameter D in.	Nail Length L in.	G=0.67 Red Oak lbs.	G=0.55 Mixed Maple Southern Pine lbs.	G=0.5 Douglas Fir-Larch lbs.	G=0.49 Douglas Fir-Larch (N) lbs.	G=0.46 Douglas Fir(S) Hem-Fir(N) lbs.	G=0.43 Hem-Fir lbs.	G=0.42 Spruce-Pine-Fir lbs.	G=0.37 Redwood lbs.	G=0.36 Eastern Softwoods Spruce-Pine-Fir (S) Western Cedars Western Woods lbs.	G=0.35 Northern Species lbs.
0.036 (20 gage)	0.135	3, 3.5	127	108	100	98	93	87	86	77	75	73
	0.148	3 - 4.5	145	123	114	111	106	100	98	87	86	83
	0.177	3 - 8	174	171	157	154	147	138	135	121	119	115
	0.200	3.5 - 8	178	178	172	168	160	150	147	132	129	126
	0.207	4 - 8	179	179	179	175	167	157	154	137	135	131
0.048 (18 gage)	0.135	3, 3.5	128	109	101	99	94	88	87	78	76	74
	0.148	3 - 4.5	145	124	115	112	107	101	99	88	87	84
	0.177	3 - 8	201	171	158	155	147	138	136	122	119	116
	0.200	3.5 - 8	219	187	172	169	161	151	148	133	130	126
	0.207	4 - 8	229	195	179	176	167	157	154	138	136	132
0.060 (16 gage)	0.135	3, 3.5	129	111	102	100	96	90	88	79	78	76
	0.148	3 - 4.5	147	126	116	114	109	102	100	90	88	86
	0.177	3 - 8	202	172	159	156	149	140	137	123	121	117
	0.200	3.5 - 8	220	188	173	170	162	152	149	134	131	128
	0.207	4 - 8	229	195	180	177	168	158	155	139	137	133
0.075 (14 gage)	0.135	3, 3.5	132	113	105	103	98	93	91	82	80	78
	0.148	3 - 4.5	150	129	119	117	111	105	103	92	91	88
	0.177	3 - 8	204	175	162	158	151	142	139	125	123	120
	0.200	3.5 - 8	222	190	176	172	164	154	151	136	134	130
	0.207	4 - 8	231	198	183	179	171	161	157	141	139	135
0.105 (12 gage)	0.135	3, 3.5	141	122	113	111	106	100	98	88	87	84
	0.148	3 - 4.5	159	137	127	125	119	113	110	99	98	95
	0.177	3 - 8	213	183	169	166	159	149	147	132	130	126
	0.200	3.5 - 8	230	198	183	179	171	161	158	142	140	136
	0.207	4 - 8	238	205	190	186	177	167	164	147	145	141
0.120 (11 gage)	0.135	3, 3.5	147	127	118	116	110	104	102	92	91	88
	0.148	3 - 4.5	165	143	133	130	124	117	115	104	102	99
	0.177	3 - 8	218	188	174	171	163	154	151	136	134	130
	0.200	3.5 - 8	235	203	188	184	176	166	163	146	144	140
	0.207	4 - 8	244	210	194	191	182	172	168	151	149	145
0.134 (10 gage)	0.135	3, 3.5	153	132	123	121	115	109	107	96	95	92
	0.148	3 - 4.5	172	148	138	135	129	122	120	108	106	104
	0.177	3 - 8	224	194	180	176	169	159	156	141	138	135
	0.200	3.5 - 8	241	208	193	189	181	171	167	151	148	144
	0.207	4 - 8	249	215	199	196	187	176	173	156	153	149
0.179 (7 gage)	0.135	3, 3.5	175	152	141	138	131	123	121	108	105	100
	0.148	3 - 4.5	195	170	158	155	148	140	137	123	121	117
	0.177	3 - 8	249	215	200	197	188	178	174	157	155	151
	0.200	3.5 - 8	265	229	213	209	200	189	185	167	164	160
	0.207	4 - 8	272	236	219	215	205	194	190	172	169	164
0.239 (3 gage)	0.135	3, 3.5	180	153	141	138	131	123	121	108	105	100
	0.148	3 - 4.5	205	174	160	157	149	140	137	123	121	117
	0.177	3 - 8	284	241	222	218	207	195	191	170	167	162
	0.200	3.5 - 8	303	264	243	238	226	213	208	186	183	178
	0.207	4 - 8	310	270	251	246	236	222	217	194	191	185

1. Tabulated lateral design values, Z, shall be multiplied by all applicable adjustment factors (see Table 11.3.1).
2. Tabulated lateral design values, Z, are for post frame ring shank nails (see Appendix Table L5) inserted in side grain with nail axis perpendicular to wood fibers; nail penetration, p, into the main member equal to 10D; and nail bending yield strengths, F_{yb}, of 100,000 psi for 0.120"< D ≤0.142" 90,000 psi for 0.142"< D ≤0.192", and 80,000 psi for 0.192"< D ≤0.207".
3. Where the post-frame ring shank nail penetration, p, is less than 10D but not less than 6D, tabulated lateral design values, Z, shall be multiplied by p/10D or lateral design values shall be calculated using the provisions of 12.3 for the reduced penetration.

SPLIT RING AND SHEAR PLATE CONNECTORS

AMERICAN WOOD COUNCIL

13

13.1 General

13.1.1 Scope

Chapter 13 applies to the engineering design of connections using split ring connectors or shear plate connectors in sawn lumber, structural glued laminated timber, and structural composite lumber. Design of split ring and shear plate connections in cross-laminated timber is beyond the scope of these provisions.

13.1.2 Terminology

A connector unit shall be defined as one of the following:

(a) One split ring with its bolt or lag screw in single shear (see Figure 13A).

(b) Two shear plates used back to back in the contact faces of a wood-to-wood connection with their bolt or lag screw in single shear (see Figures 13B and 13C).

(c) One shear plate with its bolt or lag screw in single shear used in conjunction with a steel strap or shape in a wood-to-metal connection (see Figures 13B and 13C).

Figure 13A Split Ring Connector

Figure 13B Pressed Steel Shear Plate Connector

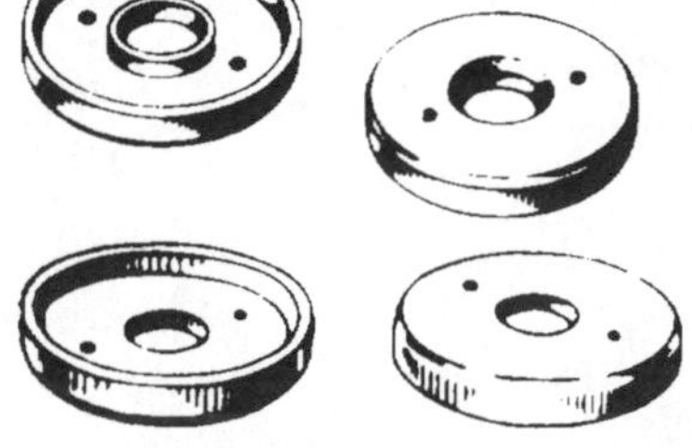

Figure 13C Malleable Iron Shear Plate Connector

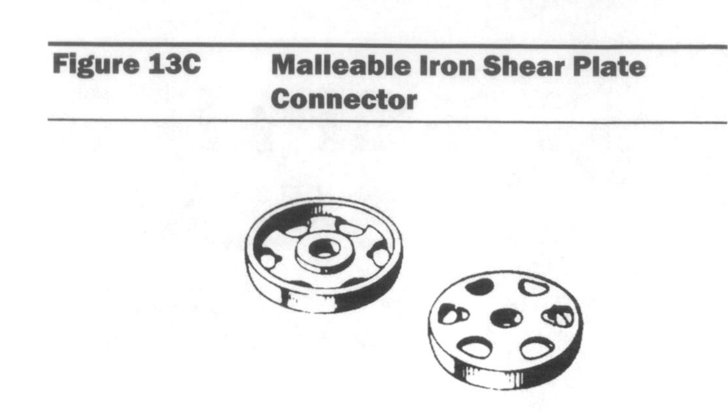

13.1.3 Quality of Split Ring and Shear Plate Connectors

13.1.3.1 Design provisions and reference design values herein apply to split ring and shear plate connectors of the following quality:

(a) Split rings manufactured from SAE 1010 hot rolled carbon steel (Reference 37). Each ring shall form a closed true circle with the principal axis of the cross section of the ring metal parallel to the geometric axis of the ring. The ring shall fit snugly in the precut groove. This shall be accomplished with a ring, the metal section of which is beveled from the central portion toward the edges to a thickness less than at midsection, or by any other method which will accomplish equivalent performance. It shall be cut through in one place in its circumference to form a tongue and slot (see Figure 13A).

(b) Shear plate connectors:

(1) 2-5/8" Pressed Steel Type—Pressed steel shear plates manufactured from SAE 1010 (Reference 37) hot rolled carbon steel. Each plate shall be a true circle with a flange around the edge, extending at right angles to the face of the plate and extending from one face only, the plate portion having a central bolt hole, with an integral hub concentric to the hole or without an integral hub, and two small perforations on opposite sides of the hole and midway from the center and circumference (see Figure 13B).

(2) 4" Malleable Iron Type—Malleable iron shear plates manufactured according to Grade 32510 of ASTM Standard A47 (Reference 11). Each casting shall consist of a perforated round plate with a flange around

the edge extending at right angles to the face of the plate and projecting from one face only, the plate portion having a central bolt hole with an integral hub extending from the same face as the flange (see Figure 13C).

13.1.3.2 Dimensions for typical split ring and shear plate connectors are provided in Appendix K. Dimensional tolerances of split ring and shear plate connectors shall not be greater than those conforming to standard practices for the machine operations involved in manufacturing the connectors.

13.1.3.3 Bolts used with split ring and shear plate connectors shall conform to 12.1.3. The bolt shall have an unreduced nominal or shank (body) diameter in accordance with ANSI/ASME Standard B18.2.1 (Reference 7).

13.1.3.4 Where lag screws are used in place of bolts, the lag screws shall conform to 12.1.3 and the shank of the lag screw shall have the same diameter as the bolt specified for the split ring or shear plate connector (see Tables 13.2A and 13.2B). The lag screw shall have an unreduced nominal or shank (body) diameter and threads in accordance with ANSI/ASME Standard B18.2.1 (see Reference 7).

13.1.4 Fabrication and Assembly

13.1.4.1 The grooves, daps, and bolt holes specified in Appendix K shall be accurately cut or bored and shall be oriented in contacting faces. Since split ring and shear plate connectors from different manufacturers differ slightly in shape and cross section, cutter heads shall be designed to produce daps and grooves conforming accurately to the dimensions and shape of the particular split ring or shear plate connectors used.

13.1.4.2 Where lag screws are used in place of bolts, the hole for the unthreaded shank shall be the same diameter as the shank. The diameter of the hole for the threaded portion of the lag screw shall be approximately 70% of the shank diameter, or as specified in 12.1.4.2.

13.1.4.3 In installation of split ring or shear plate connectors and bolts or lag screws, a nut shall be placed on each bolt, and washers, not smaller than the size specified in Appendix K, shall be placed between the outside wood member and the bolt or lag screw head and between the outside wood member and nut. Where an outside member of a shear plate connection is a steel strap or shape, the washer is not required, except where a longer bolt or lag screw is used, in which case, the washer prevents the metal plate or shape from bearing on the threaded portion of the bolt or lag screw.

13.1.4.4 Reference design values for split ring and shear plate connectors are based on the assumption that the faces of the members are brought into contact when the connector units are installed, and allow for seasonal variations after the wood has reached the moisture content normal to the conditions of service. Where split ring or shear plate connectors are installed in wood which is not seasoned to the moisture content normal to the conditions of service, the connections shall be tightened by turning down the nuts periodically until moisture equilibrium is reached.

13.2 Reference Design Values

13.2.1 Reference Design Values

13.2.1.1 Tables 13.2A and 13.2B contain reference design values for a single split ring or shear plate connector unit with bolt in single shear, installed in the side grain of two wood members (Table 13A) with sufficient member thicknesses, edge distances, end distances, and spacing to develop reference design values. Reference design values (P, Q) shall be multiplied by all applicable adjustment factors (see Table 11.3.1) to obtain adjusted design values (P', Q').

13.2.1.2 Adjusted design values (P', Q') for shear plate connectors shall not exceed the limiting reference design values specified in Footnote 2 of Table 13.2B. The limiting reference design values in Footnote 2 of Table 13.2B shall not be multiplied by adjustment factors in this Specification since they are based on strength of metal rather than strength of wood (see 11.2.3).

Table 13A Species Groups for Split Ring and Shear Plate Connectors

Species Group	Specific Gravity, G
A	$G \geq 0.60$
B	$0.49 \leq G < 0.60$
C	$0.42 \leq G < 0.49$
D	$G < 0.42$

Table 13.2A Split Ring Connector Unit Reference Design Values

Tabulated design values[1] apply to ONE split ring and bolt in single shear.

Split ring diameter	Bolt diameter	Number of faces of member with connectors on same bolt	Net thickness of member	Loaded parallel to grain (0°) Design value, P, per connector unit and bolt, lbs.				Loaded perpendicular to grain (90°) Design value, Q, per connector unit and bolt, lbs.			
in.	in.		in.	Group A species	Group B species	Group C species	Group D species	Group A species	Group B species	Group C species	Group D species
2-1/2	1/2	1	1" minimum	2630	2270	1900	1640	1900	1620	1350	1160
			1-1/2" or thicker	3160	2730	2290	1960	2280	1940	1620	1390
		2	1-1/2" minimum	2430	2100	1760	1510	1750	1500	1250	1070
			2" or thicker	3160	2730	2290	1960	2280	1940	1620	1390
4	3/4	1	1" minimum	4090	3510	2920	2520	2840	2440	2040	1760
			1-1/2"	6020	5160	4280	3710	4180	3590	2990	2580
			1-5/8" or thicker	6140	5260	4380	3790	4270	3660	3050	2630
		2	1-1/2" minimum	4110	3520	2940	2540	2980	2450	2040	1760
			2"	4950	4250	3540	3050	3440	2960	2460	2120
			2-1/2"	5830	5000	4160	3600	4050	3480	2890	2500
			3" or thicker	6140	5260	4380	3790	4270	3660	3050	2630

1. Tabulated lateral design values (P,Q) for split ring connector units shall be multiplied to all applicable adjustment factors (see Table 11.3.1).

Table 13.2B Shear Plate Connector Unit Reference Design Values

Tabulated design values[1,2,3] apply to ONE shear plate and bolt in single shear.

Shear plate diameter	Bolt diameter	Number of faces of member with connectors on same bolt	Net thickness of member	Loaded parallel to grain (0°) Design value, P, per connector unit and bolt, lbs.				Loaded perpendicular to grain (90°) Design value, Q, per connector unit and bolt, lbs.			
in.	in.		in.	Group A species	Group B species	Group C species	Group D species	Group A species	Group B species	Group C species	Group D species
2-5/8	3/4	1	1-1/2" minimum	3110*	2670	2220	2010	2170	1860	1550	1330
		2	1-1/2" minimum	2420	2080	1730	1500	1690	1450	1210	1040
			2"	3190*	2730	2270	1960	2220	1910	1580	1370
			2-1/2" or thicker	3330*	2860	2380	2060	2320	1990	1650	1440
4	3/4 or 7/8	1	1-1/2" minimum	4370	3750	3130	2700	3040	2620	2170	1860
			1-3/4" or thicker	5090*	4360	3640	3140	3540	3040	2530	2200
		2	1-3/4" minimum	3390	2910	2420	2090	2360	2020	1680	1410
			2"	3790	3240	2700	2330	2640	2260	1880	1630
			2-1/2"	4310	3690	3080	2660	3000	2550	2140	1850
			3"	4830*	4140	3450	2980	3360	2880	2400	2060
			3-1/2" or thicker	5030*	4320	3600	3110	3500	3000	2510	2160

1. Tabulated lateral design values (P,Q) for shear plate connector units shall be multiplied to all applicable adjustment factors (see Table 11.3.1).
2. Allowable design values for shear plate connector units shall not exceed the following:
   (a) 2-5/8" shear plate .... 2900 pounds
   (b) 4" shear plate with 3/4" bolt .... 4400 pounds
   (c) 4" shear plate with 7/8" bolt .... 6000 pounds
   The design values in Footnote 2 shall be permitted to be increased in accordance with the American Institute of Steel Construction (AISC) Manual of Steel Construction, 9th edition, Section A5.2 "Wind and Seismic Stresses", except when design loads have already been reduced by load combination factors (see 11.2.3).
3. Loads followed by an asterisk (*) exceed those permitted by Footnote 2, but are needed for determination of design values for other angles of load to grain. Footnote 2 limitations apply in all cases.

13.2.2 Thickness of Wood Members

13.2.2.1 Reference design values shall not be used for split ring or shear plate connectors installed in any piece of wood of a net thickness less than the minimum specified in Tables 13.2A and 13.2B.

13.2.2.2 Reference design values for split ring or shear plate connectors installed in any piece of wood of net thickness intermediate between the minimum thickness and that required for maximum reference design value, as specified in Tables 13.2A and 13.2B, shall be obtained by linear interpolation.

13.2.3 Penetration Depth Factor, C_d

Where lag screws instead of bolts are used with split ring or shear plate connectors, reference design values shall be multiplied by the appropriate penetration depth factor, C_d, specified in Table 13.2.3. Lag screw penetration into the member receiving the point shall not be less than the minimum penetration specified in Table 13.2.3. Where the actual lag screw penetration into the member receiving the point is greater than the minimum penetration, but less than the minimum penetration for $C_d = 1.0$, the penetration depth factor, C_d, shall be determined by linear interpolation. The penetration depth factor shall not exceed unity, $C_d \leq 1.0$.

13.2.4 Metal Side Plate Factor, C_{st}

Where metal side members are used in place of wood side members, the reference design values parallel to grain, P, for 4" shear plate connectors shall be multiplied by the appropriate metal side plate factor specified in Table 13.2.4.

Table 13.2.4 Metal Side Plate Factors, C_{st}, for 4" Shear Plate Connectors Loaded Parallel to Grain

Species Group	C_{st}
A	1.18
B	1.11
C	1.05
D	1.00

The adjusted design values parallel to grain, P', shall not exceed the limiting reference design values given in Footnote 2 of Table 13.2B (see 13.2.1.2).

13.2.5 Load at Angle to Grain

13.2.5.1 Where a load acts in the plane of the wood surface at an angle to grain other than 0° or 90°, the adjusted design value, N', for a split ring or shear plate connector unit shall be determined as follows (see Appendix J):

$$N' = \frac{P'Q'}{P' \sin^2\theta + Q' \cos^2\theta} \quad (13.2\text{-}1)$$

where:

θ = angle between direction of load and direction of grain (longitudinal axis of member), degrees

13.2.5.2 Adjusted design values at an angle to grain, N', for shear plate connectors shall not exceed the limiting reference design values specified in Footnote 2 of Table 13.2.B (see 13.2.1.2).

Table 13.2.3 Penetration Depth Factors, C_d, for Split Ring and Shear Plate Connectors Used with Lag Screws

	Side Member	Penetration	Penetration of Lag Screw into Main Member (number of shank diameters) Species Group (see Table 13A) Group A	Group B	Group C	Group D	Penetration Depth Factor, C_d
2-1/2" Split Ring 4" Split Ring 4" Shear Plate	Wood or Metal	Minimum for $C_d = 1.0$	7	8	10	11	1.0
		Minimum for $C_d = 0.75$	3	3-1/2	4	4-1/2	0.75
2-5/8" Shear Plate	Wood	Minimum for $C_d = 1.0$	4	5	7	8	1.0
		Minimum for $C_d = 0.75$	3	3-1/2	4	4-1/2	0.75
	Metal	Minimum for $C_d = 1.0$	3	3-1/2	4	4-1/2	1.0

13.2.6 Split Ring and Shear Plate Connectors in End Grain

13.2.6.1 Where split ring or shear plate connectors are installed in a surface that is not parallel to the general direction of the grain of the member, such as the end of a square-cut member, or the sloping surface of a member cut at an angle to its axis, or the surface of a structural glued laminated timber cut at an angle to the direction of the laminations, the following terminology shall apply:

- "Side grain surface" means a surface parallel to the general direction of the wood fibers ($\alpha = 0°$), such as the top, bottom, and sides of a straight beam.
- "Sloping surface" means a surface cut at an angle, α, other than 0° or 90° to the general direction of the wood fibers.
- "Square-cut surface" means a surface perpendicular to the general direction of the wood fibers ($\alpha = 90°$).
- "Axis of cut" defines the direction of a sloping surface relative to the general direction of the wood fibers. For a sloping cut symmetrical about one of the major axes of the member, as in Figures 13D, 13G, 13H, and 13I, the axis of cut is parallel to a major axis. For an asymmetrical sloping surface (i.e., one that slopes relative to both major axes of the member), the axis of cut is the direction of a line defining the intersection of the sloping surface with any plane that is both normal to the sloping surface and also is aligned with the general direction of the wood fibers (see Figure 13E).

α = the least angle formed between a sloping surface and the general direction of the wood fibers (i.e., the acute angle between the axis of cut and the general direction of the fibers. Sometimes called the slope of the cut. See Figures 13D through 13I).

φ = the angle between the direction of applied load and the axis of cut of a sloping surface, measured in the plane of the sloping surface (see Figure 13I).

P' = adjusted design value for a split ring or shear plate connector unit in a side grain surface, loaded parallel to grain ($\alpha = 0°$, $\varphi = 0°$).

Q' = adjusted design value for a split ring or shear plate connector unit in a side grain surface, loaded perpendicular to grain ($\alpha = 0°$, $\varphi = 90°$).

Q'_{90} = adjusted design value for a split ring or shear plate connector unit in a square-cut surface, loaded in any direction in the plane of the surface ($\alpha = 90°$).

P'_{α} = adjusted design value for a split ring or shear plate connector unit in a sloping surface, loaded in a direction parallel to the axis of cut ($0° < \alpha < 90°$, $\varphi = 0°$).

Q'_{α} = adjusted design value for a split ring or shear plate connector unit in a sloping surface, loaded in a direction perpendicular to the axis of cut ($0° < \alpha < 90°$, $\varphi = 90°$).

N'_{α} = adjusted design value for a split ring or shear plate connector unit in a sloping surface, where direction of load is at an angle φ from the axis of cut.

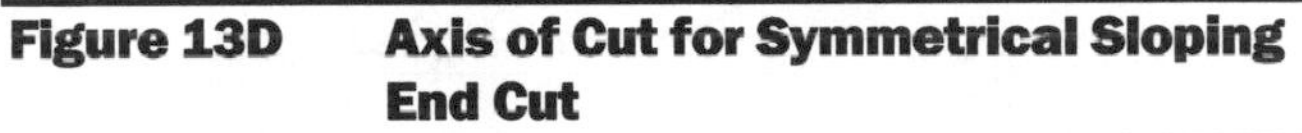

Figure 13D Axis of Cut for Symmetrical Sloping End Cut

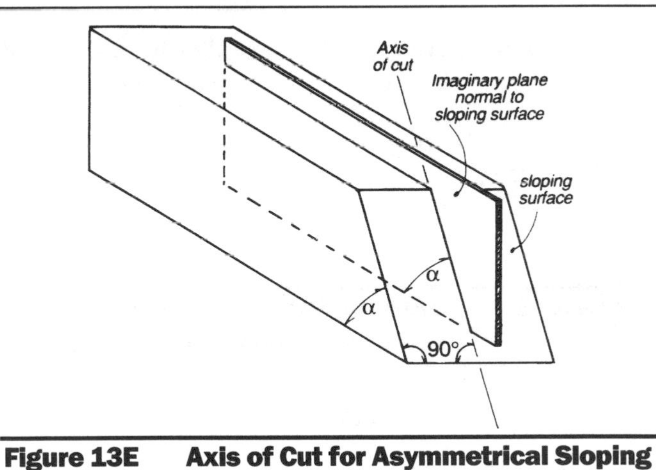

Figure 13E Axis of Cut for Asymmetrical Sloping End Cut

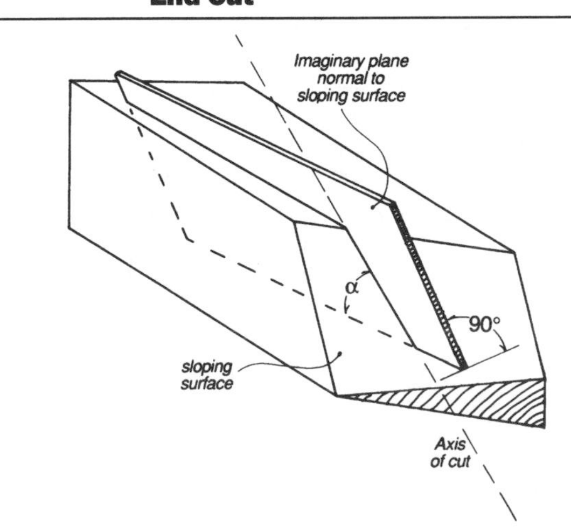

13.2.6.2 Where split ring or shear plate connectors are installed in square-cut end grain or sloping surfaces, adjusted design values shall be determined as follows (see 11.2.2):

(a) Square-cut surface; loaded in any direction ($\alpha = 90°$, see Figure 13F).

$$Q_{90}' = 0.60Q' \quad (13.2\text{-}2)$$

Figure 13F Square End Cut

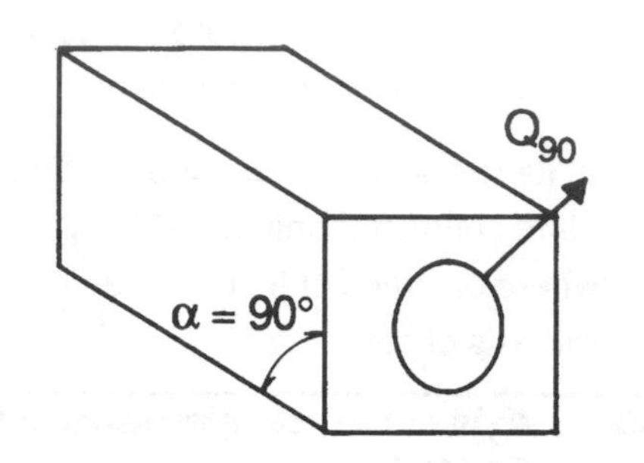

(b) Sloping surface; loaded parallel to axis of cut ($0° < \alpha < 90°$, $\varphi = 0°$, see Figure 13G).

$$P'_{\alpha} = \frac{P' Q_{90}'}{P' \sin^2 \alpha + Q_{90}' \cos^2 \alpha} \quad (13.2\text{-}3)$$

Figure 13G Sloping End Cut with Load Parallel to Axis of Cut ($\varphi = 0°$)

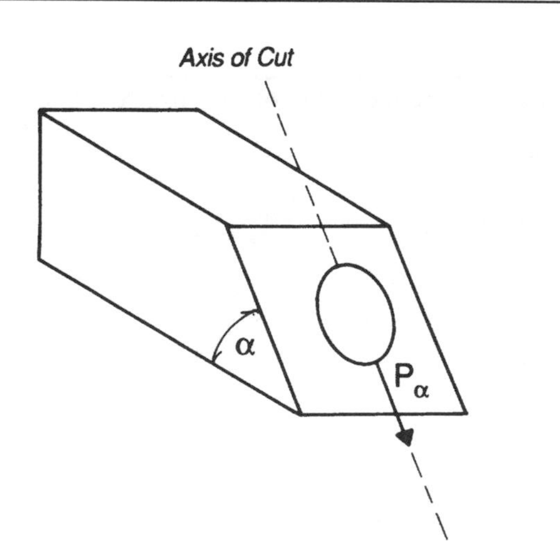

(c) Sloping surface; loaded perpendicular to axis of cut ($0° < \alpha < 90°$, $\varphi = 90°$, see Figure 13H).

$$Q'_{\alpha} = \frac{Q' Q_{90}'}{Q' \sin^2 \alpha + Q_{90}' \cos^2 \alpha} \quad (13.2\text{-}4)$$

Figure 13H Sloping End Cut with Load Perpendicular to Axis of Cut ($\varphi = 90°$)

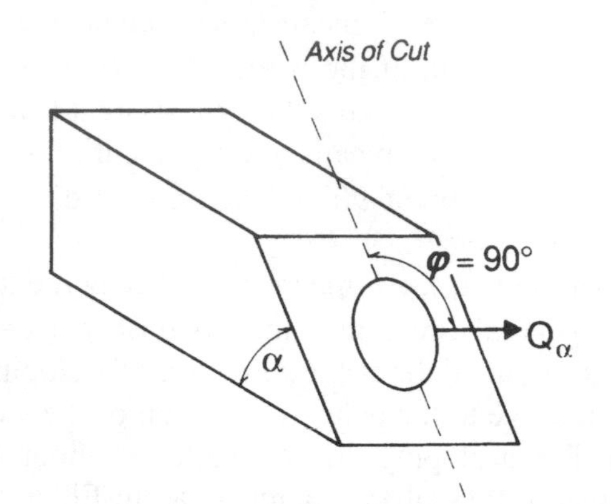

(d) Sloping surface; loaded at angle φ to axis of cut ($0° < \alpha < 90°$, $0° < \varphi < 90°$, see Figure 13I).

$$N'_{\alpha} = \frac{P_{\alpha}' Q_{\alpha}'}{P_{\alpha}' \sin^2 \varphi + Q_{\alpha}' \cos^2 \varphi} \quad (13.2\text{-}5)$$

Figure 13I Sloping End Cut with Load at an Angle φ to Axis of Cut

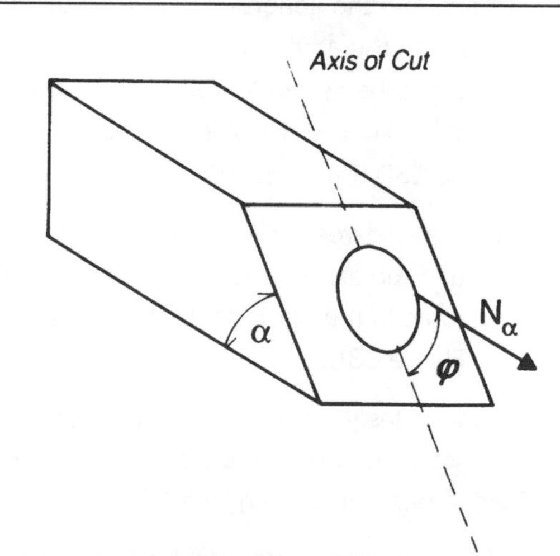

13.3 Placement of Split Ring and Shear Plate Connectors

13.3.1 Terminology

13.3.1.1 "Edge distance" is the distance from the edge of a member to the center of the nearest split ring or shear plate connector, measured perpendicular to grain. Where a member is loaded perpendicular to grain, the loaded edge shall be defined as the edge toward which the load is acting. The unloaded edge shall be defined as the edge opposite the loaded edge (see Figure 13J).

13.3.1.2 "End distance" is the distance measured parallel to grain from the square-cut end of a member to the center of the nearest split ring or shear plate connector (see Figure 13J). If the end of a member is not cut at a right angle to its longitudinal axis, the end distance, measured parallel to the longitudinal axis from any point on the center half of the transverse connector diameter, shall not be less than the end distance required for a square-cut member. In no case shall the perpendicular distance from the center of a connector to the sloping end cut of a member, be less than the required edge distance (see Figure 13K).

Figure 13J Connection Geometry for Split Rings and Shear Plates

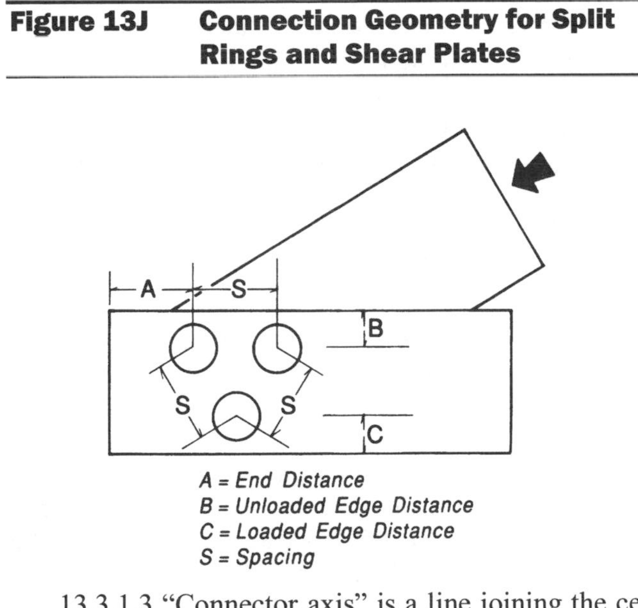

13.3.1.3 "Connector axis" is a line joining the centers of any two adjacent connectors located in the same face of a member (see Figure 13L).

13.3.1.4 "Spacing" is the distance between centers of split ring or shear plate connectors measured along their connector axis (see Figure 13J).

Figure 13K End Distance for Members with Sloping End Cut

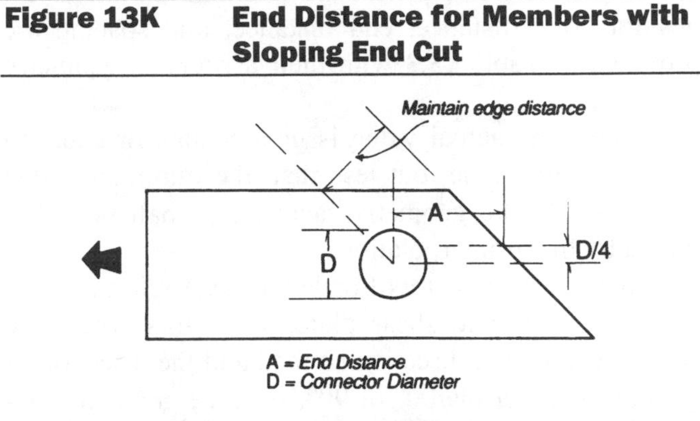

Figure 13L Connector Axis and Load Angle

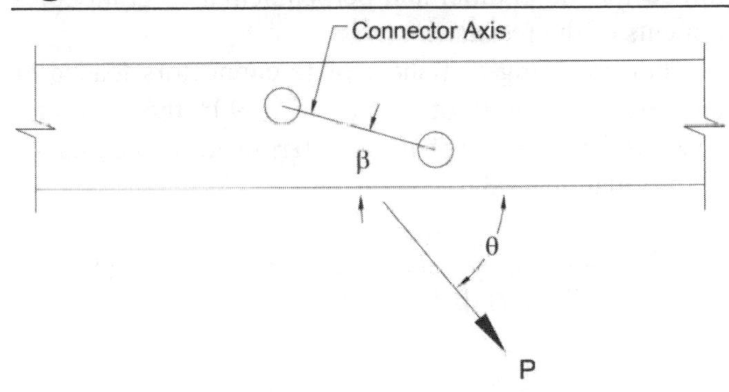

13.3.2 Geometry Factor, C_Δ, for Split Ring and Shear Plate Connectors in Side Grain

Reference design values are for split ring and shear plate connectors installed in side grain with edge distance, end distance, and spacing greater than or equal to the minimum required for $C_\Delta = 1.0$. Where the edge distance, end distance, or spacing provided is less than the minimum required for $C_\Delta = 1.0$, reference design values shall be multiplied by the smallest applicable geometry factor, C_Δ, determined from the edge distance, end distance, and spacing requirements for split ring and shear plate connectors. The smallest geometry factor for any split ring or shear plate connector in a group shall apply to all split ring and shear plate connectors in the group. Edge distance, end distance, and spacing shall not be less than the minimum values specified in 13.3.2.1 and 13.3.2.2.

13.3.2.1 Connectors Loaded Parallel or Perpendicular to Grain. For split ring and shear plate connectors loaded parallel or perpendicular to grain, minimum values for edge distance, end distance, and spacing are provided in Table 13.3 with their associated geometry factors, C_Δ.

Where the actual value is greater than or equal to the minimum value, but less than the minimum value for $C_\Delta = 1.0$, the geometry factor, C_Δ, shall be determined by linear interpolation.

13.3.2.2. Connectors Loaded at an Angle to Grain. For split rings and shear plate connectors where the angle between the direction of load and the direction of grain, θ, is other than 0° or 90°, separate geometry factors for edge distance and end distance shall be determined for the parallel and perpendicular to grain components of the resistance.

For split ring and shear plate connectors loaded at an angle to grain, θ, other than 0° or 90°, the minimum spacing for $C_\Delta = 1.0$ shall be determined in accordance with Equation 13.3-1.

$$S_\beta = \frac{S_A S_B}{\sqrt{S_A^2 \sin^2 \beta + S_B^2 \cos^2 \beta}} \quad (13.3\text{-}1)$$

where:

S_β = minimum spacing along connector axis

S_A = factor from Table 13.3.2.2

S_B = factor from Table 13.3.2.2

β = angle of connector axis to the grain

Table 13.3.2.2 Factors for Determining Minimum Spacing Along Connector Axis for $C_\Delta = 1.0$

Connector	Angle of Load to Grain[1] (degrees)	S_A in.	S_B in.
2-1/2" split ring or 2-5/8" shear plate	0	6.75	3.50
	15	6.00	3.75
	30	5.13	3.88
	45	4.25	4.13
	60-90	3.5	4.25
4" split ring or 4" shear plate	0	9.00	5.00
	15	8.00	5.25
	30	7.00	5.50
	45	6.00	5.75
	60-90	5.00	6.00

1. Interpolation shall be permitted for intermediate angles of load to grain.

The minimum spacing shall be 3.50" for 2-1/2" split rings and 2-5/8" shear plates and shall be 5.0" for 4" split ring or shear plate connectors. For this minimum spacing, $C_\Delta = 0.5$.

Where the actual spacing between split ring or shear plate connectors is greater than the minimum spacing but less than the minimum spacing for $C_\Delta = 1.0$, the geometry factor, C_Δ, shall be determined by linear interpolation. The geometry factor calculated for spacing shall be applied to reference design values for both parallel and perpendicular-to-grain components of the resistance.

13.3.3 Geometry Factor, C_Δ, for Split Ring and Shear Plate Connectors in End Grain

For split ring and shear plate connectors installed in end grain, a single geometry factor shall be determined and applied to reference design values for both parallel and perpendicular to grain components of the resistance. Edge distance, end distance, and spacing shall not be less than the minimum values specified in 13.3.3.1 and 13.3.3.2.

13.3.3.1 The provisions for geometry factors, C_Δ, for split ring and shear plate connectors installed in square-cut surfaces and sloping surfaces shall be as follows (see 13.2.6 for definitions and terminology):

(a) Square-cut surface, loaded in any direction (see Figure 13F) - provisions for perpendicular to grain loading for connectors installed in side grain shall apply except for end distance provisions.

(b) Sloping surface loaded parallel to axis of cut (see Figure 13G).

(b.1) Spacing. The minimum spacing parallel to the axis of cut for $C_\Delta = 1.0$ shall be determined in accordance with Equation 13.3-2.

The minimum spacing parallel to the axis of cut shall be 3.5" for 2-1/2" split rings and 2-5/8" shear plates and shall be 5.0" for 4" split ring or shear plate connectors. For this minimum spacing, $C_\Delta = 0.5$.

Where the actual spacing parallel to the axis of cut between split ring or shear plate connectors is greater than the minimum spacing for $C_\Delta = 0.5$, but less than the minimum spacing for $C_\Delta = 1.0$, the geometry factor, C_Δ shall be determined by linear interpolation.

$$S_\alpha = \frac{S_\parallel S_\perp}{\sqrt{S_\parallel^2 \sin^2\alpha + S_\perp^2 \cos^2\alpha}} \quad (13.3\text{-}2)$$

where:

S_α = minimum spacing parallel to axis of cut

$S_\parallel$ = factor from Table 13.3.3.1-1

$S_\perp$ = factor from Table 13.3.3.1-1

α = angle of sloped cut (see Figure 13G)

Table 13.3.3.1-1 Factors for Determining Minimum Spacing Along Axis of Cut of Sloping Surfaces

Connector	Geometry Factor	$S_\parallel$ in.	$S_\perp$ in.
2-1/2" split ring or 2-5/8" shear plate	$C_\Delta = 1.0$	6.75	4.25
4" split ring or 4" shear plate	$C_\Delta = 1.0$	9.0	6.0

(b.2) Loaded Edge Distance. The minimum loaded edge distance parallel to the axis of cut for $C_\Delta = 1.0$ shall be determined in accordance with Equation 13.3-3.

For split rings, the minimum loaded edge distance parallel to the axis of cut for $C_\Delta = 0.70$ shall be determined in accordance with Equation 13.3-3. For shear plates, the minimum loaded edge distance parallel to the axis of cut for $C_\Delta = 0.83$ shall be determined in accordance with Equation 13.3-3.

Where the actual loaded edge distance parallel to the axis of cut is greater than the minimum loaded edge distance parallel to the axis of cut for $C_\Delta = 0.70$ for split rings or for $C_\Delta = 0.83$ for shear plates, but less than the minimum loaded edge distance parallel to the axis of cut for $C_\Delta = 1.0$, the geometry factor, C_Δ, shall be determined by linear interpolation.

$$E_\alpha = \frac{E_\parallel E_\perp}{\sqrt{E_\parallel^2 \sin^2\alpha + E_\perp^2 \cos^2\alpha}} \quad (13.3\text{-}3)$$

where:

E_α = minimum loaded edge distance parallel to axis of cut

$E_\parallel$ = factor from Table 13.3.3.1-2

$E_\perp$ = factor from Table 13.3.3.1-2

α = angle of sloped cut (see Figure 13G)

Table 13.3.3.1-2 Factors for Determining Minimum Loaded Edge Distance for Connectors in End Grain

Connector	Geometry Factor	$E_\parallel$ in.	$E_\perp$ in.
2-1/2" split ring	$C_\Delta = 1.0$	5.5	2.75
	$C_\Delta = 0.70$	3.3	1.5
2-5/8" shear plate	$C_\Delta = 1.0$	5.5	2.75
	$C_\Delta = 0.83$	4.25	1.5
4" split ring	$C_\Delta = 1.0$	7.0	3.75
	$C_\Delta = 0.70$	4.2	2.5
4" shear plate	$C_\Delta = 1.0$	7.0	3.75
	$C_\Delta = 0.83$	5.4	2.5

(b.3) Unloaded Edge Distance. The minimum unloaded edge distance parallel to the axis of cut for $C_\Delta = 1.0$, shall be determined in accordance with Equation 13.3-4.

The minimum unloaded edge distance parallel to the axis of cut for $C_\Delta = 0.63$ shall be determined in accordance with Equation 13.3-4.

Where the actual unloaded edge distance parallel to the axis of cut is greater than the minimum unloaded edge distance for $C_\Delta = 0.63$, but less than the minimum unloaded edge distance for $C_\Delta = 1.0$, the geometry factor, C_Δ, shall be determined by linear interpolation.

$$U_\alpha = \frac{U_{||}U_\perp}{\sqrt{U_{||}^2 \sin^2\alpha + U_\perp^2 \cos^2\alpha}} \quad (13.3\text{-}4)$$

where:

U_α = minimum unloaded edge distance parallel to axis of cut

$U_{||}$ = factor from Table 13.3.3.1-3

$U_\perp$ = factor from Table 13.3.3.1-3

α = angle of sloped cut (see Figure 13G)

Table 13.3.3.1-3 Factors for Determining Minimum Unloaded Edge Distance Parallel to Axis of Cut

Connector	Geometry Factor	$U_{\|\|}$ in.	$U_\perp$ in.
2-1/2" split ring or 2-5/8" shear plate	$C_\Delta = 1.0$	4.0	1.75
	$C_\Delta = 0.63$	2.5	1.5
4" split ring or 4" shear plate	$C_\Delta = 1.0$	5.5	2.75
	$C_\Delta = 0.63$	3.25	2.5

(b.4) Geometry factors for unloaded edge distance perpendicular to the axis of cut and for spacing perpendicular to the axis of cut shall be determined following the provisions for unloaded edge distance and perpendicular-to-grain spacing for connectors installed in side grain and loaded parallel to grain.

(c) Sloping surface loaded perpendicular to axis of cut (see Figure 13H) - provisions for perpendicular to grain loading for connectors installed in end grain shall apply, except that:

(1) The minimum end distance parallel to the axis of cut for $C_\Delta = 1.0$ shall be determined in accordance with Equation 13.3-5.

(2) The minimum end distance parallel to the axis of cut for $C_\Delta = 0.63$ shall be determined in accordance with Equation 13.3-5.

(3) Where the actual end distance parallel to the axis of cut is greater than the minimum end distance for $C_\Delta = 0.63$, but less than the minimum unloaded edge distance for $C_\Delta =$ 1.0, the geometry factor, C_Δ, shall be determined by linear interpolation.

$$e_\alpha = \frac{E_{||}U_\perp}{\sqrt{E_{||}^2 \sin^2\alpha + U_\perp^2 \cos^2\alpha}} \quad (13.3\text{-}5)$$

where:

e_α = minimum end distance parallel to axis of cut

$E_{||}$ = factor from Table 13.3.3.1-4

$U_\perp$ = factor from Table 13.3.3.1-4

α = angle of sloped cut (see Figure 13G)

Table 13.3.3.1-4 Factors for Determining Minimum End Distance Parallel to Axis of Cut

Connector	Geometry Factor	$E_{\|\|}$ in.	$U_\perp$ in.
2-1/2" split ring or 2-5/8" shear plate	$C_\Delta = 1.0$	5.5	1.75
	$C_\Delta = 0.63$	2.75	1.5
4" split ring or 4" shear plate	$C_\Delta = 1.0$	7.0	2.75
	$C_\Delta = 0.63$	3.5	2.5

(d) Sloping surface loaded at angle φ to axis of cut (see Figure 13I) - separate geometry factors, C_Δ, shall be determined for the components of resistance parallel and perpendicular to the axis of cut prior to applying Equation 13.2-5.

13.3.3.2 Where split ring or shear plate connectors are installed in end grain, the members shall be designed for shear parallel to grain in accordance with 3.4.3.3.

13.3.4 Multiple Split Ring or Shear Plate Connectors

13.3.4.1 Where a connection contains two or more split ring or shear plate connector units which are in the same shear plane, are aligned in the direction of load, and on separate bolts or lag screws, the group action factor, C_g, shall be as specified in 11.3.6 and the total adjusted design value for the connection shall be as specified in 11.2.2.

13.3.4.2 If grooves for two sizes of split rings are cut concentric in the same wood surface, split ring connectors shall be installed in both grooves and the reference design value shall be taken as the reference design value for the larger split ring connector.

13.3.4.3 Local stresses in connections using multiple fasteners shall be evaluated in accordance with principles of engineering mechanics (see 11.1.2).

Table 13.3 Geometry Factors, C_Δ, for Split Ring and Shear Plate Connectors

		2-1/2" Split Ring Connectors & 2-5/8" Shear Plate Connectors				4" Split Ring Connectors & 4" Shear Plate Connectors			
		Parallel to grain loading		Perpendicular to grain loading		Parallel to grain loading		Perpendicular to grain loading	
		Minimum Value	Minimum for $C_\Delta = 1.0$	Minimum Value	Minimum for $C_\Delta = 1.0$	Minimum Value	Minimum for $C_\Delta = 1.0$	Minimum Value	Minimum for $C_\Delta = 1.0$
Edge Distance	Unloaded Edge	1-1/2"	1-3/4"	1-1/2"	1-3/4"	2-1/2"	2-3/4"	2-1/2"	2-3/4"
	C_Δ	0.88	1.0	0.88	1.0	0.93	1.0	0.93	1.0
	Loaded Edge	–	–	1-1/2"	2-3/4"	–	–	2-1/2"	3-3/4"
	C_Δ for Split Rings	–	–	0.70	1.0	–	–	0.70	1.0
	C_Δ for Shear Plates	–	–	0.83	1.0	–	–	0.83	1.0
End Distance	Tension Member	2-3/4"	5-1/2"	2-3/4"	5-1/2"	3-1/2"	7"	3-1/2"	7"
	C_Δ	0.63	1.0	0.63	1.0	0.63	1.0	0.63	1.0
	Compression Member	2-1/2"	4"	2-3/4"	5-1/2"	3-1/4"	5-1/2"	3-1/2"	7"
	C_Δ	0.63	1.0	0.63	1.0	0.63	1.0	0.63	1.0
Spacing	Spacing parallel to grain	3-1/2"	6-3/4"	3-1/2"	3-1/2"	5"	9"	5"	5"
	C_Δ	0.5	1.0	1.0	1.0	0.5	1.0	1.0	1.0
	Spacing perpendicular to grain	3-1/2"	3-1/2"	3-1/2"	4-1/4"	5"	5"	5"	6"
	C_Δ	1.0	1.0	0.5	1.0	1.0	1.0	0.5	1.0

TIMBER RIVETS

14

AMERICAN WOOD COUNCIL

14.1 General

14.1.1 Scope

Chapter 14 applies to the engineering design of timber rivet connections with steel side plates on Douglas Fir-Larch or Southern Pine structural glued laminated timber complying with Chapter 5 and loaded in single shear. Design of timber rivet connections in cross-laminated timber is beyond the scope of these provisions.

14.1.2 Quality of Rivets and Steel Side Plates

14.1.2.1 Design provisions and reference design values herein apply to timber rivets that are hot-dip galvanized in accordance with ASTM A 153 and manufactured from AISI 1035 steel to have the following properties tested in accordance with ASTM A 370:

Hardness	Ultimate tensile strength, F_u
Rockwell C32-39	145,000 psi, minimum

See Appendix M for rivet dimensions.

14.1.2.2 Steel side plates shall conform to ASTM Standard A 36 with a minimum 1/8" thickness. See Appendix M for steel side plate dimensions.

14.1.2.3 For wet service conditions, steel side plates shall be hot-dip galvanized in accordance with ASTM A 153.

14.1.3 Fabrication and Assembly

14.1.3.1 Each rivet shall, in all cases, be placed with its major cross-sectional dimension aligned parallel to the grain. Design criteria are based on rivets driven through circular holes in the side plates until the conical heads are firmly seated, but rivets shall not be driven flush. (Timber rivets at the perimeter of the group shall be driven first. Successive timber rivets shall be driven in a spiral pattern from the outside to the center of the group.)

14.1.3.2 The maximum penetration of any rivet shall be 70% of the thickness of the wood member. Except as permitted by 14.1.3.3, for joints with rivets driven from opposite faces of a wood member, the rivet length shall be such that the points do not overlap.

14.1.3.3 For joints where rivets are driven from opposite faces of a wood member such that their points overlap, the minimum spacing requirements of 14.3.1 shall apply to the distance between the rivets at their points and the maximum penetration requirement of 14.1.3.2 shall apply. The reference lateral design value of the connection shall be calculated in accordance with 14.2 considering the connection to be a one sided timber rivet joint, with:

(a) the number of rivets associated with the one plate equalling the total number of rivets at the joint, and
(b) s_p and s_q determined as the distances between the rivets at their points.

14.2 Reference Design Values

14.2.1 Parallel to Grain Loading

For timber rivet connections (one plate and rivets associated with it) where:

(a) the load acts perpendicular to the axis of the timber rivets
(b) member thicknesses, edge distances, end distances, and spacing are sufficient to develop full adjusted design values (see 14.3)
(c) timber rivets are installed in the side grain of wood members the reference design value per rivet joint parallel to grain, P, shall be calculated as the lesser of reference rivet capacity, P_r, and reference wood capacity, P_w:

$$P_r = 188\, p^{0.32}\, n_R\, n_C \qquad (14.2\text{-}1)$$

P_w = reference wood capacity design values parallel to grain (Tables 14.2.1A through 14.2.1F) using wood member thickness for the member dimension in Tables 14.2.1A through 14.2.1F for connections with steel plates on opposite sides; and twice the wood member thickness for the member dimension in Tables 14.2.1A through 14.2.1F for connections having only one plate, lbs.

where:

p = depth of penetration of rivet in wood member (see Appendix M), in.

= rivet length - plate thickness - 1/8"

n_R = number of rows of rivets parallel to direction of load

n_C = number of rivets per row

Reference design values, P, for timber rivet connections parallel to grain shall be multiplied by all applicable adjustment factors (see Table 11.3.1) to obtain adjusted design values, P'.

14.2.2 Perpendicular to Grain Loading

For timber rivet connections (one plate and rivets associated with it) where:

(a) the load acts perpendicular to the axis of the timber rivets

(b) member thicknesses, edge distances, end distances, and spacing are sufficient to develop full adjusted design values (see 14.3)

(c) timber rivets are installed in the side grain of wood members the reference design value per rivet joint perpendicular to grain, Q, shall be calculated as the lesser of reference rivet capacity, Q_r, and reference wood capacity, Q_w.

$$Q_r = 108\, p^{0.32}\, n_R\, n_C \qquad (14.2\text{-}2)$$

$$Q_w = q_w\, p^{0.8}\, C_\Delta \qquad (14.2\text{-}3)$$

where:

p = depth of penetration of rivet in wood member (see Appendix M), in.

= rivet length - plate thickness - 1/8"

n_R = number of rows of rivets parallel to direction of load

n_C = number of rivets per row

q_w = value determined from Table 14.2.2A, lbs.

C_Δ = geometry factor determined from Table 14.2.2B

Reference design values, Q, for timber rivet connections perpendicular to grain shall be multiplied by all applicable adjustment factors (see Table 11.3.1) to obtain adjusted design values, Q'.

14.2.3 Metal Side Plate Factor, C_{st}

The reference design value parallel to grain, P, or perpendicular to grain, Q, for timber rivet connections, when reference rivet capacity (P_r, Q_r) controls, shall be multiplied by the appropriate metal side plate factor, C_{st}, specified in Table 14.2.3:

Table 14.2.3 Metal Side Plate Factor, C_{st}, for Timber Rivet Connections

Metal Side Plate Thickness, t_s	C_{st}
$t_s \geq 1/4"$	1.00
$3/16" \leq t_s < 1/4"$	0.90
$1/8" \leq t_s < 3/16"$	0.80

14.2.4 Load at Angle to Grain

When a load acts in the plane of the wood surface at an angle, θ, to grain other than 0° or 90°, the adjusted design value, N', for a timber rivet connection shall be determined as follows (see Appendix J):

$$N' = \frac{P'Q'}{P'\sin^2\theta + Q'\cos^2\theta} \qquad (14.2\text{-}4)$$

14.2.5 Timber Rivets in End Grain

Where timber rivets are used in end grain, the factored lateral resistance of the joint shall be 50% of that for perpendicular to side grain applications where the slope of cut is 90° to the side grain. For sloping end cuts, these values can be increased linearly to 100% of the applicable parallel or perpendicular to side grain value.

14.2.6 Design of Metal Parts

Metal parts shall be designed in accordance with applicable metal design procedures (see 11.2.3).

14.3 Placement of Timber Rivets

14.3.1 Spacing Between Rivets

Minimum spacing of rivets shall be 1/2" perpendicular to grain, s_q, and 1" parallel to grain, s_p. The maximum distance perpendicular to grain between outermost rows of rivets shall be 12".

14.3.2 End and Edge Distance

Minimum values for end distance (a_p, a_q) and edge distance (e_p, e_q) as shown and noted in Figure 14A, are listed in Table 14.3.2.

Table 14.3.2 Minimum End and Edge Distances for Timber Rivet Joints

Number of rivet rows, n_R	Minimum end distance, a, in.		Minimum edge distance, e, in.	
	Load Parallel to grain, a_p	Load perpendicular to grain, a_q	Unloaded Edge e_p	Loaded edge e_q
1, 2	3	2	1	2
3 to 8	3	3	1	2
9, 10	4	3-1/8	1	2
11, 12	5	4	1	2
13, 14	6	4-3/4	1	2
15, 16	7	5-1/2	1	2
17 and greater	8	6-1/4	1	2

Note: End and edge distance requirements are shown in Figure 14A.

Figure 14A End and Edge Distance Requirements for Timber Rivet Joints

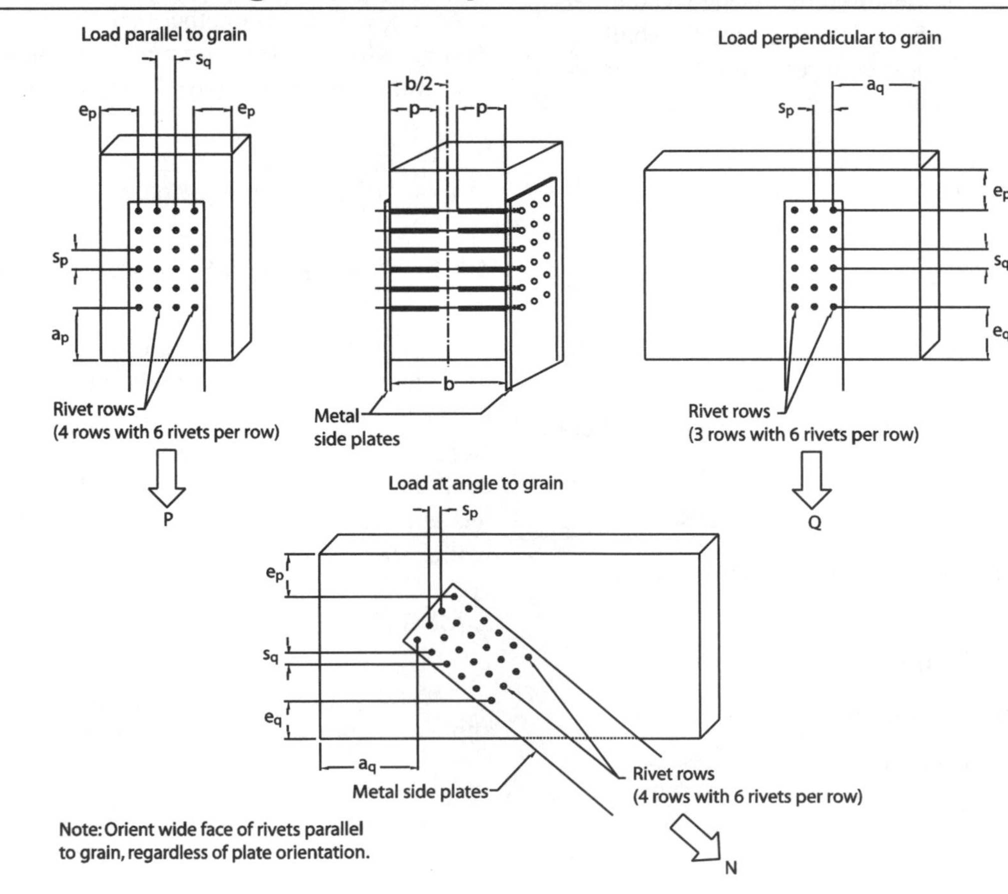

Table 14.2.1A Reference Wood Capacity Design Values Parallel to Grain, P_w, for Timber Rivets

Rivet Length = 1-1/2" s_p = 1" s_q = 1"

Member Thickness in.	Rivets per row	P_w (lbs.) No. of rows per side 2	4	6	8	10	12
3	2	2050	4900	7650	10770	14100	17050
	4	3010	6460	9700	13530	17450	20840
	6	4040	8010	11770	16320	20870	24770
	8	5110	9480	13970	18840	23910	28230
	10	5900	10930	15880	21390	26940	32020
	12	6670	12100	17760	23980	29980	35010
	14	7310	13540	19400	26380	32740	38610
	16	7670	14960	21380	28260	35470	41670
	18	8520	16250	23290	30440	38010	44500
	20	9030	17770	24950	32300	40160	46880
5	2	2680	5160	5980	7250	9280	10860
	4	3930	6610	7610	9050	11460	13390
	6	5280	8190	9290	10890	13770	15870
	8	6690	9700	10940	12740	15950	18230
	10	7720	11160	12550	14550	18120	20600
	12	8730	12680	14170	16240	20100	23100
	14	9560	14160	15720	17980	22210	25460
	16	10030	15610	17330	19650	24200	27680
	18	11150	17020	18770	21450	26110	29780
	20	11800	18410	20310	23000	28270	32260
6.75	2	2930	4810	5550	6740	8630	10110
	4	4300	6170	7080	8420	10680	12490
	6	5780	7650	8640	10150	12840	14820
	8	7320	9060	10190	11880	14890	17040
	10	8440	10420	11690	13580	16920	19260
	12	9540	11850	13210	15150	18780	21610
	14	10450	13230	14650	16790	20760	23820
	16	10970	14590	16160	18350	22630	25910
	18	12190	15910	17510	20040	24420	27890
	20	12910	17210	18950	21490	26450	30210
8.5 and greater	2	2930	4740	5460	6630	8500	9950
	4	4300	6080	6970	8290	10520	12300
	6	5780	7530	8510	10000	12650	14600
	8	7320	8920	10030	11700	14670	16790
	10	8440	10270	11520	13370	16680	18980
	12	9540	11670	13010	14930	18510	21300
	14	10450	13040	14430	16540	20460	23480
	16	10970	14370	15920	18080	22310	25540
	18	12190	15670	17250	19750	24070	27490
	20	12910	16950	18670	21180	26070	29790

Note: Member dimension is identified as "b" in Figure 14A for connections with steel side plates on opposite sides. For connections having only one plate, member dimension is twice the thickness of the wood member. Linear interpolation for intermediate values shall be permitted.

Table 14.2.1B Reference Wood Capacity Design Values Parallel to Grain, P_w, for Timber Rivets

Rivet Length = 1-1/2" s_p = 1-1/2" s_q = 1"

Member Thickness in.	Rivets per row	P_w (lbs.) No. of rows per side					
		2	4	6	8	10	12
3	2	2320	5650	8790	12270	16000	19800
	4	3420	7450	11150	15420	19810	24200
	6	4580	9230	13530	18600	23690	28760
	8	5810	10920	16060	21480	27150	32780
	10	6700	12600	18250	24380	30590	37180
	12	7570	13940	20420	27340	34040	40650
	14	8290	15600	22310	30070	37180	44840
	16	8710	17250	24580	32220	40280	48400
	18	9680	18720	26770	34700	43150	51680
	20	10250	20480	28680	36820	45600	54450
5	2	3040	5360	6740	8600	11930	14870
	4	4470	7660	9560	11970	16430	20450
	6	5990	9910	12180	15050	20610	25320
	8	7590	12000	14680	18020	24440	29760
	10	8760	14010	17090	20880	28170	34120
	12	9900	16080	19480	23530	31570	38650
	14	10850	18080	21770	26240	35120	42890
	16	11390	20040	24140	28830	38490	46900
	18	12660	21950	26250	31620	41690	50680
	20	13400	23810	28500	34010	45310	55090
6.75	2	3320	5000	6260	8000	11110	13850
	4	4890	7150	8900	11150	15330	19090
	6	6560	9250	11340	14040	19240	23660
	8	8310	11210	13680	16810	22840	27840
	10	9580	13090	15930	19500	26330	31930
	12	10830	15020	18170	21980	29520	36180
	14	11860	16900	20310	24520	32860	40180
	16	12460	18730	22520	26950	36030	43940
	18	13840	20520	24500	29560	39040	47500
	20	14660	22270	26610	31810	42440	51650
8.5 and greater	2	3320	4930	6160	7880	10930	13640
	4	4890	7050	8760	10990	15100	18800
	6	6560	9110	11170	13830	18960	23310
	8	8310	11040	13480	16560	22510	27440
	10	9580	12890	15690	19210	25960	31480
	12	10830	14800	17900	21660	29100	35670
	14	11860	16650	20000	24170	32390	39610
	16	12460	18450	22190	26560	35520	43330
	18	13840	20220	24140	29140	38490	46850
	20	14660	21940	26220	31360	41840	50940

Note: Member dimension is identified as "b" in Figure 14A for connections with steel side plates on opposite sides. For connections having only one plate, member dimension is twice the thickness of the wood member. Linear interpolation for intermediate values shall be permitted.

Table 14.2.1C Reference Wood Capacity Design Values Parallel to Grain, P_w, for Timber Rivets

Rivet Length = 2-1/2" s_p = 1" s_q = 1"

Member Thickness in.	Rivets per row	P_w (lbs.) No. of rows per side					
		2	4	6	8	10	12
5	2	2340	5610	8750	12310	16120	19500
	4	3440	7390	11100	15470	19950	23830
	6	4620	9160	13460	18660	23860	28320
	8	5850	10840	15980	21550	27350	32280
	10	6750	12500	18160	24460	30810	36610
	12	7630	13830	20310	27420	34280	40030
	14	8360	15480	22190	30170	37450	44150
	16	8770	17110	24450	32320	40570	47660
	18	9750	18580	26630	34810	43460	50890
	20	10320	20320	28530	36940	45920	53610
6.75	2	2710	6490	10130	14260	18660	22570
	4	3980	8550	12850	17910	22580	26120
	6	5350	10600	15590	20390	25510	29030
	8	6770	12550	18500	22880	28260	31840
	10	7810	14480	21020	25280	30980	34680
	12	8830	16020	23510	27430	33360	37720
	14	9670	17920	25690	29640	35930	40500
	16	10160	19810	28310	31700	38300	43040
	18	11290	21510	30160	33950	40490	45390
	20	11950	23530	32140	35770	43070	48280
8.5	2	3070	7350	10580	13060	16620	19300
	4	4510	9690	12400	14710	18410	21240
	6	6060	12000	14390	16700	20790	23640
	8	7670	13920	16320	18720	23050	25970
	10	8850	15730	18150	20680	25290	28330
	12	10010	17590	19970	22430	27270	30870
	14	10960	19360	21660	24250	29400	33190
	16	11510	21050	23410	25950	31370	35320
	18	12790	22670	24900	27810	33200	37290
	20	13540	24220	26510	29310	35350	39720
10.5	2	3400	7730	9830	11980	15210	17650
	4	5000	9490	11460	13490	16860	19460
	6	6710	11400	13250	15310	19060	21690
	8	8490	13150	15020	17170	21150	23850
	10	9800	14810	16700	18980	23230	26040
	12	11080	16520	18360	20600	25060	28400
	14	12130	18140	19910	22280	27040	30560
	16	12740	19680	21520	23850	28870	32550
	18	14160	21160	22900	25570	30570	34390
	20	14990	22580	24380	26970	32570	36640
12.5 and greater	2	3540	7610	9540	11590	14710	17060
	4	5210	9300	11100	13040	16300	18820
	6	6990	11140	12840	14810	18440	20990
	8	8860	12840	14540	16620	20470	23090
	10	10220	14440	16160	18370	22490	25230
	12	11550	16090	17770	19940	24270	27520
	14	12650	17650	19270	21580	26190	29620
	16	13290	19140	20840	23100	27970	31560
	18	14760	20570	22170	24770	29630	33350
	20	15630	21940	23600	26130	31570	35550

Note: Member dimension is identified as "b" in Figure 14A for connections with steel side plates on opposite sides. For connections having only one plate, member dimension is twice the thickness of the wood member. Linear interpolation for intermediate values shall be permitted.

Table 14.2.1D Reference Wood Capacity Design Values Parallel to Grain, P_w, for Timber Rivets

Rivet Length = 2-1/2" s_p = 1-1/2" s_q = 1"

Member Thickness in.	Rivets per row	P_w (lbs.) No. of rows per side 2	4	6	8	10	12
5	2	2660	6460	10050	14040	18300	22640
	4	3910	8520	12750	17640	22650	27670
	6	5240	10560	15480	21270	27090	32890
	8	6640	12490	18370	24560	31050	37490
	10	7660	14410	20870	27880	34980	42520
	12	8660	15950	23350	31260	38920	46490
	14	9480	17840	25510	34390	42520	51270
	16	9960	19720	28110	36850	46060	55340
	18	11070	21410	30610	39680	49350	59090
	20	11720	23420	32800	42110	52140	62260
6.75	2	3070	7480	11640	16250	21190	26210
	4	4520	9860	14770	20420	26230	32040
	6	6070	12220	17920	24630	31370	38080
	8	7690	14460	21260	28440	35950	43400
	10	8870	16690	24160	32280	40500	49230
	12	10030	18460	27030	36200	45060	53820
	14	10980	20660	29530	39820	49220	59360
	16	11530	22830	32550	42660	53320	64070
	18	12810	24790	35440	45940	57130	68420
	20	13560	27110	37970	48750	60370	72080
8.5	2	3480	8230	11610	14990	20600	25440
	4	5120	11170	14980	18590	25140	30870
	6	6880	13850	18020	21920	29500	35710
	8	8710	16390	20820	25060	33380	40030
	10	10050	18910	23430	28020	37080	44230
	12	11360	20920	25960	30640	40320	48610
	14	12440	23410	28300	33320	43740	52600
	16	13070	25860	30710	35810	46880	56250
	18	14520	27900	32770	38510	49810	59620
	20	15370	29860	34970	40700	53190	63690
10.5	2	3860	7930	10760	13740	18860	23280
	4	5670	10740	13810	17050	23050	28310
	6	7610	13360	16580	20110	27080	32800
	8	9640	15700	19140	23010	30670	36830
	10	11130	17870	21540	25740	34110	40740
	12	12580	20050	23860	28170	37130	44820
	14	13770	22110	26020	30660	40300	48540
	16	14460	24060	28240	32970	43240	51950
	18	16070	25920	30140	35470	45960	55110
	20	17020	27710	32170	37520	49120	58920
12.5 and greater	2	4020	7800	10440	13290	18230	22500
	4	5920	10500	13370	16490	22300	27390
	6	7940	13040	16050	19460	26210	31770
	8	10060	15300	18530	22270	29710	35680
	10	11600	17390	20850	24930	33050	39490
	12	13120	19490	23110	27290	35980	43460
	14	14370	21480	25200	29700	39080	47090
	16	15080	23370	27350	31950	41930	50420
	18	16760	25170	29200	34380	44590	53500
	20	17750	26900	31170	36380	47660	57220

Note: Member dimension is identified as "b" in Figure 14A for connections with steel side plates on opposite sides. For connections having only one plate, member dimension is twice the thickness of the wood member. Linear interpolation for intermediate values shall be permitted.

Table 14.2.1E Reference Wood Capacity Design Values Parallel to Grain, P_w, for Timber Rivets

Rivet Length = 3-1/2" s_p = 1" s_q = 1"

Member Thickness in.	Rivets per row	P_w (lbs.) No. of rows per side 2	4	6	8	10	12
6.75	2	2440	5850	9130	12850	16820	20350
	4	3590	7710	11580	16150	20820	24870
	6	4820	9560	14050	19480	24910	29560
	8	6100	11310	16680	22490	28550	33700
	10	7040	13050	18950	25530	32160	38220
	12	7960	14440	21200	28630	35780	41780
	14	8720	16160	23160	31490	39090	46090
	16	9160	17860	25530	33740	42340	49740
	18	10170	19390	27790	36330	45370	53120
	20	10770	21210	29780	38560	47930	55960
8.5	2	2710	6490	10130	14250	18660	22570
	4	3980	8550	12840	17910	23090	27580
	6	5350	10600	15590	21600	27620	32790
	8	6770	12550	18500	24940	31660	37370
	10	7810	14480	21020	28320	35670	42390
	12	8830	16020	23510	31750	39680	46340
	14	9670	17920	25690	34920	43350	51110
	16	10160	19810	28310	37420	46960	55170
	18	11280	21510	30830	40300	50310	58910
	20	11950	23520	33030	42760	53160	62060
10.5	2	3020	7240	11300	15900	20820	25180
	4	4440	9540	14330	19980	25760	30770
	6	5960	11830	17390	24100	30820	36580
	8	7550	14000	20630	27830	35320	40570
	10	8720	16150	23450	31420	38000	41760
	12	9850	17870	26230	32850	39220	43470
	14	10790	19990	28660	34370	40770	45050
	16	11330	22100	31580	35730	42190	46510
	18	12590	23990	33750	37340	43510	47850
	20	13330	26240	35340	38490	45290	49850
12.5	2	3320	7960	12420	17490	22890	27690
	4	4890	10490	15760	21970	28330	33840
	6	6560	13010	19120	25230	31370	35100
	8	8310	15390	22350	26580	32170	35480
	10	9580	17760	24250	27850	33280	36450
	12	10830	19650	25950	28920	34280	37940
	14	11870	21990	27400	30150	35610	39340
	16	12460	24300	28890	31290	36860	40660
	18	13840	26360	30040	32670	38030	41880
	20	14660	28020	31320	33670	39620	43680
14.5 and greater	2	3580	8580	13390	18850	24670	29840
	4	5270	11020	16940	22830	29290	33640
	6	7070	13590	19540	23990	29520	32900
	8	8950	15930	21540	25060	30160	33200
	10	10330	18090	23150	26150	31160	34110
	12	11680	20230	24620	27120	32090	35530
	14	12790	22170	25890	28250	33350	36870
	16	13430	23950	27220	29310	34540	38120
	18	14920	25580	28250	30610	35650	39300
	20	15800	27070	29430	31550	37160	41020

Note: Member dimension is identified as "b" in Figure 14A for connections with steel side plates on opposite sides. For connections having only one plate, member dimension is twice the thickness of the wood member. Linear interpolation for intermediate values shall be permitted.

Table 14.2.1F Reference Wood Capacity Design Values Parallel to Grain, P_w, for Timber Rivets

Rivet Length = 3-1/2" s_p = 1-1/2" s_q = 1"

Member Thickness in.	Rivets per row	P_w (lbs.) No. of rows per side 2	4	6	8	10	12
5	2	2770	6740	10490	14650	19100	23630
	4	4080	8890	13310	18410	23640	28880
	6	5470	11020	16160	22200	28280	34330
	8	6930	13040	19170	25640	32410	39130
	10	8000	15040	21780	29110	36510	44380
	12	9040	16640	24370	32630	40630	48520
	14	9900	18630	26630	35900	44380	53520
	16	10390	20590	29340	38460	48080	57770
	18	11550	22350	31950	41420	51510	61680
	20	12230	24450	34230	43960	54430	64990
6.75	2	3070	7480	11640	16250	21190	26210
	4	4520	9860	14760	20420	26220	32030
	6	6070	12220	17920	24630	31360	38080
	8	7690	14460	21260	28440	35950	43400
	10	8870	16680	24160	32280	40500	49220
	12	10020	18460	27030	36190	45060	53820
	14	10980	20660	29530	39810	49220	59360
	16	11530	22830	32540	42660	53320	64070
	18	12810	24790	35440	45940	57130	68410
	20	13560	27110	37970	48750	60360	72070
8.5	2	3430	8340	12980	18130	23640	29240
	4	5040	11000	16470	22780	29250	35740
	6	6770	13630	19990	27470	34990	42480
	8	8570	16130	23720	31720	40100	48420
	10	9890	18610	26950	36010	45180	54910
	12	11180	20590	30150	40380	50270	60040
	14	12250	23040	32940	43530	54910	65690
	16	12860	25470	36300	45490	58120	68370
	18	14290	27650	39530	47750	60310	70840
	20	15130	30250	42360	49450	63130	74240
10.5	2	3770	8940	14280	19930	25990	32150
	4	5550	12090	18110	25050	32170	39300
	6	7440	14990	21980	30210	38480	46710
	8	9430	17740	26080	32640	42400	49720
	10	10880	20470	29450	34550	44560	52030
	12	12300	22640	31480	36220	46470	54910
	14	13470	25340	33270	38080	48780	57570
	16	14140	28010	35150	39800	50920	60030
	18	15710	30410	36640	41810	52910	62310
	20	16640	33260	38300	43320	55450	65400
12.5 and greater	2	4060	8940	15370	21480	28010	34650
	4	5980	12730	19520	26990	34670	42350
	6	8020	16160	23590	28890	37960	44900
	8	10160	19120	25880	30610	39690	46550
	10	11720	21820	27800	32370	41740	48760
	12	13250	24280	29620	33930	43560	51520
	14	14520	26450	31250	35680	45760	54070
	16	15240	28390	32980	37310	47800	56430
	18	16940	30160	34370	39220	49710	58630
	20	17930	31770	35920	40670	52140	61590

Note: Member dimension is identified as "b" in Figure 14A for connections with steel side plates on opposite sides. For connections having only one plate, member dimension is twice the thickness of the wood member. Linear interpolation for intermediate values shall be permitted.

Table 14.2.2A Values of q_w (lbs) Perpendicular to Grain for Timber Rivets

sp = 1"

s_q in.	Rivets per row	Number of rows 2	4	6	8	10
1	2	776	809	927	1089	1255
	3	768	806	910	1056	1202
	4	821	870	963	1098	1232
	5	874	923	1013	1147	1284
	6	959	1007	1094	1228	1371
	7	1048	1082	1163	1297	1436
	8	1173	1184	1256	1391	1525
	9	1237	1277	1345	1467	1624
	10	1318	1397	1460	1563	1752
	11	1420	1486	1536	1663	1850
	12	1548	1597	1628	1786	1970
	13	1711	1690	1741	1882	2062
1-1/2	2	905	921	1042	1211	1395
	3	896	918	1024	1174	1337
	4	958	990	1083	1221	1370
	5	1020	1051	1140	1276	1428
	6	1119	1146	1231	1365	1524
	7	1223	1232	1308	1442	1597
	8	1368	1348	1413	1547	1695
	9	1811	1731	1772	1905	2110

Table 14.2.2B Geometry Factor, C_Δ, for Timber Rivet Connections Loaded Perpendicular to Grain

$\frac{e_p}{(n_c-1)S_q}$	C_Δ	$\frac{e_p}{(n_c-1)S_q}$	C_Δ
0.1	5.76	3.2	0.79
0.2	3.19	3.6	0.77
0.3	2.36	4.0	0.76
0.4	2.00	5.0	0.72
0.5	1.77	6.0	0.70
0.6	1.61	7.0	0.68
0.7	1.47	8.0	0.66
0.8	1.36	9.0	0.64
0.9	1.28	10.0	0.63
1.0	1.20	12.0	0.61
1.2	1.10	14.0	0.59
1.4	1.02	16.0	0.57
1.6	0.96	18.0	0.56
1.8	0.92	20.0	0.55
2.0	0.89	25.0	0.53
2.4	0.85	30.0	0.51
2.8	0.81		

SPECIAL LOADING CONDITIONS

AMERICAN WOOD COUNCIL

15.1 Lateral Distribution of a Concentrated Load

15.1.1 Lateral Distribution of a Concentrated Load for Moment

When a concentrated load at the center of the beam span is distributed to adjacent parallel beams by a wood or concrete-slab floor, the load on the beam nearest the point of application shall be determined by multiplying the load by the following factors:

Table 15.1.1 Lateral Distribution Factors for Moment

Kind of Floor	Load on Critical Beam (for one traffic lane[2])
2" plank	S/4.0[1]
4" nail laminated	S/4.5[1]
6" nail laminated	S/5.0[1]
Concrete, structurally designed	S/6.0[1]

1. S = average spacing of beams, ft. If S exceeds the denominator of the factor, the load on the two adjacent beams shall be the reactions of the load, with the assumption that the floor slab between the beams acts as a simple beam.
2. See Reference 48 for additional information concerning two or more traffic lanes.

15.1.2 Lateral Distribution of a Concentrated Load for Shear

When the load distribution for moment at the center of a beam is known or assumed to correspond to specific values in the first two columns of Table 15.1.2, the distribution to adjacent parallel beams when loaded at or near the quarter point (the approximate point of maximum shear) shall be assumed to be the corresponding values in the last two columns of Table 15.1.2.

Table 15.1.2 Lateral Distribution in Terms of Proportion of Total Load

Load Applied at Center of Span		Load Applied at 1/4 Point of Span	
Center Beam	Distribution to Side Beams	Center Beam	Distribution to Side Beams
1.00	0	1.00	0
0.90	0.10	0.94	0.06
0.80	0.20	0.87	0.13
0.70	0.30	0.79	0.21
0.60	0.40	0.69	0.31
0.50	0.50	0.58	0.42
0.40	0.60	0.44	0.56
0.33	0.67	0.33	0.67

15.2 Spaced Columns

15.2.1 General

15.2.1.1 The design load for a spaced column shall be the sum of the design loads for each of its individual members.

15.2.1.2 The increased load capacity of a spaced column due to the end-fixity developed by the split ring or shear plate connectors and end blocks is effective only in the direction perpendicular to the wide faces of the individual members (direction parallel to dimension d_1, in Figure 15A). The capacity of a spaced column in the direction parallel to the wide faces of the individual members (direction parallel to dimension d_2 in Figure 15A) shall be subject to the provisions for simple solid columns, as set forth in 15.2.3.

Figure 15A Spaced Column Joined by Split Ring or Shear Plate Connectors

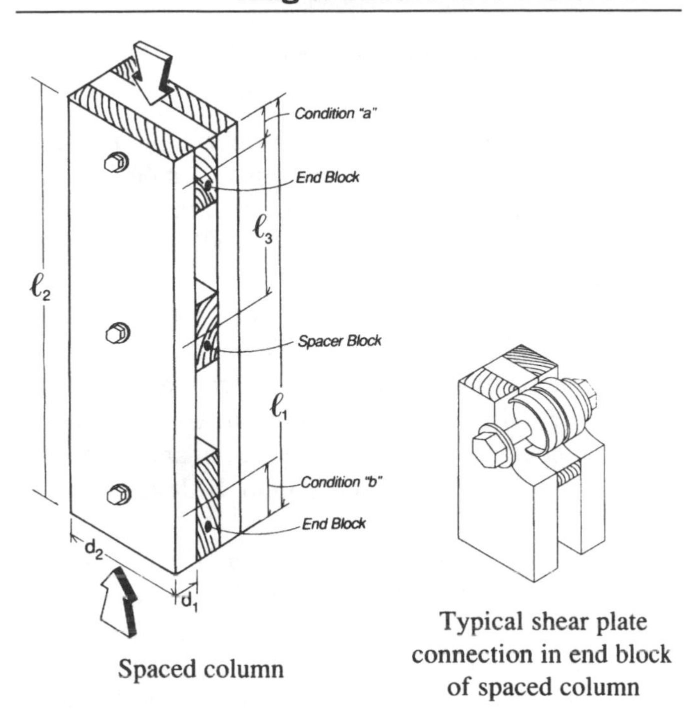

Spaced column

Typical shear plate connection in end block of spaced column

Condition "a": end distance $\leq \ell_1/20$

ℓ_1 and ℓ_2 = distances between points of lateral support in planes 1 and 2, measured from center to center of lateral supports for continuous spaced columns, and measured from end to end for simple spaced columns, inches.

ℓ_3 = Distance from center of spacer block to centroid of the group of split ring or shear plate connectors in end blocks, inches.

d_1 and d_2 = cross-sectional dimensions of individual rectangular compression members in planes of lateral support, inches.

Condition "b": $\ell_1/20 <$ end distance $\leq \ell_1/10$

15.2.2 Spacer and End Block Provisions

15.2.2.1 Spaced columns shall be classified as to end fixity either as condition "a" or condition "b" (see Figure 15A), as follows:

(a) For condition "a", the centroid of the split ring or shear plate connector, or the group of connectors, in the end block shall be within $\ell_1/20$ from the column end.

(b) For condition "b", the centroid of the split ring or shear plate connector, or the group of connectors, in the end block shall be between $\ell_1/20$ and $\ell_1/10$ from the column end.

15.2.2.2 Where a single spacer block is located within the middle 1/10 of the column length, ℓ_1, split ring or shear plate connectors shall not be required for this block. If there are two or more spacer blocks, split ring or shear plate connectors shall be required and the distance between two adjacent blocks shall not exceed ½ the distance between centers of split ring or shear plate connectors in the end blocks.

15.2.2.3 For spaced columns used as compression members of a truss, a panel point which is stayed laterally shall be considered as the end of the spaced column, and the portion of the web members, between the individual pieces making up a spaced column, shall be permitted to be considered as the end blocks.

15.2.2.4 Thickness of spacer and end blocks shall not be less than that of individual members of the spaced column nor shall thickness, width, and length of spacer and end blocks be less than required for split ring or shear plate connectors of a size and number capable of carrying the load computed in 15.2.2.5.

15.2.2.5 To obtain spaced column action the split ring or shear plate connectors in each mutually contacting surface of end block and individual member at each end of a spaced column shall be of a size and number to provide a load capacity in pounds equal to the required cross-sectional area in square inches of one of the individual members times the appropriate end spacer block constant, K_S, determined from the following equations:

Species Group	End Spacer Block Constant, K_S
A	$K_S = 9.55\ (\ell_1/d_1 - 11) \leq 468$
B	$K_S = 8.14\ (\ell_1/d_1 - 11) \leq 399$
C	$K_S = 6.73\ (\ell_1/d_1 - 11) \leq 330$
D	$K_S = 5.32\ (\ell_1/d_1 - 11) \leq 261$

If spaced columns are a part of a truss system or other similar framing, the split ring or shear plate connectors required by the connection provisions in Chapter 13 of this Specification shall be checked against the end spacer block constants, K_S, specified above.

15.2.3 Column Stability Factor, C_P

15.2.3.1 The effective column length, ℓ_e, for a spaced column shall be determined in accordance with principles of engineering mechanics. One method for determining effective column length, when end-fixity conditions are known, is to multiply actual column length by the appropriate effective length factor specified in Appendix G, $\ell_e = (K_e)(\ell)$, except that the effective column length, ℓ_e, shall not be less than the actual column length, ℓ.

15.2.3.2 For individual members of a spaced column (see Figure 15A):

(a) ℓ_1/d_1 shall not exceed 80, where ℓ_1 is the distance between lateral supports that provide restraint perpendicular to the wide faces of the individual members.

(b) ℓ_2/d_2 shall not exceed 50, where ℓ_2 is the distance between lateral supports that provide restraint in a direction parallel to the wide faces of the individual members.

(c) ℓ_3/d_1 shall not exceed 40, where ℓ_3 is the distance between the center of the spacer block and the centroid of the group of split ring or shear plate connectors in an end block.

15.2.3.3 The column stability factor shall be calculated as follows:

$$C_P = \frac{1+(F_{cE}/F_c^*)}{2c} - \sqrt{\left[\frac{1+(F_{cE}/F_c^*)}{2c}\right]^2 - \frac{F_{cE}/F_c^*}{c}} \quad (15.2\text{-}1)$$

where:

F_c^* = reference compression design value parallel to grain multiplied by all applicable adjustment factors except C_P (see 2.3)

$$F_{cE} = \frac{0.822\, K_x\, E_{min}'}{(\ell_e/d)^2}$$

K_x = 2.5 for fixity condition "a"

= 3.0 for fixity condition "b"

c = 0.8 for sawn lumber

= 0.9 for structural glued laminated timber or structural composite lumber

15.2.3.4 Where individual members of a spaced column are of different species, grades, or thicknesses, the lesser adjusted compression parallel to grain design value, F_c', for the weaker member shall apply to both members.

15.2.3.5 The adjusted compression parallel to grain design value, F_c', for a spaced column shall not exceed the adjusted compression parallel to grain design value, F_c', for the individual members evaluated as solid columns without regard to fixity in accordance with 3.7 using the column slenderness ratio ℓ_2/d_2 (see Figure 15A).

15.2.3.6 For especially severe service conditions and/or extraordinary hazard, use of lower adjusted design values may be necessary. See Appendix H for background information concerning column stability calculations and Appendix F for information concerning coefficient of variation in modulus of elasticity (COV_E).

15.2.3.7 The equations in 3.9 for combined flexure and axial loading apply to spaced columns only for uniaxial bending in a direction parallel to the wide face of the individual member (dimension d_2 in Figure 15A).

15.3 Built-Up Columns

15.3.1 General

The following provisions apply to nailed or bolted built-up columns with 2 to 5 laminations in which:

(a) each lamination has a rectangular cross section and is at least 1-1/2" thick, $t \geq$ 1-1/2".

(b) all laminations have the same depth (face width), d.

(c) faces of adjacent laminations are in contact.

(d) all laminations are full column length.

(e) the connection requirements in 15.3.3 or 15.3.4 are met.

Nailed or bolted built-up columns not meeting the preceding limitations shall have individual laminations designed in accordance with 3.6.3 and 3.7. Where individual laminations are of different species, grades, or thicknesses, the lesser adjusted compression parallel to grain design value, F_c', and modulus of elasticity for beam and column stability, E_{min}', for the weakest lamination shall apply.

15.3.2 Column Stability Factor, C_P

15.3.2.1 The effective column length, ℓ_e, for a built-up column shall be determined in accordance with principles of engineering mechanics. One method for determining effective column length, when end-fixity conditions are known, is to multiply actual column length by the appropriate effective length factor specified in Appendix G, $\ell_e = (K_e)(\ell)$.

15.3.2.2 The slenderness ratios ℓ_{e1}/d_1 and ℓ_{e2}/d_2 (see Figure 15B) where each ratio has been adjusted by the appropriate buckling length coefficient, K_e, from Appendix G, shall be determined. Each ratio shall be used to calculate a column stability factor, C_P, per section 15.3.2.4 and the smaller C_P shall be used in determining the adjusted compression design value parallel to grain, F_c', for the column. F_c' for built-up columns need not be less than F_c' for the individual laminations designed as individual solid columns per section 3.7.

15.3.2.3 The slenderness ratio, ℓ_e/d, for built-up columns shall not exceed 50, except that during construction ℓ_e/d shall not exceed 75.

15.3.2.4 The column stability factor shall be calculated as follows:

$$C_P = K_f \left[\frac{1+(F_{cE}/F_c^*)}{2c} - \sqrt{\left[\frac{1+(F_{cE}/F_c^*)}{2c}\right]^2 - \frac{F_{cE}/F_c^*}{c}} \right] \quad (15.3\text{-}1)$$

where:

F_c^* = reference compression design value parallel to grain multiplied by all applicable modification factors except C_P (see 2.3)

$$F_{cE} = \frac{0.822\, E_{min}'}{(\ell_e/d)^2}$$

K_f = 0.6 for built-up columns where ℓ_{e2}/d_2 is used to calculate F_{cE} and the built-up columns are nailed in accordance with 15.3.3

K_f = 0.75 for built-up columns where ℓ_{e2}/d_2 is used to calculate F_{cE} and the built-up columns are bolted in accordance with 15.3.4

K_f = 1.0 for built-up columns where ℓ_{e1}/d_1 is used to calculate F_{cE} and the built-up columns are either nailed or bolted in accordance with 15.3.3 or 15.3.4, respectively

c = 0.8 for sawn lumber

c = 0.9 for structural glued laminated timber or structural composite lumber

15.3.2.5 For especially severe service conditions and/or extraordinary hazard, use of lower adjusted design values may be necessary. See Appendix H for background information concerning column stability calculations and Appendix F for information concerning coefficient of variation in modulus of elasticity (COV_E).

Figure 15B Mechanically Laminated Built-Up Columns

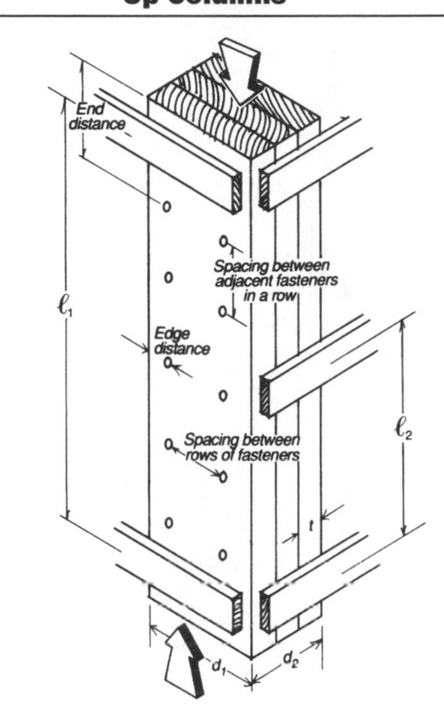

15.3.3 Nailed Built-Up Columns

15.3.3.1 The provisions in 15.3.1 and 15.3.2 apply to nailed built-up columns (see Figure 15C) in which:

(a) adjacent nails are driven from opposite sides of the column
(b) all nails penetrate all laminations and at least 3/4 of the thickness of the outermost lamination
(c) $15D \leq$ end distance $\leq 18D$
(d) $20D \leq$ spacing between adjacent nails in a row $\leq 6t_{min}$
(e) $10D \leq$ spacing between rows of nails $\leq 20D$
(f) $5D \leq$ edge distance $\leq 20D$
(g) 2 or more longitudinal rows of nails are provided where $d > 3t_{min}$

where:

D = nail diameter

d = depth (face width) of individual lamination

t_{min} = thickness of thinnest lamination

Where only one longitudinal row of nails is required, adjacent nails shall be staggered (see Figure 15C). Where three or more longitudinal rows of nails are used, nails in adjacent rows shall be staggered.

Figure 15C Typical Nailing Schedules for Built-Up Columns

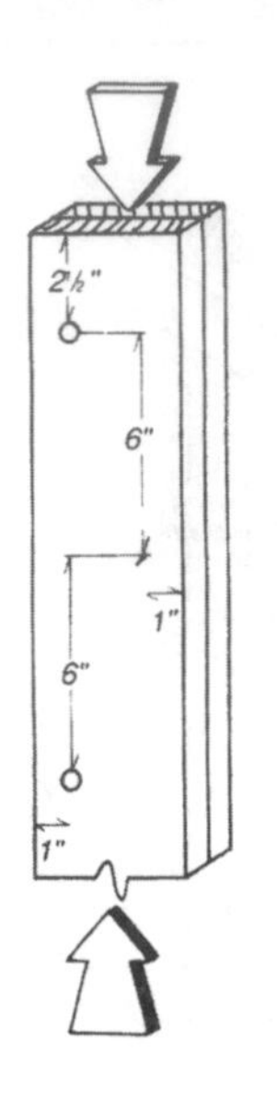

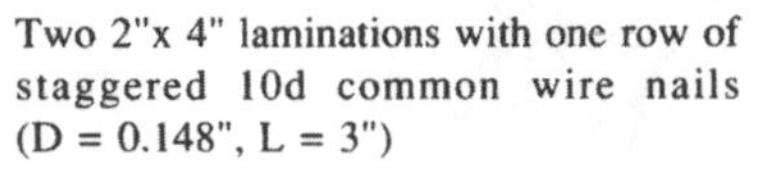
Two 2"x 4" laminations with one row of staggered 10d common wire nails (D = 0.148", L = 3")

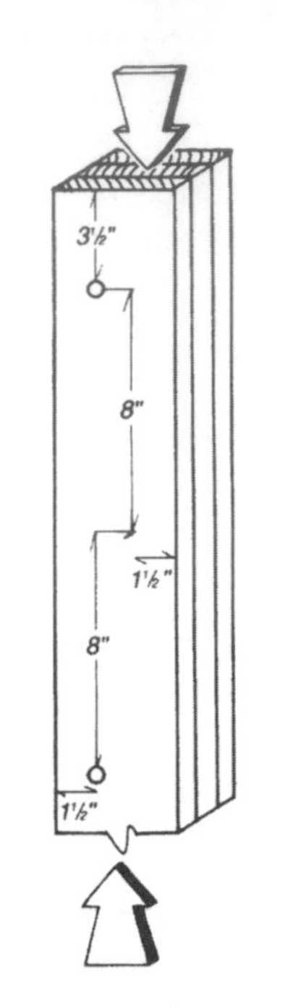

Three 2"x 4" laminations with one row of staggered 30d common wire nails (D = 0.207", L = 4-1/2")

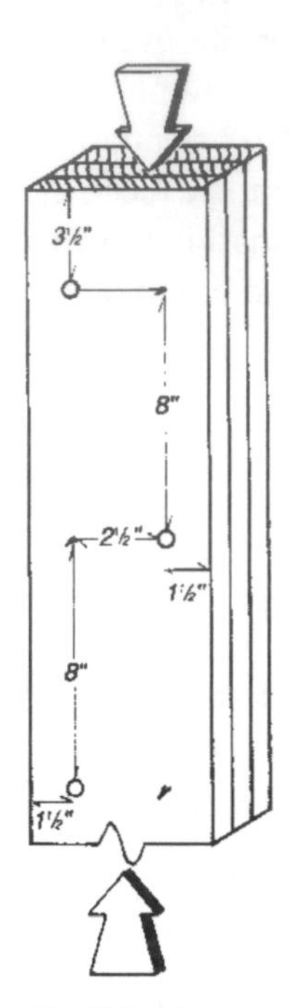

Three 2"x 6" laminations with two rows of 30d common wire nails (D = 0.207", L = 4-1/2")

15.3.4 Bolted Built-Up Columns

15.3.4.1 The provisions in 15.3.1 and 15.3.2 apply to bolted built-up columns in which:

(a) a metal plate or washer is provided between the wood and the bolt head, and between the wood and the nut
(b) nuts are tightened to insure that faces of adjacent laminations are in contact
(c) for softwoods: $7D \leq$ end distance $\leq 8.4D$
for hardwoods: $5D \leq$ end distance $\leq 6D$
(d) $4D \leq$ spacing between adjacent bolts in a row $\leq 6t_{min}$
(e) $1.5D \leq$ spacing between rows of bolts $\leq 10D$
(f) $1.5D \leq$ edge distance $\leq 10D$
(g) 2 or more longitudinal rows of bolts are provided where $d > 3t_{min}$

where:

D = bolt diameter

d = depth (face width) of individual lamination

t_{min} = thickness of thinnest lamination

15.3.4.2 Figure 15D provides an example of a bolting schedule which meets the preceding connection requirements.

Figure 15D Typical Bolting Schedules for Built-Up Columns

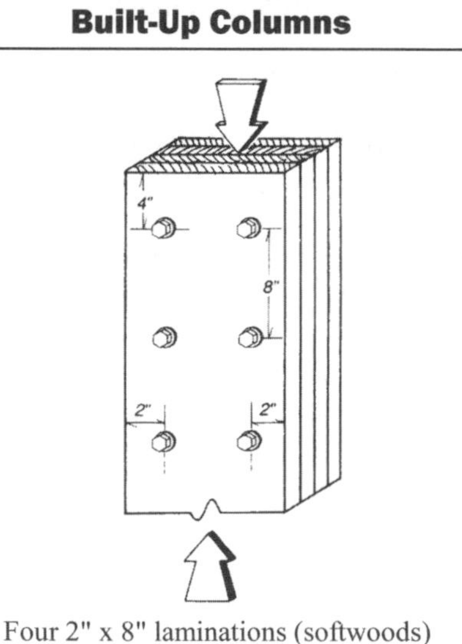

Four 2" x 8" laminations (softwoods) with two rows of ½" diameter bolts.

15.4 Wood Columns with Side Loads and Eccentricity

15.4.1 General Equations

One design method that allows calculation of the direct compression load that an eccentrically loaded column, or one with a side load, is capable of sustaining is as follows:

(a) Members subjected to a combination of bending from eccentricity and/or side loads about one or both principal axes, and axial compression, shall be proportioned so that:

$$\left(\frac{f_c}{F_c'}\right)^2 + \frac{f_{b1} + f_c(6e_1/d_1)[1 + 0.234(f_c/F_{cE1})]}{F_{b1}'[1-(f_c/F_{cE1})]} + \frac{f_{b2} + f_c(6e_2/d_2)\left\{1 + 0.234(f_c/F_{cE2}) + 0.234\left[\frac{f_{b1} + f_c(6e_1/d_1)}{F_{bE}}\right]^2\right\}}{F_{b2}'\left\{1-(f_c/F_{cE2}) - \left[\frac{f_{b1} + f_c(6e_1/d_1)}{F_{bE}}\right]^2\right\}} \leq 1.0 \qquad (15.4\text{-}1)$$

and

$$\frac{f_c}{F_{cE2}} + \left(\frac{f_{b1} + f_c(6e_1/d_1)}{F_{bE}}\right)^2 < 1.0 \qquad (15.4\text{-}2)$$

(b) Members subjected to a combination of bending and compression from an eccentric axial load about one or both principal axes, shall be proportioned so that:

$$\left(\frac{f_c}{F_c'}\right)^2 + \frac{f_c(6e_1/d_1)[1 + 0.234(f_c/F_{cE1})]}{F_{b1}'[1-(f_c/F_{cE1})]} + \frac{f_c(6e_2/d_2)\left\{1 + 0.234(f_c/F_{cE2}) + 0.234\left[\frac{f_c(6e_1/d_1)}{F_{bE}}\right]^2\right\}}{F_{b2}'\left\{1-(f_c/F_{cE2}) - \left[\frac{f_c(6e_1/d_1)}{F_{bE}}\right]^2\right\}} \leq 1.0 \qquad (15.4\text{-}3)$$

and

$$\frac{f_c}{F_{cE2}} + \left(\frac{f_c(6e_1/d_1)}{F_{bE}}\right)^2 < 1.0 \qquad (15.4\text{-}4)$$

where:

$f_c < F_{cE1} = \dfrac{0.822\,E_{min}'}{(\ell_{e1}/d_1)^2}$ for either uniaxial edgewise bending or biaxial bending

and

$f_c < F_{cE2} = \dfrac{0.822\,E_{min}'}{(\ell_{e2}/d_2)^2}$ for uniaxial flatwise bending or biaxial bending

and

$f_{b1} < F_{bE} = \dfrac{1.20\,E_{min}'}{R_B^2}$ for biaxial bending

f_c = compression stress parallel to grain due to axial load

f_{b1} = edgewise bending stress due to side loads on narrow face only

f_{b2} = flatwise bending stress due to side loads on wide face only

F_c' = adjusted compression design value parallel to grain that would be permitted if axial compressive stress only existed, determined in accordance with 2.3 and 3.7

F_{b1}' = adjusted edgewise bending design value that would be permitted if edgewise bending stress only existed, determined in accordance with 2.3 and 3.3.3

F_{b2}' = adjusted flatwise bending design value that would be permitted if flatwise bending stress only existed, determined in accordance with 2.3 and 3.3.3

R_B = slenderness ratio of bending member (see 3.3.3)

d_1 = wide face dimension

d_2 = narrow face dimension

e_1 = eccentricity, measured parallel to wide face from centerline of column to centerline of axial load

e_2 = eccentricity, measured parallel to narrow face from centerline of column to centerline of axial load

Effective column lengths, ℓ_{e1} and ℓ_{e2}, shall be determined in accordance with 3.7.1.2. F_{cE1} and F_{cE2} shall be determined in accordance with 3.7. F_{bE} shall be determined in accordance with 3.3.3.

15.4.2 Columns with Side Brackets

15.4.2.1 The formulas in 15.4.1 assume that the eccentric load is applied at the end of the column. One design method that allows calculation of the actual bending stress, f_b, if the eccentric load is applied by a bracket within the upper quarter of the length of the column is as follows.

15.4.2.2 Assume that a bracket load, P, at a distance, a, from the center of the column (Figure 15E), is replaced by the same load, P, centrally applied at the top of the column, plus a side load, P_s, applied at mid-height. Calculate P_s from the following formula:

$$P_s = \frac{3P\,a\,\ell_p}{\ell^2} \qquad (15.4\text{-}5)$$

where:

P = actual load on bracket, lbs.

P_s = assumed horizontal side load placed at center of height of column, lbs.

a = horizontal distance from load on bracket to center of column, in.

ℓ = total length of column, in.

ℓ_p = distance measured vertically from point of application of load on bracket to farther end of column, in.

The assumed centrally applied load, P, shall be added to other concentric column loads, and the calculated side load, P_s, shall be used to determine the actual bending stress, f_b, for use in the formula for concentric end and side loading.

Figure 15E Eccentrically Loaded Column

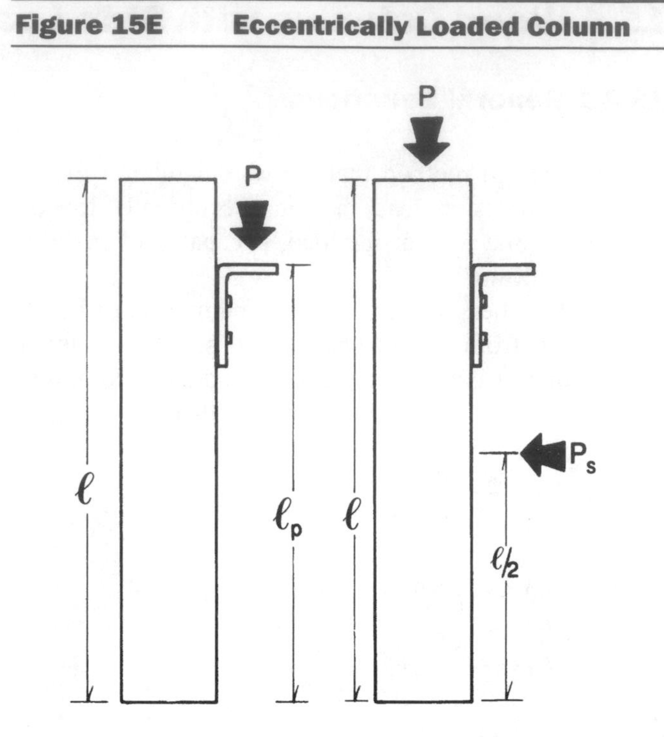

FIRE DESIGN OF WOOD MEMBERS

AMERICAN WOOD COUNCIL

16.1 General

Chapter 16 establishes general fire design provisions that apply to all wood structural members and connections covered under this Specification, unless otherwise noted. Each wood member or connection shall be of sufficient size and capacity to carry the applied loads without exceeding the design provisions specified herein. Reference design values and specific design provisions applicable to particular wood products or connections to be used with the provisions of this Chapter are given in other Chapters of this Specification.

16.2 Design Procedures for Exposed Wood Members

The induced stress shall not exceed the resisting strength which has been adjusted for fire exposure. Wood member design provisions herein are limited to fire resistance calculations not exceeding 2 hours.

16.2.1 Char Rate

16.2.1.1 The non-linear char rate to be used in this procedure can be estimated from published nominal 1-hour char rate data using the following equation:

$$\beta_t = \beta_n \text{ at one hour} \quad (16.2\text{-}1)$$

where:

β_t = non-linear char rate (in./hr.$^{0.813}$), adjusted for exposure time, t

β_n = nominal char rate (in./hr.), linear char rate based on 1-hour exposure

t = exposure time (hr.)

A nominal char rate, β_n, of 1.5 in./hr. is commonly assumed for sawn lumber, structural glued laminated softwood timber, laminated veneer lumber, parallel strand lumber, laminated strand lumber, and cross-laminated timber.

16.2.1.2 For sawn lumber, structural glued laminated softwood timber, laminated veneer lumber, parallel strand lumber, and laminated strand lumber, the char depth, a_{char}, for each exposed surface shall be calculated as:

$$a_{char} = \beta_t t^{0.813} \quad (16.2\text{-}2)$$

16.2.1.3 For cross-laminated timber manufactured with laminations of equal thickness, the char depth, a_{char}, shall be calculated as follows:

$$a_{char} = n_{lam} h_{lam} + \beta_t \left(t - \left(n_{lam} t_{gi}\right)\right)^{0.813} \quad (16.2\text{-}3)$$

$$t_{gi} = \left(\frac{h_{lam}}{\beta_t}\right)^{1.23}$$

where:

t_{gi} = time for char front to reach glued interface (hr.)

h_{lam} = lamination thickness (in.)

and

$$n_{lam} = \frac{t}{t_{gi}}$$

n_{lam} = number of laminations charred (rounded to lowest integer)

t = exposure time (hr.)

16.2.1.4 For structural calculations, section properties shall be calculated using standard equations for area, section modulus, and moment of inertia using the reduced cross-sectional dimensions. The dimensions are reduced by the effective char depth, a_{eff}, for each surface exposed to fire, where:

$$a_{eff} = 1.2 a_{char} \quad (16.2\text{-}4)$$

For sawn lumber, structural glued laminated softwood timber, laminated veneer lumber, parallel strand lumber, and laminated strand lumber, assuming a nominal char rate, β_n = 1.5 in./hr., the char depth, a_{char}, and effective char depth, a_{eff}, are shown in Table 16.2.1A.

Table 16.2.1A Char Depth and Effective Char Depth (for β_n = 1.5 in./hr.)

Required Fire Resistance (hr.)	Char Depth, a_{char} (in.)	Effective Char Depth, a_{eff} (in.)
1-Hour	1.5	1.8
1½-Hour	2.1	2.5
2-Hour	2.6	3.2

For cross-laminated timber manufactured with laminations of equal thickness and assuming a nominal char rate, β_n, of 1.5 in./hr., the effective char depth, a_{eff}, for each exposed surface is shown in Table 16.2.1B.

Table 16.2.1B Effective Char Depths (for CLT with β_n = 1.5in./hr.)

Required Fire Resistance (hr.)	Effective Char Depths, a_{eff} (in.)								
	lamination thicknesses, h_{lam} (in.)								
	5/8	3/4	7/8	1	1-1/4	1-3/8	1-1/2	1-3/4	2
1-Hour	2.2	2.2	2.1	2.0	2.0	1.9	1.8	1.8	1.8
1½-Hour	3.4	3.2	3.1	3.0	2.9	2.8	2.8	2.8	2.6
2-Hour	4.4	4.3	4.1	4.0	3.9	3.8	3.6	3.6	3.6

16.2.1.5 For cross-laminated timber, reduced section properties shall be calculated using equations provided by the cross-laminated timber manufacturer based on the actual layup used in the manufacturing process.

16.2.2 Member Strength

For sawn lumber, structural glued laminated softwood timber, laminated veneer lumber, parallel strand lumber, laminated strand lumber, and cross-laminated timber, the average member strength can be approximated by multiplying reference design values (F_b, F_t, F_c, F_{bE}, F_{cE}) by the adjustment factors specified in Table 16.2.2.

The F_b, F_t, F_c, F_{bE}, and F_{cE} values and cross-sectional properties shall be adjusted prior to use of Equations 3.3-6, 3.7-1, 3.9-1, 3.9-2, 3.9-3, 3.9-4, 15.2-1, 15.3-1, 15.4-1, 15.4-2, 15.4-3, or 15.4-4.

16.2.3 Design of Members

The induced stress calculated using reduced section properties determined in 16.2.1 shall not exceed the member strength determined in 16.2.2.

16.2.4 Special Provisions for Structural Glued Laminated Softwood Timber Beams

For structural glued laminated softwood timber bending members given in Table 5A and rated for 1-hour fire resistance, an outer tension lamination shall be substituted for a core lamination on the tension side for unbalanced beams and on both sides for balanced beams. For structural glued laminated softwood timber bending members given in Table 5A and rated for 1½- or 2-hour fire resistance, 2 outer tension laminations shall be substituted for 2 core laminations on the tension side for unbalanced beams and on both sides for balanced beams.

16.2.5 Provisions for Timber Decks

Timber decks consist of planks that are at least 2" (actual) thick. The planks shall span the distance between supporting beams. Single and double tongue-and-groove (T&G) decking shall be designed as an assembly of wood beams fully exposed on one face. Butt-jointed decking shall be designed as an assembly of wood beams partially exposed on the sides and fully exposed on one face. To compute the effects of partial exposure of the decking on its sides, the char rate for this limited exposure shall be reduced to 33% of the effective char rate. These calculation procedures do not address thermal separation.

Table 16.2.2 Adjustment Factors for Fire Design[1]

			ASD					
			Design Stress to Member Strength Factor	Size Factor[2]	Volume Factor[2]	Flat Use Factor[2]	Beam Stability Factor[3]	Column Stability Factor[3]
Bending Strength	F_b	x	2.85	C_F	C_V	C_{fu}	C_L	-
Beam Buckling Strength	F_{bE}	x	2.03	-	-	-	-	-
Tensile Strength	F_t	x	2.85	C_F	-	-	-	-
Compressive Strength	F_c	x	2.58	C_F	-	-	-	C_P
Column Buckling Strength	F_{cE}	x	2.03	-	-	-	-	-

1. See 4.3, 5.3, 8.3, and 10.3 for applicability of adjustment factors for specific products.
2. Factor shall be based on initial cross-section dimensions.
3. Factor shall be based on reduced cross-section dimensions.

16.3 Wood Connections

Wood connections, including connectors, fasteners, and portions of wood members included in the connection design, shall be protected from fire exposure for the required fire resistance time. Protection shall be provided by wood, fire-rated gypsum board, other approved materials, or a combination thereof.

A

APPENDIX

Appendix A (Non-mandatory) Construction and Design Practices

A.1 Care of Material

Lumber shall be so handled and covered as to prevent marring and moisture absorption from snow or rain.

A.2 Foundations

A.2.1 Foundations shall be adequate to support the building or structure and any required loads, without excessive or unequal settlement or uplift.

A.2.2 Good construction practices generally eliminate decay or termite damage. Such practices are designed to prevent conditions which would be conducive to decay and insect attack. The building site shall be graded to provide drainage away from the structure. All roots and scraps of lumber shall be removed from the immediate vicinity of the building before backfilling.

A.3 Structural Design

Consideration shall be given in design to the possible effect of cross-grain dimensional changes which may occur in lumber fabricated or erected in a green condition (i.e., provisions shall be made in the design so that if dimensional changes caused by seasoning to moisture equilibrium occur, the structure will move as a whole, and the differential movement of similar parts and members meeting at connections will be a minimum).

A.4 Drainage

In exterior structures, the design shall be such as to minimize pockets in which moisture can accumulate, or adequate caps, drainage, and drips shall be provided.

A.5 Camber

Adequate camber in trusses to give proper appearance and to counteract any deflection from loading should be provided. For timber connector construction, such camber shall be permitted to be estimated from the formula:

$$\Delta = \frac{K_1 L^3 + K_2 L^2}{H} \quad \text{(A-1)}$$

where:

Δ = camber at center of truss, in.

L = truss span, ft

H = truss height at center, ft

K_1 = 0.000032 for any type of truss

K_2 = 0.0028 for flat and pitched trusses

K_2 = 0.00063 for bowstring trusses (i.e., trusses without splices in upper chord)

A.6 Erection

A.6.1 Provision shall be made to prevent the overstressing of members or connections during erection.

A.6.2 Bolted connections shall be snugly tightened, but not to the extent of crushing wood under washers.

A.6.3 Adequate bracing shall be provided until permanent bracing and/or diaphragms are installed.

A.7 Inspection

Provision should be made for competent inspection of materials and workmanship.

A.8 Maintenance

There shall be competent inspection and tightening of bolts in connections of trusses and structural frames.

A.9 Wood Column Bracing

In buildings, for forces acting in a direction parallel to the truss or beam, column bracing shall be permitted to be provided by knee braces or, in the case of trusses, by extending the column to the top chord of the truss where the bottom and top chords are separated sufficiently to provide adequate bracing action. In a direction perpendicular to the truss or beam, bracing shall be permitted to be provided by wall construction, knee braces, or bracing between columns. Such bracing between columns should be installed preferably in the same bays as the bracing between trusses.

A.10 Truss Bracing

In buildings, truss bracing to resist lateral forces shall be permitted as follows:

(a) Diagonal lateral bracing between top chords of trusses shall be permitted to be omitted when the provisions of Appendix A.11 are followed or when the roof joists rest on and are securely fastened to the top chords of the trusses and are covered with wood sheathing. Where sheathing other than wood is applied, top chord diagonal lateral bracing should be installed.

(b) In all cases, vertical sway bracing should be installed in each third or fourth bay at intervals of approximately 35 feet measured parallel to trusses. Also, bottom chord lateral bracing should be installed in the same bays as the vertical sway bracing, where practical, and should extend from side wall to side wall. In addition, struts should be installed between bottom chords at the same truss panels as vertical sway bracing and should extend continuously from end wall to end wall. If the roof construction does not provide proper top chord strut action, separate additional members should be provided.

A.11 Lateral Support of Arches, Compression Chords of Trusses and Studs

A.11.1 When roof joists or purlins are used between arches or compression chords, or when roof joists or purlins are placed on top of an arch or compression chord, and are securely fastened to the arch or compression chord, the largest value of ℓ_e/d, calculated using the depth of the arch or compression chord or calculated using the breadth (least dimension) of the arch or compression chord between points of intermittent lateral support, shall be used. The roof joists or purlins should be placed to account for shrinkage (for example by placing the upper edges of unseasoned joists approximately 5% of the joist depth above the tops of the arch or chord), but also placed low enough to provide adequate lateral support.

A.11.2 When planks are placed on top of an arch or compression chord, and securely fastened to the arch or compression chord, or when sheathing is nailed properly to the top chord of trussed rafters, the depth rather than the breadth of the arch, compression chord, or trussed rafter shall be permitted to be used as the least dimension in determining ℓ_e/d.

A.11.3 When stud walls in light frame construction are adequately sheathed on at least one side, the depth, rather than breadth of the stud, shall be permitted to be taken as the least dimension in calculating the ℓ_e/d ratio. The sheathing shall be shown by experience to provide lateral support and shall be adequately fastened.

Appendix B (Non-mandatory) Load Duration (ASD Only)

B.1 Adjustment of Reference Design Values for Load Duration

B.1.1 Normal Load Duration. The reference design values in this Specification are for normal load duration. Normal load duration contemplates fully stressing a member to its allowable design value by the application of the full design load for a cumulative duration of approximately 10 years and/or the application of 90% of the full design load continuously throughout the remainder of the life of the structure, without encroaching on the factor of safety.

B.1.2 Other Load Durations. Since tests have shown that wood has the property of carrying substantially greater maximum loads for short durations than for long durations of loading, reference design values for normal load duration shall be multiplied by load duration factors, C_D, for other durations of load (see Figure B1). Load duration factors do not apply to reference modulus of elasticity design values, E, nor to reference compression design values perpendicular to grain, $F_{c\perp}$, based on a deformation limit.

(a) When the member is fully stressed to the adjusted design value by application of the full design load permanently, or for a cumulative total of more than 10 years, reference design values for normal load duration (except E and $F_{c\perp}$ based on a deformation limit) shall be multiplied by the load duration factor, $C_D = 0.90$.

(b) Likewise, when the duration of the full design load does not exceed the following durations, reference design values for normal load duration (except E and $F_{c\perp}$ based on a deformation limit) shall be multiplied by the following load duration factors:

C_D	Load Duration
1.15	two months duration
1.25	seven days duration
1.6	ten minutes duration
2.0	impact

(c) The 2 month load duration factor, $C_D = 1.15$, is applicable to design snow loads based on ASCE 7. Other load duration factors shall be permitted to be used where such adjustments are referenced to the duration of the design snow load in the specific location being considered.

(d) The 10 minutes load duration factor, $C_D = 1.6$, is applicable to design earthquake loads and design wind loads based on ASCE 7.

(e) Load duration factors greater than 1.6 shall not apply to structural members pressure-treated with water-borne preservatives (see Reference 30), or fire retardant chemicals. The impact load duration factor shall not apply to connections.

B.2 Combinations of Loads of Different Durations

When loads of different durations are applied simultaneously to members which have full lateral support to prevent buckling, the design of structural members and connections shall be based on the critical load combination determined from the following procedures:

(a) Determine the magnitude of each load that will occur on a structural member and accumulate subtotals of combinations of these loads. Design loads established by applicable building codes and standards may include load combination factors to adjust for probability of simultaneous occurrence of various loads (see Appendix B.4). Such load combination factors should be included in the load combination subtotals.

(b) Divide each subtotal by the load duration factor, C_D, for the shortest duration load in the combination of loads under consideration.

Shortest Load Duration in the Combination of Loads	Load Duration Factor, C_D
Permanent	0.9
Normal	1.0
Two Months	1.15
Seven Days	1.25
Ten Minutes	1.6
Impact	2.0

(c) The largest value thus obtained indicates the critical load combination to be used in designing the structural member or connection.

EXAMPLE: Determine the critical load combination for a structural member subjected to the following loads established by applicable building code or standard:

D = dead load
L = live load

S = snow load
W = wind load

The actual stress due to any combination of the above loads shall be less than or equal to the adjusted design value modified by the load duration factor, C_D, for the shortest duration load in that combination of loads:

Actual stress due to	(C_D)	x (Design value)
D	≤ (0.9)	x (design value)
D+L	≤ (1.0)	x (design value)
D+W	≤ (1.6)	x (design value)
D+L+S	≤ (1.15)	x (design value)
D+L+W	≤ (1.6)	x (design value)
D+S+W	≤ (1.6)	x (design value)
D+L+S+W	≤ (1.6)	x (design value)

The equations above may be specified by the applicable building code and shall be checked as required. Load combination factors specified by the applicable building code or standard should be included in the above equations, as specified in B.2(a).

B.3 Mechanical Connections

Load duration factors, $C_D \leq 1.6$, apply to reference design values for connections, except when connection capacity is based on design of metal parts (see 11.2.3).

B.4 Load Combination Reduction Factors

Reductions in total design load for certain combinations of loads account for the reduced probability of simultaneous occurrence of the various design loads. Load duration factors, C_D, account for the relationship between wood strength and time under load. Load duration factors, C_D, are independent of load combination reduction factors, and both may be used in design calculations (scc 1.4.4).

Figure B1 Load Duration Factors, C_D, for Various Load Durations

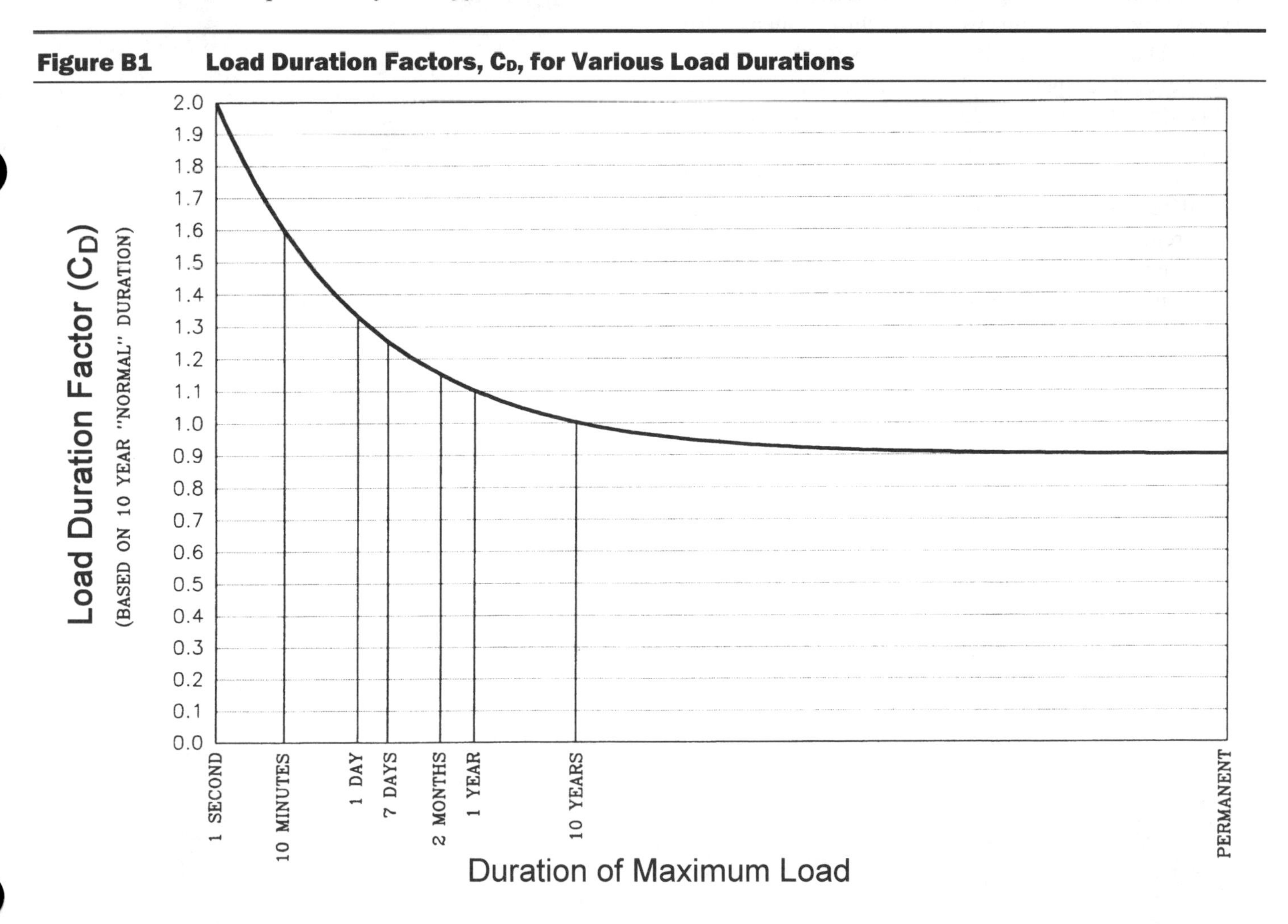

Appendix C (Non-mandatory) Temperature Effects

C.1

As wood is cooled below normal temperatures, its strength increases. When heated, its strength decreases. This temperature effect is immediate and its magnitude varies depending on the moisture content of the wood. Up to 150°F, the immediate effect is reversible. The member will recover essentially all its strength when the temperature is reduced to normal. Prolonged heating to temperatures above 150°F can cause a permanent loss of strength.

C.2

In some regions, structural members are periodically exposed to fairly elevated temperatures. However, the normal accompanying relative humidity generally is very low and, as a result, wood moisture contents also are low. The immediate effect of the periodic exposure to the elevated temperatures is less pronounced because of this dryness. Also, independently of temperature changes, wood strength properties generally increase with a decrease in moisture content. In recognition of these offsetting factors, it is traditional practice to use the reference design values from this Specification for ordinary temperature fluctuations and occasional short-term heating to temperatures up to 150°F.

C.3

When wood structural members are heated to temperatures up to 150°F for extended periods of time, adjustment of the reference design values in this Specification may be necessary (see 2.3.3 and 11.3.4). See Reference 53 for additional information concerning the effect of temperature on wood strength.

Appendix D (Non-mandatory) Lateral Stability of Beams

D.1

Slenderness ratios and related equations for adjusting reference bending design values for lateral buckling in 3.3.3 are based on theoretical analyses and beam verification tests.

D.2

Treatment of lateral buckling in beams parallels that for columns given in 3.7.1 and Appendix H. Beam stability calculations are based on slenderness ratio, R_B, defined as:

$$R_B = \sqrt{\frac{\ell_e d}{b^2}} \qquad \text{(D-1)}$$

with ℓ_e as specified in 3.3.3.

D.3

For beams with rectangular cross section where R_B does not exceed 50, adjusted bending design values are obtained by the equation (where $C_L \leq C_V$):

$$F_b' = F_b^* \left[\frac{1+\left(F_{bE}/F_b^*\right)}{1.9} - \sqrt{\left[\frac{1+\left(F_{bE}/F_b^*\right)}{1.9}\right]^2 - \frac{F_{bE}/F_b^*}{0.95}} \right] \qquad \text{(D-2)}$$

where:

$$F_{bE} = \frac{1.20\,E_{min}'}{R_B^2} \qquad \text{(D-3)}$$

F_b^* = reference bending design value multiplied by all applicable adjustment factors except C_{fu}, C_V (when $C_V \leq 1.0$), and C_L (see 2.3)

D.4

Reference modulus of elasticity for beam and column stability, E_{min}, in Equation D-3 is based on the following equation:

$$E_{min} = E\,[1 - 1.645\,COV_E](1.03)/1.66 \qquad \text{(D-4)}$$

where:

E = reference modulus of elasticity

1.03 = adjustment factor to convert E values to a pure bending basis except that the factor is 1.05 for structural glued laminated timber

1.66 = factor of safety

COV_E = coefficient of variation in modulus of elasticity (see Appendix F)

E_{min} represents an approximate 5% lower exclusion value on pure bending modulus of elasticity, plus a 1.66 factor of safety.

D.5

For products with less E variability than visually graded sawn lumber, higher critical buckling design values (F_{bE}) may be calculated. For a product having a lower coefficient of variation in modulus of elasticity, use of Equations D-3 and D-4 will provide a 1.66 factor of safety at the 5% lower exclusion value.

Appendix E (Non-mandatory) Local Stresses in Fastener Groups

E.1 General

Where a fastener group is composed of closely spaced fasteners loaded parallel to grain, the capacity of the fastener group may be limited by wood failure at the net section or tear-out around the fasteners caused by local stresses. One method to evaluate member strength for local stresses around fastener groups is outlined in the following procedures.

E.1.1 Reference design values for timber rivet connections in Chapter 14 account for local stress effects and do not require further modification by procedures outlined in this Appendix.

E.1.2 The capacity of connections with closely spaced, large diameter bolts has been shown to be limited by the capacity of the wood surrounding the connection. Connections with groups of smaller diameter fasteners, such as typical nailed connections in wood-frame construction, may not be limited by wood capacity.

E.2 Net Section Tension Capacity

The adjusted tension capacity is calculated in accordance with provisions of 3.1.2 and 3.8.1 as follows:

$$Z_{NT}' = F_t' A_{net} \quad \text{(E.2-1)}$$

where:

Z_{NT}' = adjusted tension capacity of net section area

F_t' = adjusted tension design value parallel to grain

A_{net} = net section area per 3.1.2

E.3 Row Tear-Out Capacity

The adjusted tear-out capacity of a row of fasteners can be estimated as follows:

$$Z_{RTi}' = n_i \frac{F_v' A_{critical}}{2} \quad \text{(E.3-1)}$$

where:

Z_{RTi}' = adjusted row tear out capacity of row i

F_v' = adjusted shear design value parallel to grain

$A_{critical}$ = minimum shear area of any fastener in row i

n_i = number of fasteners in row i

E3.1 Assuming one shear line on each side of bolts in a row (observed in tests of bolted connections), Equation E.3-1 becomes:

$$Z_{RTi}' = \frac{F_v' t}{2}[n_i s_{critical}](2 \text{ shear lines}) \quad \text{(E.3-2)}$$

$$= n_i F_v' t s_{critical}$$

where:

$s_{critical}$ = minimum spacing in row i taken as the lesser of the end distance or the spacing between fasteners in row i

t = thickness of member

The total adjusted row tear-out capacity of multiple rows of fasteners can be estimated as:

$$Z_{RT}' = \sum_{i=1}^{n_{row}} Z_{RTi}' \quad \text{(E.3-3)}$$

where:

Z_{RT}' = adjusted row tear out capacity of multiple rows

n_{row} = number of rows

E.3.2 In Equation E.3-1, it is assumed that the induced shear stress varies from a maximum value of $f_v = F_v'$ to a minimum value of $f_v = 0$ along each shear line between fasteners in a row and that the change in shear stress/strain is linear along each shear line. The resulting triangular stress distribution on each shear line between fasteners in a row establishes an apparent shear stress equal to half of the adjusted design shear stress, $F_v'/2$, as shown in Equation E.3-1. This assumption is combined with the critical area concept for evaluating stresses in fastener groups and provides good agreement with results from tests of bolted connections.

E3.3 Use of the minimum shear area of any fastener in a row for calculation of row tear-out capacity is based on the assumption that the smallest shear area between fasteners in a row will limit the capacity of the row of fasteners. Limited verification of this approach is provided from tests of bolted connections.

E.4 Group Tear-Out Capacity

The adjusted tear-out capacity of a group of "n" rows of fasteners can be estimated as:

$$Z_{GT}' = \frac{Z_{RT-1}'}{2} + \frac{Z_{RT-n}'}{2} + F_t' A_{group-net} \qquad (E.4\text{-}1)$$

where:

Z_{GT}' = adjusted group tear-out capacity

Z_{RT-1}' = adjusted row tear-out capacity of row 1 of fasteners bounding the critical group area

Z_{RT-n}' = adjusted row tear-out capacity of row n of fasteners bounding the critical group area

$A_{group-net}$ = critical group net section area between row 1 and row n

E.4.1 For groups of fasteners with non uniform spacing between rows of fasteners various definitions of critical group area should be checked for group tear-out in combination with row tear-out to determine the adjusted capacity of the critical section.

E.5 Effects of Fastener Placement

E.5.1 Modification of fastener placement within a fastener group can be used to increase row tear-out and group tear-out capacity limited by local stresses around the fastener group. Increased spacing between fasteners in a row is one way to increase row tear-out capacity. Increased spacing between rows of fasteners is one way to increase group tear-out capacity.

E.5.2 Section 12.5.1.3 limits the spacing between outer rows of fasteners paralleling the member on a single splice plate to 5 inches. This requirement is imposed to limit local stresses resulting from shrinkage of wood members. Where special detailing is used to address shrinkage, such as the use of slotted holes, the 5-inch limit can be adjusted.

E.6 Sample Solution of Staggered Bolts

Calculate the net section area tension, row tear-out, and group tear-out ASD adjusted design capacities for the double-shear bolted connection in Figure E1.

Main Member:
Combination 2 Douglas fir 3-1/8 x 12 glued laminated timber member. See *NDS Supplement* Table 5B – Members stressed primarily in axial tension or compression for reference design values. Adjustment factors C_D, C_T, and C_M are assumed to equal 1.0 and C_{vr} = 0.72 (see NDS 5.3.10) is used in this example for calculation of adjusted design values.

F_t' = 1250 psi

F_v' = 265 psi (C_{vr}) = 265 (0.72) = 191 psi

Main member thickness, t_m: 3.125 in.
Main member width, w: 12 in.

Side Member:
A36 steel plates on each side
Side plate thickness, t_s: 0.25 in.

Connection Details:
Bolt diameter, D: 1 inch
Bolt hole diameter, D_h: 1.0625 in.
Adjusted ASD bolt design value, $Z_{||}'$: 4380 lbs (see Table 12I. For this trial design, the group action factor, C_g, is taken as 1.0).
Spacing between rows: s_{row} = 2.5D

Adjusted ASD Connection Capacity, $nZ_{||}'$:

$nZ_{||}'$ = (8 bolts)(4,380 lbs) = 35,040 lbs

Figure E1 Staggered Rows of Bolts

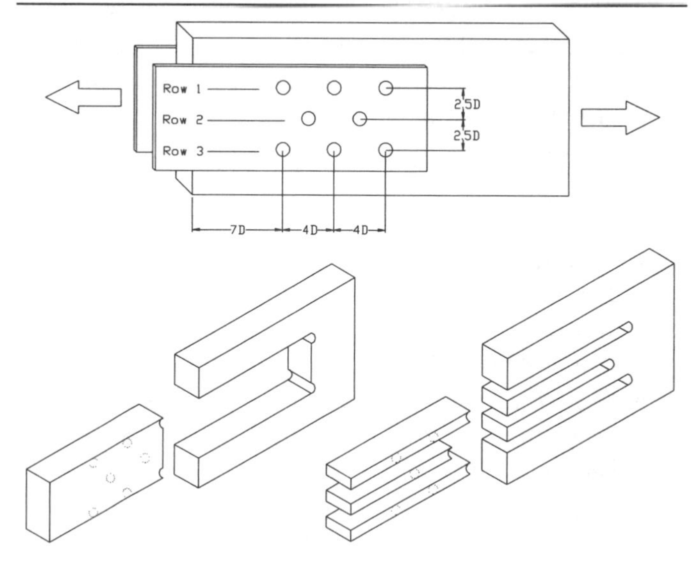

Adjusted ASD Net Section Area Tension Capacity, Z_{NT}':

$$Z_{NT}' = F_t' t[w - n_{row} D_h]$$

$Z_{NT}' = (1{,}250 \text{ psi})(3.125")[12" - 3(1.0625")]$

$= 34{,}424$ lbs

Adjusted ASD Row Tear-Out Capacity, Z_{RT}':

$$Z_{RTi}' = n_i F_v' t s_{critical}$$

$Z_{RT\text{-}1}' = 3(191 \text{ psi})(3.125")(4") = 7{,}163$ lbs

$Z_{RT\text{-}2}' = 2(191 \text{ psi})(3.125")(4") = 4{,}775$ lbs

$Z_{RT\text{-}3}' = 3(191 \text{ psi})(3.125")(4") = 7{,}163$ lbs

$$Z_{RT}' = \sum_{i=1}^{n_{row}} Z_{RTi}'$$

$= 7{,}163 + 4{,}775 + 7{,}163 = 19{,}101$ lbs

Adjusted ASD Group Tear-Out Capacity, Z_{GT}':

$$Z_{GT}' = \frac{Z_{RT-1}'}{2} + \frac{Z_{RT-3}'}{2} + F_t' t\left[(n_{row} - 1)(s_{row} - D_h)\right]$$

$Z_{GT}' = (7{,}163 \text{ lbs})/2 + (7{,}163 \text{ lbs})/2 +$

$(1{,}250 \text{ psi})(3.125")[(3 - 1)(2.5" - 1.0625")]$

$= 18{,}393$ lbs

In this sample calculation, the adjusted ASD connection capacity is limited to 18,393 pounds by group tear-out, Z_{GT}'.

E.7 Sample Solution of Row of Bolts

Calculate the net section area tension and row tear-out adjusted ASD design capacities for the single-shear single-row bolted connection represented in Figure E2.

Main and Side Members:
#2 grade Hem-Fir lumber. See *NDS Supplement* Table 4A – Visually Graded Dimension Lumber for reference design values. Adjustment factors C_D, C_T, C_M, and C_i are assumed to equal 1.0 in this example for calculation of adjusted design values.

$F_t' = 525 \text{ psi } (C_F) = 525(1.5) = 788$ psi

$F_v' = 150$ psi

Connection Details:
Bolt diameter, D: 1/2 in.
Bolt hole diameter, D_h: 0.5625 in.
Adjusted ASD bolt design value, $Z_{||}'$: 550 lbs (See NDS Table 12A for 3-1/2" main member thickness and 1-1/2" side member thickness. For this trial design, the group action factor, C_g, is taken as 1.0).

Adjusted ASD Connection Capacity, $nZ_{||}'$:

$nZ_{||}' = (3 \text{ bolts})(550 \text{ lbs}) = 1{,}650$ lbs

For side member, adjusted ASD Net Section Area Ten-sion Capacity, Z_{NT}':

$$Z_{NT}' = F_t' t[w - n_{row} D_h]$$

$Z_{NT}' = (788 \text{ psi})(1.5")[3.5" - 1(0.5625")] = 3{,}470$ lbs

Figure E2 Single Row of Bolts

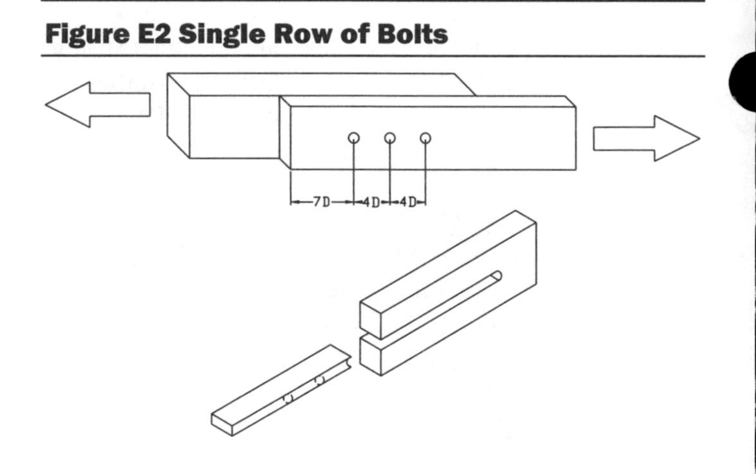

For side member, adjusted ASD Row Tear-Out Capaci-ty, Z_{RT}':

$$Z_{RTi}' = n_i F_v' t s_{critical}$$

$Z_{RT1}' = 3(150 \text{ psi})(1.5")(2") = 1{,}350$ lbs

In this sample calculation, the adjusted ASD connection capacity is limited to 1,350 pounds by row tear-out, Z_{RT}'.

E.8 Sample Solution of Row of Split Rings

Calculate the net section area tension and row tear-out adjusted ASD design capacities for the single-shear single-row split ring connection represented in Figure E3.

Main and Side Members:
#2 grade Southern Pine 2x4 lumber. See *NDS Supplement* Table 4B – Visually Graded Southern Pine Dimension Lumber for reference design values. Adjustment factors C_D, C_T, C_M, and C_i are assumed to equal 1.0 in this example for calculation of adjusted design values.

$F_t' = 675$ psi

$F_v' = 175$ psi

Main member thickness, t_m: 1.5 in.
Side member thickness, t_s: 1.5 in.
Main and side member width, w: 3.5 in.

Connection Details:
Split ring diameter, D: 2.5 in. (see Appendix K for connector dimensions)
Adjusted ASD split ring design value, P′: 2,730 lbs (see Table 13.2A. For this trial design, the group action factor, C_g, is taken as 1.0).

Adjusted ASD Connection Capacity, nP′:

$nP' = $ (2 split rings)(2,730 lbs) = 5,460 lbs

Adjusted ASD Net Section Area Tension Capacity, Z_{NT}':

$$Z_{NT}' = F_t' A_{net}$$

$Z_{NT}' = F_t' [A_{2x4} - A_{bolt\text{-}hole} - A_{split\ ring\ projected\ area}]$

$Z_{NT}' = $ (675 psi)[5.25 in.^{2} – 1.5" (0.5625") – 1.1 in.^{2}]

= 2,232 lbs

Figure E3 Single Row of Split Ring Connectors

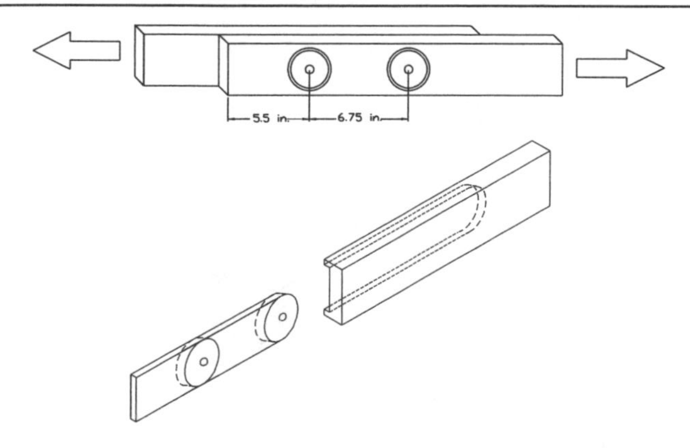

Adjusted ASD Row Tear-Out Capacity, Z_{RT}':

$$Z_{RTi}' = n_i \frac{F_v' A_{critical}}{2}$$

$Z_{RT1}' = $ [(2 connectors)(175 psi)/2](21.735 in.^{2})

= 3,804 lbs

where:

$A_{critical} = 21.735$ in.^{2} (See Figures E4 and E5)

In this sample calculation, the adjusted ASD connection capacity is limited to 2,232 pounds by net section area tension capacity, Z_{NT}'.

Figure E4 $A_{critical}$ for Split Ring Connection (based on distance from end of member)

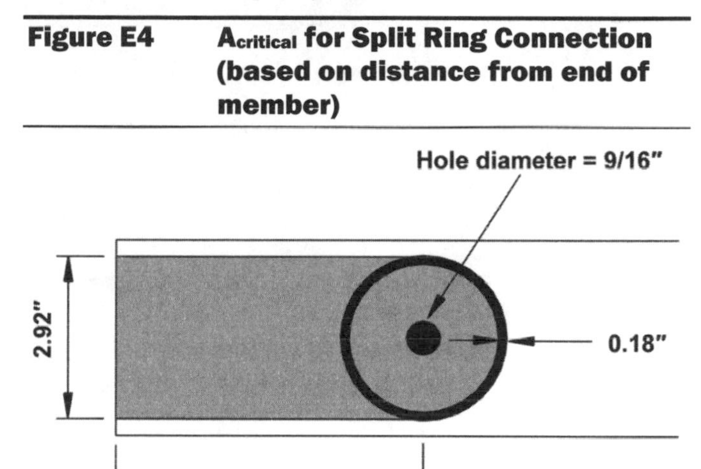

$A_{edge\ plane}$ = (2 shear lines) (groove depth)($s_{critical}$)

= (2 shear lines) (0.375")(5.5") = 4.125 in.^{2}

$A_{bottom\ plane\ net}$ = ($A_{bottom\ plane}$) – ($A_{split\ ring\ groove}$) – ($A_{bolt\ hole}$)

= [(5.5")(2.92") + (π)(2.92")^2/8] – (π/4)[(2.92")^2 – (2.92" – 0.18" – 0.18")^2] – (π/4)(0.5625")^2

= 17.61 in.^{2}

$A_{criticial}$ = $A_{edge\ plane}$ + $A_{bottom\ plane\ net}$

= 21.735 in.^{2}

Figure E5 **$A_{critical}$ for Split Ring Connection (based on distance between first and second split ring)**

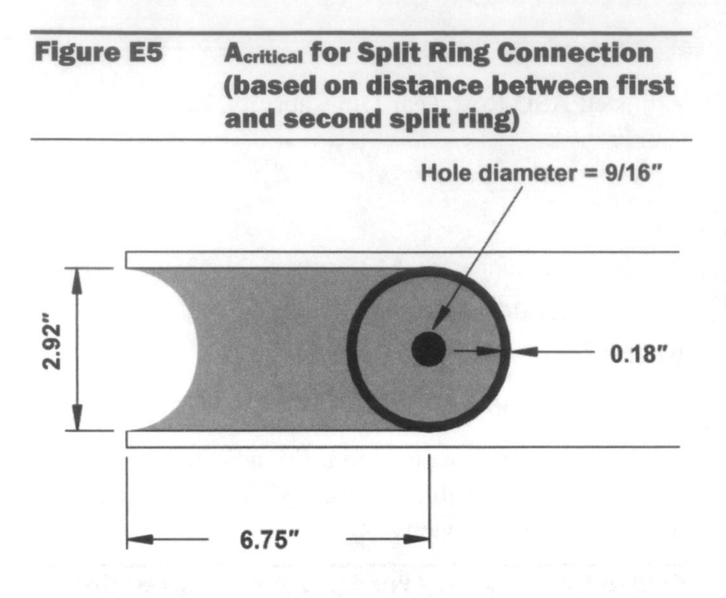

$A_{edge\ plane}$ = (2 shear lines) (groove depth)($s_{critical}$)

= (2 shear lines) (0.375")(6.75") = 5.063 in.^{2}

$A_{bottom\ plane\ net}$ = ($A_{bottom\ plane}$) – ($A_{split\ ring\ groove}$) – ($A_{bolt\ hole}$)

= (6.75")(2.92") - (π/4)[(2.92")^2-(2.92" - 0.18" - 0.18")^2] - (π/4)(0.5625")^2

= 17.91 in.^{2}

$A_{criticial}$ = $A_{edge\ plane}$ + $A_{bottom\ plane\ net}$

= 5.063 + 17.91 in.^{2} = 22.973 in.^{2}

Therefore $A_{critical}$ is governed by the case shown in Figure E4 and is equal to 21.735 in.^{2}

Appendix F (Non-mandatory) Design for Creep and Critical Deflection Applications

F.1 Creep

F.1.1 Reference modulus of elasticity design values, E, in this Specification are intended for the calculation of immediate deformation under load. Under sustained loading, wood members exhibit additional time dependent deformation (creep) which usually develops at a slow but persistent rate over long periods of time. Creep rates are greater for members drying under load or exposed to varying temperature and relative humidity conditions than for members in a stable environment and at constant moisture content.

F.1.2 In certain bending applications, it may be necessary to limit deflection under long-term loading to specified levels. This can be done by applying an increase factor to the deflection due to long-term load. Total deflection is thus calculated as the immediate deflection due to the long-term component of the design load times the appropriate increase factor, plus the deflection due to the short-term or normal component of the design load.

F.2 Variation in Modulus of Elasticity

F.2.1 The reference modulus of elasticity design values, E, listed in Tables 4A, 4B, 4C, 4D, 4E, 4F, 5A, 5B, 5C, and 5D (published in the Supplement to this Specification) are average values and individual pieces having values both higher and lower than the averages will occur in all grades. The use of average modulus of elasticity values is customary practice for the design of normal wood structural members and assemblies. Field experience and tests have demonstrated that average values provide an adequate measure of the immediate deflection or deformation of these wood elements.

F.2.2 In certain applications where deflection may be critical, such as may occur in closely engineered, innovative structural components or systems, use of a reduced modulus of elasticity value may be deemed appropriate by the designer. The coefficient of variation in Table F1 shall be permitted to be used as a basis for modifying reference modulus of elasticity values listed in Tables 4A, 4B, 4C, 4D, 4E, 4F, 5A, 5B, 5C, and 5D to meet particular end use conditions.

F.2.3 Reducing reference average modulus of elasticity design values in this Specification by the product of the average value and 1.0 and 1.65 times the applicable coefficients of variation in Table F1 gives estimates of the level of modulus of elasticity exceeded by 84% and 95%, respectively, of the individual pieces, as specified in the following formulas:

$$E_{0.16} = E\left(1 - 1.0\, COV_E\right) \tag{F-1}$$

$$E_{0.05} = E\left(1 - 1.645\, COV_E\right) \tag{F-2}$$

Table F1 Coefficients of Variation in Modulus of Elasticity (COV_E) for Lumber and Structural Glued Laminated Timber

	COV_E
Visually graded sawn lumber (Tables 4A, 4B, 4D, 4E, and 4F)	0.25
Machine Evaluated Lumber (MEL) (Table 4C)	0.15
Machine Stress Rated (MSR) lumber (Table 4C)	0.11
Structural glued laminated timber (Tables 5A, 5B, 5C, and 5D)	0.10

F.3 Shear Deflection

F.3.1 Reference modulus of elasticity design values, E, listed in Tables 4A, 4B, 4C, 4D, 4E, 4F, 5A, 5B, 5C, and 5D are apparent modulus of elasticity values and include a shear deflection component. For sawn lumber, the ratio of shear-free E to reference E is 1.03. For structural glued laminated timber, the ratio of shear-free E to reference E is 1.05.

F.3.2 In certain applications use of an adjusted modulus of elasticity to more accurately account for the shear component of the total deflection may be deemed appropriate by the designer. Standard methods for adjusting modulus of elasticity to other load and span-depth conditions are available (see Reference 54). When reference modulus of elasticity values have not been adjusted to include the effects of shear deformation, such as for prefabricated wood I-joists, consideration for the shear component of the total deflection is required.

F.3.3 The shear component of the total deflection of a beam is a function of beam geometry, modulus of elasticity, shear modulus, applied load and support conditions. The ratio of shear-free E to apparent E is

1.03 for the condition of a simply supported rectangular beam with uniform load, a span to depth ratio of 21:1, and elastic modulus to shear modulus ratio of 16:1. The ratio of shear-free E to apparent E is 1.05 for a similar beam with a span to depth ratio of 17:1. See Reference 53 for information concerning calculation of beam deflection for other span-depth and load conditions.

Appendix G (Non-mandatory) Effective Column Length

G.1

The effective column length of a compression member is the distance between two points along its length at which the member is assumed to buckle in the shape of a sine wave.

G.2

The effective column length is dependent on the values of end fixity and lateral translation (deflection) associated with the ends of columns and points of lateral support between the ends of column. It is recommended that the effective length of columns be determined in accordance with good engineering practice. Lower values of effective length will be associated with more end fixity and less lateral translation while higher values will be associated with less end fixity and more lateral translation.

G.3

In lieu of calculating the effective column length from available engineering experience and methodology, the buckling length coefficients, K_e, given in Table G1 shall be permitted to be multiplied by the actual column length, ℓ, or by the length of column between lateral supports to calculate the effective column length, ℓ_e.

G.4

Where the bending stiffness of the frame itself provides support against buckling, the buckling length coefficient, K_e, for an unbraced length of column, ℓ, is dependent upon the amount of bending stiffness provided by the other in-plane members entering the connection at each end of the unbraced segment. If the combined stiffness from these members is sufficiently small relative to that of the unbraced column segments, K_e could exceed the values given in Table G1.

Table G1 Buckling Length Coefficients, K_e

Buckling modes	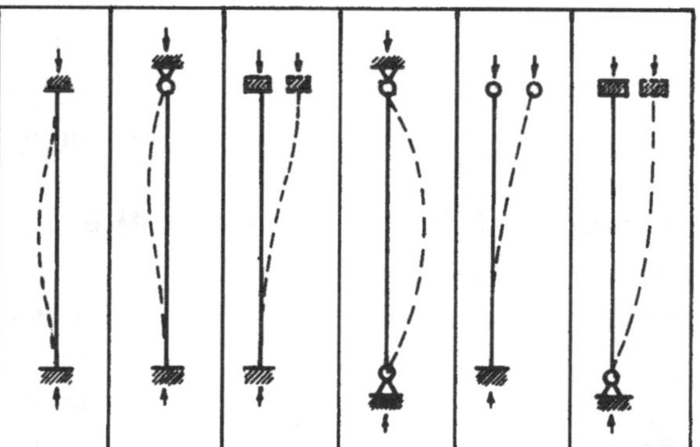 (a)	(b)	(c)	(d)	(e)	(f)
Theoretical K_e value	0.5	0.7	1.0	1.0	2.0	2.0
Recommended design K_e when ideal conditions approximated	0.65	0.80	1.2	1.0	2.10	2.4

End condition code	
(symbol)	Rotation fixed, translation fixed
(symbol)	Rotation free, translation fixed
(symbol)	Rotation fixed, translation free
(symbol)	Rotation free, translation free

Appendix H (Non-mandatory) Lateral Stability of Columns

H.1

Solid wood columns can be classified into three length classes, characterized by mode of failure at ultimate load. For short, rectangular columns with a small ratio of length to least cross-sectional dimension, ℓ_e/d, failure is by crushing. When there is an intermediate ℓ_e/d ratio, failure is generally a combination of crushing and buckling. At large ℓ_e/d ratios, long wood columns behave essentially as Euler columns and fail by lateral deflection or buckling. Design of these three length classes are represented by the single column Equation H-1.

H.2

For solid columns of rectangular cross section where the slenderness ratio, ℓ_e/d, does not exceed 50, adjusted compression design values parallel to grain are obtained by the equation:

$$F_c' = F_c^* \left[\frac{1+(F_{cE}/F_c^*)}{2c} - \sqrt{\left[\frac{1+(F_{cE}/F_c^*)}{2c}\right]^2 - \frac{F_{cE}/F_c^*}{c}} \right] \quad \text{(H-1)}$$

where:

$$F_{cE} = \frac{0.822\, E_{min}'}{(\ell_e/d)^2} \quad \text{(H-2)}$$

F_c^* = reference compression design value parallel to grain multiplied by all applicable adjustment factors except C_P (see 2.3)

c = 0.8 for sawn lumber

c = 0.85 for round timber poles and piles

c = 0.9 for structural glued laminated timber, cross-laminated timber, or structural composite lumber

Equation H-2 is derived from the standard Euler equation, with radius of gyration, r, converted to the more convenient least cross-sectional dimension, d, of a rectangular column.

H.3

The equation for adjusted compression design value, F_c', in this Specification is for columns having rectangular cross sections. It may be used for other column shapes by substituting $r\sqrt{12}$ for d in the equations, where r is the applicable radius of gyration of the column cross section.

H.4

The 0.822 factor in Equation H-2 represents the Euler buckling coefficient for rectangular columns calculated as $\pi^2/12$. Modulus of elasticity for beam and column stability, E_{min}, in Equation H-2 represents an approximate 5% lower exclusion value on pure bending modulus of elasticity, plus a 1.66 factor of safety (see Appendix D.4).

H.5

Adjusted design values based on Equations H-1 and H-2 are customarily used for most sawn lumber column designs. Where unusual hazard exists, a larger reduction factor may be appropriate. Alternatively, in less critical end use, the designer may elect to use a smaller factor of safety.

H.6

For products with less E variability than visually graded sawn lumber, higher critical buckling design values may be calculated. For a product having a lower coefficient of variation (COV_E), use of Equation H-2 will provide a 1.66 factor of safety at the 5% lower exclusion value.

Appendix I (Non-mandatory) Yield Limit Equations for Connections

I.1 Yield Modes

The yield limit equations specified in 12.3.1 for dowel-type fasteners such as bolts, lag screws, wood screws, nails, and spikes represent four primary connection yield modes (see Figure I1). Modes I_m and I_s represent bearing-dominated yield of the wood fibers in contact with the fastener in either the main or side member(s), respectively. Mode II represents pivoting of the fastener at the shear plane of a single shear connection with localized crushing of wood fibers near the faces of the wood member(s). Modes III_m and III_s represent fastener yield in bending at one plastic hinge point per shear plane, and bearing-dominated yield of wood fibers in contact with the fastener in either the main or side member(s), respectively. Mode IV represents fastener yield in bending at two plastic hinge points per shear plane, with limited localized crushing of wood fibers near the shear plane(s).

I.2 Dowel Bearing Strength for Steel Members

Dowel bearing strength, F_e, for steel members shall be based on accepted steel design practices (see References 39, 40 and 41). Design values in Tables 12B, 12D, 12G, 12I, 12K, 12M, 12P, and 12T are for 1/4" ASTM A 36 steel plate or 3 gage and thinner ASTM A 653, Grade 33 steel plate with dowel bearing strength proportional to ultimate tensile strength. Bearing strengths used to calculate connection yield load represent nominal bearing strengths of 2.4 F_u and 2.2 F_u, respectively (based on design provisions in References 39, 40, and 41 for bearing strength of steel members at connections). To allow proper application of the load duration factor for these connections, the bearing strengths have been divided by 1.6.

I.3 Dowel Bearing Strength for Wood Members

Dowel bearing strength, F_e, for wood members may be determined in accordance with ASTM D 5764.

I.4 Fastener Bending Yield Strength, F_{yb}

In the absence of published standards which specify fastener strength properties, the designer should contact fastener manufacturers to determine fastener bending yield strength for connection design. ASTM F 1575 provides a standard method for testing bending yield strength of nails.

Fastener bending yield strength (F_{yb}) shall be determined by the 5% diameter (0.05D) offset method of analyzing load-displacement curves developed from fastener bending tests. However, for short, large diameter fasteners for which direct bending tests are impractical, test data from tension tests such as those specified in ASTM F 606 shall be evaluated to estimate F_{yb}.

Research indicates that F_{yb} for bolts is approximately equivalent to the average of bolt tensile yield strength and bolt tensile ultimate strength, $F_{yb} = F_y/2 + F_u/2$. Based on this approximation, 48,000 psi $\leq F_{yb} \leq$ 140,000 psi for various grades of SAE J429 bolts. Thus, the aforementioned research indicates that F_{yb} = 45,000 psi is reasonable for many commonly available bolts. Tests of limited samples of lag screws indicate that F_{yb} = 45,000 psi is also reasonable for many commonly available lag screws with $D \geq 3/8"$.

Tests of a limited sample of box nails and common wire nails from twelve U.S. nail manufacturers indicate that F_{yb} increases with decreasing nail diameter, and may exceed 100,000 psi for very small diameter nails. These tests indicate that the F_{yb} values used in Tables 12N through 12R are reasonable for many commonly available box nails and small diameter common wire nails ($D < 0.2"$). Design values for large diameter common wire nails ($D > 0.2"$) are based on extrapolated estimates of F_{yb} from the aforementioned limited study. For hardened-steel nails, F_{yb} is assumed to be approximately 30% higher than for the same diameter common wire nails. Design values in Tables 12J through 12M for wood screws and small diameter lag screws ($D < 3/8"$) are based on estimates of F_{yb} for common wire nails of the same diameter. Table I1 provides values of F_{yb} based on fastener type and diameter.

Figure I1 (Non-mandatory) Connection Yield Modes

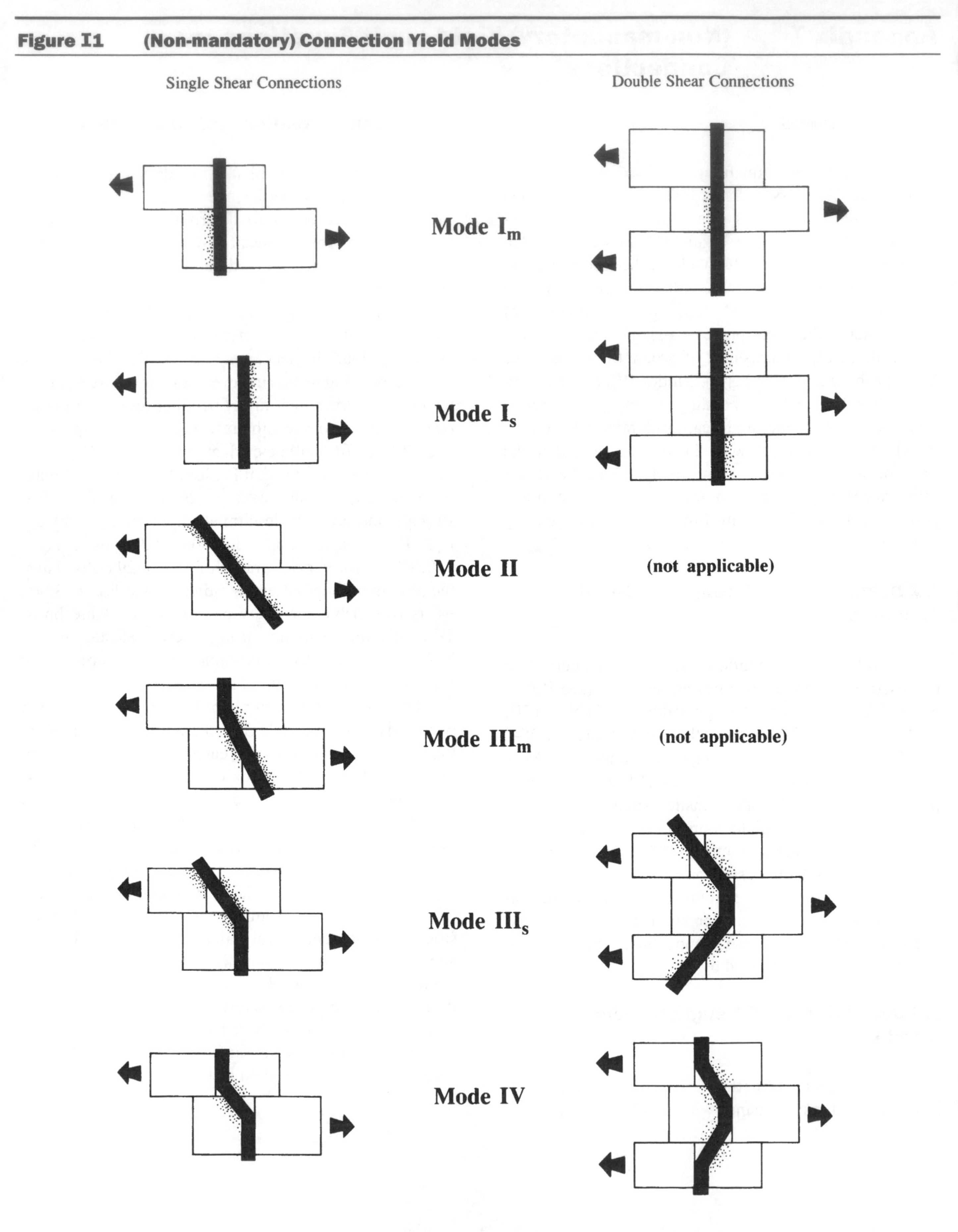

I.5 Threaded Fasteners

The reduced moment resistance in the threaded portion of dowel-type fasteners can be accounted for by use of root diameter, D_r, in calculation of reference lateral design values. Use of diameter, D, is permitted when the threaded portion of the fastener is sufficiently far away from the connection shear plane(s). For example, diameter, D, may be used when the length of thread bearing in the main member of a two member connection does not exceed 1/4 of the total bearing length in the main member (member holding the threads). For a connection with three or more members, diameter, D, may be used when the length of thread bearing in the outermost member does not exceed 1/4 of the total bearing length in the outermost member (member holding the threads).

Reference lateral design values for reduced body diameter lag screw and rolled thread wood screw connections are based on root diameter, D_r to account for the reduced diameter of these fasteners. These values may also be applicable for full-body diameter lag screws and cut thread wood screws since the length of threads for these fasteners is generally not known and/or the thread bearing length based on typical dimensions exceeds 1/4 the total bearing length in the member holding the threads. For bolted connections, reference tabulated lateral design values are based on diameter, D.

One alternate method of accounting for the moment and bearing resistance of the threaded portion of the fastener and moment acting along the length of the fastener is provided in AWC's *Technical Report 12 - General Dowel Equations for Calculating Lateral Connection Values* (see Reference 51). A general set of equations permits use of different fastener diameters for bearing resistance and moment resistance in each member.

Table I1 Fastener Bending Yield Strengths, F_{yb}

Fastener Type	F_{yb} (psi)
Bolt, lag screw (with D ≥ 3/8"), drift pin (SAE J429 Grade 1 - F_y = 36,000 psi and F_u = 60,000 psi)	45,000
Common, box, or sinker nail, spike, lag screw, wood screw (low to medium carbon steel)	
0.099" ≤ D ≤ 0.142"	100,000
0.142" < D ≤ 0.177"	90,000
0.177" < D ≤ 0.236"	80,000
0.236" < D ≤ 0.273"	70,000
0.273" < D ≤ 0.344"	60,000
0.344" < D ≤ 0.375"	45,000
Hardened steel nail (medium carbon steel) including post-frame ring shank nails	
0.120" ≤ D ≤ 0.142"	130,000
0.142" < D ≤ 0.192"	115,000
0.192" < D ≤ 0.207"	100,000

Appendix J (Non-mandatory) Solution of Hankinson Formula

J.1

When members are loaded in bearing at an angle to grain between 0° and 90°, or when split ring or shear plate connectors, bolts, or lag screws are loaded at an angle to grain between 0° and 90°, design values at an angle to grain shall be determined using the Hankinson formula.

J.2

The Hankinson formula is for the condition where the loaded surface is perpendicular to the direction of the applied load.

J.3

When the resultant force is not perpendicular to the surface under consideration, the angle θ is the angle between the direction of grain and the direction of the force component which is perpendicular to the surface.

J.4

The bearing surface for a split ring or shear plate connector, bolt or lag screw is assumed perpendicular to the applied lateral load.

J.5

The bearing strength of wood depends upon the direction of grain with respect to the direction of the applied load. Wood is stronger in compression parallel to grain than in compression perpendicular to grain. The variation in strength at various angles to grain between 0° and 90° shall be determined by the Hankinson formula as follows:

$$F_\theta' = \frac{F_c^* F_{c\perp}'}{F_c^* \sin^2\theta + F_{c\perp}' \cos^2\theta} \qquad \text{(J-1)}$$

where:

F_c^* = adjusted compression design value parallel to grain multiplied by all applicable adjustment factors except the column stability factor

$F_{c\perp}'$ = adjusted compression design value perpendicular to grain

F_θ' = adjusted bearing design value at an angle to grain

θ = angle between direction of load and direction of grain (longitudinal axis of member)

When determining dowel bearing design values at an angle to grain for bolt or lag screw connections, the Hankinson formula takes the following form:

$$F_{e\theta} = \frac{F_{e\parallel} F_{e\perp}}{F_{e\parallel} \sin^2\theta + F_{e\perp} \cos^2\theta} \qquad \text{(J-2)}$$

where:

$F_{e\parallel}$ = dowel bearing strength parallel to grain

$F_{e\perp}$ = dowel bearing strength perpendicular to grain

$F_{e\theta}$ = dowel bearing strength at an angle to grain

When determining adjusted design values for bolt or lag screw wood-to-metal connections or wood-to-wood connections with the main or side member(s) loaded parallel to grain, the following form of the Hankinson formula provides an alternate solution:

$$Z_\theta' = \frac{Z_\parallel' Z_\perp'}{Z_\parallel' \sin^2\theta + Z_\perp' \cos^2\theta} \qquad \text{(J-3)}$$

For wood-to-wood connections with side member(s) loaded parallel to grain,

$Z_\parallel'$ = adjusted lateral design value for a single bolt or lag screw connection with the main and side wood members loaded parallel to grain, $Z_\parallel$

$Z_\perp'$ = adjusted lateral design value for a single bolt or lag screw connection with the side member(s) loaded parallel to grain and main member loaded perpendicular to grain, $Z_{m\perp}$

For wood-to-wood connections with the main member loaded parallel to grain,

$Z_{\parallel}'$ = adjusted lateral design value for a single bolt or lag screw connection with the main and side wood members loaded parallel to grain, $Z_{\parallel}$

$Z_{\perp}'$ = adjusted lateral design value for a single bolt or lag screw connection with the main member loaded parallel to grain and side member(s) loaded perpendicular to grain, $Z_{s\perp}$

For wood-to-metal connections,

$Z_{\parallel}'$ = adjusted lateral design value for a single bolt or lag screw connection with the wood member loaded parallel to grain, $Z_{\parallel}$

$Z_{\perp}'$ = adjusted lateral design value for a single bolt or lag screw connection with the wood member loaded perpendicular to grain, $Z_{\perp}$

When determining adjusted design values for split ring or shear plate connectors or timber rivets, the Hankinson formula takes the following form:

$$N' = \frac{P'Q'}{P'\sin^2\theta + Q'\cos^2\theta} \tag{J-4}$$

where:

P' = adjusted lateral design value parallel to grain for a single split ring connector unit or shear plate connector unit

Q' = adjusted lateral design value perpendicular to grain for a single split ring connector unit or shear plate connector unit

N' = adjusted lateral design value at an angle to grain for a single split ring connector unit or shear plate connector unit

The nomographs presented in Figure J1 provide a graphical solution of the Hankinson formula.

Figure J1 Solution of Hankinson Formula

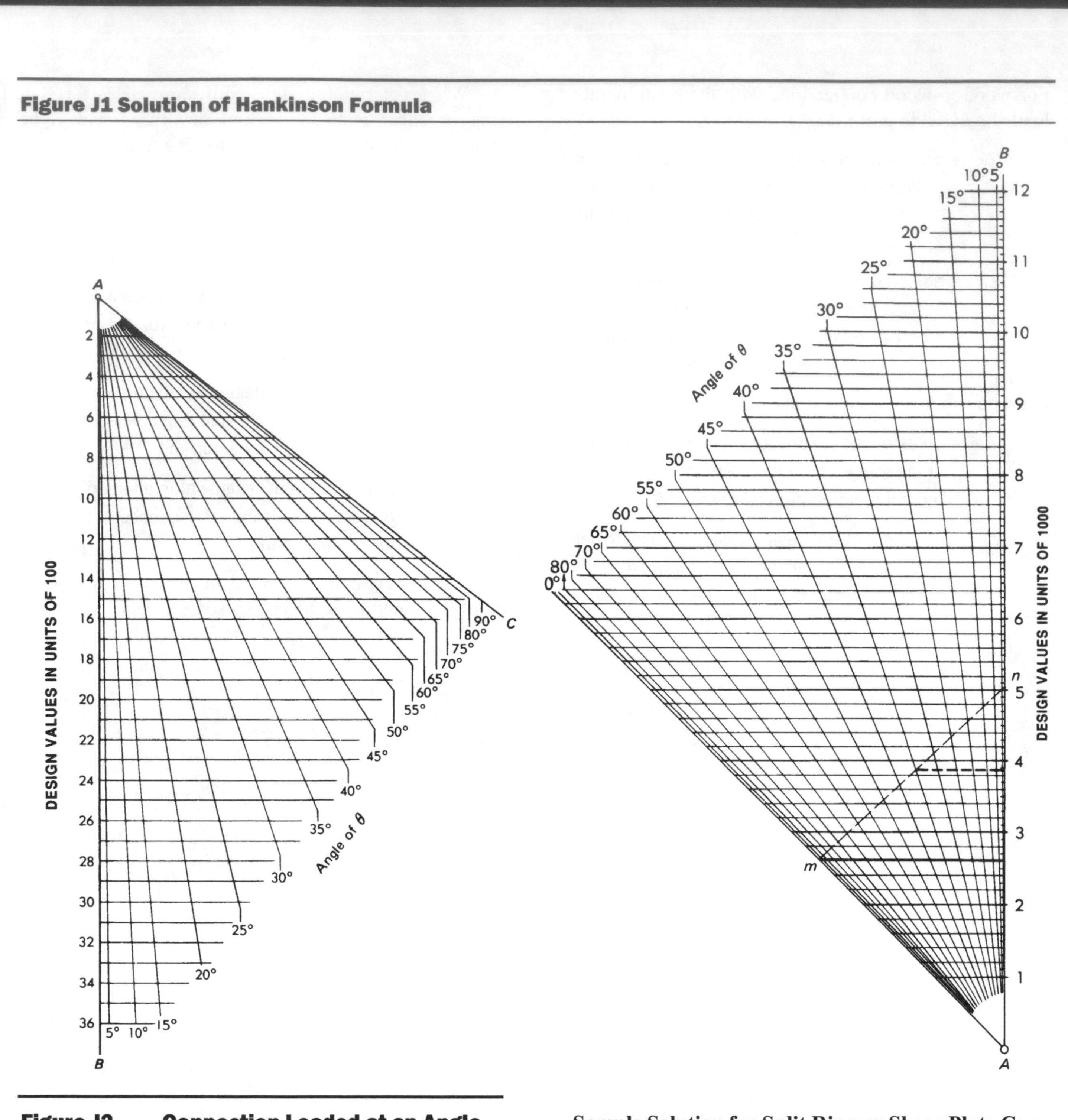

Figure J2 Connection Loaded at an Angle to Grain

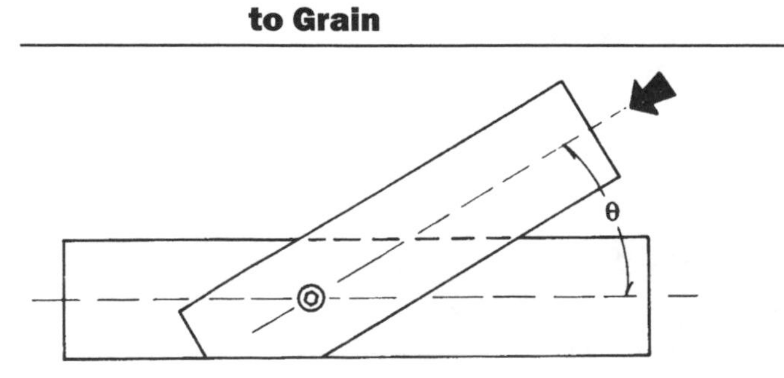

Sample Solution for Split Ring or Shear Plate Connection:

Assume that P' = 5,030 lbs, Q' = 2,620 lbs, and θ = 35° in Figure J2. On line A-B in Figure J1, locate 5,030 lbs at point n. On the same line A-B, locate 2,620 lbs and project to point m on line A-C. Where line m-n intersects the radial line for 35°, project to line A-B and read the ASD adjusted design value, N' = 3,870 lbs.

Appendix K (Non-mandatory) Typical Dimensions for Split Ring and Shear Plate Connectors

SPLIT RINGS[1]	2-1/2"	4"
Split Ring		
Inside diameter at center when closed	2.500"	4.000"
Thickness of metal at center	0.163"	0.193"
Depth of metal (width of ring)	0.750"	1.000"
Groove		
Inside diameter	2.56"	4.08"
Width	0.18"	0.21"
Depth	0.375"	0.50"
Bolt hole diameter in timber members	9/16"	13/16"
Washers, standard		
Round, cast or malleable iron, diameter	2-1/8"	3"
Round, wrought iron (minimum)		
Diameter	1-3/8"	2"
Thickness	3/32"	5/32"
Square plate		
Length of side	2"	3"
Thickness	1/8"	3/16"
Projected area: portion of one split ring within member	1.10 in.^{2}	2.24 in.^{2}

1. Courtesy of Cleveland Steel Specialty Co.

SHEAR PLATES	2-5/8"	2-5/8"	4"	4"
Shear plate[1]	Pressed	Malleable	Malleable	Malleable
Material	steel	cast iron	cast iron	cast iron
Plate diameter	2.62"	2.62"	4.02"	4.02"
Bolt hole diameter	0.81"	0.81"	0.81"	0.93"
Plate thickness	0.172"	0.172"	0.20"	0.20"
Plate depth	0.42"	0.42"	0.62"	0.62"
Bolt hole diameter in timber members and metal side plates[2]	13/16"	13/16"	13/16"	15/16"
Washers, standard				
Round, cast or malleable iron, diameter	3"	3"	3"	3-1/2"
Round, wrought iron (minimum)				
Diameter	2"	2"	2"	2-1/4"
Thickness	5/32"	5/32"	5/32"	11/64"
Square plate				
Length of side	3"	3"	3"	3"
Thickness	1/4"	1/4"	1/4"	1/4"
Projected area: portion of one shear plate within member	1.18 in.^{2}	1.00 in.^{2}	2.58 in.^{2}	2.58 in.^{2}

1. ASTM D 5933.
2. Steel straps or shapes used as metal side plates shall be designed in accordance with accepted metal practices (see 11.2.3).

Appendix L (Non-mandatory) Typical Dimensions for Dowel-Type Fasteners and Washers[1]

Table L1 Standard Hex Bolts[1]

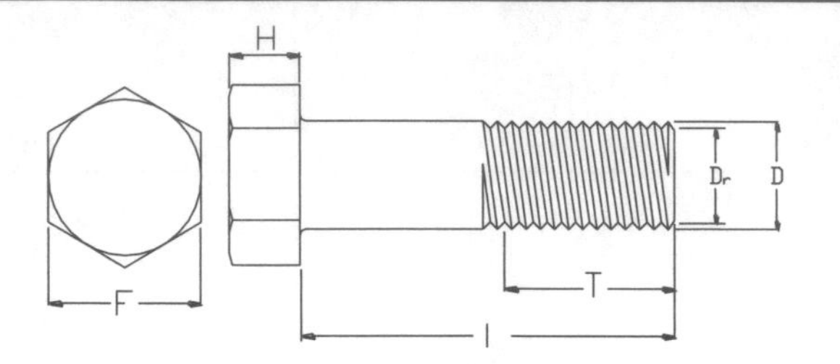

Full-Body
Diameter

D = diameter, in.
D_r = root diameter, in.
T = thread length, in.
L = bolt length, in.
F = width of head across flats, in.
H = height of head, in.

		Diameter, D							
		1/4	**5/16**	**3/8**	**1/2**	**5/8**	**3/4**	**7/8**	**1**
D_r		0.189	0.245	0.298	0.406	0.514	0.627	0.739	0.847
F		7/16	1/2	9/16	3/4	15/16	1-1/8	1-5/16	1-1/2
H		11/64	7/32	1/4	11/32	27/64	1/2	37/64	43/64
T	$L \leq 6$	3/4	7/8	1	1-1/4	1-1/2	1-3/4	2	2-1/4
	$L > 6$	1	1-1/8	1-1/4	1-1/2	1-3/4	2	2-1/4	2-1/2

1. Tolerances are specified in ANSI/ASME B18.2.1. Full-body diameter bolt is shown. Root diameter based on UNC thread series (see ANSI/ASME B1.1).

Table L2 Standard Hex Lag Screws[1]

D = diameter, in.
D_r = root diameter, in.
S = unthreaded body length, in.
T = minimum thread length[2], in.

E = length of tapered tip, in.
L = lag screw length, in.
N = number of threads/inch
F = width of head across flats, in.
H = height of head, in.

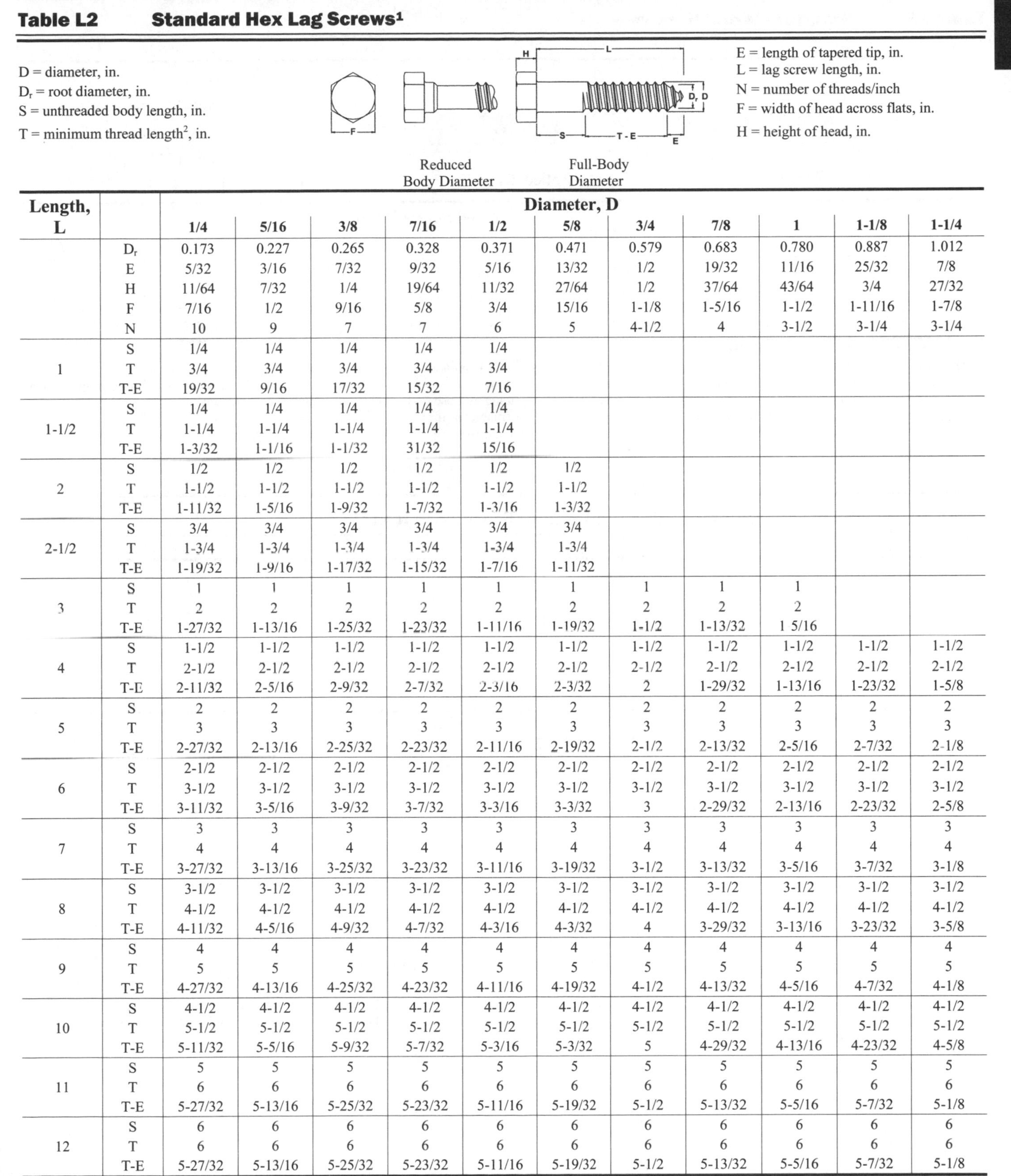

Reduced Body Diameter

Full-Body Diameter

Length, L		Diameter, D										
		1/4	5/16	3/8	7/16	1/2	5/8	3/4	7/8	1	1-1/8	1-1/4
	D_r	0.173	0.227	0.265	0.328	0.371	0.471	0.579	0.683	0.780	0.887	1.012
	E	5/32	3/16	7/32	9/32	5/16	13/32	1/2	19/32	11/16	25/32	7/8
	H	11/64	7/32	1/4	19/64	11/32	27/64	1/2	37/64	43/64	3/4	27/32
	F	7/16	1/2	9/16	5/8	3/4	15/16	1-1/8	1-5/16	1-1/2	1-11/16	1-7/8
	N	10	9	7	7	6	5	4-1/2	4	3-1/2	3-1/4	3-1/4
1	S	1/4	1/4	1/4	1/4	1/4						
	T	3/4	3/4	3/4	3/4	3/4						
	T-E	19/32	9/16	17/32	15/32	7/16						
1-1/2	S	1/4	1/4	1/4	1/4	1/4						
	T	1-1/4	1-1/4	1-1/4	1-1/4	1-1/4						
	T-E	1-3/32	1-1/16	1-1/32	31/32	15/16						
2	S	1/2	1/2	1/2	1/2	1/2	1/2					
	T	1-1/2	1-1/2	1-1/2	1-1/2	1-1/2	1-1/2					
	T-E	1-11/32	1-5/16	1-9/32	1-7/32	1-3/16	1-3/32					
2-1/2	S	3/4	3/4	3/4	3/4	3/4	3/4					
	T	1-3/4	1-3/4	1-3/4	1-3/4	1-3/4	1-3/4					
	T-E	1-19/32	1-9/16	1-17/32	1-15/32	1-7/16	1-11/32					
3	S	1	1	1	1	1	1	1	1	1		
	T	2	2	2	2	2	2	2	2	2		
	T-E	1-27/32	1-13/16	1-25/32	1-23/32	1-11/16	1-19/32	1-1/2	1-13/32	1 5/16		
4	S	1-1/2	1-1/2	1-1/2	1-1/2	1-1/2	1-1/2	1-1/2	1-1/2	1-1/2	1-1/2	1-1/2
	T	2-1/2	2-1/2	2-1/2	2-1/2	2-1/2	2-1/2	2-1/2	2-1/2	2-1/2	2-1/2	2-1/2
	T-E	2-11/32	2-5/16	2-9/32	2-7/32	2-3/16	2-3/32	2	1-29/32	1-13/16	1-23/32	1-5/8
5	S	2	2	2	2	2	2	2	2	2	2	2
	T	3	3	3	3	3	3	3	3	3	3	3
	T-E	2-27/32	2-13/16	2-25/32	2-23/32	2-11/16	2-19/32	2-1/2	2-13/32	2-5/16	2-7/32	2-1/8
6	S	2-1/2	2-1/2	2-1/2	2-1/2	2-1/2	2-1/2	2-1/2	2-1/2	2-1/2	2-1/2	2-1/2
	T	3-1/2	3-1/2	3-1/2	3-1/2	3-1/2	3-1/2	3-1/2	3-1/2	3-1/2	3-1/2	3-1/2
	T-E	3-11/32	3-5/16	3-9/32	3-7/32	3-3/16	3-3/32	3	2-29/32	2-13/16	2-23/32	2-5/8
7	S	3	3	3	3	3	3	3	3	3	3	3
	T	4	4	4	4	4	4	4	4	4	4	4
	T-E	3-27/32	3-13/16	3-25/32	3-23/32	3-11/16	3-19/32	3-1/2	3-13/32	3-5/16	3-7/32	3-1/8
8	S	3-1/2	3-1/2	3-1/2	3-1/2	3-1/2	3-1/2	3-1/2	3-1/2	3-1/2	3-1/2	3-1/2
	T	4-1/2	4-1/2	4-1/2	4-1/2	4-1/2	4-1/2	4-1/2	4-1/2	4-1/2	4-1/2	4-1/2
	T-E	4-11/32	4-5/16	4-9/32	4-7/32	4-3/16	4-3/32	4	3-29/32	3-13/16	3-23/32	3-5/8
9	S	4	4	4	4	4	4	4	4	4	4	4
	T	5	5	5	5	5	5	5	5	5	5	5
	T-E	4-27/32	4-13/16	4-25/32	4-23/32	4-11/16	4-19/32	4-1/2	4-13/32	4-5/16	4-7/32	4-1/8
10	S	4-1/2	4-1/2	4-1/2	4-1/2	4-1/2	4-1/2	4-1/2	4-1/2	4-1/2	4-1/2	4-1/2
	T	5-1/2	5-1/2	5-1/2	5-1/2	5-1/2	5-1/2	5-1/2	5-1/2	5-1/2	5-1/2	5-1/2
	T-E	5-11/32	5-5/16	5-9/32	5-7/32	5-3/16	5-3/32	5	4-29/32	4-13/16	4-23/32	4-5/8
11	S	5	5	5	5	5	5	5	5	5	5	5
	T	6	6	6	6	6	6	6	6	6	6	6
	T-E	5-27/32	5-13/16	5-25/32	5-23/32	5-11/16	5-19/32	5-1/2	5-13/32	5-5/16	5-7/32	5-1/8
12	S	6	6	6	6	6	6	6	6	6	6	6
	T	6	6	6	6	6	6	6	6	6	6	6
	T-E	5-27/32	5-13/16	5-25/32	5-23/32	5-11/16	5-19/32	5-1/2	5-13/32	5-5/16	5-7/32	5-1/8

1. Tolerances are specified in ANSI/ASME B18.2.1. Full-body diameter and reduced body diameter lag screws are shown. For reduced body diameter lag screws, the unthreaded body diameter may be reduced to approximately the root diameter, D_r.
2. Minimum thread length (T) for lag screw lengths (L) is 6 or 1/2 the lag screw length plus 0.5, whichever is less. Thread lengths may exceed these minimums up to the full lag screw length (L).

Table L3 Standard Wood Screws[1,6]

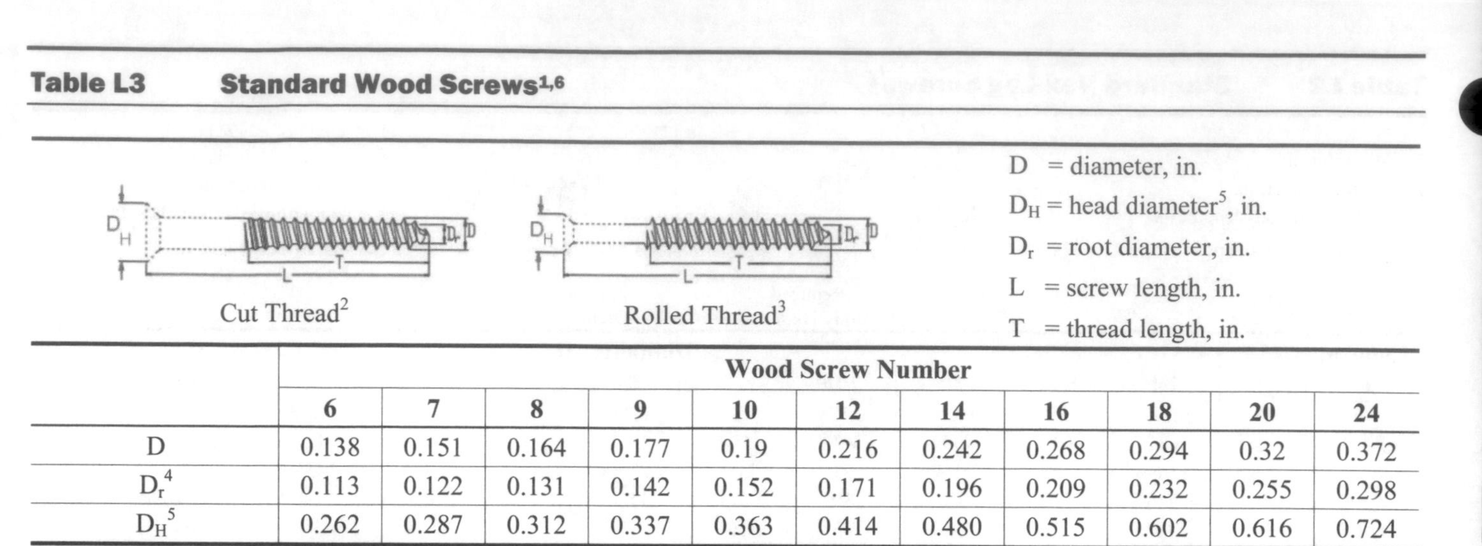

Cut Thread[2]

Rolled Thread[3]

D = diameter, in.
D_H = head diameter[5], in.
D_r = root diameter, in.
L = screw length, in.
T = thread length, in.

	Wood Screw Number										
	6	7	8	9	10	12	14	16	18	20	24
D	0.138	0.151	0.164	0.177	0.19	0.216	0.242	0.268	0.294	0.32	0.372
D_r[4]	0.113	0.122	0.131	0.142	0.152	0.171	0.196	0.209	0.232	0.255	0.298
D_H[5]	0.262	0.287	0.312	0.337	0.363	0.414	0.480	0.515	0.602	0.616	0.724

1. Tolerances specified in ANSI/ASME B18.6.1.
2. Thread length on cut thread wood screws is approximately 2/3 of the wood screw length, L.
3. Single lead thread shown. Thread length is at least four times the screw diameter or 2/3 of the wood screw length, whichever is greater. Wood screws which are too short to accommodate the minimum thread length, have threads extending as close to the underside of the head as practicable.
4. Taken as the average of the specified maximum and minimum limits for body diameter of rolled thread wood screws.
5. Taken as the average of the specified maximum and minimum limits for head diameter.
6. It is permitted to assume the length of the tapered tip is 2D.

Table L4 Standard Common, Box, and Sinker Steel Wire Nails[1,2]

L
H
D

Common or Box

L
H
D

Sinker

D = diameter, in.
L = length, in.
H = head diameter, in.

Type		Pennyweight										
		6d	7d	8d	10d	12d	16d	20d	30d	40d	50d	60d
Common	L	2	2-1/4	2-1/2	3	3-1/4	3-1/2	4	4-1/2	5	5-1/2	6
	D	0.113	0.113	0.131	0.148	0.148	0.162	0.192	0.207	0.225	0.244	0.263
	H	0.266	0.266	0.281	0.312	0.312	0.344	0.406	0.438	0.469	0.5	0.531
Box	L	2	2-1/4	2-1/2	3	3-1/4	3-1/2	4	4-1/2	5		
	D	0.099	0.099	0.113	0.128	0.128	0.135	0.148	0.148	0.162		
	H	0.266	0.266	0.297	0.312	0.312	0.344	0.375	0.375	0.406		
Sinker	L	1-7/8	2-1/8	2-3/8	2-7/8	3-1/8	3-1/4	3-3/4	4-1/4	4-3/4		5-3/4
	D	0.092	0.099	0.113	0.12	0.135	0.148	0.177	0.192	0.207		0.244
	H	0.234	0.250	0.266	0.281	0.312	0.344	0.375	0.406	0.438		0.5

1. Tolerances are specified in ASTM F1667. Typical shape of common, box, and sinker steel wire nails shown. See ASTM F 1667 for other nail types.
2. It is permitted to assume the length of the tapered tip is 2D.

Table L5 Post-Frame Ring Shank Nails[1]

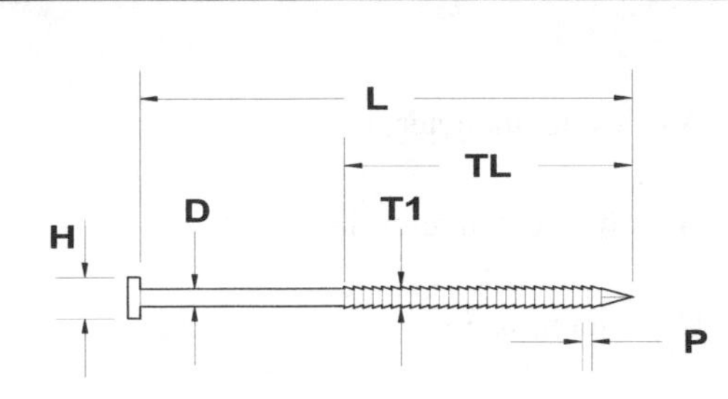

D = diameter, in.
L = length, in.
H = head diameter, in.
TL = minimum length of threaded shank, in.
T1 = crest diameter, in.
$D + 0.005 \text{ in.} \leq T1 \leq D + 0.010 \text{ in.}$
P = pitch or spacing of threads, in.
$0.05 \text{ in.} \leq P \leq 0.077 \text{ in.}$

D	L	TL	H	Root Diameter[2], D_r
0.135	3, 3.5	2.25	5/16	0.128
0.148	3, 3.5, 4	2.25	5/16	0.140
	4.5	3		
0.177	3, 3.5, 4	2.25	3/8	0.169
	4.5, 5, 6, 8	3		
0.200	3.5, 4	2.25	15/32	0.193
	4.5, 5, 6, 8	3		
0.207	4	2.25	15/32	0.199
	4.5, 5, 6, 8	3		

1. Tolerances are specified in ASTM F1667.
2. Root diameter is a calculated value and is not specified as a dimension to be measured.

Table L6 Roof Sheathing Ring Shank Nails[1]

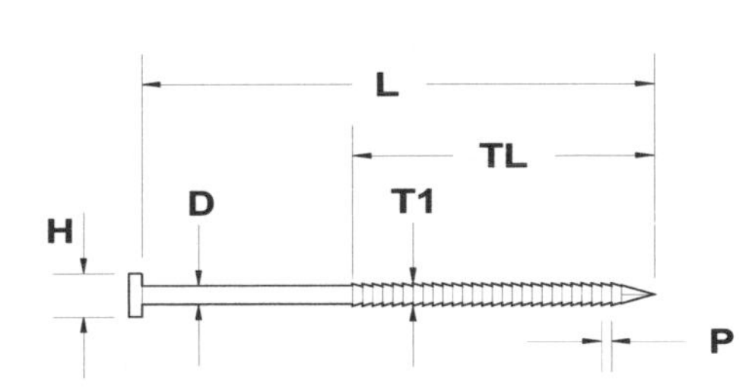

D = diameter, in.
L = length, in.
H = head diameter, in.
TL = minimum length of threaded shank, in.
T1 = crest diameter, in.
$D + 0.005 \text{ in.} \leq T1 \leq D + 0.012 \text{ in.}$
P = pitch or spacing of threads, in.
$0.05 \text{ in.} \leq P \leq 0.077 \text{ in.}$

Dash No.	D	L	TL	H
01	0.113	2-3/8	1-1/2	0.281
02	0.120	2-1/2	1-1/2	0.281
03	0.131	2-1/2	1-1/2	0.281
04	0.120	3	1-1/2	0.281
05	0.131	3	1-1/2	0.281

1. Tolerances are specified in ASTM F1667.

Table L7 Standard Cut Washers[1]

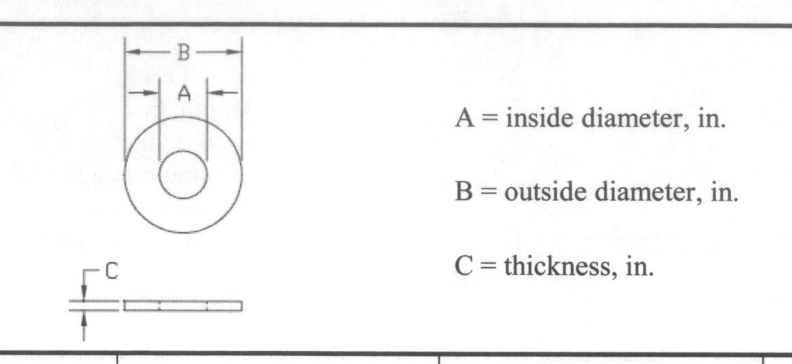

Nominal Washer Size	A Inside Diameter	B Outside Diameter	C Thickness
	Basic	Basic	Basic
3/8	0.438	1.000	0.083
1/2	0.562	1.375	0.109
5/8	0.688	1.750	0.134
3/4	0.812	2.000	0.148
7/8	0.938	2.250	0.165
1	1.062	2.500	0.165

1. Tolerances are provided in ANSI/ASME B18.22.1. For other standard cut washers, see ANSI/ASME B18.22.1.

Appendix M (Non-mandatory) Manufacturing Tolerances for Rivets and Steel Side Plates for Timber Rivet Connections

Rivet dimensions are taken from ASTM F 1667.

Rivet Dimensions

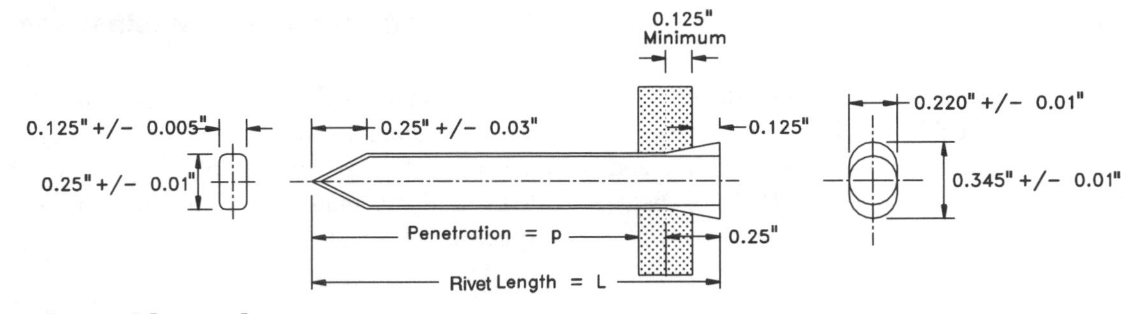

Steel Side Plate Dimensions

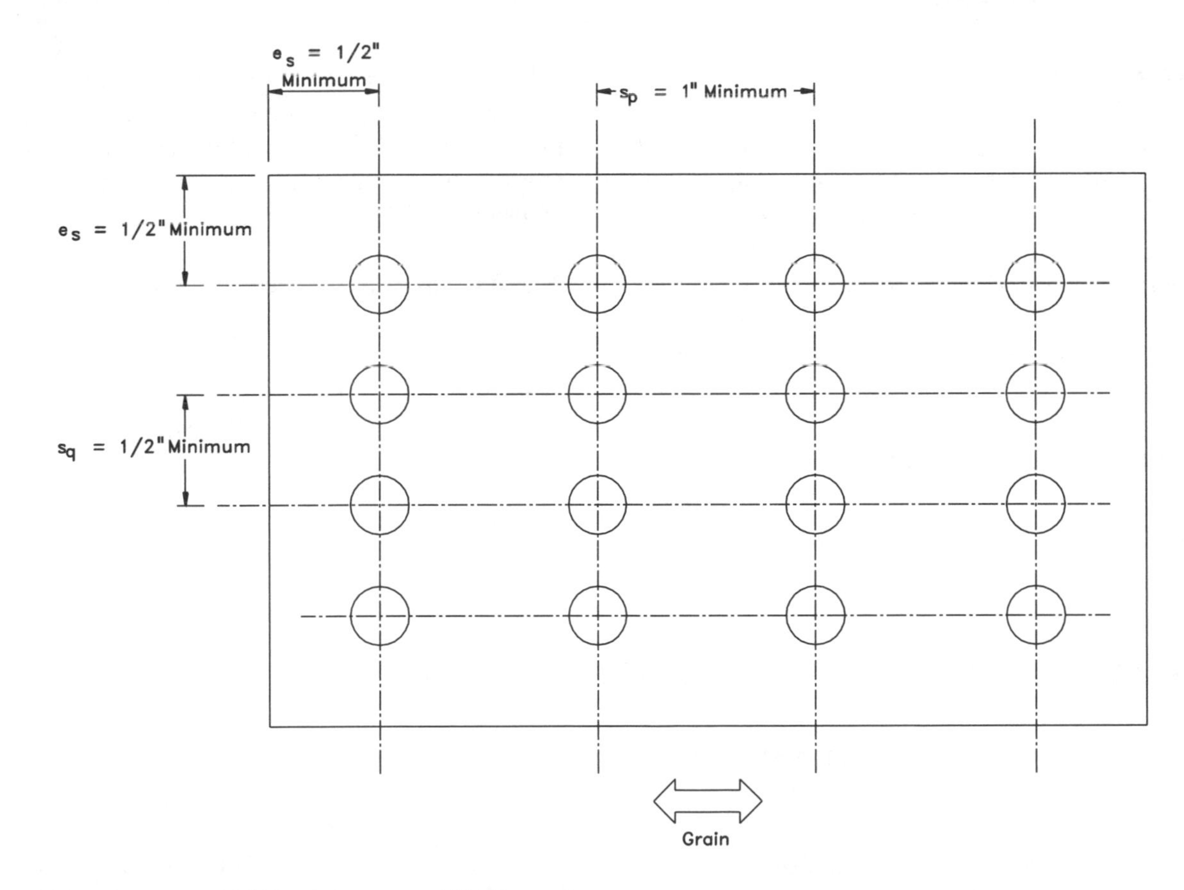

Notes:

1. Hole diameter: 17/64 minimum to 18/64 maximum.
2. Tolerances in location of holes: 1/8 maximum in any direction.
3. All dimensions are prior to galvanizing in inches.
4. s_p and s_q are defined in 14.3.
5. e_s is the end and edge distance as defined by the steel.
6. Orient wide face of rivets parallel to grain, regardless of plate orientation.

Appendix N (Mandatory) Load and Resistance Factor Design (LRFD)

N.1 General

N.1.1 Application

LRFD designs shall be made in accordance with Appendix N and all applicable provisions of this Specification. Applicable loads and load combinations, and adjustment of design values unique to LRFD are specified herein.

N.1.2 Loads and Load Combinations

Nominal loads and load combinations shall be those required by the applicable building code. In the absence of a governing building code, the nominal loads and associated load combinations shall be those specified in ASCE 7.

N.2 Design Values

N.2.1 Design Values

Adjusted LRFD design values for members and connections shall be determined in accordance with ASTM Specification D 5457 and design provisions in this Specification or in accordance with N.2.2 and N.2.3. Where LRFD design values are determined by the reliability normalization factor method in ASTM D 5457, the format conversion factor shall not apply (see N.3.1).

N.2.2 Member Design Values

Reference member design values in this Specification shall be adjusted in accordance with 4.3, 5.3, 6.3, 7.3, 8.3, 9.3, and 10.3 for sawn lumber, structural glued laminated timber, poles and piles, prefabricated wood I-joists, structural composite lumber, panel products, and cross-laminated timber, respectively, to determine the adjusted LRFD design value.

N.2.3 Connection Design Values

Reference connection design values in this Specification shall be adjusted in accordance with Table 11.3.1 to determine the adjusted LRFD design value.

N.3 Adjustment of Reference Design Values

N.3.1 Format Conversion Factor, K_F (LRFD Only)

Reference design values shall be multiplied by the format conversion factor, K_F, as specified in Table N1. Format conversion factors in Table N1 adjust reference ASD design values (based on normal duration) to the LRFD reference resistances (see Reference 55). Format conversion factors shall not apply where LRFD reference resistances are determined in accordance with the reliability normalization factor method in ASTM D 5457.

Table N1 Format Conversion Factor, K_F (LRFD Only)

Application	Property	K_F
Member	F_b	2.54
	F_t	2.70
	F_v, F_{rt} F_s	2.88
	F_c,	2.40
	$F_{c\perp}$	1.67
	E_{min}	1.76
All Connections	(all design values)	3.32

N.3.2 Resistance Factor, ϕ (LRFD Only)

Reference design values shall be multiplied by the resistance factor, ϕ, as specified in Table N2 (see Reference 55).

Table N2 Resistance Factor, ϕ (LRFD Only)

Application	Property	Symbol	Value
Member	F_b	ϕ_b	0.85
	F_t	ϕ_t	0.80
	F_v, F_{rt}, F_s	ϕ_v	0.75
	F_c, $F_{c\perp}$	ϕ_c	0.90
	E_{min}	ϕ_s	0.85
All Connections	(all design values)	ϕ_z	0.65

N.3.3 Time Effect Factor, λ (LRFD Only)

Reference design values shall be multiplied by the time effect factor, λ, as specified in Table N3.

Table N3 Time Effect Factor, λ (LRFD Only)

Load Combination[2]	λ
1.4D	0.6
1.2D + 1.6L + 0.5(L_r or S or R)	0.7 when L is from storage 0.8 when L is from occupancy 1.25 when L is from impact[1]
1.2D + 1.6(L_r or S or R) + (L or 0.5W)	0.8
1.2D + 1.0W + L + 0.5(L_r or S or R)	1.0
1.2D + 1.0E + L + 0.2S	1.0
0.9D + 1.0W	1.0
0.9D + 1.0E	1.0

1. Time effect factors, λ, greater than 1.0 shall not apply to connections or to structural members pressure-treated with water-borne preservatives (see Reference 30) or fire retardant chemicals.
2. Load combinations and load factors consistent with ASCE 7-16 are listed for ease of reference. Nominal loads shall be in accordance with N.1.2. D = dead load; L = live load; L_r = roof live load; S = snow load; R = rain load; W = wind load; and E = earthquake load.

REFERENCES

AMERICAN WOOD COUNCIL

1. ACI 318-14 Building Code Requirements for Structural Concrete, American Concrete Institute, Farmington Hills, MI, 2014.
2. ACI 530/530.1-13 Building Code Requirements and Specification for Masonry Structures and Companion Commentaries, American Concrete Institute, Farmington Hills, MI, 2013.
3. AISI 1035 Standard Steels, American Iron and Steel Institute, Washington, DC, 1985.
4. ANSI A190.1-2017, Standard for Wood Products - Structural Glued Laminated Timber, APA - The Engineered Wood Association, Tacoma, WA. 2017.
5. ASCE/SEI Standard 7-16, Minimum Design Loads for Buildings and Other Structures, American Society of Civil Engineers, Reston, VA, 2016.
6. ANSI/ASME Standard B1.1-2003, Unified Inch Screw Threads UN and UNR Thread Form, American Society of Mechanical Engineers, New York, NY, 2003.
7. ANSI/ASME Standard B18.2.1-2012, Square, Hex, Heavy Hex, and Askew Head Bolts and Hex, Heavy Hex, Hex Flange, Lobed Head, and Lag Screws (Inch Series), American Society of Mechanical Engineers, New York, NY, 2012.
8. ANSI/ASME Standard B18.6.1-1981 (Reaffirmed 1997), Wood Screws (Inch Series), American Society of Mechanical Engineers, New York, NY, 1982.
9. ANSI/TPI 1-2014 National Design Standard for Metal Plate Connected Wood Truss Construction, Truss Plate Institute, 2014.
10. ASTM Standard A 36-08, Standard Specification for Carbon Structural Steel, ASTM, West Conshohocken, PA, 2008.
11. ASTM Standard A 47-99 (2009), Standard Specification for Ferritic Malleable Iron Castings, ASTM, West Conshohocken, PA, 2009.
12. ASTM A 153-09, Standard Specification for Zinc Coating (Hot-Dip) on Iron and Steel Hardware, ASTM, West Conshohocken, PA, 2009.
13. ASTM A 370-11, Standard Test Methods and Definitions for Mechanical Testing of Steel Products, ASTM, West Conshohocken, PA, 2011.
14. ASTM Standard A653-10, Standard Specification for Steel Sheet, Zinc-Coated (Galvanized) or Zinc-Iron Alloy-Coated (Galvannealed) by the Hot-Dip Process, ASTM, West Conshohocken, PA, 2010.
15. ASTM Standard D 25-12 (2012), Standard Specification for Round Timber Piles, ASTM, West Conshohocken, PA, 2012.
16. ASTM Standard D 245-06 (2011), Standard Practice for Establishing Structural Grades and Related Allowable Properties for Visually Graded Lumber, ASTM, West Conshohocken, PA, 2011.
17. ASTM Standard D 1760-01, Pressure Treatment of Timber Products, ASTM, West Conshohocken, PA, 2001.
18. ASTM Standard D 1990-16, Standard Practice for Establishing Allowable Properties for Visually Graded Dimension Lumber from In-Grade Tests of Full-Size Specimens, ASTM, West Conshohocken, PA, 2016.
19. ASTM Standard D 2555-16, Standard Practice for Establishing Clear Wood Strength Values, ASTM, West Conshohocken, PA, 2016.
20. ASTM Standard D 2899-12, Standard Practice for Establishing Allowable Stresses for Round Timber Piles, ASTM, West Conshohocken, PA, 2012.
21. ASTM Standard D 3200-74 (2012), Standard Specification and Test Method for Establishing Recommended Design Stresses for Round Timber Construction Poles, ASTM, West Conshohocken, PA, 2012.
22. ASTM Standard D 3737-12, Standard Practice for Establishing Stresses for Structural Glued Laminated Timber (Glulam), ASTM, West Conshohocken, PA, 2012.
23. ASTM Standard D 5055-16, Standard Specification for Establishing and Monitoring Structural Capacities of Prefabricated Wood I-Joists, ASTM, West Conshohocken, PA, 2016.
24. ASTM Standard D 5456-14b, Standard Specification for Evaluation of Structural Composite Lumber Products, ASTM, West Conshohocken, PA, 2014.
25. ASTM Standard D 5764-97a (2013), Standard Test Method for Evaluating Dowel Bearing Strength of Wood and Wood Based Products, ASTM, West Conshohocken, PA, 2013.

26. ASTM Standard D 5933-96 (2013), Standard Specification for 2-5/8 in. and 4 in. Diameter Metal Shear Plates for Use in Wood Construction, ASTM, West Conshohocken, PA, 2013.

27. ASTM Standard F 606-16, Standard Test Methods for Determining the Mechanical Properties of Externally and Internally Threaded Fasteners, Washers, Direct Tension Indicators, and Rivets, ASTM, West Conshohocken, PA, 2016.

28. ASTM Standard F 1575-03 (2013), Standard Test Method for Determining Bending Yield Moment of Nails, ASTM, West Conshohocken, PA, 2013.

29. ASTM Standard F 1667-17, Standard Specification for Driven Fasteners: Nails, Spikes, and Staples, ASTM, West Conshohocken, PA, 20175.

30. AWPA Book of Standards, American Wood Protection Association, Birmingham, AL, 2011.

31. American Softwood Lumber Standard, Voluntary Product Standard PS 20-15, National Institute of Standards and Technology, U.S. Department of Commerce, 2015.

32. Design/Construction Guide-Diaphragms and Shear Walls, Form L350, APA-The Engineered Wood Association, Tacoma, WA, 2007.

33. Engineered Wood Construction Guide, Form E30, APA-The Engineered Wood Association, Tacoma, WA, 2007.

34. Plywood Design Specification and Supplements, Form Y510, APA-The Engineered Wood Association, Tacoma, WA, 1998.

35. PS1-09, Structural Plywood, United States Department of Commerce, National Institute of Standards and Technology, Gaithersburg, MD, 2009.

36. PS2-10, Performance Standard for Wood-Based Structural-Use Panels, U.S. Department of Commerce, National Institute of Standards and Technology, Gaithersburg, MD, 2011.

37. SAE J412, General Characteristics and Heat Treatment of Steels, Society of Automotive Engineers, Warrendale, PA, 1995.

38. SAE J429, Mechanical and Material Requirements for Externally Threaded Fasteners, Society of Automotive Engineers, Warrendale, PA, 1999.

39. Specification for Structural Joints Using High-Strength Bolts, Research Council on Structural Connections, Chicago, IL, 2009.

40. Specification for Structural Steel Buildings (ANSI/AISC 360-10), American Institute of Steel Construction (AISC), Chicago, IL, 2010.

41. North American Standard for Cold-Formed Steel Framing, American Iron and Steel Institute (AISI), Washington, DC, 2007.

42. Standard Grading Rules for Canadian Lumber, National Lumber Grades Authority (NLGA), Surrey, BC, Canada, 2014.

43. Standard Grading Rules for Northeastern Lumber, Northeastern Lumber Manufacturers Association (NELMA), Cumberland Center, ME, 2013.

44. Standard Grading Rules, Northern Softwood Lumber Bureau (NSLB), Cumberland Center, ME, 2007.

45. Standard Grading Rules for Southern Pine Lumber, Southern Pine Inspection Bureau (SPIB), Pensacola, FL, 2014.

46. Standard Grading Rules for West Coast Lumber, West Coast Lumber Inspection Bureau (WCLIB), Portland, OR, 2004.

47. Standard Specifications for Grades of California Redwood Lumber, Redwood Inspection Service (RIS), Novato, CA, 2000.

48. Standard Specifications for Highway Bridges, American Association of State Highway and Transportation Officials (AASHTO), Washington, DC, 2002.

49. Western Lumber Grading Rules, Western Wood Products Association (WWPA), Portland, OR, 2017.

50. Design Manual for TECO Timber Connectors Construction, TECO/Lumberlok, Colliers, WV, 1973.

51. Technical Report 12 General Dowel Equations for Calculating Lateral Connection Values, American Wood Council (AWC), Washington, DC, 2014.

52. Timber Construction Manual, American Institute of Timber Construction (AITC), John Wiley & Sons, 2012.

53. Wood Handbook: Wood as an Engineering Material, General Technical Report FPL-GTR-190, Forest Products Laboratory, U.S. Department of Agriculture, 2010.

54. ASTM Standard D 2915-10, Practice for Sampling and Data Analysis for Structural Wood and Wood Based Products, ASTM West Conshohocken, PA, 2010.

55. ASTM Standard D 5457-15, Standard Specification for Computing the Reference Resistance of Wood-Based Materials and Structural Connections for Load and Resistance Factor Design, ASTM, West Conshohocken, PA, 2015.

56. ANSI/AWC SDPWS-2015, Special Design Provisions for Wind and Seismic, American Wood Council, Leesburg, VA, 2014.

57. ANSI/APA PRG 320-2017, Standard for Performance-Rated Cross-Laminated Timber, APA-The Engineered Wood Association, Tacoma, WA, 2017.

FOREWORD TO THE NDS COMMENTARY

The *National Design Specification® for Wood Construction (NDS®)* was first issued in 1944 as the *National Design Specification for Stress-Grade Lumber and Its Fastenings*. In 1977 the title of the Specification was changed to its present form. The 2015 edition is the sixteenth edition of the publication.

The Commentary presented herein is intended to respond to user needs for background information and interpretive discussion of the provisions of the Specification. The Commentary follows the same subject matter organization as the Specification itself. Discussion of a particular provision in the Specification is identified in the Commentary by the same section or subsection number assigned to that provision in the Specification. The Commentary on each provision addressed consists of one or more of the following: background, interpretation, and example. Information presented under background is intended to give the reader an understanding of the data and/or experience on which the provision is based. References containing more detailed information on the subject are included. Interpretive discussion of how a provision should be applied is given where users have suggested the intent of a requirement is ambiguous.

It is intended that this NDS Commentary be used in conjunction with competent engineering design, accurate fabrication, and adequate supervision of construction. AWC does not assume any responsibility for errors or omissions in the document, nor for engineering designs, plans, or construction prepared from it. Particular attention is directed to Section C2.1.2, relating to the designer's responsibility to make adjustments for particular end uses of structures.

Those using this document assume all liability arising from its use. The design of engineered structures is within the scope of expertise of licensed engineers, architects, or other licensed professionals for applications to a particular structure.

Inquiries, comments, and suggestions from the readers of this document are invited.

American Wood Council

C1 GENERAL REQUIREMENTS FOR STRUCTURAL DESIGN

C1.1 Scope

C1.1.1 Practice Defined

C1.1.1.1 This Specification defines a national standard of practice for the structural design of wood elements and their connections.

C1.1.1.2 Where the structural performance of assemblies utilizing panel products are dependent upon the capacity of the connections between the materials, such as in shear walls or diaphragms, the design provisions for mechanical connections in the Specification may be used for such assemblies when such application is based on accepted engineering practice or when experience has demonstrated such application provides for satisfactory performance in service.

C1.1.1.3 Requirements for the design of structural assemblies utilizing metal connector plates in accordance with principles of engineering mechanics were moved from the mechanical connections chapter to NDS 1.1.1.3 in the 2012 edition of the Specification in recognition of the scope of the referenced ANSI/TPI standard for design of metal plate-connected wood truss construction which includes more than design of the metal connector plates alone. This relocation was also coordinated with removal of metal connector plate requirements from the Specification, such as applicability of adjustment factors and the wet service factor, because they were redundant with those in the ANSI/TPI standard. It is the intent of this section to require design of structural assemblies utilizing metal connector plates in accordance with principles of engineering mechanics such as those addressed in the ANSI/TPI standard for design of metal plate connected wood truss construction.

C1.1.1.5 The data and engineering judgments on which the Specification are founded are based on principles of engineering mechanics and satisfactory performance in service. However, they are not intended to preclude the use of other products or design procedures where it can be demonstrated that these products or design procedures provide for satisfactory performance in the intended application. Other criteria for demonstrating satisfactory performance may be proprietary or specialized design standards applicable to a particular component type. The appropriateness and acceptability of alternate criteria are determined by the designer and the code authority having jurisdiction.

C1.1.2 Competent Supervision

There are several areas in which competent supervision should be required such as joint details and placement of fasteners. Special attention should be given to end details of columns and beam-columns to assure that design assumptions related to load eccentricity are met.

C1.2 General Requirements

C1.2.1 Conformance with Standards

The provisions of this Specification assume conformance with the standards specified.

C1.2.2 Framing and Bracing

Unless otherwise specified in the Specification, all reference design values assume that members are adequately framed, anchored, tied and braced. Adequate bracing and anchorage of trusses and truss members to assure appropriate resistance to lateral loads is particularly important. Good practice recommendations (142) for installation between trusses of vertical sway (cross) bracing, continuous horizontal bottom chord struts and bottom chord cross bracing are given in NDS Appendix A.10.

In addition to providing adequate permanent bracing and bridging in the structure to resist wind and other racking forces, sufficient temporary bracing of load-carrying members should be used during construction to assure such members will withstand wind and temporary construction loads before adjacent members and cladding materials required by the design are installed.

C1.3 Standard as a Whole

The provisions of this Specification are intended to be used together. Unless otherwise noted, pertinent provisions from each chapter apply to every other chapter.

C1.4 Design Procedures

The Specification addresses both allowable stress design (ASD) and load and resistance factor design (LRFD) formats for design with wood structural members and their connections. In general, design of elements throughout a structure will utilize either the ASD or LRFD format; however, specific requirements to use a single design format for all elements within a structure are not included in this Specification. The suitability of mixing formats within a structure is the responsibility of the designer. Consideration should be given to building code limitations, where available. *ASCE 7 – Minimum Design Loads for Buildings and Other Structures* (3), referenced in building codes, limits mixing of design formats to cases where there are changes in materials.

C1.4.1 Loading Assumptions

The design provisions in the Specification assume adequacy of specified design loads.

C1.4.2 Governed by Codes

Design loads shall be based on the building code or other recognized minimum design loads such as ASCE 7 - *Minimum Design Loads and Associated Criteria for Buildings and Other Structures* (3).

C1.4.3 Loads Included

This section identifies types of loads to consider in design but is not intended to provide a comprehensive list of required loading considerations.

C1.4.4 Load Combinations

The reduced probability of the simultaneous occurrence of combinations of various loads on a structure, such as dead, live, wind, snow and earthquake, is recognized for both ASD and LRFD in the model building codes and ASCE 7(3). Specific load reductions for ASD or load combinations for LRFD apply when multiple transient loads act simultaneously.

For ASD, some codes provide for a reduction in design load for wind or earthquake even when both are not considered to act simultaneously. This particular load reduction is accounted for in such codes by allowing all materials a 1/3 increase in allowable stress for these loading conditions. Because individual jurisdictions and code regions may account for load combinations differently, the building code governing the structural design should be consulted to determine the proper method.

All modifications for load combinations are entirely separate from adjustments for load duration, C_D, or time effect, λ, which are directly applicable to wood design values (see C2.3.2 and C2.3.7). It should be emphasized that reduction of design loads to account for the probability of simultaneous occurrence of loads and the adjustment of wood resistances to account for the effect of the duration of the applied loads are independent of each other and both adjustments are applicable in the design calculation.

C1.5 Specifications and Plans

C1.5.1 Sizes

To assure that the building is constructed of members with the capacity and stiffness intended by the designer, the basis of the sizes of wood products given in the plans and specifications should be clearly referenced in these documents. The use of nominal dimensions in the distribution and sale of lumber and panel products has been a source of confusion to some designers, particularly those unfamiliar with wood structural design practices. The standard nominal sizes and the standard net sizes for sawn lumber are established for each product in national product standards (152). For proprietary or made-to-order products, special sizes should be specified.

C1.6 Notation

The system of notation used in the Specification helps to identify the meaning of certain frequently used symbols. Adjustment factors, identified by the symbol "C", modify reference design values for conditions of use, geometry, or stability. The subscripts "D", "F", "L", etc., are used to distinguish between different adjustment factors. In certain cases, upper and lower case subscripts of the same letter ("D" and "d") are used to denote two different adjustments (load duration factor and penetration depth factor for split ring and shear plate connections, respectively). There is no particular significance to the use of the same letter with different cases for different adjustment factors. The symbols "F" and "F'" denote reference and adjusted design values, respectively; where adjusted design values represent reference design values multiplied by all applicable adjustment factors. The symbol "f" indicates the actual or induced stress caused by the applied loads. The subscripts "b", "t", "c", "v", and "c⊥" indicate bending, tension parallel to grain, compression parallel to grain, shear, and compression perpendicular to grain stress, respectively.

C2 DESIGN VALUES FOR STRUCTURAL MEMBERS

C2.1 General

C2.1.1 General Requirement

The Specification addresses both ASD and LRFD formats for structural design with wood products (see C1.4).

C2.1.2 Responsibility of Designer to Adjust for Conditions of Use

The Specification identifies adjustments to reference design values for service conditions generally encountered in wood construction. However, this Specification does not address all possible design applications or end use conditions.

The designer has the final responsibility for determining the proper adjustment of design values for specific loading and end use conditions. Particular attention is required to those uses where two or more extreme conditions of service converge. An example of such a use is one where it is known that the full design load will be applied continuously and the structural members will be consistently exposed to water at elevated temperatures. Assessment of the consequences of a failure of an individual member in the structure is an integral part of the designer's responsibility of relating design assumptions with design value adjustments appropriate to the end use conditions.

C2.2 Reference Design Values

Reference design values used in this Specification and tabulated in the NDS Supplement are ASD values based on normal load duration and moisture conditions specified.

C2.3 Adjustment of Reference Design Values

C2.3.1 Applicability of Adjustment Factors

The Specification requires adjustment of reference design values for specific conditions of use, geometry and stability. Such modifications are made through application of adjustment factors. The adjustment factors are cumulative except where indicated otherwise. In addition to the adjustment factors given in this section, other adjustments of reference design values for special conditions of use may be required. Such additional adjustments may include modifications for creep effects, variability in modulus of elasticity, and fire retardant treatment.

Each product chapter of the Specification provides a unique table to identify the applicability of adjustment factors for determining design values for sawn lumber, structural glued laminated timber, structural composite lumber, prefabricated wood I-joists, and wood structural panels. The approach of adjusting a reference value in accordance with the applicable adjustment factors to arrive at either an ASD or LRFD adjusted design value is illustrated in the following example for sawn lumber bending stress, F_b:

ASD: $F_b' = F_b(C_D)(C_M)(C_t)(C_L)(C_F)(C_{fu})(C_i)(C_r)$

LRFD: $F_b' = F_b(C_M)(C_t)(C_L)(C_F)(C_{fu})(C_i)(C_r)(2.54)(0.85)(\lambda)$

where:

F_b = Reference bending design value, psi

C_D = Load duration factor applicable for ASD only

$(C_M)(C_t)(C_L)(C_F)(C_{fu})(C_i)(C_r)$ = Adjustment factors from NDS 4.3 and Table 4.3.1

2.54 = Format conversion factor, K_F, from Table 4.3.1 applicable for LRFD only

0.85 = Resistance factor, ϕ, from Table 4.3.1 applicable for LRFD only

λ = Time effect factor, applicable for LRFD only

C2.3.2 Load Duration Factor, C_D (ASD Only)

C2.3.2.1 Load duration factors (C_D) are applicable to all reference design values except modulus of elasticity and compression perpendicular to grain. Exclusion of modulus of elasticity from load duration adjustment has been a provision of the Specification since the first edition. Load duration factors are based on the effect of time under load on ultimate load-carrying capacity. Increased deflection or deformation is a separate consideration, independent of ultimate strength. Compression perpendicular to grain design values were subject to adjustment for load duration when such values were based on proportional limit test values. For compression perpendicular to grain design values that are based on a deformation limit, the load duration factor does not apply.

Table 2.3.2 Frequently Used Load Duration Factors, C_D

Permanent Loads. In addition to construction dead loads due to materials, foundation soil loads and concentrated loads from equipment designed as part of the structure should be considered long-term loads that will be applied continuously or cumulatively for more than ten years. Special continuous loadings related to the particular purpose or use of the structure, such as water loads in cooling towers or heavy machinery in industrial buildings, also may be associated with durations exceeding ten years.

Ten Year or Normal Loading. Loads traditionally characterized as normal are code specified floor loads, either uniform live or concentrated, which include furniture, furnishings, movable appliances and equipment, all types of storage loads, and all people loads. Although maximum human traffic loads may be infrequent and of short duration, such as those occurring on balconies, exterior walkways and stairways, this type of loading is considered normal loading.

Two Month Loads. A two month load duration adjustment factor of 1.15 was used for all code specified snow loads prior to 1986. Maximum snow loads published in ASCE 7 (3) based on probability of occurrence are significantly greater in some high snow regions than the loads previously used in those areas. Evaluation of annual snow load records available for some of these areas shows that the duration of the maximum snow load specified in ASCE 7 is much shorter than the two months duration previously assumed for all snow loads. The Specification provides for use of a larger snow load adjustment than 1.15 when information is available on the duration of the design snow load for a specific area.

Seven Day Loads. Where the minimum roof uniform load specified by the applicable building code exceeds the design snow load for the area and the specific building design, it is conventional practice to consider this load a construction type load for which a seven day or 1.25 load duration factor is applicable. If the roof snow load is less than 92 percent of the minimum roof load specified, the latter will be the limiting of the two load conditions.

One Day Loads. Prior to 1987, a one day or 1.33 factor was used as the load duration adjustment for wind and earthquake loads. In the current Specification, the load duration factor for these loads has been based on a 10 minute load duration.

Ten Minute Loads. The ten minute or 1.6 load duration factor is to be used with wind and earthquake loads in the current Specification. For allowable stress design (ASD), wind loads in the model building codes and ASCE 7 are maximum loads expected to occur less than once in 50 years and to have durations of from one to 10 seconds. Peak earthquake loads are known to have cumulative durations less than 5 minutes rather than the one day duration traditionally assigned. The ten minute load duration factor is conservatively estimated as the adjustment for the cumulative effect of these two load conditions.

Impact Loads. Loads in this category are considered to be those in which the load duration is one second or less. Such a duration is associated with an adjustment factor of 2.0 based on the general relationship between strength and load duration (see NDS Appendix B). Pressure treatment of wood with preservatives or fire retardant chemicals may reduce energy absorbing capacity as measured by work-to-maximum-load in bending; therefore, use of the 2.0 load duration factor in these applications is not permitted (173). Connections or wood structural panels are also not permitted to use the 2.0 load duration factor.

C2.3.2.2 Design of structural members is based on the critical combination of loads representing different durations and resistances adjusted for these different durations. Note that load duration adjustments are not applicable to modulus of elasticity (see C2.3.2.1), hence, a member subject to buckling should be analyzed for the critical load combination after the critical buckling design value has been calculated.

C2.3.2.3 Reduction of design loads to account for the probability of simultaneous occurrence of loads and the adjustment of wood resistances to account for the effect of the duration of the applied loads are independent of each other and both adjustments are applicable in the design calculation (see C1.4.4).

C2.3.3 Temperature Factor, C_t

Temperature adjustments in the Specification apply when structural members are exposed to temperatures between 100°F and 150°F for extended periods of time, such as in industrial applications in which structural members are in close proximity to or in contact with heated fluids used in manufacturing processes. In general, adjustment of reference design values in the Specification for temperature should be considered for applications involving sustained heavy dead or equipment loads, or water immersion, or wet or high moisture content service conditions, when sustained or frequent extended exposure to elevated temperatures up to 150°F will occur.

Use of lumber or glued-laminated timber members in applications involving prolonged exposure to temperatures over 150°F should be avoided. Where such exposures do occur, adjustments for both immediate and permanent strength reductions should be made. Permanent effects should be based on the cumulative time the members will be exposed to temperature levels over 150°F during the life of the structure and the strength losses associated with these levels (183). Roof systems and other assemblies subject to diurnal temperature fluctuations from solar radiation are not applications that normally require adjustment of reference design values for temperature.

Reversible Effects at or Below 150°F. The increase in the strength properties of wood when cooled below normal temperatures and the decrease in these properties when it is heated up to 150°F are immediate and generally reversible. When the temperature of the wood returns to normal temperature levels, it recovers its original properties. In general, these reversible effects are linear with temperature for a given moisture content (51). The magnitude of the increase or decrease, however, varies with moisture content. The higher the moisture content, the larger the increase in wood strength properties with decreasing temperature and the larger the decrease in wood strength properties with increasing temperature.

Permanent Effects Over 150°F. Prolonged exposure to temperatures over 150°F can cause a permanent loss in strength when cooled and tested at normal temperatures. The permanent effect is in addition to the immediate or reversible effect that occurs at the exposure temperature. Permanent losses in strength resulting from exposures over 212°F are greater for heating in steam than in water (183). For temperatures over 150°F, permanent decreases in strength are greater for heating in water than in dry air.

The use of 150°F as a nominal threshold for the beginning of permanent strength loss is substantiated by available test data showing an approximate 10 percent loss in bending strength (modulus of rupture) for material exposed for 300 days in water at 150°F and then tested at room temperature (183). Exposure in air at the same temperature would result in a smaller permanent strength loss.

Cold Temperatures. Adjustments for increasing reference design values for cooling below normal temperatures are difficult to establish in building design because of the variable nature of low temperature environments. Structural members that might be exposed to below freezing temperatures continuously for up to several months also are exposed to normal temperatures during periods of the year when the full design load might be resisted. For special applications such as arctic construction or transportation of cryogenic materials where the design load is always associated with low temperature environments, data from other sources may be used to make appropriate adjustments of design values (183, 51).

Elevated Temperatures Encountered in Normal Service. Temperatures higher than ambient can be reached in roof systems as a result of solar radiation. The temperatures reached in such systems are a function of many variables, including hour of day, season of year, cloud cover, wind speed, color of roofing, orientation, ventilation rate, presence of insulation and thickness of sheathing. Measurements of roof system temperatures in actual buildings (64) show that structural framing members in such roofs seldom if ever reach a temperature of 150°F, and when such levels are reached the duration is very short and is confined to the face of the member on which the sheathing is attached. Even in the severest of radiation and design conditions, the temperature of structural beams, rafters, and truss members in wood roofs generally do not reach 140°F. Normal temperature environments return as the sun sets.

The foregoing considerations and successful field experience are the basis for the long standing practice of applying the reference design values tabulated in the Specification without adjustment for temperature to structural wood roof members in systems designed to meet building code ventilation requirements. Reference design values also are appropriate for use with wood members directly exposed to solar radiation but otherwise surrounded by ambient air, such as members used in bridges, exterior balconies and stairways, and exterior vertical and horizontal structural framing.

C2.3.4 Fire Retardant Treatment

Fire retardant treatments are proprietary and chemical formulations vary between manufacturers. The fire retardant treatment manufacturers have established design values for wood products treated with their commercial formulations. It should be noted that use of individual company design value recommendations for fire retardant treated wood products is subject to approval of the authority having jurisdiction.

C2.3.5 Format Conversion Factor, K_f (LRFD Only)

Format conversion factors convert reference design values (allowable stress design values based on normal load duration) to *LRFD reference resistances* as described in ASTM D5457 (17). Specified format conversion factors, K_F, in NDS Table 2.3.5 and Applicability of Adjustment Factor Tables in Chapters 4, 5, 6, 7, 8, 9, and 10 and Appendix Table N1 are based on similar factors contained in ASTM D5457.

The *LRFD reference resistance* is a strength level design value for short term loading conditions. Consequently, the format conversion factor includes: 1) a conversion factor to adjust an allowable design value to a higher strength-level design value, 2) a conversion factor to adjust from a 10-year to a 10-minute (short-term) load basis, and 3) a conversion factor to adjust for a specified resistance factor, ϕ.

The term, *LRFD reference resistance,* is not specifically defined or calculated in the Specification but is included as part of the LRFD adjusted design value which includes all applicable adjustments to the reference design value. Because format conversion factors are based on calibrating ASD and LRFD formats for certain reference conditions, they apply only to reference design values in this Specification and should not apply where LRFD reference resistances are determined in accordance with the reliability normalization factor method in ASTM D5457.

To be consistent with ASD, which does not adjust compression perpendicular to grain stresses for duration of load and to parallel changes in ASTM D5457, the format conversion factor, K_F, for compression perpendicular to grain was changed from 2.08 to 1.67 in the 2012 edition of the Specification and the adjustment for time effect was removed. Also, beginning with the 2012 edition of the Specification, the numeric value of the format conversion factor, K_F, for each material property is tabulated in lieu of the equation format of K_F (i.e., K_F = constant/ϕ) used in prior editions of the Specification.

C2.3.6 Resistance Factor, ϕ (LRFD Only)

Specified resistance factors, ϕ, in NDS Table 2.3.6 and Appendix N, Table N2 are based on resistance factors defined in ASTM D5457 (17). Resistance factors are assigned to various wood properties with only one factor assigned to each stress mode (i.e., bending, shear, compression, tension, and stability). In general, the magnitude of the resistance factor is considered to, in part, reflect relative variability of wood product properties. Actual differences in product variability are accounted for in the derivation of reference design values.

C2.3.7 Time Effect Factor, λ (LRFD Only)

The time effect factor, λ (LRFD counterpart to the ASD load duration factor, C_D), varies by load combination and is intended to establish a consistent target reliability index for load scenarios represented by applicable load combinations. With the exception of the load combination for dead load only, each load combination can be viewed as addressing load scenarios involving peak values of one or more "primary" loads in combination with other transient loads. Specific time effect factors for various *ASCE 7* (3) load combinations are largely dependent on the magnitude, duration, and variation of the primary load in each combination. For example, a time-effect factor of 0.8 is associated with the load combination 1.2D + 1.6 (L_r or S or R) + (L or 0.8W) to account for the duration and variation of the primary loads in that combination (roof live, snow, or rain water, or ice loads). The effect of transient loads in a particular load combination or even changes in the load factors within a given combination is considered to be small relative to the effect of the primary load on the load duration response of the wood. Consequently, specific time-effect factors need not change to address load factor or load combination changes over time. Footnote 2 of NDS Table N3 provides clarification that the specific load factors shown are for reference only and are intended to provide flexibility in assignment of the time effect factor in the event of changes to specified load factors.

C3 DESIGN PROVISIONS AND EQUATIONS

C3.1 General

C3.1.1 Scope

This Chapter provides general design provisions for structural wood members and connections. Product-specific adjustments to these provisions are included in product Chapters 4 through 9 of the Specification. Specific connection design provisions are addressed in NDS Chapters 11 through 14.

C3.1.2 Net Section Area

C3.1.2.1 These provisions direct the designer to take into account the effects of removing material from the cross-sectional area. Specific provisions pertaining to notches in bending members are given in NDS 3.2.3. Provisions for calculation of shear strength in notched bending members are given in NDS 3.4.3. For compression parallel to grain, NDS 3.6.3 provides for the use of gross section area when the reduced section of a column does not occur in the critical part of the length that is most subject to potential buckling.

C3.1.2.2 To avoid possible misapplication when non-uniform patterns are used, the provision requires staggered or offset fasteners in adjacent rows to be considered in the same critical section if the parallel to grain distance between them is less than 4 diameters.

C3.1.2.3 Where the parallel to grain distance between staggered split ring or shear plate connectors is less than or equal to one diameter, they should be considered to occur in the same critical section and used to determine net area. The limit should be applied to the parallel to grain offset or stagger of split rings or shear plates in adjacent rows.

C3.1.3 Connections

Particular attention should be given to the design of joints involving multiple fasteners and to those subject to moment forces. Only fastener types having the same general load-slip or stiffness characteristics should be employed in the same joint (see C11.1.4).

The provisions are intended to ensure each member in the joint carries its portion of the design load and that symmetrical members and fasteners are used unless the induced moments are taken into account. A lapped joint is an example of an unsymmetrical connection where the induced bending moments need to be considered.

C3.1.4 Time Dependent Deformations

Consideration of time dependent deformations in built-up members should provide for equal inelastic deformation of the components. One application addressed by this section is the use of a flange member to strengthen or stiffen a single main member in a truss without increasing the size of other members in the same plane (142). Because component connections in these built-up systems do not provide full composite action, judgment must be used to establish the level of contribution of these components and the time dependent effects on these connections. Member creep effects should also be considered in making this assessment.

C3.1.5 Composite Construction

Structural composites of lumber and other materials utilize the characteristics of each to obtain desirable structural efficiencies and/or extended service life. Timber-concrete bridge decks, timber-steel flitch beams and plywood-lumber stress-skin panels and box beams are such composites. Proven design procedures for timber-concrete beams and timber-steel members are available in wood engineering handbooks and textbooks (58, 142). Detailed design and fabrication information for plywood-lumber structural components are available from APA-The Engineered Wood Association (106). The American Institute of Timber Construction provides design information for composites involving glued laminated timber (140).

C3.2 Bending Members - General

C3.2.1 Span of Bending Members

The design span length for simple, continuous, and cantilevered bending members is defined as the clear span plus one-half the required bearing length at each reaction to avoid unrealistic moment determinations where supports are wider than the required bearing.

C3.2.2 Lateral Distribution of Concentrated Load

Lateral distribution of concentrated loads to adjacent parallel bending members can be estimated using accepted engineering practice (see C15.1).

C3.2.3 Notches

C3.2.3.1 Notches are a special problem in bending members due to the stress concentrations occurring at the corners and the difficulty of calculating the effects of shear and perpendicular to grain stresses occurring at such locations. These stress concentrations can be reduced by using gradually tapered rather than square corner notches (181).

C3.2.3.2 A notch having a depth of up to 1/6 the bending member depth and a length up to 1/3 the bending member depth is assumed to have little practical effect on bending member stiffness (184, 181).

C3.3 Bending Members - Flexure

C3.3.3 Beam Stability Factor, C_L

The beam stability factor, C_L, adjusts the reference bending design value for the effects of lateral-torsional buckling. Lateral-torsional buckling is a limit state where beam deformation includes in-plane deformation, out-of-plane deformation and twisting. The load causing lateral instability is called the elastic lateral-torsional buckling load and is influenced by many factors such as loading and support conditions, member cross-section, and unbraced length. In the 2012 and prior editions of the Specification, the limit state of lateral torsional buckling is addressed using an effective length format whereby unbraced lengths are adjusted to account for load and support conditions that influence the lateral-torsional buckling load. Another common format uses an equivalent moment factor to account for these conditions. AWC Technical Report 14 (138) describes the basis of the current effective length approach used in the NDS and summarizes the equivalent moment factor approach and provides a comparison between the two approaches.

It is common to assume buckling is not an issue in designing load-bearing beams used as headers over openings. However, long span header beams of slender cross-sections demand particular attention to stability issues. An example would be dropped garage door headers in which the load is transferred into the beam through a cripple wall that does not provide lateral support to the beam. In this instance, raising the beam in the wall and attaching it directly to the top plate which is braced by a horizontal floor or ceiling diaphragm can be assumed to provide effective lateral support. Alternatively, the beam can be braced at points of bearing and designed as an unbraced member in accordance with NDS 3.3.3.

C3.3.3.1 For rectangular members, lateral-torsional buckling does not occur where the breadth of the bending member is equal to or greater than the depth and the load is applied in the plane of the member depth (184, 60). Note that lateral-torsional buckling does not occur in circular members.

C3.3.3.2 The rules for determining lateral support requirements based on depth to breadth ratios for sawn lumber bending members given in NDS 4.4.1 are alternate provisions to those of NDS 3.3.3. Specific span and loading conditions may be checked to compare the relative restrictiveness of the respective provisions.

C3.3.3.3 When the compression edge of a bending member is continuously supported along its length and bearing points are restrained against rotation and lateral displacement, lateral-torsional buckling under loads inducing compressive stresses in the supported edge are generally not a concern. However, the possibility of stress reversal, such as that associated with wind loading, should be considered to assure that the tension side of the bending member under the predominant loading case is adequately supported to carry any expected compressive forces. Also, bending members with large depth to breadth ratios should be braced on the tension edges.

C3.3.3.4 Where load is applied to the compression edge of a bending member using uniformly-spaced purlins that are adequately attached to the compression edge, the unsupported length, ℓ_u, of the bending member is the distance between purlins (61). The bending member must also be braced at points of bearing. Consistent with the intent of NDS 3.3.3.4, the nonmandatory phrase "and/or lateral displacement" was removed and does not appear in 2012 and later editions of the Specification because the requirement to "prevent rotation" at points of bearing is not optional and prevention of lateral displacement does not necessarily prevent rotation.

C3.3.3.5 Formulas are provided for determining the effective span length, ℓ_e, from the unsupported length, ℓ_u, for different loading and support conditions (138). The ℓ_e values for small span-to-depth ratios, $\ell_u/d < 7$ are limited to address unrealistically large ℓ_e values that otherwise would be calculated for these short, deep bending members (60).

The constants in the formulas for effective length in NDS Table 3.3.3 include a 15 percent increase in ℓ_u to account for the possibility of imperfect torsional restraint at lateral supports. The formulas given in the table are applicable where loads are applied to the compression edge of the bending member, the most conservative loading case. Formulas given in the footnote for load conditions not covered by the formulas in the body of the table represent the most limiting formula for the ℓ_u/d range from those given for specified load conditions. For more information on the derivation of these formulas, see *TR14* (138).

C3.3.3.6 The beam slenderness ratio, R_B, is comparable to the slenderness ratio for solid columns, ℓ_e/d, in terms of its effect on bending member design strength.

C3.3.3.7 Limiting the beam slenderness ratio, R_B, to a maximum value of 50 is a good practice recommendation intended to preclude design of bending members with high buckling potential. This limit parallels the limit on slenderness ratio for columns, ℓ_e/d (60).

C3.3.3.8 The beam stability factor equation is applicable to all beam slenderness ratios (R_B). This equation provides a means of combining the bending design stress (F_b^*) with the critical buckling design stress (F_{bE}) to estimate an "effective" bending design value. The volume factor, C_V, shall be included in the calculation of F_b^* when C_V is greater than 1.0 which can be the case for SCL per Section 8.3.6.

C3.3.3.10 See C3.9.2 on biaxial bending.

C

COMMENTARY: DESIGN PROVISIONS AND EQUATIONS

C3.4 Bending Members - Shear

C3.4.1 Strength in Shear Parallel to Grain (Horizontal Shear)

C3.4.1.1 Shear strength perpendicular to the grain, also referred to as cross-grain or vertical shear, refers to shear stresses in the radial-tangential plane tending to cut the wood fibers perpendicular to their long axis. The strength of wood in this plane is very high relative to shear strength parallel to grain, or horizontal shear, which refers to shear stresses in the longitudinal-radial or longitudinal-tangential plane tending to slide one fiber past another along their long axes. As both parallel and perpendicular to grain shear occur simultaneously, parallel to grain shear strength is always the limiting case. Therefore, reference shear design values, F_v, are horizontal or parallel to grain shear stresses.

Shear in the tangential-longitudinal or radial-longitudinal plane tending to roll one fiber over another perpendicular to their long axes is termed rolling shear. Rolling shear, which occurs in structural plywood applications as shear in the plane of the plies, is not a design consideration in most lumber or timber product applications.

C3.4.1.2 Shear design provisions in NDS 3.4 are limited to solid flexural members such as sawn lumber, structural glued laminated timber, structural composite lumber, and mechanically laminated timber. Built-up components, such as trusses, are specifically excluded because of field experience that indicated the procedures might not be adequate for shear design of top-hung parallel chord trusses and similar components that contained load-bearing web and top chord connections near points of support. Shear design of built-up components is required to be based on testing, theoretical analysis, and/or documented experience due to the complexity of determining the effects of stress concentrations, the influence of embedded metal connectors, and questions regarding the applicability of the general practice of ignoring loads close to supports.

C3.4.2 Shear Design Equations

Actual shear stress parallel to grain, f_v, in a circular bending member may be determined as:

$$f_v = 4V / 3A \qquad \text{(C3.4.2-1)}$$

where:

V = shear force, lbs

A = cross-sectional area of circular member, in.

For cross-laminated timber, the reference design shear, V_r, is provided by the CLT manufacturer and is designated in NDS Chapter 10 as $F_s(Ib/Q)_{eff}$.

C3.4.3 Shear Design

C3.4.3.1 (a) For purposes of calculating shear forces, ignoring uniform loads within a distance equal to the bending member depth, "d", of the support face assumes such loads are carried directly to the support by diagonal compression through the member depth. Concentrated loads within a distance "d" may be reduced proportionally to the distance from the face of the support. Where a member is loaded with a series of closely-spaced framing members (such as a girder loaded by floor joists), a uniform load condition may be assumed even though the framing members can be viewed as individual point loads.

C3.4.3.1 (b) Placement of the critical moving load is assumed to be one beam depth from the support. Other loads within a distance, d, of the support are permitted to be ignored similar to the provisions of NDS 3.4.3.1(a).

C3.4.3.1 (c) Placement of two or more moving loads should be evaluated to determine the location that provides the maximum shear stress. Other loads within a distance, d, of the support are permitted to be ignored similar to the provisions of NDS 3.4.3.1(a).

C3.4.3.2 (a) The equation for determining the adjusted design shear of a tension-side notched member reduces the effective shear capacity by the square of the ratio of the remaining member depth (d_n) to the unnotched member depth (d). This relationship has been verified by tests of bending members at various depths (115) and is related to the concentration of tension and shear stresses occurring at the reentrant corner of the notch. Both d and d_n are measured perpendicular to the length of the member where member length is represented by the longitudinal axis of the member. Therefore, for a sloped member such as a roof rafter, d and d_n are measured as the distance perpendicular to the rafter's longitudinal axis, not the horizontal projected length of the rafter.

C3.4.3.2 (b) The equation for calculating the adjusted shear in members of circular cross section end-notched on the tension face parallels that for end-notched rectangular bending members. The area of the circular member (A_n) at the notch replaces the width (b) and depth at the notch (d_n) in the equation for the rectangular beam. It has been shown that maximum shear stresses near the neutral axis of an unnotched circular member calculated using (VQ)/(Ib), *or* (4V)/(3A), are within 5 percent of actual stresses (108). Therefore, the adjusted design shear of a tension-side notched circular member is conservatively estimated using the factor 2/3 rather than 3/4 in the equation.

C3.4.3.2 (c) Procedures used to calculate the adjusted shear in bending members of other than rectangular or circular cross section containing end notches on the tension face should account for any effects of stress concentrations that may occur at reentrant corners.

C3.4.3.2 (d) See C3.2.3.1.

C3.4.3.2 (e) Shear strength of bending members is less affected by end notches on the compression face than on the tension face (181).

C3.4.3.3 The shear force, V, is the shear in the beam determined as a result of structural analysis of the bending member for all loads including those imparted by connections (as shown in Figures 3E and 3I in the NDS). It is not the load applied at the connection which can be either less than or greater than the actual shear in the beam.

C3.4.3.3 (a) An equation for calculating the shear resistance at connections located less than five times the depth of the member from its end is similar to that for end-notched rectangular bending members where the ratio d_e/d is comparable to the factor d_n/d.

C3.4.3.3 (b) For connections that are at least five times the member depth from the end, net section is permitted to be used for calculating the shear resistance.

C3.4.3.3 (c) Bending members supported by concealed or partially hidden hangers whose installation involves kerfing or notching of the member are designed for shear using the notched bending member provisions of NDS 3.4.3.2.

C3.5 Bending Members - Deflection

C3.5.1 Deflection Calculations

Reference modulus of elasticity design values, E, in the Specification for wood bending members are average values. Individual pieces will have modulus of elasticity values higher or lower than the reference average value.

For solid rectangular and circular bending members, reference modulus of elasticity values are considered to contain a shear deflection component equivalent to that occurring in a rectangular bending member on a span-depth ratio of between 17 and 21 under uniformly distributed load. Assuming a modulus of elasticity to modulus of rigidity ratio (E/G) of 16, shear-free modulus of elasticity may be taken as 1.03 and 1.05 times the reference value for sawn lumber and glued laminated timber, respectively. Standard methods for adjusting modulus of elasticity to other load and span-depth conditions are available (4).

Experience has shown that use of average modulus of elasticity values provide an adequate measure of the immediate deflection of bending members used in normal wood structural applications. It should be noted that the reduced modulus of elasticity value, E_{min}, is used in beam stability analyses and contains both a statistical and a safety level reduction.

C3.5.2 Long Term Loading

The reference modulus of elasticity values provide a measure of the immediate deflection of a member that occurs when a load is applied. If the load is sustained, the member will exhibit a slow but continual increase in deflection over time, otherwise known as creep. At moderate to low levels of sustained stress and under stable environmental conditions, the rate of creep will decrease over time (52, 62).

Where creep is decreasing over time, total creep occurring in a specific period of time is approximately proportional to the stress level (123, 185). Total bending creep increases with increase in moisture content (34, 139) and temperature (112); and is greater under variable compared to constant relative humidity conditions (112). Creep deflection that is increasing at a constant rate should be considered a possible danger signal; and when creep deflection is increasing at an increasing rate, imminent failure is indicated (8, 139, 185).

Code specified maximum wind, snow, and live loads are pulse type loadings with low frequency of occurrence. Thus creep deflection is not a significant factor in most situations. Where dead loads or sustained live loads represent a relatively high percentage of the total design load, creep may be a design consideration. In such situations, total deflection from long-term loading, Δ_T, is estimated by increasing the immediate deflection, Δ_{LT}, associated with the long-term load component by the time dependent deformation factor, K_{cr}, provided in the Specification.

C3.6 Compression Members - General

C3.6.2 Column Classifications

C3.6.2.1 Simple solid columns are defined as single piece members or those made of pieces glued together to form a single member. Such glued members are considered to have the grain of all component pieces oriented in the same direction and to be made with a phenolic, resorcinol, or other rigid adhesive. The performance of columns made using elastomeric adhesives are not covered by the provisions of the Specification except where it has been established that the adhesive being used possesses strength and creep properties comparable to those of standard rigid adhesives.

C3.6.2.2 Design provisions for spaced columns are covered in NDS 15.2.

C3.6.2.3 Mechanically-laminated built-up columns are not designed as solid columns. Design provisions for these built-up columns are covered in NDS 15.3.

C3.6.3 Strength in Compression Parallel to Grain

In reduced section members, the actual compression stress parallel to grain, f_c, shall be checked as follows:

1. When the reduced section occurs in the critical buckling zone, the net section area shall be used to calculate $f_{c(net)}$, and $f_{c(net)} \leq F_c'$.
2. When the reduced section occurs outside the critical buckling zone, the gross section area shall be used to calculate $f_{c(gross)}$ and $f_{c(gross)} \leq F_c'$. In addition, the net section area shall be used to check for crushing, $f_{c(net)} \leq F_c^*$.

C3.6.4 Compression Members Bearing End to End

Compression design values parallel to grain (F_c^*) are applicable for bearing stresses occurring at the ends of compression members. See C3.10.1.

C3.6.5 Eccentric Loading or Combined Stresses

See C3.9 and C15.4.

C3.6.6 Column Bracing

Column bracing should be designed using accepted engineering practice. Design of bracing systems is beyond the scope of the Specification; however, prescriptive recommendations are provided in Appendix A.

C3.6.7 Lateral Support of Arches, Studs, and Compression Chords of Trusses

Where roof joists or purlins are used between arches or compression chords, the column stability factor, C_P, should be calculated using the larger of:

(i) the slenderness ratio, ℓ_{e1}/d_1, based on distance between points of lateral support and the depth of the arch or chord (NDS Figure 3F).

(ii) the slenderness ratio, ℓ_{e2}/d_2, based on the distance between purlins or joists and the breadth of the arch or chord (NDS Figure 3F).

When continuous decking or sheathing is attached to the top of the arch or compression chord, it is common practice to assume that the slenderness ratio is the length between points of lateral support divided by the depth of the arch or chord, ℓ_{e1}/d_1.

Use of the depth of the stud as the least dimension in calculating the slenderness ratio in determining the axial load-carrying capacity of sheathed or clad light-frame wall systems is a long standing practice. Experience has shown that wood structural panels, fiberboard, hardboard, gypsumboard, or other sheathing materials provide adequate lateral support of the stud across its thickness when properly fastened.

C3.7 Solid Columns

C3.7.1 Column Stability Factor, C_P

C3.7.1.2 In general, the effective length of a column is the distance between points of support that prevent lateral displacement of the member in the plane of buckling. It is common practice in wood construction to assume most column end conditions to be pin connected (translation fixed, rotation free) even though in many cases some partial rotational fixity is present. Where the end conditions in the plane of buckling are significantly different from the pinned assumption, recommended coefficients, K_e, for adjustment of column lengths are provided in Appendix G of the Specification.

As shown in Table G1 of NDS Appendix G, the recommended coefficients are larger than the theoretical values for all cases where rotational restraint of one or both ends of the column is assumed. This conservatism is introduced in recognition that full fixity is generally not realized in practice. The recommended values of K_e are the same as those used in steel design (125) except for the sixth case (rotation and translation fixed one end, rotation free and translation fixed other end) where a more conservative coefficient (20 percent larger than the theoretical value) is specified based on the ratio of theoretical/recommended value in the third case.

C3.7.1.4 The limitation on the slenderness ratio of solid columns to 50 precludes the use of column designs susceptible to potential buckling. The ℓ_e/d limit of 50 is comparable to the $K\ell/r$ limit of 200 (ℓ_e/d of 58) used in steel design (125).

Allowing a temporary ℓ_e/d ratio of 75 during construction is based on satisfactory experience with temporary bracing of trusses installed in accordance with truss industry standards (148); recognition that in most cases the assembly will carry only dead loads until load distributing and racking resisting sheathing elements are installed; and experience with a similar provision in steel design. In the latter regard, a $K\ell/r$ limit of 300 (ℓ_e/d of 87) is permitted during construction with cold-formed steel structural members (126). The critical buckling design load of a column with an ℓ_e/d ratio of 75 is approximately 45 percent that of a column with an equivalent cross-section and an ℓ_e/d ratio of 50.

C3.7.1.5 The column stability factor equation is applicable to all column slenderness ratios (ℓ_e/d). This equation provides a means of combining the compression design stress (F_c^*) with the critical buckling design stress (F_{cE}) to estimate an "effective" compression design value (30, 68, 81, 97, 191).

The parameter "c" was empirically established from the stress-strain relationship of very short columns (ℓ_e/d of 2.5). The column stability factor equation provides a good approximation of column strength if the short column tests adequately characterize the properties and non-uniformities of the longer columns (101). By empirically fitting the column stability factor equation to column strength data, estimates of "c" closely predicted test results at all ℓ_e/d ratios (189, 191, 190). A significant advantage of the methodology is that by selecting column test material representative of the non-uniform properties across the cross section and along the length that are associated with permitted grade characteristics such as knots, slope of grain and warp, the combined effects of these variables on column behavior are included in the resultant value of "c" (190).

NDS equation 3.7-1 is formulated based on the assumption of a rectangular cross section and design property presentation in terms of adjusted stress (i.e. F_c^* and E'_{min}). An alternative format applicable for rectangular and non-rectangular sections where member properties are given in terms of adjusted stress times applicable section property (i.e. F_c^*A and $E_{min}'I$) is given as:

$$C_p = \frac{1+\alpha_c}{2c} - \sqrt{\left[\frac{1+\alpha_c}{2c}\right]^2 - \frac{\alpha_c}{c}} \qquad \text{(C3.7.1-1)}$$

where:

$$\alpha_c = \frac{P_{cE}}{P_c^*} \qquad \text{(C3.7.1-2)}$$

$$P_c^* = F_c^* A \qquad \text{(C3.7.1-3)}$$

$$P_{cE} = \frac{\pi^2 E_{min}'I}{\ell_e^2} \qquad \text{(C3.7.1-4)}$$

and

α_c = ratio of the critical column buckling resistance to reference compression resistance parallel to grain

P_{cE} = column buckling resistance, lbs

P_c^* = reference axial compression resistance parallel to grain multiplied by all applicable adjustment factors except C_P (i.e. F_c^*A), lbs

F_c^* = reference compression design value parallel to grain multiplied by all applicable adjustment factors except C_P, psi

A = area of cross section, in.^{2}

E_{min}' = adjusted modulus of elasticity for beam stability and column stability calculations, psi

I = moment of inertia, in^4

ℓ_e = effective length of compression member between planes of lateral support, in.

For rectangular cross sections, column buckling resistance, P_{cE}, is based on the smaller of $E_{min}'I_1/\ell_{e1}$ and $E_{min}'I_2/\ell_{e2}$ where subscripts 1 and 2 denote principal axes between planes of lateral support.

C3.7.1.6 Continuous exposure to elevated temperature and moisture in combination with continuous application of full design loads is an example of a severe service condition. Particularly when such design environments are coupled with design uncertainties, such as end fixity or stiffness of unsupported spliced connections, use of a reduced K_{cE} value should be considered. Included in such evaluations should be the possibility of eccentric application of the axial load and the need to design the member as a beam-column (see NDS 15.4).

C3.7.2 Tapered Columns

Analyses showed the general one-third rule (NDS Equation 3.7-3) was conservative for some end support conditions but unconservative for others (36). The use of a dimension taken at 1/3 the length from the smaller end underestimated the buckling load by 35 percent for a tapered column fixed at the large end and unsupported at the small end, and 16 percent for a tapered column simply supported (translation fixed) at both ends. Alternatively, the 1/3 rule was shown to overestimate the buckling load by 13 percent for a tapered column fixed at the small end and unsupported at the large end. These estimates were for a minimum to maximum diameter (dimension) ratio of 0.70. For these specific support conditions, NDS Equation 3.7-2 provides more realistic estimates of column strength. NDS Equation 3.7-3 remains applicable for other support conditions.

The one end fixed - one end unsupported or simply supported conditions referenced in NDS 3.7.2 correspond to the fifth and sixth buckling mode cases in NDS Appendix G. The condition of both ends simply supported corresponds to the fourth case. Values for the constant "a", given under "Support Conditions" in NDS 3.7.2, are considered applicable when the ratio of minimum to maximum diameter equals or exceeds 1/3 (36).

The effective length factor, K_e, from NDS Appendix G is used in conjunction with the representative dimension (equivalent prism) when determining the stability factor, C_P, for tapered columns. It is to be noted that the actual compression stress parallel to grain, f_c, based on the minimum dimension of the column is not to exceed F_c^*.

C3.7.3 Round Columns

Round columns are designed as square columns of equivalent cross-sectional area and taper since the solid column provisions and equations in NDS 3.7.1 have been derived in terms of rectangular cross-sections. An alternative form of the equations in NDS 3.7.1, applicable to both rectangular and nonrectangular cross-sections, is provided in Section C3.7.1.5.

C3.8 Tension Members

C3.8.2 Tension Perpendicular to Grain

Average strength values for tension perpendicular to grain that are available in reference documents (181, 183) apply to small, clear specimens that are free of shakes, checks and other seasoning defects. Such information indicates that tension design values perpendicular to grain of clear, check- and shake-free wood may be considered to be about one-third the shear design value parallel to grain of comparable quality material of the same species (9). However, because of undetectable ring shakes, checking and splitting that can occur as a result of drying in service, very low strength values for the property can be encountered in commercial grades of lumber. For this reason, no sawn lumber tension design values perpendicular to grain have been published in the Specification. Cautionary provisions have been provided to alert the designer to avoid design configurations that induce tension perpendicular to grain stresses wherever possible. Connections where moderate to heavy loads are acting through the tension side of a bending member (see NDS Table 12.5.1C, footnote 2) should be avoided. These connections should be designed to ensure that perpendicular to grain loads are applied through the compression side of the bending member, either through direct connections or top-bearing connectors.

If perpendicular to grain tension stresses are not avoidable, use of stitch bolts or other mechanical reinforcement to resist these loads should be considered. When such a solution is used, care should be taken to ensure that the reinforcement itself does not cause splitting of the member as a result of drying in service (140). Ultimately, the designer is responsible for avoiding tension perpendicular to grain stresses or for assuring that mechanical reinforcing methods are adequate.

Radial stresses are induced in curved, pitch tapered, and certain other shapes of glued laminated timber beams. Radial tension design values perpendicular to grain are given in NDS 5.2.2 and have been shown to be adequate by both test (23, 24, 113) and experience.

C3.9 Combined Bending and Axial Loading

C3.9.1 Bending and Axial Tension

Theoretical analyses and experimental results show the linear interaction equation for combined bending and tension stresses yields conservative results (189). It can be shown that the effect of moment magnification, which is not included in the equation, serves to reduce the effective bending ratio rather than increase it.

Where eccentric axial tension loading is involved, the moment associated with the axial load, $(6Pe)/(bd^2)$, should be added to the actual bending stress induced by the bending load when applying the interaction equation. The eccentricity, e, should carry the sign appropriate to the direction of eccentricity: positive when the moment associated with the axial load is increasing the moment due to the bending load and negative when it is reducing the moment.

Where biaxial bending occurs with axial tension, the interaction equation can be expanded to:

$$\frac{f_t}{F_t'} + \frac{f_{b1}}{F_{b1}^*} + \frac{f_{b2}}{F_{b2}^*} \leq 1.0 \qquad \text{(C3.9.2-1)}$$

where the subscripts indicate the principle axes.

Reference bending design values, F_b, are not adjusted for slenderness, C_L, in NDS Equation 3.9-1 because the tension load acts to reduce the buckling stress and the combined stress is not the critical buckling condition. Critical buckling is checked separately using NDS Equation 3.9-2.

An alternative formulation of Equation C3.9.2-1 in terms of induced axial tension load and induced bending moment is given as:

$$\frac{T}{T'} + \frac{M_1}{M_1^*} + \frac{M_2}{M_2^*} \leq 1.0 \qquad \text{(C3.9.2-2)}$$

T = induced axial tension load, lbs

T' = adjusted axial tension resistance (i.e. $F_t'A$), lbs

M_1 = induced bending moment in the strong axis, in.-lbs

M_1^* = reference strong axis moment resistance multiplied by all applicable adjustment factors except C_L (i.e. $F_{b1}^* S_1$), in.-lbs

M_2 = induced bending moment in the weak axis, in.-lbs

M_2^* = reference weak axis moment resistance multiplied by all applicable adjustment factors except C_L (i.e. $F_{b2}{}^*S_2$), in.-lbs

C3.9.2 Bending and Axial Compression

The interaction equation given in NDS 3.9.2 (NDS Equation 3.9-3) addresses effects of beam buckling and bending about both principal axes, and closely matches beam-column test data for in-grade lumber as well as similar earlier data for clear wood material (189, 187).

The ratio of actual (induced) to adjusted compression stress in NDS Equation 3.9-3 is squared based on tests of short beam-columns made from various species of 2×4 and 2×6 lumber (68, 193, 189). The squared relationship in Equation 3.9-3 is intended to be used for all wood member sizes.

The moment magnification adjustment for edgewise bending in NDS Equation 3.9-3 is $(1-f_c/F_{cE1})$. This adjustment is consistent with similar adjustments for other structural materials, and is based on theoretical analysis, confirmed by tests of intermediate and long wood beam-columns (189, 187).

The moment magnification adjustment for flatwise bending in NDS Equation 3.9-3 is $[1-(f_c/F_{cE2})-(f_{b1}/F_{bE})^2]$. The first term, $(1-f_c/F_{cE2})$, is consistent with the adjustment for edgewise bending discussed previously. The second term, $(f_{b1}/F_{bE})^2$, represents the amplification of f_{b2} from f_{b1}. This second term is based on theoretical analysis (187) and has been verified using beam-column tests made on clear Sitka spruce (99, 187). The biaxial bending calculations in NDS Equation 3.9-3 conservatively model cantilever and multi-span beam-columns subject to biaxial loads (192).

NDS Equation 3.9-4 checks an intermediate calculation for members subjected to flatwise bending in combination with axial compression, with or without edgewise bending. When a flatwise bending load is checked with the third term of the stress interaction equation (NDS Equation 3.9-3), the axial and edgewise bending interaction in the denominator can become a negative value. The occurrence of the negative value indicates an overstress. However, use of this negative term in the stress interaction equation (NDS Equation 3.9-3) overlooks the overstress in flatwise bending and incorrectly reduces the overall interaction.

An alternative formulation of Equation C3.9-3 presented in terms of induced axial load and induced bending moment follows:

$$\left(\frac{P}{P'}\right)^2 + \frac{M_1}{M_1'(1-\frac{P}{P_{cE1}})} + \frac{M_2}{M_2'(1-\frac{P}{P_{cE2}}-\frac{M_1}{M_{bE}})} \leq 1.0 \quad \text{(C3.9.2-3)}$$

where:

P = induced axial compression load, lbs

P' = adjusted axial compression resistance (i.e. F_{cA}'), lbs

M_1 = induced bending moment in the strong axis, in.-lbs

M_1' = adjusted strong axis moment resistance (i.e. $F_{b1}'S_1$), in.-lbs

M_2 = induced bending moment in the weak axis, in.-lbs

M_2' = adjusted weak axis moment resistance (i.e. $F_{b2}'S_2$), in.-lbs

P_{cE1} = critical column buckling resistance in the strong axis, lbs (see C3.7.1.5)

P_{cE2} = critical column buckling resistance in the weak axis, lbs (see C3.7.1.5)

M_{bE} = critical beam buckling moment (i.e. 2.4 $E_{min}'\,I_2/\ell_e$), in.-lbs where $E_{min}'I_2$ represents adjusted weak axis stiffness for beam stability and column stability calculations

and

$$\frac{P}{P_{cE2}} + \left(\frac{M_1}{M_{bE}}\right)^2 \leq 1.0 \quad \text{(C3.9.2-4)}$$

where:

$$P < P_{cE1} = \frac{\pi^2 E_{min}' I_1}{\ell_{e1}^2} \quad \text{(C3.9.2-5)}$$

$$P < P_{cE2} = \frac{\pi^2 E_{min}' I_2}{\ell_{e2}^2} \quad \text{(C3.9.2-6)}$$

$$M < M_{bE} = \frac{2.4\ E_{min}' I_2}{\ell_e} \quad \text{(C3.9.2-7)}$$

C

COMMENTARY: DESIGN PROVISIONS AND EQUATIONS

For additional equations involving combined bending and axial compression including eccentric axial compression loading, see C15.4.

C3.10 Design for Bearing

C3.10.1 Bearing Parallel to Grain

Where end-grain bearing is a design consideration, the actual compression stress parallel to grain, f_c, shall not exceed the compression design value parallel to grain, F_c^*. For purposes of this section, the term "actual compressive bearing stress parallel to grain" and the term "compression stress parallel to grain," f_c, are synonymous.

Examples of end-grain bearing configurations are end-to-end compression chord segments laterally supported by splice plates, butt end-bearing joints in individual laminations of mechanically laminated truss chords, roof-tied arch heel connections, notched chord truss heel joints, and columns supporting beams. Where the actual compression stress parallel to grain at the point of bearing is less than or equal to 75 percent of the compression design value parallel to grain ($f_c \leq 0.75\ F_c^*$), direct end-to-end bearing of wood surfaces is permitted provided that abutting end surfaces are parallel and appropriate lateral support is provided. The required use of a metal bearing plate or equivalently durable, rigid, homogeneous material in highly loaded end-to-end bearing joints ($f_c > 0.75\ F_c^*$) is to assure a uniform distribution of load from one member to another.

C3.10.2 Bearing Perpendicular to Grain

Ignoring any non-uniform distribution of bearing stress that may occur at the supports of a bending member as a result of the deflection or curvature of that member under load is long standing design practice.

C3.10.3 Bearing at an Angle to Grain

NDS Equation 3.10-1 for calculating the compressive stress at an angle to grain was developed from tests on Sitka spruce and verified for general applicability by tests on other species (184, 54, 59). The equation applies when the inclined or loaded surface is at right angles to the direction of load. The equation is limited to F_c' when the angle between direction of grain and direction of load, θ, is 0° and $F_{c\perp}'$ when this angle is 90°. Stresses on both inclined surfaces in a notched member should be checked if the limiting case is not apparent.

C3.10.4 Bearing Area Factor, C_b

Provisions for increasing reference compression perpendicular design values for length of bearing are based on the results of test procedures in ASTM D 143 (5) which involve loading a two-inch wide steel plate bearing on a two-inch wide by two-inch deep by six-inch long specimen. Research at the USDA Forest Products Laboratory on proportional limit stresses associated with bolt and washer loads showed that the smaller the width of the plate or bearing area relative to the length of the test specimen, the higher the proportional limit stress (146, 178). Early research conducted in Australia and Czechoslovakia confirmed the nature and magnitude of the bearing length effect (178).

The effect of length of bearing is attributed to the resisting bending and tension parallel to grain strengths in the fibers at the edges of the bearing plate (84, 178). Because of the localized nature of the edge effect, the contribution provided decreases as the length of the area under compressive load increases. When the bearing plate covers the entire surface of the supporting specimen (full bearing), test values will be lower than those obtained in the standard two-inch plate test. For the case of complete surface or full bearing (bearing length equals supporting member length), such as may occur in a pressing operation, compression perpendicular to grain is approximately 75% of the reference compression perpendicular to grain design value. Deformation will also exceed that associated with the standard test.

Note that potential buckling perpendicular to grain is a design consideration that is not evaluated as part of the ASTM D143 (5) test procedures. One method of checking for buckling perpendicular to grain would be to use the provisions for column buckling parallel to grain in NDS 3.7.1 with mechanical properties from approved sources.

Bearing adjustment factors are useful in special cases such as highly loaded washers, metal supporting straps or hangers on wood beams, highly loaded foundation studs bearing on wood plates and crossing wood members. See C4.2.6 for discussion of deformation occurring in this support condition relative to metal or end-grain bearing on side or face-grain.

C4 SAWN LUMBER

C4.1 General

C4.1.1 Scope

The design requirements given in Chapters 1 through 3 of the Specification are applicable to sawn lumber except where indicated otherwise. Chapter 4 of the Specification contains provisions which are particular to sawn lumber.

C4.1.2 Identification of Lumber

C4.1.2.1 The design provisions of the Specification applicable to sawn lumber are based on (i) use of lumber that displays the official grading mark of an agency that has been certified by the Board of Review of the American Lumber Standard Committee (ALSC), established under the U.S. Department of Commerce's *Voluntary Product Standard PS 20* (152); and (ii) use of design values tabulated in the *NDS Supplement–Design Values for Wood Construction (NDS Supplement)* are a compendium of reference design values published by grading rules-writing agencies approved by the ALSC Board of Review (152). Those agencies publishing approved grading rules and design values are given in the *Design Values Supplement* to the Specification under "List of Sawn Lumber Grading Agencies." It is the responsibility of the designer to assure that the design values given in the NDS Supplement are applicable to the material so identified. If design values other than those tabulated in the NDS Supplement are used, it is the designer's responsibility to assure that the reliability and adequacy of the assignments are such that they may be used safely with the design provisions of the Specification.

The requirement that glued lumber products bear a distinct grade mark indicating that the joint integrity is subject to qualification and quality control clarifies that the bond strength of the joint itself is to be monitored on a continuous basis under an inspection program.

C4.1.3 Definitions

C4.1.3.2 Categories and grades of "Dimension" lumber are standardized under the National Grading Rule for Softwood Dimension Lumber which was authorized by the American Softwood Lumber Standard PS20 (152). The rule provides standard use categories, grade names, and grade descriptions. The National Grading Rule includes allowable knot sizes based on the strength ratio concept. Under this concept, the effect of a knot or other permitted strength reducing characteristic is expressed as the ratio of the assumed strength of the piece containing the characteristic to the strength of clear, straight-grain wood of the same species (8).

Grades established under the National Grading Rule are:

Structural Light Framing 2"–4" thick, 2"–4" wide
Select Structural
No. 1
No. 2
No. 3

Light Framing 2"–4" thick, 2"–4" wide
Construction
Standard
Utility

Studs 2"–4" thick, 2"–6" wide
Stud

Structural Joists & Planks 2"–4" thick, 5" and wider
Select Structural
No. 1
No. 2
No. 3

Design values for dimension lumber are based on in-grade tests of full-size pieces. Design values for Structural Light Framing and Structural Joists and Planks are consolidated under the common grade names (Select Structural, No. 1, No. 2, and No. 3) and separate width adjustments or values by width are provided (see NDS Supplement Tables 4A and 4B). There has been no change in the visual descriptions or maximum size of knots and other characteristics permitted in each width class of the grades established under the National Grading Rule.

C4.1.3.3 "Beams and Stringers" are uniformly defined in certified grading rules as lumber that is 5" (nominal) or more in thickness, and width 2" or more greater than the thickness. Such members, for example 6×10, 6×12, 8×12, 8×16, and 10×14, are designed for use on edge as bending members. Grades for which design values are given in this Specification (NDS Supplement Table 4D) are:

Select Structural
No. 1
No. 2

C4.1.3.4 "Posts and Timbers" are defined as lumber that is 5" (nominal) or more in thickness and width not more than 2" greater than thickness. These members, such as 6×6, 6×8, 8×10, and 12×12, are designed to support axial column loads. Grades of lumber in this classification are the same as those for "Beams and Stringers." Posts and Timbers also may be used as beams; however, other grades and sections may be more efficient where strength in bending is a major consideration.

C4.1.4 Moisture Service Condition of Lumber

Design values tabulated in the Specification for sawn lumber apply to material surfaced in any condition and used in dry conditions of service. Such conditions are those in which the moisture content in use will not exceed a maximum of 19 percent. Adjustment factors, C_M, are provided in NDS Supplement Tables 4A through 4F for uses where this limit will be exceeded for a sustained period of time or for repeated periods.

Applications in which the structural members are regularly exposed directly to rain and other sources of moisture are typically considered wet conditions of service. Members that are protected from the weather by roofs or other means but are occasionally subjected to wind-blown moisture are generally considered dry (moisture content 19 percent or less) applications. The designer has final responsibility for determining the appropriate moisture content basis for the design.

Design values tabulated for Southern Pine timbers and Mixed Southern Pine timbers in NDS Supplement Table 4D have already been adjusted for use in wet service conditions. These values also apply when these species are used in dry service conditions.

C4.1.5 Lumber Sizes

C4.1.5.1 The minimum lumber sizes given in NDS Supplement Table 1A are minimum-dressed sizes established in the American Softwood Lumber Standard, PS 20 (152).

C4.1.5.2 Dry net sizes are used in engineering computations for dimension lumber surfaced in any condition. When lumber is surfaced in the Green condition, it is oversized to allow for shrinkage (152).

C4.1.5.3 Beams and Stringers and Posts and Timbers are manufactured in the Green condition to standard Green dimensions (152). The reference design values for such lumber, which are applicable to dry conditions of service, include adjustments for the effects of shrinkage. Standard Green sizes, therefore, are to be used in engineering computations with these grades.

C4.1.6 End-Jointed or Edge-Glued Lumber

Design values tabulated in the NDS Supplement apply to end-jointed lumber of the same species and grade as unjointed sawn lumber when such material is identified by the grademark or inspection certificate of an approved agency (see C4.1.2.1). This identification indicates the glued product is subject to ongoing quality monitoring, including joint strength evaluation, by the agency.

End-jointed, face-glued and edge-glued lumber may be used interchangeably with sawn lumber members of the same grade and species. The limitation on the use of finger-jointed lumber marked "STUD USE ONLY" or "VERTICAL USE ONLY" to those applications where any induced bending or tension stresses are of short duration is a provision to minimize possible joint creep associated with long-term loads. Bending and tension stresses associated with wind loads and seismic loads are examples of short duration stresses permitted in finger-jointed lumber marked for "STUD USE ONLY" or "VERTICAL USE ONLY."

C4.1.7 Resawn or Remanufactured Lumber

Material that has been regraded after resawing qualifies for design values tabulated in the Supplement only when identified by the grademark or inspection certificate of an approved agency (see C4.1.2.1).

C4.2 Reference Design Values

C4.2.1 Reference Design Values

Design values tabulated in NDS Supplement Tables 4A through 4F have been taken from grading rules that have been certified by the Board of Review of the American Lumber Standard Committee as conforming to the provisions of the American Softwood Lumber Standard, PS 20 (152). Such grading rules may be obtained from the rules writing agencies listed in the NDS Supplement. Information on stress-rated board grades applicable to the various species is available from the respective grading rules agencies.

C4.2.2 Other Species and Grades

Where design values other than those tabulated in the Specification are to be used, it is the designer's responsibility to assure the technical adequacy of such assignments and the appropriateness of using them with the design provisions of the Specification (see C4.1.2.1).

C4.2.3 Basis for Reference Design Values

C4.2.3.2 Visually Graded Lumber

Dimension

In 1977, the softwood lumber industry in North America and the U.S. Forest Products Laboratory began a testing program to evaluate the strength properties of in-grade full-size pieces of visually-graded dimension lumber made from most commercially important species in North America (65). The testing program, conducted over an eight year period, involved the destructive testing of over 70,000 pieces of lumber from 33 species or species groups. The test method standard, ASTM D4761, covers the mechanical test methods used in the program (14). The standard practice, ASTM D1990, provides the procedures for establishing design values for visually graded dimension lumber from test results obtained from in-grade test programs (7).

Design values for bending, F_b, tension parallel to grain, F_t, compression parallel to grain, F_c, and modulus of elasticity, E, for 14 species or species combinations listed in Tables 4A and 4B of the NDS Supplement are based on in-grade test results. Further, the grade and size models developed under ASTM D1990 have been employed to establish grade and size relationships for those species whose index strengths are established by D245 methods. All design values for shear parallel to grain, F_v, and compression perpendicular to the grain, $F_{c\perp}$, in these tables are based on ASTM D245 provisions (8).

Timbers

Design values and adjustment factors for size, wet service, and shear stress given in NDS Supplement Table 4D for Beams and Stringers and Posts and Timbers are based on the provisions of ASTM D245 (8).

Decking

Design values for Decking in NDS Supplement Table 4E are based on ASTM D245 provisions except for the wet service factor, C_M, for F_b which is based on ASTM D1990. Reference bending design values, F_b, in Table 4E for all species and species combinations except Redwood are based on a four-inch thickness. A 10 percent increase in these values applies when two-inch decking is used (see C_F adjustment factor in the Table).

C4.2.3.3 Machine Stress Rated (MSR) Lumber and Machine Evaluated Lumber (MEL)

Design values for F_b, F_t, F_c, and E given in NDS Supplement Table 4C for mechanically graded dimension lumber apply to material that meets the qualification and quality control requirements of the grading agency whose grademark appears on the piece. Stiffness-based stress-rating machines are set so that pieces passing through the machine will have the average E desired. For these machines, values of F_b are based on correlations established between minimum bending strength for lumber loaded on edge and E. Similarly, F_t and F_c values are based on test results for lumber in each F_b-E grade. Density-based grading machines operate under similar principles, using various density-based algorithms as the basis for grading decisions. For both machine types, machine settings are monitored and routinely verified through periodic stiffness and strength testing. Mechanically graded lumber also is required to meet certain visual grading requirements which include limitations on the size of edge knots and distorted grain on the wide face. Such limitations, expressed as a maximum proportion of the cross-section occupied by the characteristics, generally range from 1/2 to 1/6 depending on the level of F_b.

Machine Stress Rated (MSR) lumber is material that is categorized in classes of regularly increasing strength (F_b, F_t, and F_c) and E assignments. As F_b values increase, F_t values increase at a greater rate, starting from 0.39 of the F_b value for the 900f grade to 0.80 of the F_b value for the 2400f and higher grades. Alternatively, F_c values increase at a lower rate than F_b values, starting from 1.17 of the F_b value for the 900f grade to 0.70 of the F_b value

C

COMMENTARY: SAWN LUMBER

for the 3300f grade. F_b, F_t, and E values for MSR lumber in NDS Supplement Table 4C are essentially the same as those published in the 1986 edition. Previously, F_c values were taken as 80 percent of the corresponding F_b value. As noted, these assignments now vary depending on level of F_b.

Design values for Machine Evaluated Lumber (MEL) are characterized by several different levels of E, F_t, or F_c for each level of F_b rather than assignment of qualifying material to specific stress classes, each of which has a generally unique assignment for each property. The MEL approach allows a greater percentage of total lumber production from a mill to be mechanically rated than is possible under the MSR classification system.

C4.2.4 Modulus of Elasticity, E

Design values for Modulus of Elasticity, E, are estimates of the average values for the species and grade of material. Reference modulus of elasticity for beam and column stability, E_{min}, is based on the following equation:

$$E_{min} = \frac{E(1-1.64COV_E)(1.03)}{1.66} \qquad \text{(C4.2.4-1)}$$

where:

E = reference modulus of elasticity

1.03 = adjustment factor to convert E values to a pure bending basis

1.66 = factor of safety

COV_E = coefficient of variation in modulus of elasticity (see NDS Appendix F)

E_{min} represents an approximate 5% lower exclusion value on pure bending modulus of elasticity, a 1.03 adjustment factor to convert from an apparent bending E at a span-to-depth ratio of 17:1 to a true bending E, and a 1.66 factor of safety. For more discussion, see NDS Appendix D.

C4.2.5 Bending, F_b

C4.2.5.1 When reference F_b values for dimension grades are applied to members with the load applied to the wide face, the flat use factor, C_{fu}, is to be used (see C4.3.7).

C4.2.5.4 Grade requirements for Beams and Stringers do not consider the effects of allowable knots and other permitted characteristics on the bending strength of the member under loads applied to the wide face. Therefore, reference bending design values, F_b, for Beams and Stringers in NDS Supplement Table 4D, used when checking stresses where loads are applied on the wide face, should be adjusted by the applicable size factor in NDS Supplement Table 4D. Posts and Timbers are graded for bending in both directions and can be used in biaxial bending design situations.

C4.2.6 Compression Perpendicular to Grain, $F_{c\perp}$

Reference compression design values perpendicular to grain in the 1977 and earlier editions of the Specification were based on proportional limit stresses and were adjusted for load duration. This practice changed when ASTM D245 provisions were revised to recognize compression perpendicular to grain as a serviceability limit state where the property is used as a measure of bearing deformation (8). Since 1982, lumber $F_{c\perp}$ values referenced in the Specification have been based on a uniform 0.04-inch deformation level for the condition of a steel plate on wood bearing condition. Such values are not adjusted for load duration.

The change in the basis of compression design values perpendicular to grain was an outgrowth of the introduction of ASTM D2555 in 1966. This standard gave new clear wood property information for western species and prescribed strict criteria for assignment of properties to combinations of species (see C4.2.3.2). Implementation of this information and the grouping criteria through ASTM D245 in 1971 resulted in a significant reduction in the $F_{c\perp}$ design value for a commercially important species group. The reduction caused bearing stress to become the limiting design property for the group in truss and other structural applications even though lumber of the group in these uses had performed satisfactorily at the previous higher bearing stress level for over 25 years.

Subsequent evaluation indicated that bearing perpendicular to the grain loads are not associated with structural failure and that deformation levels at proportional limit stresses could vary 100 percent between species in the standard ASTM D143 test. This test consists of loading a 2-inch wide steel plate bearing on the middle of a 2-inch by 2-inch by 6-inch long wood specimen (5). It was concluded that a uniform deformation limit was the preferred basis for establishing design loads concerned with bearing perpendicular to the grain. New methodology was developed to enable the stress at any deformation level to be estimated for any species based on its proportional limit stress (26, 27). This methodology was coupled with field experience to establish a deformation limit of 0.04 inches in the standard 2-inch specimen as an appropriate design stress base for applied loads of any duration. Stresses at 0.04-inch deformation for individual species were subsequently published in ASTM D2555 and provisions for basing compression design values perpendicular to grain on a deformation limit were introduced into ASTM D245.

In view of the outward load redistribution that occurs through the thickness of a member not subjected to a uniform bearing load along its length, and taking into account the effects of bearing deformation on the structure, establishment of a deformation limit state in terms of strain rate (deformation divided by member thickness) was not considered appropriate. On the basis of field experience, bearing stresses and deformations derived from the standard test of steel plate on 2 inch deep wood member are judged applicable to all lumber sizes. For the same stress, deformation of a joint consisting of two wood members both loaded perpendicular to grain will be approximately 2.5 times that of a metal to wood joint. The $F_{c\perp}$ values given in the 1982 edition of the Specification and continued in the present edition are about 60 percent greater than the proportional limit–normal load based values published in earlier editions but are applicable to wind, earthquake, snow and other load durations without adjustment.

The equation given in NDS 4.2.6 for adjusting reference $F_{c\perp}$ values to a 0.02-inch deformation limit is based on regression equations relating proportional limit mean stress to deformation at the 0.04 and the 0.02 levels (27). Use of this reduced compression design value perpendicular to grain may be appropriate where bearing deformations could affect load distribution or where total deflections of members must be closely controlled. Bearing deformation is not a significant factor in most lumber designs.

C4.3 Adjustment of Reference Design Values

C4.3.1 General

Applicable adjustment factors for sawn lumber are specified in Table 4.3.1 of the Specification.

C4.3.2 Load Duration Factor, C_D (ASD Only)

See C2.3.2.

C4.3.3 Wet Service Factor, C_M

The wet service reduction value, C_M, for F_b, F_t, F_c, and E in NDS Supplement Tables 4A and 4B are based on provisions of ASTM D1990 (7). For F_v and $F_{c\perp}$, the values of C_M, are based on ASTM D245. The wet service factors account for the increase in cross-section dimensions associated with this exposure.

C4.3.4 Temperature Factor, C_t

See C2.3.3.

C4.3.5 Beam Stability Factor, C_L

See C3.3.3.

C4.3.6 Size Factor, C_F

C4.3.6.1 Design values for F_b, F_t, and F_c in NDS Supplement Table 4A for all species and species combinations are adjusted for size using the size factors, C_F, referenced at the beginning of the table. These factors and those used to develop the size specific values given in NDS Supplement Table 4B for certain species combinations are based on the adjustment equation for geometry given in ASTM D1990 (7). This equation, based on in-grade test data, accounts for differences in F_b, F_t, and F_c related to width and for differences in F_b and F_t related to length (test span). Reference values in Tables 4A and 4B for F_b and F_t are based on the following standardized lengths:

Width, in.	Length, ft
2 to 6	**12**
8 to 10	**16**
12 and wider	**20**

For constant length, the ASTM D1990 size equation provides for significantly greater reductions in bending design values, F_b, as width increases than comparable previous adjustments for this property. Width adjustments for tension design values parallel to grain, F_t, and compression design values parallel to grain, F_c, in the equation are applicable. Additionally, the modification of F_b and F_t for length is presented in the D1990 equation. Based on the total conservatism of these combined adjustments relative to past practice, use of design values in NDS Supplement Tables 4A and 4B for any member span length is considered appropriate.

C4.3.6.2 Bending design values for Beams & Stringers and Posts & Timbers in NDS Supplement Table 4D apply to a 12 inch depth. The NDS size factor equation for adjusting these values to deeper members is based on the formula given in ASTM D245.

C4.3.6.3 Beams of circular cross section (see C4.3.6.2).

C4.3.6.4 Values of F_b referenced for decking in NDS Supplement Table 4E are for members 4 inches thick. The increases of 10 and 4 percent allowed for 2 inch and 3 inch decking are based on the NDS size equation in 4.3.6.2.

C4.3.7 Flat Use Factor, C_{fu}

Adjustment factors for flat use of bending members are based on the 1/9 power size equation discussed in C4.3.6.2 and C4.3.6.4. Relative to the test results that are available, the ASTM D245 equation gives conservative C_{fu} values. The flat use factor, C_{fu}, is to be used cumulatively with the size factor, C_F. Since C_{fu} is equal to or greater than 1.0 for dimension lumber 2" to 4" thick, its use is permitted but not required in accordance with Section 4.3.7.1. For Beams and Stringers, since C_{fu} is equal to or less than 1.0, its use is required. Posts and Timbers may use the design values in Table 4D without the C_{fu} adjustment factors ($C_{fu} = 1.0$).

C4.3.8 Incising Factor, C_i

Incising involves making shallow, slit-like holes parallel-to-grain in the surfaces of refractory wood species to obtain deeper and more uniform penetration of preservatives. Treating standards require incising to improve pressure treatment of thin sapwood species such as Douglas fir, Spruce and Hemlock, which may have heartwood surfaces or tend to be resistant to side penetration of preservative solutions.

The effect of the incising process has been found to reduce the strength properties of wood (73, 74, 105). More recent work on nominal 2x4 lumber of multiple species having either 660 or 880 incisions/ft^2 has shown that incising effects are dependent on: the number of incisions (density) per square foot of surface area; the depth, width and length of individual incisions; and the damage beneath the boundaries of the incisions (199, 200). The incising adjustment factors for E, F_b, F_t, F_v, and F_c given in Table 4.3.8 of the Specification are limited to dimension lumber using patterns in which the incisions are not deeper than 0.4 inches and no more than 1,100 per square foot in number.

To verify the current practices of incising across the Western U.S., a survey was recently conducted by Western Wood Preservers Institute and Oregon State University (206). It confirmed that the current incising machines used in Pacific Northwest treating plants produced average incising densities of 377 incisions/ft^2 with a standard deviation of 145 incisions/ft^2. The 16 plants responding to the survey used incision densities between 148-638 incisions/ft^2. Incision depth ranged from 0.04-0.24 inches and averaged 0.14 inch with a standard deviation of 0.06 inch.

The incising effect on larger member sizes is generally less than nominal 2x4 size lumber due to the larger cross-section and the common practice on timbers of using lower incision densities (<800/ft^2).

Alternatively, incising factors for specific incising patterns, in conjunction with dimension lumber or timber sizes may be obtained from the company providing the incising and reported in their design documents. These incising factors may either be determined by test or by calculation using reduced section properties, and shall account for damage to wood around edges and below the bottom of incisions (199, 200).

For larger sizes, such as timbers, reviews of early testing of timbers and railway ties (105, 199) indicated that a slight decrease in strength properties for timbers was expected, but in some cases no strength reductions were reported.

For timber sizes with thicknesses larger than 5 inches, the effects of incising are small to minimal and C_i can be assumed to vary from 0.95 to 1.0 depending on timber species and size, incision depth and density, and incision damage to wood around edges and below the bottom of incisions. Thus, reductions provided in Table 4.3.8 are usually not applied to larger members such as solid sawn timbers.

C4.3.9 Repetitive Member Factor, C_r

The 15 percent repetitive member increase in reference bending design values, F_b, for lumber 2 to 4 inches thick is based on provisions in ASTM D245 (8) and D6555 (19). It is based on the increase in load-carrying capacity and stiffness obtained when multiple framing members are fastened together or appropriately joined by transverse load distributing elements. Such an increase has been demonstrated by both analysis and test (28, 107, 149, 194). It reflects two interactions: load-sharing or redistribution of load among framing members and partial composite action of the framing member and the covering materials (149). Application of the C_r adjustment requires no assumption as to which of the two types of interaction is involved or predominates. A C_r value of 15 percent is generally considered to be conservative for sawn lumber assemblies (111, 177, 179).

The criteria for use of the repetitive member increase are three or more members in contact or spaced not more than 24 inches and joined by transverse load distributing elements such that the group of members performs as a unit rather than as separate pieces. The members may be any piece of dimension lumber loaded in bending, including studs, rafters, truss chords, and decking, as well as joists.

The repetitive member increase also applies to an assembly of three or more essentially parallel members of equal size and of the same orientation which are in direct contact with each other (28). In this case the transverse elements may be mechanical fasteners such as nails, nail gluing, tongue-and-groove joints, or bearing plates. The required condition is that the three or more members act together to resist the applied moment.

C4.3.10 Column Stability Factor, C_P

See C3.7.1.

C4.3.11 Buckling Stiffness Factor, C_T

See C4.4.2.

C4.3.12 Bearing Area Factor, C_b

See C3.10.4.

C4.3.13 Pressure-Preservative Treatment

The provision in the NDS for use of reference design values with lumber that has been preservative treated (170, 169, 168, 171, 172, 175) is applicable to material that has been treated and redried in accordance with AWPA Standards. In AWPA Standards, the maximum temperature for kiln drying material after treatment is 165°F (22).

C4.3.14 Format Conversion Factor, K_F (LRFD Only)

See C2.3.5.

C4.3.15 Resistance Factor, ϕ (LRFD Only)

See C2.3.6.

C4.3.16 Time Effect Factor, λ (LRFD Only)

See C2.3.7.

C4.4 Special Design Considerations

C4.4.1 Stability of Bending Members

C4.4.1.1 Bending design values, F_b, given in NDS Supplement Tables 4A through 4F are based on a bending member having a compression edge supported throughout its length or having a depth to breadth ratio of one or less. When these conditions do not exist, F_b values are to be adjusted by the beam stability factor, C_L, calculated in accordance with the procedures of NDS 3.3.3. As an alternative method, bracing rules provided in NDS 4.4.1.2 are an acceptable method for providing restraint to prevent lateral displacement or rotation of lumber bending members (181).

C4.4.1.2 Sheathing, subflooring, or decking attached with two or more fasteners per piece provide acceptable edge restraint for a joist, rafter, or beam loaded through these load distributing elements. The requirement for bridging in the form of diagonal cross bracing or solid blocking in NDS 4.4.1.2(d) and the requirement for both edges to be supported in NDS 4.4.1.2(e) address: (i) redistribution of concentrated loads from long span members to adjacent members, and (ii) localized eccentricities due to cupping or twisting of deep members as a result of drying in service. Intermittent bridging specified in NDS 4.4.1.2(d) is not required in combination with tension and compression edge bracing specified in NDS 4.4.1.2(e).

The approximate rules of NDS 4.4.1.2(c) are equivalent to the beam stability provisions of NDS 3.3.3.3. For larger depth to breadth ratios the NDS 4.4.1.2 bracing rules are more restrictive than provisions of NDS 3.3.3.3. For smaller ratios the NDS 4.4.1.2 bracing rules are less restrictive, with the difference between effective bending stress based on the two methods increasing as F_b increases and E decreases.

C4.4.1.3 Tests of heavily stressed biaxial beam-columns showed that the bracing members could buckle as a result of the combination of loads applied directly on the bracing member and the loads induced by the beam-column as it buckles (147). Bracing members providing lateral support to a beam-column will typically have only one edge braced (such as a sheathed purlin bracing a rafter). The bracing member should have sufficient capacity to carry the additional compression load produced by the beam-column as it tends to buckle.

C4.4.2 Wood Trusses

C4.4.2.1 These provisions recognize the contribution of wood structural panel (WSP) sheathing to the buckling resistance of compression truss chords (in the plane of the chord depth). Quantification of the increase in chord buckling resistance from plywood sheathing was based on research (53, 55) involving stiffness tests of sheathed 2×4 members, nail slip tests, use of existing methodology for estimating the nail slip modulus of combinations of materials (155, 159), and application of a finite element analysis program for layered wood systems (149). It was found that the sheathing contribution increases with decrease in modulus of elasticity of the chord, with increase in span, and with increase in fastener slip modulus. Effects of plywood thickness and chord specific gravity were found to be of lesser significance.

While research was conducted using plywood, the application applies to all WSP including OSB.

The difference between the two K_m factors reflects the effect of drying on the nail load-slip modulus. The equations apply to chord lengths up to 96 inches, 2×4 or smaller chords in trusses spaced 24 inches or less, and 3/8 inch or thicker WSP nailed to the narrow face of the chord using recommended schedules (38).

The analyses on which the equations are based assumed nails adjacent to joints between panel edges were located one inch from the panel edge, a chord specific gravity (oven dry volume basis) of 0.42 and an open joint without H clips between sheathing panels. Clips were estimated to increase the C_T factor by 5 percent (53).

Because the buckling stiffness factor decreases with increase in chord modulus of elasticity, the 1977 equations were based on the 5 percent exclusion value of E for the visually graded lumber species and grade having the highest reference design value. The 5 percent value was used because this is the basis for the E value used to establish the Euler column buckling load. It should be noted that the decrease in the relative contribution of sheathing that occurs as chord E increases above the 5 percent exclusion level is more than offset by the increase in the E of the chord itself.

C4.4.3 Notches

Prior to 1977, the Specification provided for the use of the net section at the notch for determining the bending strength of a notched bending member. This provision was based on early research which indicated that use of the net section at the notch was a sufficiently conservative design basis for commercial grades of sawn lumber (184, 181). It was recognized even at that time that stress concentrations at the corners of the notch caused lower proportional limit loads and caused failure to begin at lower loads than those expected from an unnotched bending member having a depth equal to the net depth of the notched bending member (184, 181).

In the 1977 edition, as a result of field experience and new research related to crack propagation, the use of the net section procedure for determining induced bending moment in notched bending members was discontinued and specific notch limitations were established for different bending member sizes. These new provisions were continued in the 1986 and 1991 editions. The field performance history considered included: (i) large bending members end-notched to the quarter points of the span which exhibited splitting and tension perpendicular to grain separations at relatively low loads; and (ii) the long record of satisfactory performance of light-frame construction joists notched using good practice recommendations. Fracture mechanics research also confirmed and quantified the propensity of cracks to develop at square-cornered notches at relatively low bending loads (92, 91, 132). Narrow slit notches (3/32 inch long) were found to cause greater strength reductions than wide (greater than two inches long) notches of the same depth. The interaction of size and crack propagation has been characterized, with crack initiation increasing in proportion to the square root of the bending member depth for a given relative notch depth and constant induced bending and shear stress (183).

C4.4.3.1 Tension perpendicular to grain stresses occur with shear stresses at end notches to make a bending member more susceptible to splitting at the corner of such notches. The limitation on end notches in sawn lumber bending members to 1/4 or less the bending member depth is a good practice recommendation that also reflects experience and the effects of shrinkage stresses.

C4.4.3.2 The allowance of notches on both the tension and compression sides of two and three inch thick sawn lumber bending members up to 1/6 the depth of the member in the outer thirds of a single span is consistent with good practice recommendations for light-frame construction (180). The satisfactory field performance of notched joists meeting these limitations, without use of the net section at the notch to determine actual stress, is attributed in part to the fact that reference bending design values (F_b) for the dimension grades of lumber already include section reductions for edge knots ranging from 1/6 to 1/2 the depth of the member. The restriction on interior notches in the tension side of nominal four inch and thicker sawn lumber bending members is based on experience with larger bending members and fracture mechanics analyses, as well as consideration of the shrinkage stresses that occur in such members when seasoning in service. Such stresses contribute to the perpendicular to grain stress conditions existing at the notch corners.

C4.4.3.3 The design provisions for shear in notched bending members given in NDS 3.4.3 include a magnification factor to account for tension perpendicular to grain stresses that occur with shear stresses making a bending member more susceptible to splitting at the corner of such notches.

C5 STRUCTURAL GLUED LAMINATED TIMBER

C5.1 General

Structural glued laminated timber, consisting of multiple layers of wood glued together with the grain of all layers approximately parallel, began its growth as a significant structural material in the United States in the 1930's. Technology developed in the formulation and use of casein glues to fabricate structural members in wood aircraft during and after World War I was extended to the construction of larger structural framing members used in buildings (181). The resistance of these glues to elevated relative humidities coupled with the use of pressing systems that could provide continuous pressure to all glue lines enabled the manufacture of large beams, arches and other curved shapes with assured durability. The subsequent development of resorcinol and other synthetic resin glues with high moisture resistance expanded the uses of structural glued laminated timber to bridges, marine construction and other applications involving direct exposure to the weather.

Glued laminated members are made of dry lumber laminations in which the location and frequency of knots and other strength reducing characteristics can be controlled. The result is a structural product in which splits, checks and loosening of fasteners associated with drying in service are greatly reduced and relatively high strength is achieved.

The early development of design values for structural glued laminated timber paralleled that for visually graded lumber. In 1934, methods published in the U.S. Department of Agriculture's Miscellaneous Publication 185 for the grading and determination of working stresses for structural timbers (167) were also applied to structural glued laminated timber. Under these procedures, strength values for small, clear, straight-grained wood were reduced for load duration, variability, size and factor of safety to basic stresses; and then these stresses were further reduced to account for the effects of knots, slope of grain and other characteristics permitted in the grade of lumber being used as laminations. These design values were assigned by the manufacturers to the species and grades of structural glued laminated timber being produced.

The earliest comprehensive procedures for establishing design values that were specifically developed for structural glued laminated timber were published in 1939 in U.S. Department of Agriculture Technical Bulletin 691 (166). These procedures provided for the use of lower grades of lumber in the inner laminations than in the outer laminations. A simplified method of establishing design values from basic stresses also was given which was based on use of only two grades of lumber: one allowing knots up to one-fourth the width of the piece and one allowing up to one-eighth the width of the piece.

Design procedures for structural glued laminated timber were codified as national standards of practice in 1943 as part of the War Production Board's Directive No. 29 (153) and then in 1944 as part of the first edition of the National Design Specification (96). Design values established in the first edition were the same as those for the grade of sawn lumber used (based on the procedures in Miscellaneous Publication 185) except that increases for seasoning were permitted in compression parallel to grain and for all properties except shear parallel to grain when lumber two inches or less in thickness was used. In addition, increases were permitted for constructions in which knot limitations were twice as restrictive as those applicable to inner laminations. The procedures published in 1939 in Technical Bulletin 691 also were allowed as alternative methods.

The regional lumber rules writing agencies used the new Forest Products Laboratory procedures (49) to establish specifications for the design and fabrication of structural glued laminated lumber which provided design values for various species and lamination grade combinations. Design values established by these regional agencies were published in the Specification from 1951 through the 1968 editions.

A national consensus product standard covering minimum requirements for the production of structural glued laminated timber was promulgated as Commercial Standard CS253-63 by the U.S. Department of Commerce in 1963 (133).

In 1970, the American Institute of Timber Construction (AITC) assumed responsibility for developing laminating combinations and related design values for structural glued laminated timber. Beginning with the 1971 edition of the Specification, the design values established by AITC (130, 131) have been those published in the Specification.

In 1973, the CS253 standard was revised and repromulgated by the U.S. Department of Commerce as Voluntary Product Standard PS 56-73 (134). In 1983, the standard was adopted as an American National Standard through American National Standards Institute's (ANSI) consensus process, it is now published as ANSI/AITC A190.1 (2). This product standard includes requirements for sizes, grade combinations, adhesives, inspection, testing and certification of structural glued laminated timber products. Under A190.1, the grade combinations and related design values for structural glued laminated timber are required to be developed in accordance with ASTM D3737 or obtained by performance testing and analysis in accordance with recognized standards. Procedures embodied in this ASTM standard, first published in 1978, reflect the previously used methodology (49) as modified by data from a succession of more recent full-scale test programs (2).

C5.1.1 Scope

C5.1.1.1 The design requirements given in Chapters 1 through 3 of the Specification are applicable to structural glued laminated timber except where indicated otherwise. Chapter 5 of the Specification contains provisions which are particular to structural glued laminated timber.

The provisions of Chapter 5 contain only the basic requirements applicable to engineering design of structural glued laminated timber. Specific detailed requirements, such as those for curved and tapered members and connection details, are available from the American Institute of Timber Construction (140) and APA – The Engineered Wood Association.

C5.1.1.2 Where design values other than those given in NDS Supplement Tables 5A, 5B, 5C, and 5D, or as provided in the adjustments and footnotes of these tables are used, it shall be the designer's responsibility to assure that the values have been developed in accordance with all applicable provisions of ASTM D3737 and ANSI/AITC A190.1.

The design provisions in the Specification for structural glued laminated timber apply only to material certified by an approved agency as conforming to ANSI/AITC A190.1. The local building code body having jurisdiction over the structural design is the final authority as to the competency of the certifying agency and the acceptability of its grademarks.

C5.1.2 Definition

Laminations of structural glued laminated timber are usually made of sawn lumber. Laminated veneer lumber, consisting of graded veneers bonded together with grain parallel longitudinally, and manufactured lumber, lumber of two or more pieces glued together, may be used for tension laminations where high tensile strength is required (2).

Adhesives and glued joints in structural glued laminated timber members are required to meet the testing and related requirements of ANSI/AITC A190.1.

C5.1.3 Standard Sizes

C5.1.3.1 The finished widths of structural glued laminated timber members are typically less than the dimensions of surfaced lumber from which it is made in order to allow for removal of excess adhesive from the edges of the laminations and preparation of a smooth surface. This is done by removing from 3/8 to 3/4 inch of the width from the original lumber width by planing or sanding.

For applications where appearance is not important, structural glued laminated timbers having a finished width matching the dimensions of standard framing lumber widths are available in a Framing appearance grade. This appearance grade is not generally suitable for members which will be exposed to view (128).

Widths other than standard sizes can be specified. These special widths require use of larger nominal lumber which may result in significant waste. For example, a 7 inch glued laminated beam would require the use 2x10 (9.25 inch) lumber laminations while a 6-3/4 inch beam would require 2x8 (7.25 inch) lumber laminations. While not specified as a standard size, other widths such as 3-1/2 inch and 5-1/2 inch may be available as stock items.

NDS Table 5.1.3 indicates standard widths for structural glued laminated timber members made from laminations of the indicated nominal widths. For example, structural glued laminated timber members with a net width of 3 inches or 3-1/8 inches are manufactured from nominal 4 inch wide lumber laminations and structural glued laminated timber members with a net width of 10-1/2 inches or 10-3/4 inches are made from nominal 12 inch wide lumber laminations. Dimension lumber is not typically available in nominal widths greater than 12 inches, so structural glued laminated timber members wider than 10-3/4 inches are typically manufactured from multiple-piece laminations (across the width). A 12 inch or 12-1/4 inch wide member is typically manufactured from a nominal 6 inch wide piece of lumber placed next to a nominal 8 inch wide piece of lumber (total nominal width of lamination is 14 inches). It could also be made from a nominal 10 inch wide piece of lumber placed next to a nominal 4 inch wide piece (total nominal width of lamination is 14 inches). A 14 inch or 14-1/4 inch wide member, is made from a nominal 10 inch piece of lumber placed next to a nominal 6 inch piece of lumber (total nominal width of lamination is 16 inches). In members composed of multiple-piece laminations across the width, edge joints in the laminations are staggered so they don't align in adjacent laminations. Edge joints in members with multiple-piece laminations (across the width) are not typically bonded unless specifically required by the design.

C5.1.3.2 The sizes of structural glued laminated timber are designated by the actual size after manufacture. Depths are usually produced in increments of the thickness of the lamination used. For straight or slightly curved members, this is a multiple of 1-1/2 inches for western species and 1-3/8 inches for southern pine. The faces of southern pine lumber generally are resurfaced prior to gluing, thereby reducing the thickness of this material an additional 1/8 inch. For sharply curved members, nominal 1 inch rather than 2 inch thick lumber is used (140).

When members are tapered, the depth at the beginning and the end of the taper should be designated. In all cases, the length and net cross-section dimensions of all members should be specified.

C5.1.4 Service Conditions

C5.1.4.1 Where the equilibrium moisture content of members in service is less than 16 percent, the dry service design values tabulated in NDS Supplement Tables 5A, 5B, 5C, and 5D apply. A dry service condition for structural glued laminated timber prevails in most covered structures. However, members used in interior locations of high humidity, such as may occur in certain industrial operations or over unventilated swimming pools, may reach an equilibrium moisture content of 16 percent or more. In such conditions, wet service factors should be applied to reference design values.

C5.1.4.2 Glued laminated members used in exterior exposures that are not protected from the weather by a roof, overhang, or eave and are subject to water exposure for a sustained period of time are generally considered wet conditions of use. Adjustment factors, C_M, are provided in NDS Supplement Tables 5A through 5D for uses where this limit will be exceeded. Bridges, towers, and loading docks represent typical wet service applications. Uses in which the member is in contact with the ground should be considered wet use for those portions of the member that will attain a moisture content of 16 percent or more. Where wet service conditions apply, the susceptibility of the member to decay and the need for preservative treatment (see C5.3.11) should also be considered.

C5.2 Reference Design Values

C5.2.1 Reference Design Values

Reference design values in NDS Supplement Tables 5A (and Table 5A Expanded) and 5B are for members made with softwood species. Reference design values in NDS Supplement Tables 5C and 5D are for members made with hardwood species.

NDS Supplement Table 5A. Reference design values in this table are for softwood laminating combinations that have been optimized for members stressed in bending about the x-x axis (loads applied perpendicular to the wide face of the laminations). These values apply to members having 4 or more laminations. The stress class in the first column represents multiple laminating combinations, which have at least the indicated design properties. The stress class system was developed to simplify the design and specification of structural glued laminated timbers and to allow the manufacturer to supply laminated timbers which meet the stress class requirements, while making the most efficient use of available resources. Specification of a particular laminating combination from NDS Supplement Table 5A Expanded is also permissible.

NDS Supplement Table 5A Expanded. Reference design values in this table are for softwood laminating combinations that have been optimized for members stressed in bending about the x-x axis (loads applied perpendicular to the wide face of the laminations). These values apply to members having 4 or more laminations and are divided into stress classes for which the combination qualifies. The combination symbol in the first column designates a specific combination and lay-up of grades of lumber. For example, 16F-V6 indicates a combination with a bending design value, F_{bx}, of 1600 psi (column 3–tension zone stressed in tension) made with visually graded lumber (V). In the same format, 24F-E1 indicates an F_{bx} of 2400 psi (column 3–tension zone stressed in tension) made with E-rated lumber. The second column of NDS Supplement Table 5A Expanded indicates the species used for the outer laminations and for the core laminations of the member. For example, DF/HF indicates Douglas Fir-Larch is used for the outer laminations and Hem-Fir is used for the core laminations. Lay-up details for softwood combinations are available in AITC 117(131).

NDS Supplement Table 5B. Reference design values in this table are for softwood laminating combinations that have been optimized for stresses due to axial loading or to bending about the y-y axis (loads applied parallel to the wide face of the laminations). Each combination consists of a single grade of one species of lumber. The grade associated with each numbered combination can be obtained from AITC 117 (131).

NDS Supplement Table 5C. Reference design values in this table are for hardwood laminating combinations that have been optimized for members stressed in bending about the x-x axis (loads applied perpendicular to the wide face of the laminations). These values apply to members having 4 or more laminations. The combination symbol in the first column designates a specific combination and lay-up of grades of lumber. For example, 16F-V1 indicates a combination with a bending design value, F_{bx}, of 1600 psi (column 2–tension zone stressed in tension) made with visually graded lumber (V). In the same format, 24F-E2 indicates an F_{bx} of 2400 psi (column 2–tension zone stressed in tension) made with E-rated lumber. Lay-up details for hardwood combinations are available in AITC 119 (130).

NDS Supplement Table 5D. Reference design values in this table are for hardwood laminating combinations that have been optimized for stresses due to axial loading or to bending about the y-y axis (loads applied parallel to the wide face of the laminations). Each combination consists of a single grade of one species of lumber. The grade associated with each numbered combination can be obtained from the AITC 119 (130).

C5.2.2 Orientation of Member

Reference design values for structural glued laminated timber are primarily developed using provisions from ASTM D3737 (13). The various models contained in D3737 result in different design values based on the orientation of the member with respect to transverse loads. These different values reflect both the use of mixed-grade layups and differences in the placement of strength-reducing characteristics between laminations on edge and laminations used flatwise. The x-x and y-y axes are defined relative to the orientation of the laminations, not the overall dimensions of the laminated timber cross section.

C5.2.3 Balanced and Unbalanced Layups

Multiple-grade layups of structural glued laminated timber are optimized for bending by placing high grade laminations near the top and bottom of the section and lower grade laminations in the core. Testing of glulam beams has demonstrated that the strength of tension laminations is critical and that laminations of a somewhat lower grade can be used in the compression zone of a beam without reducing the capacity of the beam. These *unbalanced* layups are more resource-efficient for applications such as simply-supported beams where the beam is bent in only one direction. *Balanced* layups are recommended for applications involving both positive and negative bending. The top faces of glulam beams are marked "TOP" to ensure proper installation.

C5.2.4 Bending, F_{bx}^+, F_{bx}^-, F_{by}

Positive and negative bending design values are tabulated for bending about the x-x axis. The positive bending design value, F_{bx}^+, is used for both flexural tension and flexural compression in sections subjected to bending causing compression at the top edge and tension at the bottom edge. The negative bending design value, F_{bx}^-, is used for both flexural tension and flexural compression in sections subject to bending causing tension at the top edge and compression at the bottom edge.

C5.2.5 Compression Perpendicular to Grain, $F_{c\perp x}$, $F_{c\perp y}$

The appropriate design value for compression perpendicular to grain is based on the density of the lamination(s) at the location of bearing stress. Design values for compression perpendicular to grain on the top and bottom of the beam are assigned based on the grade of the laminations at those locations. Design values for bearing on the side of glulam beams are assigned based on the lowest grade of lumber used in the layup. Because the laminations used on the top and bottom of glulam beams are commonly more dense than the core laminations, higher values of compression perpendicular to grain are commonly used for bearing on the top or bottom faces than on the side.

C5.2.6 Shear Parallel to Grain, F_{vx}, F_{vy}

Reference design values for shear have traditionally been derived from tests of small shear-block specimens. The current reference design values are based on tests of full-scale prismatic beams subjected to quasi-static loading conditions. Application of the shear reduction factor reduces the reference stress to approximately the value derived from the shear-block tests for cases which were not tested as part of the full-scale test program.

The shear stress reduction of 0.84 and 0.95 for use with members of only two laminations or three laminations, respectively, shall be applied cumulatively with the Shear Reduction Factor, C_{vr}, in 5.3.10.

C5.2.7 Modulus of Elasticity, E_x, $E_{x\ min}$, E_y, $E_{y\ min}$

Reference design values for E_x and E_y represent the average bending moduli for bending about the x-x and y-y axes, respectively. These values include a 5% reduction to account for shear deformations and are customarily used for serviceability calculations. For calculations of beam and column stability, the appropriate reference design values (E_{xmin} and E_{ymin}) are determined using the following equation:

$$E_{min} = \frac{E[1-1.645(CoV_E)][1.05]}{1.66} = \frac{E[1-1.645(0.10)][1.05]}{1.66} = 0.528$$

where:

E = reference modulus of elasticity

1.05 = adjustment factor to convert E values to a pure bending basis

1.66 = factor of safety

CoV_E = coefficient of variation in modulus of elasticity (see NDS Appendix F)

C5.2.8 Radial Tension, F_{rt}

Radial tension stresses are induced in curved bending members when bending loads tend to flatten out the curve or increase the radius of curvature. In earlier editions, radial tension design values perpendicular to grain were established as 1/3 the corresponding shear design value parallel to grain for all species. This provision was based on strength data for small, clear specimens free of checks and other seasoning effects (9). It is important to note that the factor of 1/3 applies to the shear value for non-prismatic members ($F_{vx}C_{vr}$). As a result of field experience, the radial tension reference design value perpendicular to grain for Douglas Fir-Larch was limited to 15 psi except for conditions created by wind and earthquake loading. In 1991, this limit was expanded to all western species.

C5.2.9 Radial Compression, F_{rc}

Because radial stresses are maximum at the neutral axis of a curved beam, the appropriate design value to use for radial compression is the compression perpendicular to grain design value for the laminations used in the core of the beam. This value is equal to the design value for bearing on the side face of a beam, $F_{c\perp y}$.

C5.2.10 Other Species and Grades

See C5.1.1.2.

C5.3 Adjustment of Reference Design Values

C5.3.1 General

Applicable adjustment factors for structural glued laminated timbers are specified in Table 5.3.1 of the Specification.

C5.3.2 Load Duration Factor, C_D (ASD Only)

See C2.3.2.

C5.3.3 Wet Service Factor, C_M

The wet service reduction value, C_M, for F_b, F_t, F_v, $F_{c\perp}$ F_c, and E in NDS Supplement Tables 5A, 5B, 5C, and 5D are based on provisions of ASTM D3737 (13). The wet service factors account for both the decrease in mechanical properties and the increase in cross-section dimensions associated with this exposure. Since radial tension, F_{rt}, is based on shear parallel to grain, F_v, Footnote 2 in Table 5.3.1 is intended to clarify that C_M for F_v is also applicable to F_{rt}.

C5.3.4 Temperature Factor, C_t

See C2.3.3. Since radial tension, F_{rt}, is based on shear parallel to grain, F_v, Footnote 2 in Table 5.3.1 is intended to clarify that C_t for F_v is also applicable to F_{rt}.

C5.3.5 Beam Stability Factor, C_L

Reference bending design values, F_b, given in NDS Supplement Tables 5A, 5B, 5C, and 5D are based on members having a compression edge supported throughout its length or having a depth to breadth ratio of one or less. When these conditions do not exist, F_b values are to be adjusted by the beam stability factor, C_L, calculated in accordance with the procedures of NDS 3.3.3. Because the tendency of the compression portion of the beam to buckle is a function of beam stiffness about the y-y axis for beams loaded in bending about the x-x axis, all glued laminated beam stability factor calculations are to be made with values of modulus of elasticity for bending about the y-y axis, E_{ymin}, modified by all applicable adjustment factors (see also C3.3.3).

C5.3.6 Volume Factor, C_V

The volume factor adjustment for structural glued laminated timber beams includes terms for the effects of width, length, and depth. The volume factor (C_V) equation (NDS Equation 5.3-1) is based on research involving tests of beams 5-1/8 and 8-3/4 inches wide, 6 to 48 inches deep, and 10 to 68 feet in length (90). This equation is based on the volume effect equation given in ASTM D3737 (13). The volume factor, C_V, applies when structural glued laminated timber bending members are loaded in bending about the x-x axis.

As indicated in Footnote 1 to NDS Table 5.3.1, the volume factor, C_V, is not applied simultaneously with the beam stability factor, C_L. The smaller of the two adjustment factors applies. This provision is a continuation of the practice of considering beam stability and bending size modifications separately. The practice is based on design experience and the position that beam buckling is associated with stresses on the compression side of the beam, whereas bending design values and the effect of volume on such values are related primarily to the properties of the laminations stressed in tension.

C5.3.7 Flat Use Factor, C_{fu}

The flat use factor, C_{fu}, applies where glued laminated timber bending members are loaded in bending about the y-y axis. The C_{fu} factors given in NDS Supplement Tables 5A, 5B, 5C, and 5D are applied only to the tabulated F_{byy} design values in these tables and cover only those members which are less than 12" in dimension parallel to the wide face of the laminations, d_y. For bending members loaded parallel to the wide face of the laminations with the dimension of the member in this direction greater than 12", a flat use factor based on Equation 4.3-1 of the Specification should be used.

Provisions reflect standard nomenclature used by the glued-laminated timber industry. The term "d_y" refers to the member dimension parallel to the wide faces of the laminations. NDS Figure 5B clarifies the dimension "d_y", member orientation, and direction of loading, for applicability of the flat use factor.

C5.3.8 Curvature Factor, C_c

When the individual laminations of structural glued laminated timber members are bent to shape in curved forms, bending stresses are induced in each lamination that remain after gluing. In addition, the distribution of stresses about the neutral axis of curved members is not linear. The curvature factor, C_c, is an adjustment of reference bending design values, F_b, to account for the effects of these two conditions.

The curvature factor equation given in NDS 5.3.8 is based on early tests (166). The limits on the ratio of lamination thickness to radius of curvature of 1/100 for southern pine and hardwoods and 1/125 for other softwood species are imposed to avoid overstressing or possible breaking of the laminations.

Radii of curvature used in practice generally are larger than those allowed by the specified minimum thickness/radius of curvature ratios. For nominal 1 inch thick laminations (3/4 inch net), radii of curvature of 7 feet and 9.3 feet are typically used with southern pine and other softwood species, respectively. For nominal 2 inch laminations (1.5 inches net), a radius of curvature of 27.5 feet is commonly used for all species.

C5.3.9 Stress Interaction Factor, C_I

Prismatic beam design neglects the potential interaction of shear and bending stresses, because the maximum values of these stresses occur at different locations in the cross section. For beams with a tapered edge, the shear stress distribution is altered. In addition, perpendicular to grain stresses are developed along the tapered edge. Taper cuts are, therefore, not recommended on the tension faces of beams since they cause tension stresses to develop perpendicular to grain. The stress interaction factor, C_I, accounts for the interaction of flexure, shear, and perpendicular-to-grain stresses along the tapered edge.

The stress interaction factor, C_I, does not apply simultaneously with the volume effect factor, C_V, for members tapered on the compression face, because, in this case, the volume factor accounts for tension-side effects, and the combined beam stability factor and stress interaction factor account for compression-side effects. Therefore, in the case of a tapered compression face, the lesser of C_V or C_LC_I applies. Similarly, the stress interaction factor, C_I, does not apply simultaneously with the lateral stability factor, C_L, for members tapered on the tension face, because in this case the beam stability factor accounts for compression side effects and the combined volume factor and stress interaction factor account for tension side effects. Therefore, in the case of a tapered tension face, the lesser of C_VC_I or C_L applies.

C5.3.10 Shear Reduction Factor, C_{vr}

The shear reduction factor, C_{vr}, previously appearing as a footnote to glued-laminated timber design value tables in the NDS Supplement, was added to the 2012 edition of the Specification as an adjustment factor applicable for shear design of other than prismatic beams such as for the design of notched members, curved members, tapered members, design for radial tension, and shear design at connections.

The term "non-prismatic" is used to designate a broad range of products including curved beams and arches, tapered beams, pitched and tapered curved beams, and generally members with any geometry other than straight or mildly cambered with constant depth.

C5.3.11 Column Stability Factor, C_P

See C3.7.1.

C5.3.12 Bearing Area Factor, C_b

See C3.10.4.

C5.3.13 Pressure-Preservative Treatment

The provision in the NDS for use of reference design values with structural glued laminated timber that has been preservative treated is applicable to material that has been treated and redried in accordance with AWPA Standards. In AWPA Standards, the maximum temperature for kiln drying material after treatment is 165°F (22).

C5.3.14 Format Conversion Factor, K_F (LRFD Only)

See C2.3.5.

C5.3.15 Resistance Factor, ϕ (LRFD Only)

See C2.3.6.

C5.3.16 Time Effect Factor, λ (LRFD Only)

See C2.3.7.

C5.4 Special Design Considerations

C5.4.1 Curved Bending Members with Constant Cross Section

C5.4.1.3 The equation for determining radial stress in a curved member of constant rectangular cross section is based on research published in 1939 (166). Radial stresses in curved members having variable cross section are determined by different procedures (46, 56). Complete design procedures for such members are available from other recognized sources (140).

Where the bending moment acts to reduce curvature, the radial stress is to be checked against the adjusted radial tension design value perpendicular to grain, F_{rt}' (see C5.2.2). When mechanical reinforcing is provided which is sufficient to resist all induced radial stresses, the actual radial stress is still limited to no more than (1/3) F_{vx}'.

Where the bending moment acts to increase curvature, the radial stress is to be checked against the adjusted compression design value perpendicular to grain. The appropriate compression perpendicular-to-grain design value for use is the value corresponding to the lamination grades used in the core of the beam, $F_{c\perp}$.

C5.4.1.4 The downward deflection of curved beams results in lateral displacement of the unrestrained beam ends. This lateral displacement must be considered in the design of beams and in the connection between beams and walls.

C5.4.2 Double-Tapered Curved Bending Members

C5.4.2.1 The bending stress, f_b, for curved beams of variable cross section, such as pitched tapered curved beams, is greater than for straight prismatic members and is increased by the bending stress factor, K_ϕ, (NDS Equation 5.4-2) due to the shape of the member.

C5.4.2.2 Design of double-tapered curved members for shear is identical to the design of prismatic members, except loads within a distance d from the support are not permitted to be neglected and the shear stress reduction factor is applied.

C5.4.2.3 The shape of double-tapered curved members alters the stress distribution for radial stresses in the curved segment of the beam, rendering Equation 5.4-1 inapplicable. The empirical radial stress factor, K_{rs}, is used with the flexure formula at the section through the beam apex to estimate the value of the radial stress at that section for the case of a beam subject to pure bending moment. The empirical load-shape radial stress reduction factor, C_{rs}, accounts for reduced radial stresses that exist in a uniformly loaded beam.

C5.4.2.4 Due to the variable cross section, strict evaluation of the deflection of a double-tapered curved beam requires more advanced analysis techniques such as virtual work or finite element modeling. A simplified approach has been developed that uses a prismatic rectangular beam of *equivalent depth* to estimate the deflection. This approach is permitted to be used in lieu of more complex methods.

Vertical deflection of double-tapered curved beams results in lateral displacement of the beam ends. NDS Equation 5.4-5 provides an estimate of the displacement at each support. The total horizontal displacement is equal to $2\Delta_H$.

C5.4.3 Lateral Stability for Tudor Arches

Prescriptive limitations on the ratio of tangent point depth to breadth (d/b) for glulam arches are based on long-standing industry recommendations and field experience over many years.

In determining the adequacy of lateral support, decking or subflooring applied directly to a beam with two or more fasteners per piece is acceptable edge restraint for a beam loaded through such decking or subflooring. Rafters, joists, or purlins attached two feet or less on center to the side of a beam and stabilized through the attachment of sheathing or subflooring are acceptable edge restraint for a beam that is loaded through such rafters, joists, or purlins. Recent research has shown that the bottom edges of rafters, joists, or purlins attached to the sides of beams by strap hangers or similar means do not have to be fixed to provide adequate lateral support to the beam if their top edges are restrained (164, 165).

C5.4.4 Tapered Straight Bending Members

C5.4.4.1 Because glulam beams are typically manufactured with high grades of lumber in the top and bottom laminations and lower grades in the core (see C5.2.2 and C5.2.3), field-tapering a member will result in reductions in the reference design values for the section. For beams manufactured with taper in the laminating plant, the high grades are maintained along the full length of the taper cut to ensure that the full design value is maintained. Manufacturers or trade associations representing the manufacturers should be contacted to determine the appropriate reference design values for field-tapered members (see also C5.3.9).

C5.4.4.2 Design of tapered straight members for shear is identical to the design of prismatic members, except loads within a distance d from the support are not permitted to be neglected and the shear stress reduction factor is applied.

C.5.4.4.3 Due to the variable cross section, strict evaluation of the deflection of a tapered beam requires more advanced analysis techniques such as virtual work or finite element. A simplified approach has been developed that uses a prismatic rectangular beam of *equivalent depth* to estimate the deflection. This approach is permitted to be used in lieu of more complex methods.

C5.4.5 Notches

The designer has the responsibility of determining if structural glued laminated timber bending members should be notched and how load-carrying capacity should be calculated. Current good engineering practice is to avoid all notching of such bending members on the tension side except where end notching at the supports is necessary. End notches on the tension face are limited to the lesser of 1/10 of the bending member depth or 3 inches (140). Notches on the compression face of the beam are less severe and consequently less restrictive, particularly for taper cuts.

The effect of notches located at the ends of beams is generally limited to a reduction of shear capacity for the beam. However, notches that extend a long distance from the end of the member may also reduce the bending load-carrying capacity and increase the deflection. For notches extending more than 1/3 of the length of the member, the effects of the notch on bending and deflection must also be considered based on 5.4.4. The methods of NDS 3.4.3 are used to calculate the design shear of glued laminated timber members with end notches (140). The shear reduction factor of 5.3.10 applies for the analysis of members with notches.

The provisions for compression-side notches do not consider the case of a taper cut combined with a square-cornered notch such as illustrated in Figure C5.4.5. At a minimum, for such a case, each type of modification must comply with the applicable limitation. No further guidance is available for the evaluation of this case.

Figure C5.4.5 Taper Cut Combined with a Square-Cornered Notch

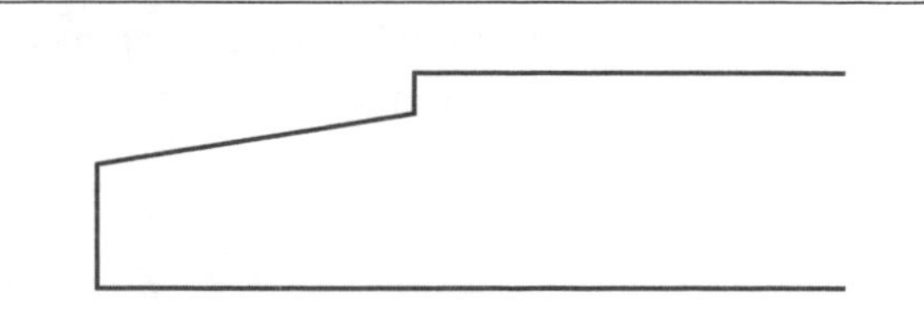

C6 ROUND TIMBER POLES AND PILES

C6.1 General

Round timber piles have been widely used in the United States in the construction of railroads, highways, harbors and dams, as well as for building foundations, since the middle of the 18th century. In addition to availability and cost, the natural taper of round timber piles makes them relatively easy to drive, compacts the soil around the pile during driving, and provides a larger diameter butt end capable of withstanding driving forces and supporting loads from other structural members (176).

The earliest standardization effort involving timber piles was the establishment of uniform size and grade characteristics in ASTM D25, *Standard Specification for Round Timber Piles* (10). First developed in 1915, the current edition of this standard includes specifications for minimum butt and tip sizes for various pile lengths, establishes limits on crook and knot sizes, and sets minimum rate of growth and percent summerwood quality requirements.

The establishment of standard physical characteristics for timber piles in ASTM D25 was subsequently followed by the development of standard requirements for preservative treatment. Such specifications were available from the American Wood Preservers' Association (AWPA) since well before World War II (184). This Association's Standard C3, *Piles-Preservative Treatment by Pressure Processes*, establishes conditioning, pressure, temperature, retention, and penetration limitations and requirements for various preservative treatments by species and pile use (22). Because of the effect treatment processes can have on strength properties, standardization of the processes used are an important element in the specification and use of timber piles.

Engineering design with timber piles in the early years was largely based on experience, observation of the performance of piles under similar loading conditions, and the results of static loading tests. Piles were considered to fall into two groups: those in which the pile tip bears on a solid layer and were designed as columns, and those in which the pile receives most of its support from soil friction on the sides and were designed from driving records or empirical formulas (184). Standard design procedures were not available.

To meet the growing need for uniform design recommendations, the American Association of State Highway Officials (AASHTO) began to specify allowable pile compression design values of 1200 psi for Douglas fir and slightly lower values for other species in the 1940's (176). However, maximum pile loads in the order of 36,000 to 50,000 pounds per pile also were specified which generally was the limiting criterion.

In the 1950's, AASHTO, the American Railway Engineering Association, and other user groups began to establish pile design values using the procedures of ASTM D245, *Standard Methods for Establishing Structural Grades of Lumber* (176) (see C4.2.3.2). Building codes also began to establish allowable pile stresses using basic stresses and other information given in ASTM D245 (161).

Uniform national standards for development of strength values for timber piles became available in 1970 with the publication of ASTM D2899, *Standard Method for Establishing Design Stresses for Round Timber Piles* (11). This consensus standard provided for the establishment of stresses for piles of any species meeting the size and quality requirements of ASTM D25. Under D2899, clear wood property information from ASTM D2555 (9) were adjusted for grade, relation of pile tip strength to clear wood strength, variability of pile strength to that of small clear specimens, load duration, and treatment conditioning effects.

In 1997, reference design values were added for construction poles based on D2899 per reference in ASTM D3200.

In 2003, the provisions of D2899 were revised to derive single pile design values rather than pile cluster design values derived in previous versions of D2899. As a result, beginning with the 2012 edition of the Specification the single pile basis became the reference condition for pile design values and adjustments to pile design values.

C6.1.1 Scope

C6.1.1.2 The provisions of Chapter 6 of the Specification relate solely to the properties of round timber poles and piles. It is the responsibility of the designer to determine soil loads, such as frictional forces from subsiding soils and fills, the adequacy of the surrounding soil or water to provide sufficient lateral bracing, the method of pole or pile placement that will preclude damage to the wood member, the bearing capacity of the strata at the pile tip, and the effects of any other surrounding environmental factors on the supporting or loading of poles or piles.

C6.1.2 Specifications

C6.1.2.1 In addition to setting standard pile sizes, ASTM D25 (10) establishes minimum quality requirements, straightness criteria, and knot limitations. All pile tips are required to have an average rate of growth of 6 or more rings per inch and percent summerwood of 33 percent or more in the outer 50 percent of the radius; except less than 6 rings per inch growth rate is acceptable if the summerwood percentage is 50 percent or more in the outer 50 percent of the tip radius. Thus, 75 percent of the cross-sectional area of pile tips conforming to ASTM D25 essentially meets lumber requirements for dense material (8).

Knots in piles are limited by ASTM D25 to a diameter of not more than one-sixth of the circumference of the pile at the point where they occur. The sum of knot diameters in any one-foot length of pile is limited to one-third or less of the circumference.

ASTM D3200 establishes standard sizes and minimum grades for construction poles based on ASTM D25 for piles.

C6.1.2.2 Preservative treatment requirements and limitations differ depending upon where the piles are to be used. Designation of the applicable treatment standard and use condition defines the treatment desired by the specifier.

C6.1.3 Standard Sizes

Standard sizes (10) for round timber piles range from 7 to 18 inches in diameter measured 3 feet from the butt. Pile lengths range from 20 to 85 feet for southern pine and to 120 feet for Douglas fir and other species. Pile taper is controlled by establishing a minimum tip circumference associated with a minimum circumference 3 feet from the butt for each length class; or by establishing a minimum circumference 3 feet from the butt associated with a minimum tip circumference for each length class. This provides a known tip area for use in engineering design as well as a conservative estimate of the area at any point along the length of the pile.

Standard sizes (12) for round timber construction poles range from 5 to 12 inches in diameter measured at the tip. Pole lengths range from 10 to 40 feet.

C6.1.4 Preservative Treatment

C6.1.4.1 Green timber piles are generally conditioned prior to pressure treatment (22). For southern pine the conditioning usually involves steaming under pressure to obtain a temperature of 245°F and then applying a vacuum. The process results in water being forced out of the outer part of the pile, but does not dry it to a seasoned condition (181, 63). Conditioning of Douglas fir is usually done by the Boulton or boiling-under-a-vacuum-process. This method of conditioning, which partially seasons the sapwood portion of the pile, involves heating the material in the preservative oil under a vacuum at temperatures up to 220°F (181, 63). The Boulton process also is used with hardwood species.

Both the steaming and Boulton conditioning processes affect pile strength properties (11, 176). The effects of conditioning (steaming, Boultonizing, and drying) are not included in pile design values given in Table 6A of the NDS Supplement and must be addressed with the reduction factors in 6.3.5.

C6.1.4.2 Decay does not occur in softwood species and in most hardwoods that are completely saturated and an air supply is not available (63, 127). Permanently submerged piles meet these conditions.

C6.2 Reference Design Values

C6.2.1 Reference Design Values

C6.2.1.1 Reference design values for round timber piles are specified in NDS Supplement Table 6A and are based on ASTM D2899 (11). All values are derived from the properties of small clear specimens of the applicable species as given in ASTM D2555 (9) adjusted as appropriate for the specific property for variability, load duration, grade, lower strength of pile tip, and lower variability of piles compared to small clear specimens (160).

C6.2.1.2 Design values for round timber poles are specified in NDS Supplement Table 6B and are based on ASTM D3200 which uses provisions from ASTM D2899 (11) with similar adjustments used for round timber piles.

C6.2.2 Other Species or Grades

Where piles of species other than those listed in NDS Supplement Table 6A are used, it is the designer's responsibility to assure that the methods of ASTM D2899 for establishing design values are properly applied, including appropriate adjustments for conditioning process.

C6.3 Adjustment of Reference Design Values

C6.3.1 General

Adjustment factors for round timber poles and piles are specified in Table 6.3.1 of the Specification.

C6.3.2 Load Duration Factor, C_D (ASD Only)

See C2.3.2. As shown in NDS Table 6.3.1, the load duration factor, C_D, is not applicable to compression design values perpendicular to grain, $F_{c\perp}$ for round timber poles and piles. Pressure impregnation of water-borne preservatives or fire retardant chemicals to retentions of 2.0 pcf or more may significantly reduce energy absorbing ability as measured by work-to-maximum-load in bending. For this reason, the impact load duration adjustment is not to be applied to members pressure-treated with preservative oxides for salt water exposure or those pressure-treated with fire retardant chemicals.

C6.3.4 Temperature Factor, C_t

See C2.3.3.

C6.3.5 Condition Treatment Factor, C_{ct}

Reference design values for poles and piles are based on air dried conditioning. Kiln-drying, steam conditioning, or boultonizing prior to treatment will have the effect of reducing the reference design value.

C6.3.6 Beam Stability Factor, C_L

A round member can be considered to have a d/b ratio of 1 and therefore, in accordance with NDS 3.3.3.1, C_L equals 1.0.

C6.3.7 Size Factor, C_F

Bending design values, F_b, for round timber poles and piles that are larger than 13.5 inches in diameter at the critical section in bending are adjusted for size using the same equation used to make size adjustments with sawn lumber Beams & Stringers and Posts & Timbers (see NDS 4.3.6.3 and C4.3.6.2). When applied to round timbers, Equation 4.3-1 is entered with a d equal to the depth of a square beam having the same cross-sectional area as that of the round member. The equivalency of the load-carrying capacity of a circular member and a conventionally loaded square member of the cross-sectional area has long been recognized (98).

C6.3.8 Column Stability Factor, C_P

See C3.7.1. Column stability provisions from NDS 3.7.1 can be used for round timber poles and piles by substituting $r\sqrt{12}$ for the depth, d, in the equations, where r is the applicable radius of gyration of the column cross section.

C6.3.9 Critical Section Factor, C_{cs}

The critical section factor, C_{cs}, accounts for the effect of tree height on compression design values parallel to grain. The specific adjustment, based on D2899, provides for an increase in the design value as the critical section moves from the pile tip toward the pile butt and is limited to a maximum increase of 10%.

C6.3.10 Bearing Area Factor, C_b

See C3.10.4.

C6.3.11 Load Sharing Factor (Pile Group Factor), C_{ls}

Reference design values in NDS Supplement Table 6A are based on a single pile. Where piles are used in clusters such that the pile group deforms as a single element,, the single pile reference compression design value parallel to grain, F_c, and the single pile reference bending design value, F_b, are permitted to be multiplied by C_{ls} in NDS Table 6.3.11.

The load sharing factor (pile group factor) is applicable to F_b and F_c and is not applicable to soil-related properties such as pile tip bearing or skin friction.

C6.3.12 Format Conversion Factor, K_F (LRFD Only)

See C2.3.5.

C6.3.13 Resistance Factor, ϕ (LRFD Only)

See C2.3.6.

C6.3.14 Time Effect Factor, λ (LRFD Only)

See C2.3.7.

C7 PREFABRICATED WOOD I-JOISTS

C7.1 General

Prefabricated wood I-joists utilize the geometry of the cross-section and high strength components to maximize the strength and stiffness of the wood fiber. Flanges are manufactured from solid sawn lumber or structural composite lumber, while webs typically consist of plywood or oriented strand board. Wood I-joists are generally produced as proprietary products. Acceptance reports and product literature should be consulted for current design information.

C7.1.1 Scope

The general requirements given in Chapters 1, 2, and 3 of the Specification are applicable to prefabricated wood I-joists except where indicated otherwise. Chapter 7 of the Specification contains provisions which specifically apply to prefabricated wood I-joists manufactured and evaluated in accordance with ASTM D 5055 (15). The provisions of NDS Chapter 7 contain only the basic requirements applicable to engineering design of prefabricated wood I-joists. Specific detailed requirements, such as those for bearing, web stiffeners, web holes, and notches, are available in the prefabricated wood I-joist manufacturer's literature and code evaluation reports. Code evaluation reports, where available for a specific product and application, contain information to assist in the approval and use of the specific product in accordance with requirements of the applicable building code.

C7.1.2 Definition

Prefabricated wood I-joists are specialized products, manufactured with specially designed equipment. Expertise in adhesives, wood products, manufacturing, and quality assurance are necessary ingredients for the fabrication of high-quality prefabricated wood I-joists.

Standard Sizes

Prefabricated wood I-joists are available in a range of sizes to handle a variety of applications. Common I-joist depths for residential flooring applications are 9.5", 11.875", 14", and 16". These sizes do not match standard sawn lumber depths to minimize the combined use of sawn lumber with wood I-joists in the same floor system. Mixing I-joists and sawn lumber in the same system is not recommended because differences in dimensional change between sawn lumber and wood I-joists can affect load distribution as the products reach equilibrium moisture content.

C7.1.3 Identification

Prefabricated wood I-joists are typically identified by product series and company name, plant location or number, qualified agency name or logo, code evaluation report numbers, and a means for establishing the date of manufacture.

C7.1.4 Service Conditions

Prefabricated wood I-joists are typically used in dry service conditions (where moisture content of sawn lumber is less than 16%). I-joist manufacturers state dry service conditions based on the moisture content of lumber since the equilibrium moisture content (EMC) of I-joists is lower under the same environmental conditions and varies based on the manufacturing process. For other conditions, the I-joist manufacturer should be consulted.

C7.2 Reference Design Values

Prefabricated wood I-joists are proprietary products and reference design values vary among manufacturers and product lines. Reference design values are obtained from the manufacturer through the manufacturer's literature or code evaluation report.

C7.3 Adjustment of Reference Design Values

C7.3.1 General

Applicable adjustment factors for prefabricated wood I-joists are specified in Table 7.3.1 of the Specification. Volume effects are accounted for either directly in testing or indirectly in analysis as detailed in ASTM D 5055 (15) and need not be considered in design.

C7.3.2 Load Duration Factor, C_D (ASD Only)

See C2.3.2. Duration of load effects in NDS 2.3.2 apply to all prefabricated wood I-joist design values except for those relating to stiffness, EI, EI_{min}, and K.

C7.3.3 Wet Service Factor, C_M

Prefabricated wood I-joists are limited to use in dry service conditions unless specifically allowed by the manufacturer (see NDS 7.1.4). I-joists are assembled with exterior adhesives and can tolerate the environmental conditions of typical jobsites. Care should be taken, however, to follow the manufacturer's recommendations for proper jobsite storage to minimize dimensional changes associated with changes in moisture content.

C7.3.4 Temperature Factor, C_t

See C2.3.3. Prefabricated wood I-joist reference design values are adjusted by the same temperature adjustment factors as other wood products (see Table C7.3-1).

C7.3.5 Beam Stability Factor, C_L

Bending design values provided in manufacturers' code evaluation reports are based on the I-joist having the compression flange supported throughout its entire length to prevent lateral displacement. This condition is ensured by direct attachment of sheathing to the I-joist. In addition, wood I-joists should be provided with lateral support at points of bearing to prevent cross-sectional rotation (twisting). Provisions applicable to wood I-joists are consistent with provisions in NDS 3.3.3 as follows:

a) NDS 7.3.5.1 permits C_L=1.0 when the compression flange of an I-joist is supported throughout its length to prevent lateral displacement, consistent with NDS 3.3.3.3.

b) NDS 7.3.5.2 provides a method for designing the compression flange of an I-joist as an unbraced or partially braced column when the compression flange is not braced throughout its length, consistent with NDS 3.3.3.4.

Derivation of the beam stability equations in the NDS are based on the assumption that the beam is braced against cross-sectional rotation (twisting) and lateral displacement at points of bearing (i.e., the tension edge and the compression edge of the beam are held in line see Figure C7.3.5). As an example, bracing against cross-sectional rotation (twisting) will prevent lateral-torsional buckling, but bracing against lateral displacement will not necessarily prevent rotation at the point of bearing (e.g., set of floor joists "turning over").

Table C7.3-1 Temperature Factor, C_t, for Prefabricated Wood I-Joists

Reference Design Values	In-Service Moisture Conditions[1]	C_t		
		T≤100°F	100°F<T≤125°F	125°F<T≤150°F
EI, EI_{min}	Wet or Dry	1.0	0.9	0.9
M_r, V_r, R_r, and K	Dry	1.0	0.8	0.7
	Wet	1.0	0.7	0.5

1. Wet and dry service conditions for wood I-joists are specified in NDS 7.1.4.

Figure C7.3.5 Example of Direct Attachment of Sheathing to Support Compression Flange and Lateral Support at Points of Bearing

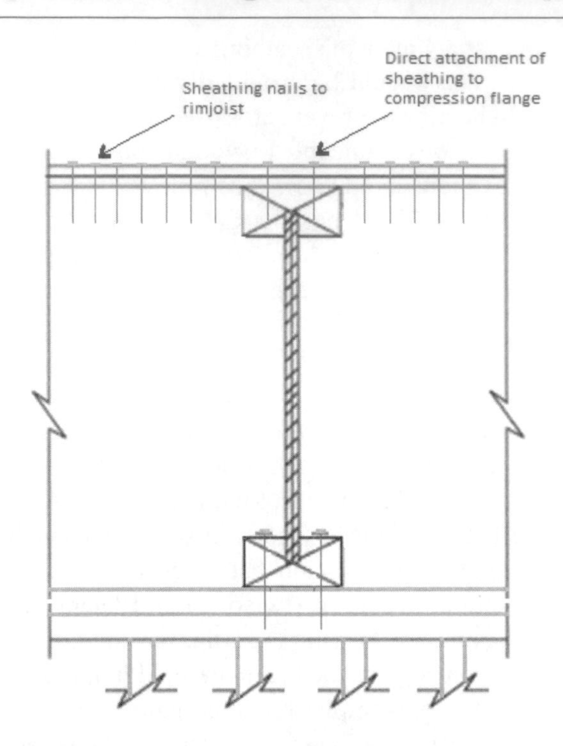

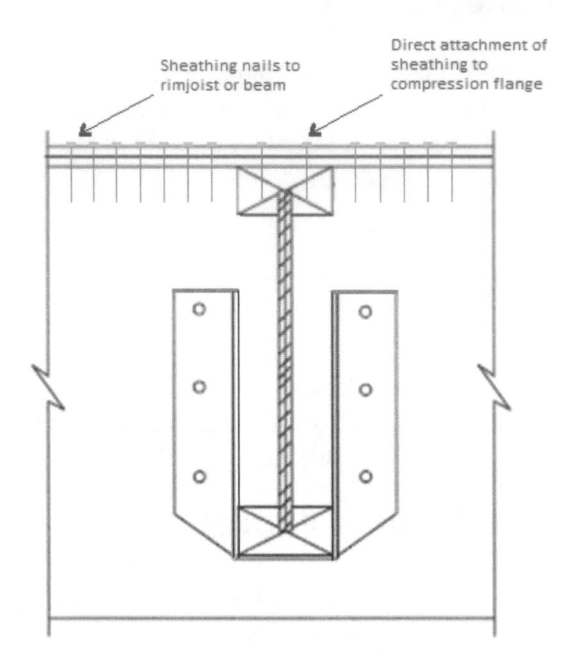

C7.3.6 Repetitive Member Factor, C_r

The repetitive member factor varies with composite action across a range of I-joist depths and series, I-joist stiffness variability, sheathing types, sheathing stiffnesses, and sheathing attachment. For several technical reasons, the magnitude of the repetitive member factor is typically much smaller than for sawn lumber. To provide a factor that could be applied across all applications, this factor was set at 1.0 in ASTM D 5055 (15) and D 6555 (19).

C7.3.7 Pressure-Preservative Treatment

Common treatments associated with I-joists include light solvent-based preservatives applied under low pressure offering protection against wood destroying fungi or insects. Any treatment of I-joists that require high pressure or harsh drying cycles should be avoided. Manufacturers should be consulted for any applications that require preservative treatment.

C7.3.8 Format Conversion Factor, K_F (LRFD Only)

See C2.3.5.

C7.3.9 Resistance Factor, ϕ (LRFD Only)

See C2.3.6.

C7.3.10 Time Effect Factor, λ (LRFD Only)

See C2.3.7.

C7.4 Special Design Considerations

C7.4.1 Bearing

The end conditions of an I-joist require specific attention by the designer when considering the differences of designing with an "I" shape versus rectangular sections. The limit states at the bearing of an I-joist include the I-joist reaction (integrity of the web/flange rout), flange compression, compression of the support, reaction hardware (hangers), and shear.

The manufacturer's literature or code evaluation reports should be consulted for design assumptions at end conditions. Reaction capacity, R_r, and shear capacity, V_r, are typically published separately and should be checked independently. Published reaction capacity is based on testing conducted at one or more bearing lengths. Extrapolation beyond tested conditions is not appropriate. For end bearing, the minimum bearing length is typically 1.75", but never less than 1.5". The reaction capacity may or may not include the compression of the flange or bearing plate. The published capacities of joist hangers only include the capacity of the hanger. A complete design would include checking the I-joist capacity for the bearing length of the particular joist hanger.

C7.4.2 Load Application

The manufacturer's literature or code evaluation reports should be consulted for design assumptions where loads are not applied to the top flange or where concentrated loads or other non-uniform loads are applied to the I-joist.

C7.4.3 Web Holes

The manufacturer's literature or code evaluation reports should be consulted for the effect of web holes on strength and stiffness.

C7.4.4 Notches

The manufacturer's literature or code evaluation reports should be consulted when notching of the flange is being considered. However, as a general rule, flange notching is not permitted.

C7.4.5 Deflection

I-joist stiffness is presented as the product of the material modulus of elasticity and the effective moment of inertia (EI). I-Joist floor systems are typically designed to L/480 deflection limits rather than the code minimum of L/360. Consideration of creep deflection for unique applications, such as those with heavy dead loads, may be done in accordance with NDS 3.5.2.

C7.4.6 Vertical Load Transfer

See C7.4.2.

C7.4.7 Shear

See C7.4.1 and C7.4.2.

C8 STRUCTURAL COMPOSITE LUMBER

C8.1 General

Structural composite lumber (SCL) is manufactured from wood strands or full sheets of veneer. The process typically includes alignment of stress-graded fiber, application of adhesive, and pressing the material together under heat and pressure. By redistributing natural growth characteristics and monitoring manufacturing through quality control procedures, the resulting material has consistent quality, and maximizes the strength and stiffness of the wood fiber.

Structural composite lumber is typically produced in a long length continuous or fixed press in a billet form. It is then resawn into required dimensions for use. Material is available in a variety of depths typically from 4-3/8" to 24" and thicknesses from 3/4" to 7".

C8.1.1 Scope

The general requirements given in Chapters 1, 2, and 3 of the Specification are applicable to structural composite lumber except where indicated otherwise. Chapter 8 of the Specification contains provisions which are particular to structural composite lumber. The provisions of NDS Chapter 8 contain only the basic requirements applicable to engineering design of structural composite lumber manufactured in accordance with ASTM D 5456 (16). Specific detailing requirements, such as those for notches, are available from structural composite lumber manufacturers' literature or code evaluation reports. Code evaluation reports, where available for a specific product and application, contain information to assist in the approval and use of the specific product in accordance with requirements of the applicable building code.

C8.1.2 Definitions

Definitions for structural composite lumber, including laminated veneer lumber and parallel strand lumber, are based on definitions in ASTM D 5456 (16).

C8.1.3 Identification

Structural composite lumber is typically identified by product grade and company name, plant location or number, quality assurance agency name or logo, code evaluation report numbers, and a means for establishing the date of manufacture.

C8.1.4 Service Conditions

Structural composite lumber (SCL) is typically used in dry service conditions (where moisture content of sawn lumber is less than 16%). SCL manufacturers state dry service conditions based on the moisture content of lumber since the equilibrium moisture content (EMC) of SCL is lower under the same environmental conditions and varies based on the manufacturing process. For other conditions, the SCL manufacturer should be consulted.

C8.2 Reference Design Values

Structural composite lumber is a proprietary product and design values vary among manufacturers and product lines. Reference design values should be obtained from the manufacturer through the manufacturer's literature or code evaluation report.

C8.3 Adjustment of Reference Design Values

C8.3.1 General

Applicable adjustment factors for structural composite lumber are specified in Table 8.3.1 of the Specification.

C8.3.2 Load Duration Factor, C_D (ASD Only)

See C2.3.2.

C8.3.3 Wet Service Factor, C_M

Structural composite lumber is limited to use in dry service conditions unless specifically allowed by the manufacturer (see NDS 8.1.4).

C8.3.4 Temperature Factor, C_t

See C2.3.3.

C8.3.5 Beam Stability, C_L

See C3.3.3.

C8.3.6 Volume Factor, C_V

C8.3.6.1 Volume effects of SCL beams are two dimensional in that increasing the width does not result in a strength reduction. Further, since SCL bending properties are established based on testing at span-to-depth ratios between 17 and 21 (representative of most applications where bending strength controls), the adjustment is based only on member depth. The volume factor is determined in accordance with ASTM D5456 (16) and uses an exponent unique to each manufacturer (based on variability of the product) to adjust the reference bending design value from a reference depth to the end-use depth in application. C_V is permitted to be greater than 1 when the end-use member depth is shallower than the reference depth.

C8.3.6.2 Similar to the volume factor for bending in SCL, ASTM D5456 requires development of a volume factor for tension which can be considered a length factor, adjusting from the length used in testing to the end-use length in application. As with bending, the exponent for the volume factor in tension is unique to each manufacturer. The SCL manufacturer may also choose to publish reference tension design values based on a reference length longer than tested, in which case C_V is permitted to be greater than 1 when the end-use member length is shorter than the reference length.

C8.3.7 Repetitive Member Factor, C_r

The repetitive member factor for SCL is based on assumptions used to develop the repetitive member factor for sawn lumber (see C4.3.9), except that lower strength and stiffness variability limits the magnitude of the factor.

C8.3.8 Column Stability Factor, C_P

See C3.7.1.

C8.3.9 Bearing Area Factor, C_b

See C3.10.4.

C8.3.10 Pressure-Preservative Treatment

Per NDS 8.1.4, structural composite lumber is limited to use in dry service conditions unless specifically allowed by the manufacturer. Manufacturers should be consulted for any applications that require preservative treatment.

C8.3.11 Format Conversion Factor, K_F (LRFD Only)

See C2.3.5.

C8.3.12 Resistance Factor, ϕ (LRFD Only)

See C2.3.6.

C8.3.13 Time Effect Factor, λ (LRFD Only)

See C2.3.7.

C8.4 Special Design Considerations

C8.4.1 Notches

The designer has the responsibility of determining if structural composite lumber bending members should be notched and how load-carrying capacity should be calculated. Current good engineering practice is to avoid all notching of such bending members on the tension side except where end notching at the supports is necessary. This end notching is limited to 1/10 of the bending member depth, similar to structural glued laminated timber (140). The methods of NDS 3.4.3, used to calculate shear force at end notches in sawn lumber and structural glued laminated timber members, are permitted for structural composite lumber under the same design assumptions. Where different assumptions are made, the manufacturer should be consulted.

C9 WOOD STRUCTURAL PANELS

C9.1 General

C9.1.1 Scope

The general requirements given in Chapters 1, 2, and 3 of the Specification are applicable to wood structural panels except where indicated otherwise. Chapter 9 of the Specification contains provisions that specifically apply to wood structural panels manufactured in accordance with USDOC PS 1 (150) or PS 2 (151). The provisions of NDS Chapter 9 contain only the basic requirements applicable to engineering design of wood structural panels. Specific requirements, such as the wet service factor, the Grade and Construction factor, and the panel size factor are available from the wood structural panel manufacturer or the qualified agency.

C9.1.2 Identification

C9.1.2.1 Panel grades for plywood manufactured in conformance with USDOC PS 1 (150), *Construction & Industrial Plywood,* are designated by the grade of the face and back veneers (e.g., C-D, C-C, A-C, etc.) or by intended end-use (e.g., Underlayment, Marine, Concrete Form, etc.). Corresponding grade names in PS 1 for Sheathing, Structural I Sheathing, and Single Floor are C-D, Structural I C-D, and Underlayment, respectively.

Panel grades for products manufactured in conformance with USDOC PS 2 *Performance Standard for Wood-Based Structural-Use Panels* (151), are identified by intended end-use and include: Sheathing, Structural I Sheathing, and Single Floor.

Sheathing grade panels are intended for use as structural covering material for roofs, subfloors, and walls. Structural I sheathing panels meet increased requirements for cross-panel strength and stiffness and are typically used in panelized roof systems, diaphragms, and shear walls. Single Floor grade panels are used as a combination subfloor and underlayment and may be used under several different types of finish flooring as well as subflooring in a two-layer floor system with underlayment.

Bond classification is related to the moisture resistance of the glue bond under intended end-use conditions and does not relate to the physical (i.e., erosion, ultraviolet) or biological (i.e., mold, fungal decay, insect) resistance of the panel. Structural-use panels manufactured in conformance with PS 1 or PS 2 must meet the bond classification requirements for *Exterior* or *Exposure 1*.

> *Exterior* is defined in PS 1 and PS 2 as a bond classification for panels that are suitable for repeated wetting and redrying or long-term exposure to weather or other conditions of similar severity. *Exterior* plywood is manufactured with a minimum C grade veneer.

> *Exposure 1* is defined in PS 1 and PS 2 as a bond classification for panels that are suitable for uses not permanently exposed to the weather. Panels classified as *Exposure 1* are intended to resist the effects of moisture on structural performance due to construction delays or other conditions of similar severity.

C9.1.2.2 Span ratings indicate the maximum on center spacing of supports, in inches, over which the panels should be placed for specific applications. The span rating system is intended for panels that are applied with the strength axis across two or more spans. The strength axis is typically the axis parallel to the orientation of oriented strand board (OSB) face strands or plywood face veneer grain and is the long dimension of the panel unless indicated otherwise by the manufacturer.

The span rating for Sheathing grade panels is provided as two numbers separated by a slash (e.g., 32/16 or 48/24). The first number is the maximum recommended on center support spacing in inches for roof applications. The second number is the maximum recommended on center support spacing when the panel is used for subflooring in residential and many light commercial applications. For example, a panel with a span rating of 32/16 may be used for roof sheathing over supports spaced up to 32 inches on center or as a subfloor over supports spaced up to 16 inches on center.

Recommendations for use of Sheathing grade panels also include wall applications. Panels with roof span ratings of 16 or 20 may be installed with their strength axis either parallel or perpendicular to the wall studs space at 16 inches or less on center. Similarly, panels with roof span ratings of 24 or maximum may be installed with their strength axis either parallel or perpendicular to the wall studs spaced at 24 inches or less on center.

Sheathing grade panels may also be used in wall applications, according to manufacturers' recommendations, both parallel and perpendicular to studs. Sheathing panels with span ratings of Wall-16 or Wall-24 are for use only as wall sheathing. The numerical index (16 or 24) corresponds to the maximum on center spacing of the studs. Wall sheathing panels are typically performance tested with the strength axis parallel to the studs. For this reason, wall sheathing panels may be applied with either the strength axis parallel to the supports or perpendicular to the supports.

The span rating for Single Floor grade panels appears as a single number and represents the maximum recommended on center (oc) support spacing in inches. Typical span ratings for Single Floor products are 20 oc and 24 oc, although 16 oc, 32 oc, and 48 oc panels are also available.

C9.1.3 Definitions

C9.1.3.3 Oriented strand board (OSB) was first commercially introduced in the early 1980s succeeding "waferboard." Waferboard is a mat-formed panel product that utilizes random distribution of rectangular wafers, whereas OSB is a mat-formed panel product with oriented layers resulting in directional properties.

C9.1.3.4 The term "ply" refers to the individual sheets of veneer used to construct plywood. A "layer" is defined as a single ply of veneer or two or more adjacent plies with grain oriented in the same direction. Veneer is classified into the following six grades:

N: Highest grade level. No knots, restricted patches.
A: Higher grade level. No knots, allows more patches than N-grade but quantity of patches is also restricted.
B: Solid surface-Small round knots. Patches and round plugs are allowed.
C Plugged: Special improved C grade.
C: Small knots, knotholes, patches. Lowest grade allowed in Exterior plywood.
D: Larger knots, knotholes, some limited white pocket in sheathing grades.

C9.1.4 Service Conditions

C9.1.4.1. When the equilibrium moisture content of wood structural panels in service is less than 16 percent (including either Exposure 1 or Exterior bond classification), the dry service design values apply. A dry service condition prevails in most covered structures. However, members used in interior locations subject to high humidity, such as may occur in certain industrial operations or over unventilated swimming pools, may reach an equilibrium moisture content of 16 percent or more. In such conditions, wet service factors (see C9.3.3) should be applied to reference design values. However, preservative treated panels should be used where there is a potential for wood decay such as when panels maintain an in-service MC of 19% or more, either from sustained high humidity levels or prolonged exposure to moisture.

Exterior exposures that are not protected from the weather are generally considered wet conditions of use. Wet service adjustment factors, C_M, are provided in Commentary Table C9.3.3 for uses where this limit will be exceeded for a sustained period of time or for repeated periods. Uses in which the panel is in contact with the ground should be considered wet use for those portions of the panel that will attain a moisture content of 16 percent or more. Where wet service conditions apply, the need for preservative treatment should be considered, as untreated panels used in these conditions are susceptible to degradation from fungal decay.

C9.2 Reference Design Values

C9.2.1 Panel Stiffness and Strength

C9.2.1.1 Minimum design stress values for wood structural panels are available from the panel manufacturer or the qualified agency for the panel grade and span rating. These unit design stress values, where provided, can be combined with the design section properties (see C9.2.4) to calculate panel stiffness and strength design capacities. Panel stiffness and strength design capacities for specific panels may be available from the panel manufacturer.

C9.2.1.2 Structural panels have a strength axis direction and a cross panel direction (see Figure C9.2.1). The direction of the strength axis is defined as the axis parallel to the orientation of OSB face strands or plywood face veneer grain and is the long dimension of the panel unless indicated otherwise by the manufacturer.

Figure C9.2.1 Structural Panel with Strength Direction Across Supports

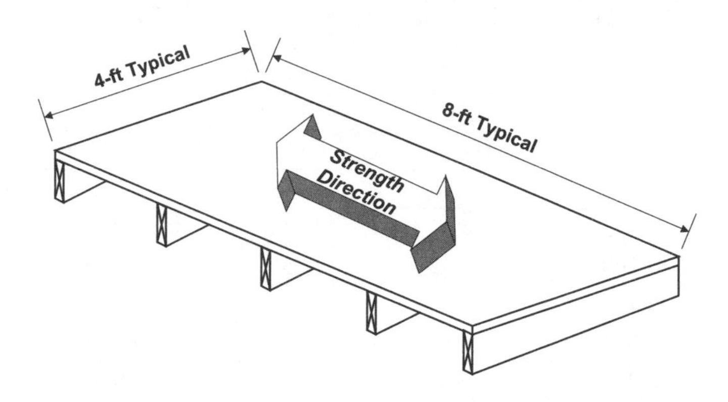

C9.2.2 Strength and Elastic Properties

Reference strength and stiffness design values are available from the panel manufacturer (see C9.2.1.1).

C9.2.3 Design Thickness

Section properties associated with the nominal panel thickness should be used in design calculations (see C9.2.4), unless otherwise indicated. The relationship between the nominal panel thickness and the span rating is provided in Table C9.2.3.

Table C9.2.3 Relationship Between Span Rating and Nominal Thickness

Span Rating	Nominal Thickness (in.)										
	3/8	7/16	15/32	1/2	19/32	5/8	23/32	3/4	7/8	1	1-1/8
Sheathing											
24/0	P	A	A	A							
24/16		P	A	A							
32/16			P	A	A	A					
40/20					P	A	A	A			
48/24							P	A	A		
Single Floor											
16 oc					P	A					
20 oc					P	A					
24 oc							P	A			
32 oc									P	A	
48 oc											P

P = Predominant nominal thickness for each span rating.
A = Alternative nominal thickness that may be available for each span rating. Check with suppliers regarding availability.

C9.2.4 Design Section Properties

The section properties associated with the nominal panel thickness and span rating are provided in Table C9.2.4. These values should be used with the panel stiffness and strength design stress values. Alternatively, these values can be combined with the panel stiffness and strength design stress values to provide panel stiffness and strength design capacities (see C9.2.1.1).

Table C9.2.4 Panel Section Properties[1]

Nominal Thickness (in.)	Approximate Weight[2] (psf)	Thickness t (in.)	Area A (in.²/ft.)	Moment of Inertia I (in.⁴/ft.)	Section Modulus S (in.³/ft.)	Statical Moment Q (in.³/ft.)	Shear Constant Ib/Q (in.²/ft.)
3/8	1.1	0.375	4.500	0.053	0.281	0.211	3.000
7/16	1.3	0.437	5.250	0.084	0.383	0.287	3.500
15/32	1.4	0.469	5.625	0.103	0.440	0.330	3.750
1/2	1.5	0.500	6.000	0.125	0.500	0.375	4.000
19/32	1.8	0.594	7.125	0.209	0.705	0.529	4.750
5/8	1.9	0.625	7.500	0.244	0.781	0.586	5.000
23/32	2.2	0.719	8.625	0.371	1.033	0.775	5.750
3/4	2.3	0.750	9.000	0.422	1.125	0.844	6.000
7/8	2.6	0.875	10.500	0.670	1.531	1.148	7.000
1	3.0	1.000	12.000	1.000	2.000	1.500	8.000
1-1/8	3.3	1.125	13.500	1.424	2.531	1.898	9.000

1. Properties based on rectangular cross section of 1-ft. width.
2. Approximate plywood weight for calculating actual dead loads. For OSB and composite panels, increase tabulated weights by 10%.

C9.3 Adjustment of Reference Design Values

C9.3.1 General

Applicable adjustment factors for wood structural panels are specified in Table 9.3.1 of the Specification.

C9.3.2 Load Duration Factor, C_D (ASD Only)

See C2.3.2.

C9.3.3 Wet Service Factor, C_M, and Temperature Factor, C_t

Wet Service Factor

Design capacities for panels can be used without adjustment for moisture effects where the panel moisture content in service is expected to be less than 16% (see C9.1.4). Adjustment factors for conditions where the panel moisture content in service is expected to be 16% or greater should be obtained from the manufacturer, industry associations, or third-party inspection agencies. Wet service adjustment factors traditionally used include:

Table C9.3.3 Wet Service Factor, C_M

Reference Design Capacity	C_M
Strength (F_bS, F_tA, F_cA, $F_s(Ib/Q)$, F_vt_v)	0.75
Stiffness (EI, EA, G_vt_v)	0.85

Wood structural panels used in structural applications such as roof and wall sheathing, subfloors, diaphragms, and built-up members must be manufactured with either an "Exposure 1" or "Exterior" bond classification (see C9.1.2).

Temperature Factor

The temperature factor, C_t, shall be applied when wood structural panels are exposed to in-service sustained temperatures in excess of 100°F (see C2.3.3). In the range of 100°F to 200°F, the temperature factor is applicable only when the moisture content of the wood structural panels can be expected to remain at or above 12%. The rationale behind the latter recommendation is that the strength increases due to panel drying under the higher temperature is sufficient to offset the strength decreases due to the temperature itself. The temperature factor can be estimated using the following equation:

$$C_t = 1.0 - 0.005\,(T - 100) \qquad \text{(C9.3-1)}$$

where:

T = Temperature (°F)

C9.3.4 Panel Size Factor, C_s

Design capacities for bending strength and axial tension strength can be used without a panel size adjustment for panels that are 24 inches or greater in width (i.e., dimension perpendicular to the strength axis). For panels less than 24 inches in width, the capacities should be reduced by applying the appropriate panel size adjustment factor, C_s, as shown in NDS Table 9.3.4 or obtained from the manufacturer, industry associations, or third-party inspection agency.

C9.3.5 Format Conversion Factor, K_F (LRFD Only)

See C2.3.5.

C9.3.6 Resistance Factor, ϕ (LRFD Only)

See C2.3.6.

C9.3.7 Time Effect Factor, λ (LRFD Only)

See C2.3.7.

C9.4 Design Considerations

C9.4.1 Flatwise Bending

Special care should be taken to ensure that the section properties associated with the proper strength axis are used to calculate the bending capacity of the panel (see Figure C9.4.1).

Figure C9.4.1 Example of Structural Panel in Bending

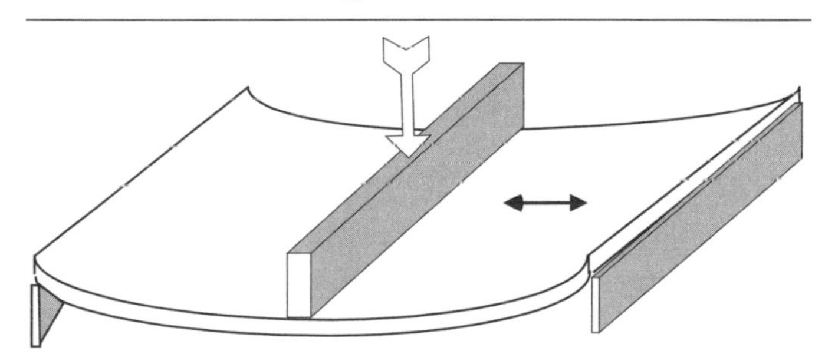

C9.4.2 Tension in the Plane of the Panel

Special care should be taken to ensure that the section properties associated with the proper strength axis are used to calculate the tensile capacity of the panel.

C9.4.3 Compression in the Plane of the Panel

Special care should be taken to ensure that the section properties associated with the proper strength axis are used to calculate the compression capacity of the panel (see Figure C9.4.3).

Figure C9.4.3 Structural Panel with Axial Compression Load in Plane of the Panel

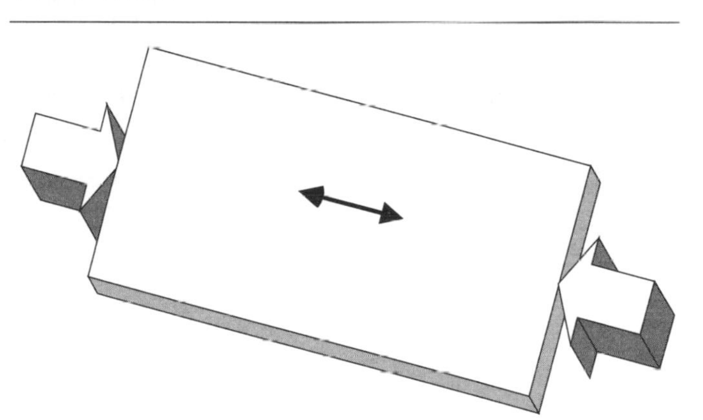

C9.4.4 Planar (Rolling) Shear

Special care should be taken to ensure that the section properties associated with the proper strength axis is used to calculate the planar shear (also called shear-in-the-plane or rolling shear) capacity of the panel (see Figure C9.4.4).

Figure C9.4.4 Shear-in-the-Plane for Wood Structural Panels

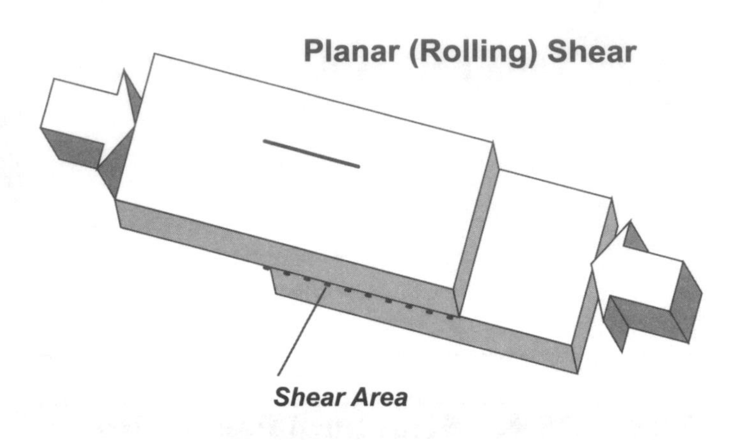

C9.4.5 Through-the-Thickness Shear

The section property for shear-through-the-thickness is the same both along the panel axis and across the panel axis (see Figure C9.4.5).

Figure C9.4.5 Through-the-Thickness Shear for Wood Structural Panels

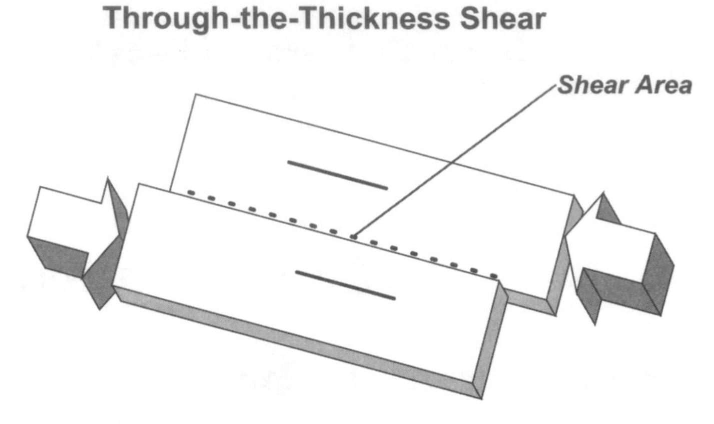

C9.4.6 Bearing

The design bearing stress on the panel face is independent of panel axis orientation.

C10 CROSS-LAMINATED TIMBER

C10.1 General

C10.1.1 Application

The general requirements given in Chapters 1, 2, and 3 of the Specification are applicable to cross-laminated timber (CLT) except where indicated otherwise. Chapter 10 of the Specification contains provisions that specifically apply to CLT manufactured in accordance with APA PRG 320 (197). The provisions of NDS Chapter 10 contain only the basic requirements applicable to engineering design of CLT. Specific requirements, such as CLT design values and the wet service factor are available from the CLT manufacturer's literature or code evaluation reports. Code evaluation reports, where available for a specific product and application, contain information to assist in the approval and use of the specific product in accordance with requirements of the applicable building code.

C10.1.2 Definitions

The definition for cross-laminated timber is based on the definition in APA PRG 320 (197).

C10.1.3 Standard Dimensions

10.1.3.1 Lamination thickness refers to the narrow face of a lamination perpendicular to the lamination length (face perpendicular to the glueline). Minimum and maximum thickness of 5/8 in. and 2 in., respectively, are based on APA PRG 320.

10.1.3.2 CLT panel thickness is measured perpendicular to the plane of the panel and is limited to 20 in. in accordance with APA PRG-320. CLT panel length is measured parallel to the major strength direction and CLT panel width is measured perpendicular to the major strength direction.

C10.1.4 Specification

The specific manufacturer's CLT product should be specified, including standard grade, where used, or the CLT configuration based on lamination grades, thicknesses, and layup (See C10.2). Standard grades of CLT consisting of specific lamination grades, thicknesses, and layups are provided in Annex A of APA PRG-320.

C10.1.5 Service Conditions

CLT design values are based on dry service conditions (moisture content in service less than 16%). For other conditions, the manufacturer should be consulted.

C10.2 Reference Design Values

Reference design values for specific grades and layups of CLT are provided in APA PRG-320. CLT design capacities are a function of the manufacturer's CLT layup and properties associated with the lamination grades. The user should contact the CLT manufacturer for design values and section properties for specific CLT products.

C10.3 Adjustment of Reference Design Values

C10.3.1 General

Applicable adjustment factors for cross-laminated timber are specified in Table 10.3.1 of the Specification.

C10.3.2 Load Duration Factor, C_D (ASD Only)

Load duration factors for CLT are the same as for other wood products (see C2.3.2) with the exception of rolling shear, $F_s(Ib/Q)_{eff}$, which is not adjusted in CLT since the value is limited by the tendency of the crossing laminations to "roll over" rather than exhibit a strength limit state associated with shear stress in the laminations.

C10.3.3 Wet Service Factor, C_M

See C10.1.5

C10.3.4 Temperature Factor, C_t

See C2.3.3.

C10.3.5 Curvature Factor, C_c

Design of curved CLT is beyond the scope of the NDS. The CLT manufacturer should be contacted to determine whether curved product is available and, if so, the proper design.

C10.3.6 Beam Stability Factor, C_L

Cross-laminated timber loaded in out-of-plane bending, such as vertical loads on floor slabs or lateral loads on walls, are not susceptible to lateral-torsional buckling and C_L=1.0. Cross-laminated timber panels loaded by in-plane bending are susceptible to lateral-torsional buckling and should be adjusted by the beam stability factor. Design capacities for CLT used as beams or headers over door and window openings have not been standardized and are not available in PRG 320. For beam applications, consult the CLT manufacturer for design capacities.

C10.3.7 Column Stability Factor, C_P

Cross-laminated timber panels loaded by in-plane compression are susceptible to buckling and should be adjusted by the column stability factor. Due to the significant shear deformation that can occur between the parallel and perpendicular CLT laminations, the effective bending stiffness, $(EI)_{eff}$, should be adjusted for shear stiffness per NDS 10.4.1 using a Shear Deformation Adjustment Factor, K_s, of 11.8 associated with the loading case of a constant moment.

C10.3.8 Bearing Area Factor, C_b

See C3.10.4.

C10.3.9 Pressure-Preservative Treatment

Per NDS 10.1.5, cross-laminated timber is limited to use in dry service conditions unless specifically allowed by the manufacturer. Manufacturers should be consulted for applications that require preservative treatment.

C10.3.10 Format Conversion Factor, K_F (LRFD Only)

See C2.3.5.

C10.3.11 Resistance Factor, ϕ (LRFD Only)

See C2.3.6.

C10.3.12 Time Effect Factor, λ (LRFD Only)

See C2.3.7.

C10.4 Special Design Considerations

C10.4.1 Deflection

C10.4.1.1 When cross-laminated panels are loaded in out-of-plane bending, the shear deformation can be a significant portion of the total deformation. The provisions of NDS 10.4.1 provide a method of calculating the "apparent" stiffness, $(EI)_{app}$, from the properties provided in PRG 320 and from the CLT manufacturer.

Effective bending stiffness values (EI_{eff}) and effective shear stiffness values (GA_{eff}) are provided by the CLT manufacturer. Apparent bending stiffness can be approximated as:

$$(EI)_{app} = \frac{EI_{eff}}{1 + \frac{K_s EI_{eff}}{GA_{eff} L^2}} \quad \text{(C10.4.1-1)}$$

To estimate $(EI)_{app\text{-}min}$ the value for $(EI)_{app}$ is adjusted per provisions of NDS Appendix D and Appendix H and the coefficient of variation of 0.10 from PRG-320:

$$(EI)_{app\text{-}min} = (EI)_{app}\,(1-1.645(0.10))(1.03)/1.66 = 0.518(EI)_{app}$$

Shear deformation adjustment factors, K_s, provided in NDS Table 10.4.1.1 and Table C10.4.1.1 are based on relationships for the specified loading and end-fixity conditions from the Wood Handbook [183]. The value of K_s is derived when the beam deformation and shear deformation equations are combined for each load case to provide an adjustment that provides an "apparent" EI_{eff} value. The beam deflection, δ, for rectangular members is estimated as:

$$\delta = \frac{k_b W L^3}{EI_{eff}} + \frac{6 k_s W L}{5 GA_{eff}} \quad \text{(C10.4.1-4)}$$

Where,

δ = beam deflection

k_b, k_s = beam constants based on beam loading, support conditions, and measurement location

W = total load on the beam

Setting the beam deformation equations equal to the bending deformation equation assuming an "apparent" stiffness, EI_{app} yields:

$$\frac{k_b W L^3}{EI_{app}} = \frac{k_b W L^3}{EI_{eff}} + \frac{6 k_s W L}{5 GA_{eff}} \quad \text{(C10.4.1-5)}$$

Solving for EI_{app}:

$$EI_{app} = \frac{EI_{eff}}{1 + \frac{6 k_s EI_{eff}}{5 k_b GA_{eff} L^2}} = \frac{EI_{eff}}{1 + \frac{K_s EI_{eff}}{GA_{eff} L^2}} \quad \text{(C10.4.1-6)}$$

From this derivation, it can be seen that $K_s = 6k_s/(5k_b)$.

For the case of Column Buckling Moment, the derivation is more complex. For a column pinned at each end, the bending deformation is estimated to be $\delta_b = A\sin(\pi x)$ and the shear deformation is estimated to be $\delta_s = A\pi^2 \sin(\pi x)$ and at midheight simplifies to $\delta_b = A$ and $\delta_s = A\pi^2$. For a column fixed at each end, the bending deformation is estimated to be δ_b=B and the shear deformation is estimated to be δ_s=$4B\pi^2$.

C

COMMENTARY: CROSS-LAMINATED TIMBER

Table C10.4.1.1 Shear Deformation Adjustment Factors

Loading	End Fixity	k_b	k_s	K_s
Uniformly Distributed	Pinned	5/384	1/8	11.5
	Fixed	1/384	1/8	57.6
Line Load at midspan	Pinned	1/48	1/4	14.4
	Fixed	1/192	1/4	57.6
Line Load at quarter points	Pinned	11/768	1/8	10.5
Constant Moment	-	1/12	0	0
Uniformly Distributed	Cantilevered	1/8	1/2	4.8
Line Load at free-end	Cantilevered	1/3	1	3.6
Column Buckling	Pinned	A	$A\pi^2$	11.8
	Fixed	B	$4B\pi^2$	47.4

Cross-laminated timber panels are designed as one-way slabs using a beam analogy. Terminology in NDS Table 10.4.1.1 and Table C10.4.1.1 has been modified from typical beam terminology to address the panel width. For example, a point load at midspan of a beam is called a "line load at midspan" to indicate that the load is assumed to be applied across the panel (perpendicular to the span) at the midspan of the cross-laminated timber. Additional loading and end-fixity conditions are available in the literature.

C11 MECHANICAL CONNECTIONS

C11.1 General

C11.1.1 Scope

C11.1.1.2 See C3.1.3, C3.1.4, and C3.1.5.

C11.1.1.3 The adequacy of alternate methods or procedures for designing and verifying the reference design values of connections that differ from those in the Specification is the responsibility of the designer or the authority accepting or approving such alternate methods or procedures. This responsibility includes providing for appropriate margins of safety; assuring the applicability of load duration, wet service and other adjustment factors in the Specification; and confirming the applicability of test results to field fabrication and service conditions (see C1.1.1.3).

C11.1.2 Stresses in Members at Connections

All connection designs should be checked for conformance of structural members to the net section area requirements of NDS 3.1.2 and the shear design provisions of NDS 3.4.3 (see C3.1.2 and C3.4.3). All single shear or lapped joints also should be checked to determine the adequacy of the member to resist the additional stresses induced by the eccentric transfer of load at the joint (see NDS 3.1.3). This often will involve bending and compression or bending and tension interaction where the bending moment induced by the eccentric load at the joint results in bending about the weak axis of the member.

Where multiple fasteners are used, the capacity of the fastener group may be limited by wood failure at the net section or by tear-out around the fasteners caused by local stresses. One method for evaluating member strength for local stresses around fastener groups is outlined in NDS Appendix E.

C11.1.3 Eccentric Connections

Fastener eccentricity that induces tension perpendicular to grain stresses in the main wood member at the connection should be avoided. Where multiple fasteners occur with eccentricity, fasteners are to be placed, insofar as possible, such that the wood between them is placed in compression rather than in tension (see NDS Figure 11A).

In 1948, provisions for shear design of bending members at connections were introduced in an attempt to limit tension perpendicular to grain stresses at eccentric connections. In 1982, a provision was added prohibiting eccentric connections that induce tension perpendicular to grain stresses unless it has been shown by analysis or testing that such joints can safely carry all applied loads. The determination of the type and extent of the analysis and/or testing required to demonstrate the adequacy of eccentric connections that induce tension perpendicular to grain stresses in the wood members is the responsibility of the designer. Use of stitch bolts or plates to resist such stresses when they cannot be avoided is a common practice.

It is to be emphasized that tension design values perpendicular to grain are not given in the Specification (see C3.8.2).

C11.1.4 Mixed Fastener Connections

The individual fasteners in a connection should generally be of the same size to assure comparable load-slip or stiffness characteristics. Such equivalency is required to obtain appropriate distribution of load among fasteners in the connection and is a condition for use of the group action factor, C_g, of NDS 11.3.6.

It is recognized that some designers have used different fastener types in the same connection where the addition of one or more fasteners of the type being used is precluded by area restrictions or is considered uneconomical. Such mixed-type connections, for example, the use of a single 1/2-inch bolt with three split-ring connectors or the use of a 16d nail with two 1/2-inch bolts, are not covered by the design provisions of the Specification. Because of the different load-slip behavior of different fastener types, the allowable load on such connections cannot be assumed to be the sum of the allowable loads for each fastener type, even when the different types are in different rows.

Allowable loads for connections employing more than one type or size of fastener shall be based on analyses that account for different connection stiffnesses, on test results, or on field experience (see C1.1.1.3). It is the designer's responsibility to assure that load capacities assigned to such connections contain adequate margins of safety and are achievable under field conditions.

C11.1.5 Connection Fabrication

Design values for connection joints have been applied to connections having both tight and loose nuts. This provision is based on the original bolted joint tests used to establish design values in which the nuts were intentionally not tightened in order to simulate the additional shrinkage that can occur during service (146). It is to be noted that these provisions only apply to the loosening of nuts that may occur from shrinkage and not the effects of moisture on bearing strength or the effects of checks and cracks that may occur from seasoning after fabrication. Reduction of connection design values for these factors is required when connections are assembled with wet or partially seasoned wood (see NDS 11.3.3).

C11.2 Reference Design Values

C11.2.1 Single Fastener Connections

Reference lateral design values for dowel-type fasteners (bolts, lag screws, wood screws, nails, and spikes) are based on a yield limit model which specifically accounts for the different ways these connections can behave under load. These behavior patterns or modes (see NDS Appendix I) are uniform bearing in the wood under the fastener, rotation of the fastener in the joint without dowel bending, and development of one or more plastic hinges in the fastener (67, 122). Equations have been developed for each mode relating the joint load to the maximum stresses in the wood members and in the fastener (67, 121). The capacity of the connection under each yield mode is keyed to the bearing strength of the wood under the fastener and the bending strength of the fastener, with the lowest capacity calculated for the various modes being taken as the design value for the connection.

The yield limit model provides a consistent basis for establishing the relative effects of side and main member thickness and bearing strength, and fastener bending strength on the load-carrying capacity of connections involving dowel-type fasteners. Because the yield strength of a wood connection is not well defined on the load-deformation curve for a connection, the limiting wood stresses used in the yield model are based on the load at which the load-deformation curve from a fastener embedment test intersects a line represented by the initial tangent modulus offset 5 percent of the fastener diameter (120). This nominal yield point is intermediate between the proportional limit and maximum load for the material and for the connection.

Reference lateral design values for connections in previous editions of the Specification represented nominal proportional limit values. For purposes of transition and to build on the long record of satisfactory performance obtained with these previous values, short-term design values based on direct application of the yield limit equations have been reduced to design levels published in previous editions for connections made with equivalent species and member sizes. This calibration was accomplished by establishing average ratios of previous Specification design values to yield limit model design values for each yield mode and direction of loading (parallel and perpendicular to grain). This soft conversion procedure retained historical safety levels while resulting in some design values for each fastener type being somewhat higher and some lower than previous values depending upon the fastener diameter and the thickness of main and side member.

C11.2.2 Multiple Fastener Connections

The reference design value for a connection containing two or more fasteners is obtained by summing the reference design values for each individual fastener. It is to be understood that this provision requires application of the group action factor of NDS 11.3.6 to the individual fastener reference design value wherever a row of two or more split ring connectors, shear plate connectors, or dowel-type fasteners are involved.

Summation of individual fastener reference design values to obtain a total reference design value for a connection containing two or more fasteners is limited to designs involving the same type and the same size of fastener (see C11.1.4). Fasteners of the same type, diameter, and length joining the same members and resisting load in the same shear plane may be assumed to exhibit the same yield mode.

C11.2.3 Design of Metal Parts

Metal parts, including fasteners, are to be designed in accordance with national standards of practice and specifications applicable to the material. Tension stresses in fasteners as a result of withdrawal loads, shear in cross-sections of fasteners, bearing of fasteners on metal side plates, tension and shear of plates, and buckling of plates and rods are included under this provision.

Standard metal design practices are not to be used to account for bending stresses occurring in dowel-type fasteners in wood connections subject to lateral loads. These stresses are accounted for in this Specification under the provisions for the particular fastener type involved. Where the design value for a connection involving metal fasteners is limited by the provisions of this Specification, the adjustment factors of NDS 11.3 are to be applied. Where the design value of the connection is limited by the strength of the metal fastener or part, the adjustment factors of NDS 11.3 are not to be applied.

C11.2.4 Design of Concrete or Masonry Parts

Concrete or masonry parts are to be designed in accordance with national standards of practice and specifications applicable to the material.

C11.3 Adjustment of Reference Design Values

C11.3.1 Applicability of Adjustment Factors

Applicable adjustment factors for connections subject to lateral loads, withdrawal loads, and fastener head pull-through loads are specified in Table 11.3.1 of the Specification.

C11.3.2 Load Duration Factor, C_D (ASD Only)

See C2.3.2. Reference design values for wood connections derived from the results of standard short-term tests (5-10 minute duration) and/or calculated using properties derived from short-term tests include a 1.6 reduction to account for the potential effects of long-term loading. When wood connections are used to resist short-term loads, the reference design values can be increased by a factor of up to 1.6 based on the provisions of NDS 2.3.2. Load duration factors greater than 1.6, including the impact load duration factor of 2.0, are not to be applied to design loads for connections.

C11.3.3 Wet Service Factor, C_M

The wet service factors in NDS Table 11.3.3 for bolts and lag screws, split ring and shear plate connectors, wood screws, and nails were recommended as part of early research on wood connections (184, 181).

The 0.80 factor for metal plate connectors installed in partially seasoned or wet lumber is based on the results of both truss and tension in-line joint tests (1,109,195).

The factor of 0.40 in NDS Table 11.3.3 for multiple rows of dowel fasteners installed in partially seasoned wood used in dry conditions of service is based on limited tests of connections fabricated with unseasoned members joined at right angles to each other and tested after drying (181).

C11.3.4 Temperature Factor, C_t

The temperature adjustment factors for connections in NDS Table 11.3.4 are equivalent to those for bending, compression, and shear design values in NDS 2.3.3 (see C2.3.3). Bearing under metal fasteners is closely correlated with compression parallel to grain or compression perpendicular to grain properties.

C11.3.5 Fire Retardant Treatment

See C2.3.4.

C11.3.6 Group Action Factors, C_g

Modification factors for two or more split ring connectors, shear plate connectors, or dowel-type fasteners in a row were added to the Specification in the 1973 edition. Earlier tests of bolted and shear plate connector joints had shown that the load capacity of connections containing multiple fasteners in a row was not directly proportional to the number of fasteners, with those located near the ends of the row carrying a greater proportion of the applied load than those located in the interior of the row (35, 39, 40, 66, 72).

The tables of factors included in the 1973 edition to account for the non-uniform loads on a row of fasteners was based on a linear analysis wherein the direct stresses in the main and side members of the connection were assumed to be uniformly distributed across their cross section, and the relationship between fastener slip and fastener load was assumed to be linear (77). This analytical procedure showed that the transfer of load from side to main members and the proportion of the total load carried by each fastener were determined by the modulii of elasticity (E) and cross-sectional areas of the side and main members, the number of fasteners in a row, the spacing between fasteners, and the joint load/slip modulus.

Two tables of modification factors for joints containing two or more fasteners in a row were developed using the linear analysis: one for connections with wood side plates and one for connections with metal side plates. For purposes of simplicity, factors were tabulated only in terms of the number of fasteners in the row and the cross-sectional areas of the members being joined. Other variables were assumed to have the following values (156):

Wood to wood connections:	
E of side and main members	1,800,000 psi
Load-slip fastener modulus	220,000 lbs/in.
Spacing between fasteners	6.5 inches
Wood to metal connections:	
E of main member	1,400,000 psi
Load-slip fastener modulus	330,000 lbs/in.
Spacing between fasteners	5.75 inches

With the foregoing constant values, the analytical procedure was used to calculate modification factors for 3 to 8 fasteners in a row and then results were extrapolated up to 12 fasteners and down to 2 fasteners in a row (156). The resulting tables of factors, ranging from 1.00 for two fasteners in a row to as low as 0.34 and 0.15 for 12 fasteners in a row in joints made with wood and metal side plates, respectively, were continued essentially unchanged through the 1986 edition. The group action factor equation given in NDS 11.3.6 consolidated the analytical procedure used to establish the modification factors given in previous editions (188). Concurrent with the development of the compact single equation for accounting for group action, more recent load-slip data for bolted joints and split ring and shear plate connectors have been used to establish new representative load-slip moduli for different types of connections (188).

It is to be noted that the variable A_s in the group action equation (NDS Equation 11.3-1) represents the sum of the cross-sectional area of the side members. Thus the equation accounts for single shear as well as double shear connections. For a connection with four or more members, each shear plane is evaluated as a single shear connection (see NDS 12.3.8). Where such a connection contains two or more fasteners in a row, a group action factor is calculated for each shear plane using an A_s based on the thinnest member adjacent to the plane being considered.

Perpendicular to Grain Loading. The number of fasteners in a row perpendicular to grain are generally limited in order to avoid splitting that can occur as a result of drying (see C11.3.3). When a row of multiple fasteners are used perpendicular to grain, it is standard practice to use the same group action factor as that for fasteners aligned parallel to grain. This practice is based on the assumption that use of the member and connection stiffnesses perpendicular to grain ($E_\perp$ and $\gamma_\perp$) in NDS Equation 11.3-1 would result in similar group action factors.

C11.3.7 Format Conversion Factor, K_F (LRFD Only)

See C2.3.5.

C11.3.8 Resistance Factor, ϕ (LRFD Only)

See C2.3.6.

C11.3.9 Time Effect Factor, λ (LRFD Only)

See C2.3.7.

C12 DOWEL-TYPE FASTENERS

C12.1 General

C12.1.1 Scope

Chapter 12 groups the design for a range of fasteners known as "dowel-type" fasteners. These include fasteners such as bolts, lag screws, wood screws, nails, spikes, drift bolts, and drift pins.

C12.1.3 Bolts

C12.1.3.1 ANSI/ASME Standard B18.2.1 *Square and Hex Bolts and Screws (Inch Series)*, is the quality reference standard for bolts. Bolt design provisions and tabulated bolt design values apply only to bolts having diameters of 1 inch or less. This limit was in response to reported field problems with connections involving large diameter bolts in structural glued laminated timber members and the results of research (31, 135). The latter showed drying in service, workmanship variables, and perpendicular to grain load components could interact to affect the capacity of connections made with multiple large diameter, relatively stiff bolts. Use of these procedures to establish reference design values for large diameter bolted connections is the sole responsibility of the designer.

C12.1.3.2 Generally, smaller diameter bolts will use the smaller oversize hole value and larger bolts the larger oversize value. The same target oversize is to be used for all holes in the same connection. Proper alignment, especially in groups of fasteners, is required to properly distribute the load into each fastener. Forcible driving of the fastener can damage the wood bearing surface and reduce the capacity of the connection.

C12.1.3.3 Use of standard cut washers or equivalent metal parts under the head and nut prevent localized crushing of the wood at bolt holes.

C12.1.3.4 Edge distance, end distance, and fastener spacing requirements have been consolidated for dowel-type fasteners in NDS 12.5.

C12.1.4 Lag Screws

C12.1.4.1 ANSI/ASME Standard B18.2.1 *Square and Hex Bolts and Screws (Inch Series)*, is the quality reference standard for lag screws. It provides standard hex lag screw dimensions (see NDS Appendix L) but does not specify metal having specific strength properties. The designer is responsible for specifying the metal strength of the lag screws that are to be used. Bending yield strength of the lag screw (see NDS Appendix I) is a required input variable to the yield equations of NDS 12.3.1. Additionally, the actual tensile stress in the lag screw at the root diameter must be checked when designing lag screw connections for withdrawal (see NDS 11.2.3).

C12.1.4.2 Lead hole requirements for three specific gravity classes are based on early lag screw research involving tests of Douglas fir, southern pine, white oak, redwood, and northern white pine (100).

C12.1.4.3 Provision for allowing 3/8 inch and smaller diameter lag screws loaded primarily in withdrawal to be inserted without a lead hole in wood of medium to low specific gravity was added to address the use of small lag screws. On the basis of field experience, early lag screw research (100), and information on the withdrawal resistance of tapping screws inserted with different size lead holes (163), use of small lag screws without lead holes is deemed acceptable when the following conditions are met:

1. The lag screws are being loaded primarily in withdrawal.
2. The lag screws are inserted in wood with specific gravity (G) ≤ 0.5.
3. Placement of lag screws avoids excessive splitting.

A lag screw subjected to combined withdrawal and lateral loading may be considered loaded primarily in withdrawal when the axis of the screw is at an angle of 75 degrees or more to the grain of the wood member holding the threaded portion of the screw. The requirement that unusual splitting be avoided when lead holes are not used is to be considered a performance requirement that (i) is related to the ability of the screw to hold the cleat or side member to the main or foundation member, and (ii) is applicable to both members being joined.

C12.1.4.5 A lubricant is sometimes used to facilitate lag screw insertion even when small diameter lag screws are inserted without the use of lead holes.

C12.1.4.6 Minimum length of lag screw penetration requirements, not including the length of the tapered tip, are provided to ensure that fasteners can achieve the design value calculated using the yield equations in NDS 12.3.1.

C12.1.4.7 Edge distances, end distances, and fastener spacing requirements have been consolidated for dowel-type fasteners in NDS 12.5.

C12.1.5 Wood Screws

C12.1.5.1 ANSI/ASME Standard B18.6.1 is the quality reference standard for wood screws. It provides standard wood screw dimensions (see NDS Appendix L) but does not specify metal having specific strength properties. The designer is responsible for specifying the metal strength of the wood screws that are to be used. Bending yield strength of the wood screw (see NDS Appendix I) is a required input variable to the lateral design value yield limit equations of NDS 12.3.1. Additionally, the actual tensile stress in the wood screw at the root diameter must be checked when designing wood screw connections for withdrawal (see C11.2.3 of Specification).

C12.1.5.2 Lead hole requirements for wood screws are based on early research involving flat head wood screws up to 24 gage and 5 inches in length in seven species, including southern pine, cypress, and oak (43).

The provision allowing the insertion of wood screws without a lead hole in species with $G \leq 0.5$ when the screw is subject to withdrawal loads parallels the provision for 3/8 inch and smaller diameter lag screws (see C12.1.4.3).

C12.1.5.3 Wood screws resisting lateral loads are required to have shank and threaded portion lead holes based on early lateral load tests of wood screws (70, 181, 184). Lead holes are required for all wood screws subject to lateral loads regardless of wood specific gravity.

C12.1.5.4 Wood screws tests (43, 70, 181) are based on inserting the screw by turning rather than driving with a hammer.

C12.1.5.5 A lubricant is sometimes used to facilitate screw insertion and avoid screw damage. Tests have shown that the lubricant has no significant effect on reference design values (43, 70, 184).

C12.1.5.6 Minimum length of wood screw penetration requirements, including the length of the tapered tip, are provided to ensure that fasteners can achieve the reference design value calculated using the yield equations in NDS 12.3.1.

C12.1.5.7 Edge distances, end distances, and fastener spacing requirements have been consolidated across all diameters for dowel-type fasteners in NDS 12.5. For diameters less than ¼", specific requirements are not provided; however, Table C12.1.5.7 may be used to establish wood screw placement recommendations. Designers should note that wood species, moisture content, and grain orientation will impact spacing effects between fasteners in a row.

Table C12.1.5.7 Recommended Minimum Spacing for Wood Screws

	Wood Side Members	
	Not Prebored	Prebored
Edge distance	2.5D	2.5D
End distance		
- tension load parallel to grain	15D	10D
- compression load parallel to grain	10D	5D
Spacing between fasteners in a row		
- parallel to grain	15D	10D
- perpendicular to grain	10D	5D
Spacing between rows of fasteners		
- in-line	5D	3D
- staggered	2.5D	2.5D
	Steel Side Members	
	Not Prebored	Prebored
Edge distance	2.5D	2.5D
End distance		
- tension load parallel to grain	10D	5D
- compression load parallel to grain	5D	3D
Spacing between fasteners in a row		
- parallel to grain	10D	5D
- perpendicular to grain	5D	2.5D
Spacing between rows of fasteners		
- in line	3D	2.5D
- staggered	2.5D	2.5D

C12.1.6 Nails and Spikes

C12.1.6.1 ASTM F 1667 *Standard Specification for Driven Fasteners: Nails, Spikes, and Staples* (202) provides standard dimensions for common, box, and sinker steel wire nails, spikes, Roof Sheathing Ring Shank (RSRS) nails, and Post Frame Ring Shank (PF) nails (See NDS Appendix L). The Supplementary Requirements of ASTM F1667 regarding Nail Bending Yield Strength are required to be used for engineered construction. The method in which F_{yb} is determined for nails is incorporated in ASTM F1575. F_{yb} requirements are referenced in the Supplementary Requirements of ASTM F1667 or section 12.1.6 of the NDS. For any deformed shank nails (e.g. RSRS, PF), moment capacity is evaluated at the transition zone (between the smooth shank and deformations) and diameter, D, of the smooth shank is used in the calculation of F_{yb}. The resulting use of F_{yb} and D produces the appropriate yield moment of the nail when D is used in yield theory calculations. Additionally, the actual tensile stress in the driven fastener must be checked when designing driven fastener connections for withdrawal (see C11.2.3 of the Specification).

C12.1.6.3 Toe-nailing procedures consisting of slant driving of nails at a 30° angle from the face of the attached member with an end distance (distance between end of side member and initial point of entry) of one-third the nail length are based on lateral and withdrawal tests of nailed joints in frame wall construction (181, 118). The toenail factors of NDS 12.5.4.1 and NDS 12.5.4.2 presume use of these driving procedures and the absence of excessive splitting. If such splitting does occur, predrilling or a smaller nail should be used. The vertically-projected length is used as the side member bearing length in yield limit equations when calculating lateral capacity of a toe-nailed connection.

C12.1.6.4 Minimum length of penetration requirements, including the length of the tapered tip, are provided to ensure that driven fasteners can achieve the design value calculated using the yield equations in NDS 12.3.1. The exception for clinching in double-shear connections is applicable to 0.148" (12d common, 20d box, or 16d sinker nails) or smaller diameter nails.

C12.1.6.5 Edge distances, end distances, and fastener spacing requirements have been consolidated across all diameters for dowel-type fasteners in NDS Table 12.5.1A through 12.5.1F. For diameters less than ¼", specific requirements are not provided; however, Table C12.1.6.6 may be used to establish nail placement recommendations. Designers should note that wood species, moisture content, and grain orientation will impact spacing effects between fasteners in a row.

C12.1.7 Drift Bolts and Drift Pins

C12.1.7.1 Drift bolts and drift pins are unthreaded rods used to join large structural members where a smooth surface without protruding metal parts is desired. The designer is responsible for specifying the metal strength of the drift bolt or pin that is to be used. Bending yield strength of the drift bolt or pin (see NDS Appendix I) is a required input variable to the reference lateral design value yield limit equations of NDS 12.3.1.

C12.1.7.2 Additional penetration into the members is required to resist withdrawal of the drift bolt or pin.

C12.1.7.3 Edge distances, end distances, and fastener spacing requirements have been consolidated across all diameters for dowel-type fasteners in NDS Table 12.5.1A through 12.5.1F.

Table C12.1.6.6 Recommended Minimum Spacing for Nails

	Wood Side Members	
	Not Prebored	Prebored
Edge distance	2.5D	2.5D
End distance		
- tension load parallel to grain	15D	10D
- compression load parallel to grain	10D	5D
Spacing between fasteners in a row		
- parallel to grain	15D	10D
- perpendicular to grain	10D	5D
Spacing between rows of fasteners		
- in-line	5D	3D
- staggered	2.5D	2.5D
	Steel Side Members	
	Not Prebored	Prebored
Edge distance	2.5D	2.5D
End distance		
- tension load parallel to grain	10D	5D
- compression load parallel to grain	5D	3D
Spacing between fasteners in a row		
- parallel to grain	10D	5D
- perpendicular to grain	5D	2.5D
Spacing between rows of fasteners		
- in line	3D	2.5D
- staggered	2.5D	2.5D

C12.1.8 Other Dowel-Type Fasteners

While specific installation instructions are not provided for all types of dowel-type fasteners, the provisions for withdrawal in NDS 12.2 and the generic yield equations in NDS 12.3.1 for lateral design apply. The designer is responsible for determining the proper installation requirements and for specifying the metal strength of these fasteners.

C12.2 Reference Withdrawal Design Values

C12.2.1 Lag Screws

C12.2.1.1 NDS Equation 12.2-1 was used to establish the lag screw reference withdrawal design values given in NDS Table 12.2A. This equation was derived from the following equation based on research (181, 100):

$$W = K_W G^{3/2} D^{3/4} \qquad \text{(C12.2.1-1)}$$

where:

W = reference withdrawal design value per inch of thread penetration into main member, lbs

K_W = 1800

G = specific gravity of main member based on oven dry weight and volume, where $0.31 \leq G \leq 0.73$

D = lag screw diameter (equivalent to unthreaded shank diameter for full body diameter lag screws), in., where $0.25" \leq D \leq 1.25"$

The value of K_W represents approximately one-fourth (one-fifth increased by 20 percent) of the average constant at oven dry weight and volume obtained from ultimate load tests of joints made with five different species and seven sizes of lag screw (100), increased by 20 percent; or

$$K_W = 1.2\left(\frac{7500}{5}\right) \qquad \text{(C12.2.1-2)}$$

The twenty percent increase was introduced as part of the World War II emergency increase in wood design values, and then subsequently codified as 10 percent for the change from permanent to normal loading and 10 percent for experience (see C2.3.2).

When the reference withdrawal capacity of a lag screw is determined by multiplying the reference unit design value by the length of penetration of the threaded portion into the side grain of the main member, the length of the tapered tip of the screw is not to be included. This tapered portion at the tip of the lag screw was not considered as part of the effective penetration depth in the original joint tests (100) and in the development of equation C12.2.1-1. In addition, the thickness of any washer used between the lag screw head and the cleat or side member should be taken into account when determining the length of penetration of the threaded portion in the main member. Standard lag screw dimensions, including minimum thread length and length of tapered tip, are given in Appendix L of the Specification.

C12.2.1.2 The unit reference withdrawal design value in lbs/in. is multiplied by the depth of thread penetration into a wood member to calculate the fastener reference withdrawal in pounds.

C12.2.1.3 Reference withdrawal design values for lag screws are reduced 25 percent when the screw is inserted in the end grain (radial-tangential plane) of the main member rather than the side grain (radial-longitudinal or tangential-longitudinal plane) based on lag screw joint tests (100). Because of the greater possibility of splitting when subject to lateral load, it has been recommended that insertion of lag screws in end grain surfaces be avoided (181, 96).

C12.2.1.4 (see C11.2.3).

C12.2.1.5 The required use of the end grain factor of 0.75 for lag screws installed into the narrow edge of CLT panels conservatively assumes the lag screw will be subject to strength reductions associated with installation in end grain. This assumption was judged practical to address varying grain orientations in the edge of cross-laminated timber panels (e.g. both end grain and side grain are present in the edge of CLT panels), and the ability to maintain minimum edge distances for larger diameter lag screws installed in the narrow face of a lamination. For cases where the narrow face of the laminations is large, such as 2 in., and the lag screw diameter is small such as ¼" and where installation is in side grain only with adequate edge distance, application of the 0.75 factor may not be warranted where strength reducing conditions associated with placement in end grain or with inadequate edge distances for side grain are not present.

C12.2.2 Wood Screws

C12.2.2.1 NDS Equation 12.2-2 was used to establish the wood screw reference withdrawal design values given in NDS Table 12.2B. This equation was based on testing of cut thread wood screws in seven wood species (43):

$$W = K_W G^2 D \qquad \text{(C12.2.2-1)}$$

where:

W = reference withdrawal design value per inch of thread penetration in the main member, lbs

K_W = 2850

G = specific gravity of main member based on oven dry weight and volume, where $0.31 \leq G \leq 0.73$

D = wood screw thread diameter, in., where $0.138" \leq D \leq 0.372"$

The value of K_W represents one-fifth (one-sixth increased by 20 percent) of the average constant at oven dry weight and volume obtained from ultimate load tests of joints (43) made with seven different species and cut-thread wood screw; or

$$K_W = \frac{14250}{6} \qquad \text{(C12.2.2-2)}$$

The twenty percent increase was introduced as part of the World War II emergency increase in wood design values, and then subsequently codified as 10 percent for the change from permanent to normal loading and 10 percent for experience (see C2.3.2).

Wood screw reference withdrawal design values are based on tests of cut thread wood screws. The shank or body diameter of a cut thread screw is the same as the outside diameter of the thread. The shank or body diameter of the rolled thread screw is the same as the root diameter. For the same nominal diameter of screw, both screw thread types have the same threads per inch, the same outside thread diameter, and the same thread depth. If the tensile strength of the screw is adequate and the lead hole provisions based on root diameter are used, the withdrawal resistance of rolled thread screws is considered equivalent to that of cut thread screws (182, 163).

The ANSI/ASME B18.6.1 standard states that the thread length is approximately two-thirds of the nominal screw length.

C12.2.2.2 The unit reference withdrawal design value in lbs/in. is multiplied by the depth of thread penetration into a wood member to calculate the fastener reference withdrawal in pounds.

C12.2.2.3 Early tests of wood screws in withdrawal from end grain surfaces of oak, southern pine, maple, and cypress gave somewhat erratic results relative to those for withdrawal from side grain (43). These irregular results were attributed to the tendency of the screw to split the wood in the end grain configuration. Average ratios of end grain withdrawal resistance to side grain withdrawal resistance ranged from 52 to 108 percent (43). Because of this variability, structural loading of wood screws in withdrawal from end grain has been prohibited. Wood screws installed in end grain are suitable for lateral resistance; however, to clarify that screws are permitted to be installed in end-grain but should not be assigned withdrawal design values, the end-grain adjustment factor, C_{eg}, is set to zero for withdrawal loading.

C12.2.2.4 Similar to the provisions of 12.2.2.3, wood screws installed in end-grain of cross-laminated timber laminations should not be assigned withdrawal design values (i.e. C_{eg}=0.0).). There is no reduction in withdrawal resistance for wood screws installed in the side grain of laminations at cross-laminated timber panel edges.

C12.2.2.5 See C11.2.3.

C12.2.3 Nails and Spikes

C12.2.3.1 Smooth shank nails or spikes

(a) NDS Equation 12.2-3 is used to establish the smooth shank (bright or galvanized) nail and spike reference withdrawal design values given in NDS Table 12.2C. This equation is based on research (94, 95):

$$W = K_W G^{5/2} D \qquad \text{(C12.2.3-1)}$$

where:

W = nail or spike withdrawal design value per inch of penetration in main member, lbs

K_W = 1380

G = specific gravity of main member based on oven dry weight and volume, where $0.31 \le G \le 0.73$

D = shank diameter of the nail or spike, in., where $0.092" \le D \le 0.375"$

The value of K_W represents one-fifth (one-sixth increased by 20 percent) of the average constant at oven dry weight and volume obtained from ultimate load tests (184), increased by 20 percent; or

$$K_W = 1.2\left(\frac{6900}{6}\right) \qquad \text{(C12.2.3-2)}$$

The twenty percent increase was introduced as part of the World War II emergency increase in wood design values, and then subsequently codified as 10 percent for the change from permanent to normal loading and 10 percent for experience (see C2.3.2).

(b) NDS Equation 12.2-4 is used to establish smooth shank stainless steel nail and spike reference withdrawal design values given in NDS Table 12.2D. Testing of A304 and A316 stainless steel nails has shown withdrawal capacity of smooth-shank stainless steel nails to be less than that of bright or galvanized carbon steel nails (203). This strength reduction is attributed to the reduced friction between nail and wood fiber. Withdrawal design values from Eq. 12.2-4 are one-fifth of the average ultimate values. Eq. 12.2-4 is slightly different than and produces smaller values than the equation proposed in the research to improve fit to data.

Clinching. Withdrawal resistance of smooth-shank nails can be significantly increased by clinching (29).

(c) The unit reference withdrawal design value in lbs/in. for nails and spikes is multiplied by the depth of penetration into a wood member, including the tip, to calculate the fastener reference withdrawal in pounds. The equations were developed assuming the tip was part of the penetration length.

C12.2.3.2 Deformed shank nails.

(a) In the 2012 edition of the Specification, provisions were added for Post-Frame Ring Shank nails and in the 2018 edition of the Specification, provisions were added for Roof Sheathing Ring Shank nails in accordance with ASTM F1667. The withdrawal design value equation (NDS

Equation 12.2-5) is based on research conducted at the Forest Products Laboratory.

(b) The constant of 1800 in NDS Equation 12.2-5 incorporates a 20% reduction to account for effects of galvanized coatings from testing in Southern pine rather than the average reduction of 15% from testing in all species (basswood, SPF, Douglas fir, Southern pine, and white oak) tested in the study (196). Therefore, when using uncoated carbon steel Post-Frame Ring Shank or Roof Sheathing Ring Shank nails, a 1.25 increase factor is permitted (e.g. 0.80x1.25=1.0). Effects of other coatings have not been quantified.

(c) The unit reference withdrawal design value in lbs/in. for Roof Sheathing Ring Shank nails and Post-Frame Ring Shank nails is multiplied by the depth of ring shank penetration into the side grain of a wood member, including the tip, to calculate the fastener reference withdrawal in pounds. The equations were developed assuming that the tip was part of the penetration length.

(d) Reference withdrawal design values for smooth shank nails are permitted to be used for other deformed shank nails of the same shank diameter, D, recognizing that tests of deformed shank nails indicate that shank deformations do not reduce the withdrawal value below the values for smooth shank nails. The permissible use of the smooth shank nail withdrawal value replaces criteria in the 2015 NDS and prior editions that recognized slightly larger withdrawal strengths for "threaded nails" with unspecified geometry of deformations.

C12.2.3.3 Reduction of withdrawal design values up to 50 percent have been reported for nails driven in end grain surfaces (radial-tangential plane) as compared to side grain (radial-longitudinal or tangential-longitudinal planes) surfaces (184, 118). When coupled with the effects of seasoning in-service after fabrication, such reductions are considered too great for reliable design. On this basis, structural loading of nails in withdrawal from end grain has been prohibited. Nails installed in end grain are suitable for lateral resistance; however, to clarify that nails are permitted to be installed in end-grain but should not be assigned withdrawal design values, the end-grain adjustment factor, C_{eg}, is set to zero for withdrawal loading.

C12.2.3.4 Similar to the provisions of 12.2.3.5, nails installed in end-grain of cross-laminated timber laminations should not be assigned withdrawal design values (i.e. C_{eg}=0.0). There is no reduction in withdrawal resistance for nails installed in the side grain of laminations at cross-laminated timber panel edges.

C12.2.4 Drift Bolts and Drift Pins

C12.2.4.1 While specific provisions for determining withdrawal design values for round drift bolts or pins are not specifically included in the Specification, the following equation has been used where friction and workmanship can be maintained (184, 181):

$$W = 1200\, G^2\, D \qquad \text{(C12.2.4-1)}$$

where:

W = drift bolt or drift pin reference withdrawal design value per inch of penetration, lbs

G = specific gravity based on oven dry weight and volume

D = drift bolt or drift pin diameter, in.

Equation C12.2.4-1 assumes the fastener is driven into a prebored hole having a diameter 1/8 inch less than the fastener diameter (184). The reference withdrawal design values calculated with Equation C12.2.4-1 are approximately one-fifth average ultimate test values (184, 181).

C12.2.5 Fastener Head Pull-Through

C12.2.5.1 Fastener head pull-through data used to set industry recommendations for wood structural panels, combined with historical results of pull-through data from tests of various fastener head shapes and washer diameters pulled through lumber and wood structural panels, were analyzed to develop fastener head pull-through provisions (204). NDS Equation 12.2-6a is based on the fastener head diameter model and was used to establish the reference pull-through design values, W_H, given in NDS Table 12.2F. NDS Equation 12.2-6b was added to limit the head pull-through capacity for net side member thicknesses greater than 2.5 times the fastener head diameter based on analysis of available data which indicated that the increased head pull-through capacity reached a limit where no further increase for side member thickness was appropriate.

For fasteners where the head is driven flush with the side member surface, the net side member thickness, t_{ns}, is the thickness of the side member (see Figure C12.2.5A). For fasteners that are installed in counter-bored holes, the net side member thickness is measured from the bottom of the hole (see Figure C12.2.5B).

Head pull-through equations in NDS Section 12.2.5 (see Equation C12.2.5-1) are for round-head fasteners and washers. For fasteners with other than round heads, such as clipped or oval head nails and hex head bolts and lag screws, analysis of underlying data is considered to support the use of a more general fastener head perimeter model (see Equation C12.2.5-2).

Figure C12.2.5 Net Side Member Thickness, t_{ns}

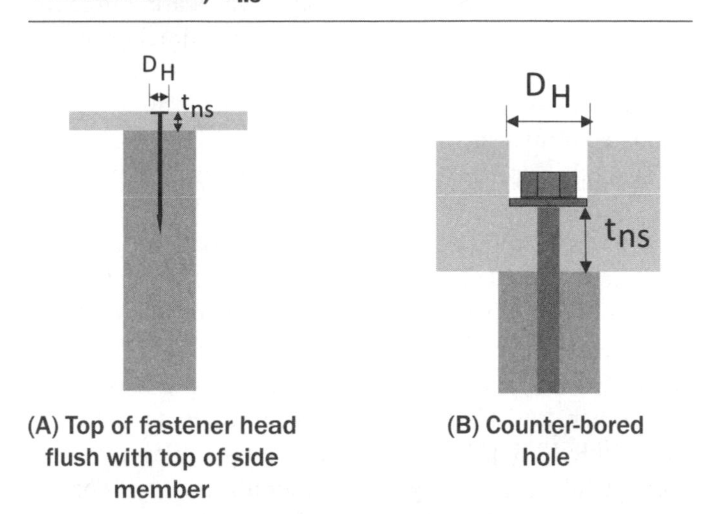

(A) Top of fastener head flush with top of side member

(B) Counter-bored hole

Fastener head diameter equation for establishing fastener head pull-through reference design values:

$$W_H = 690\ \pi\ D_H\ G^2\ t_{ns}\ \text{for}\ t_{ns} \leq 2.5D_H \qquad (C12.2.5\text{-}1)$$

Fastener head perimeter equation for establishing fastener head pull-through reference design values:

$$W_H = 690\ P_H\ G^2\ t_{ns}\ \ \text{for}\ t_{ns} \leq 0.8P_H \qquad (C12.2.5\text{-}2)$$

where:

$\pi\ D_H$ = perimeter for fasteners with round heads, in.

D_H = fastener head diameter, in.

G = specific gravity of side member

t_{ns} = net side member thickness, in.

P_H = fastener head perimeter, P_H, in.

C12.3 Reference Lateral Design Values

Reference lateral design values for dowel-type fasteners (bolts, lag screws, wood screws, nails and spikes) are based on a yield limit model which specifically accounts for the different ways these connections can behave under load. These behavior patterns or modes (see NDS Appendix I) are uniform bearing in the wood under the fastener, rotation of the fastener in the joint without bending, and development of one or more plastic hinges in the fastener (67, 122). Equations have been developed for each mode relating the joint load to the maximum stresses in the wood members and in the fastener (67, 121). The capacity of the connection under each yield mode is keyed to the bearing strength of the wood under the fastener and the bending strength of the fastener, with the lowest capacity calculated for the various modes being taken as the reference design value for the connection.

Although the yield limit model represents significantly different methodology than that used previously to establish fastener design values, the relative effects of various joint variables shown by both procedures are generally similar (85, 86, 89, 121). Short-term design values obtained from application of the yield limit equations have been reduced to the design value levels published in previous editions of the Specification for connections made with the same species and member sizes.

Bolts: Reference lateral design values for bolted connections are indexed to proportional limit estimates from bolted connection tests (44, 57, 146, 162) at reference conditions (seasoned dry, normal load duration).

Lag Screws: Reference lateral design values for lag screw connections are indexed to average short-term proportional limit test values (100) divided by 1.875. The 1.875 factor is based on an original reduction factor of 2.25, increased 20 percent for normal loading and experience. The twenty percent increase was introduced as part of the World War II emergency increase in wood design values, and then subsequently codified as 10 percent for the change from permanent to normal loading and 10 percent for experience (see C2.3.2).

Wood Screws: Reference lateral design values for wood screw connections are indexed to average short-term proportional limit test values (184, 70) divided by 1.33. The 1.33 factor is based on an original reduction factor of 1.6, increased 20 percent for normal loading and experience. The twenty percent increase was introduced as part of the World War II emergency increase in wood design values, and then subsequently codified as 10 percent for the change from permanent to normal loading and 10 percent for experience (see C2.3.2). Lateral design values for wood screw connections at reference conditions (seasoned dry, normal load duration) are about one-fifth of maximum tested capacities (184).

Nails & Spikes: Reference lateral design values for nailed connections are indexed to average short-term proportional limit test values (184, 50) divided by 1.33. The 1.33 factor is based on an original reduction factor of 1.6, increased 20 percent for normal loading and experience. The twenty percent increase was introduced as part of the World War II emergency increase in wood design values, and then subsequently codified as 10 percent for the change from permanent to normal loading and 10 percent for experience (see C2.3.2). Lateral design values for nailed connections at reference conditions (seasoned dry, normal load duration) are about one-fifth of maximum tested capacities for softwoods and one-ninth of maximum tested capacities for hardwoods (184, 50).

C12.3.1 Yield Limit Equations

The yield limit equations for single shear connections (NDS Equations 12.3-1 to 12.3-6) and for double shear connections (NDS Equations 12.3-7 to 12.3-10) were developed from European research (121, 78) and have been confirmed by tests of connections made with domestic species (21, 20, 88, 120, 121, 122). The limiting yield modes covered by these equations are bearing in the main or side members (Mode I), fastener rotation without bending (Mode II), development of a plastic hinge in the fastener in main or side member (Mode III) and development of plastic hinges in the fastener in both main and side members (Mode IV) (see NDS Appendix I).

The reduction term, R_d, in NDS Equations 12.3-1 through 12.3-10, reduces the values calculated using the yield limit equations to approximate estimates of the nominal proportional limit design values in previous editions of the Specification (157). For fasteners loaded perpendicular to grain with diameters equal to or greater than 0.25 inches, the reduction term is increased 25% ($K_\theta = 1.25$) to match previous design values for connections loaded perpendicular to grain.

For detailed technical information on lateral design equations, see *AWC's Technical Report 12: General Dowel Equations for Calculating Lateral Connection Values* (137) available at www.awc.org.

C12.3.2 Common Connection Conditions

Reference lateral design values, Z, for connections with bolts, lag screws, wood screws, nails and spikes are calculated for common connection conditions and assumed fastener bending yield strengths using the yield limit equations in NDS 12.3.1. Assumptions used in the yield limit equations to develop the tables are provided in the table headings and footnotes.

C12.3.3 Dowel Bearing Strength

C12.3.3.1 The limiting wood stresses used in the yield limit equations are based on the load at which the load-deformation curve from a fastener embedment test intersects a line represented by the initial tangent modulus offset 5 percent of the fastener diameter (120). This nominal yield point is intermediate between the proportional limit and maximum loads for the material.

The effect of specific gravity on dowel bearing strength was established from 3/4-inch dowel embedment tests on Douglas fir, southern pine, spruce-pine-fir, sitka spruce, red oak, yellow poplar, and aspen. Diameter effects were evaluated from tests of 1/4, 1/2, 3/4, 1, and 1-1/2 inch dowels in southern pine using bolt holes 1/16-inch larger than the dowel diameter. Diameter was found to be a significant variable only in perpendicular to grain loading. Bearing specimens were 1/2-inch or thicker such that width and number of growth rings did not influence results (158).

The specific gravity values given in NDS Table 12.3.3A for each specie or species group are those used to establish dowel bearing strength values, F_e, tabulated in NDS Table 12.3.3. These specific gravity values represent average values from in-grade lumber test programs or are based on information from ASTM D 2555.

The equations provided in footnote 2 of NDS Table 12.3.3 were used to calculate tabulated values in NDS Table 12.3.3. These equations were derived from test data using methods described in ASTM D 5764 (158, 18).

C12.3.3.2 Dowel bearing strengths for wood structural panels using a dowel diameter of less than or equal to ¼ inch are provided in NDS Table 12.3.3B and are based on research conducted by APA-The Engineered Wood Association (25). Dowel bearing values for larger diameters in wood structural panels are available in APA 825E.

C12.3.3.3 Dowel bearing strengths for structural composite lumber are determined for each product using equivalency methods described in ASTM D5456 (16).

C12.3.3.4 For fasteners with $D \geq 1/4"$ installed in end-grain, the dowel bearing strength is equal to the perpendicular to grain value, $F_{e\perp}$.

C12.3.3.5 For fasteners in the wide face of CLT, dowel bearing strength is based on the dowel bearing strength of the layer at the shear plane. The orientation of the layer at the shear plane may either be parallel or perpendicular to the major strength axis of the panel and should be part of the specification of the cross-laminated timber panel (see Commentary C10.1.4). For connections where the loading direction is parallel to grain for the layer at the shear plane, the dowel bearing strength is the parallel to grain dowel bearing strength, $F_{e\parallel}$. For connections where the loading direction is perpendicular to grain for the layer at the shear plane, the dowel bearing strength is the perpendicular to grain dowel bearing strength, $F_{e\perp}$. The influence of different dowel bearing strengths of crossing layers on cross-laminated connection design values is accounted for by adjustment of the bearing length in the crossing layers (See NDS 12.3.5.2).

C12.3.3.6 For fasteners with $D \geq 1/4"$ that are installed into the edge of cross-laminated timber, the dowel bearing strength is assumed to be the same as for fasteners installed into end-grain (See NDS 12.3.3.4) which conservatively addresses varying grain orientations and the ability to maintain minimum edge distances within the narrow face of a cross-laminated timber lamination. For fasteners with $D<1/4"$, the same dowel bearing strength, F_e, applies for either parallel or perpendicular to grain loading.

C12.3.4 Dowel Bearing Strength at an Angle to Grain

NDS Equation 12.3-11 (and Equation J-2 in NDS Appendix J) is used to calculate the dowel bearing strength for a main or side member loaded at an angle to grain. This equation is a form of the bearing angle to grain equation (NDS Equation J-1). The equation is entered with the parallel and perpendicular dowel bearing strengths for the member and the reference bolt design value is determined from the yield limit equations using $F_{e\theta}$ as the dowel bearing strength for the main or side member.

The reference design value obtained from the yield limit equations using dowel bearing strength at an angle to grain is similar to that obtained from using parallel to grain and perpendicular to grain *Z* values in NDS Equation J-3 to obtain a Z_θ design value for the connection (157). Determining a Z_θ design value using this latter approach can be used as an alternative to calculating $F_{e\theta}$ for use in each yield limit equation and allows the use of tabulated *Z* values from the Specification.

C12.3.5 Dowel Bearing Length

C12.3.5.2 For fasteners with $D \geq 1/4"$, crossing layers in cross-laminated timbers will have different dowel bearing strengths than the layer at the shear plane due to the difference in grain orientation. The influence of varying dowel bearing strengths in crossing layers on connection design values is addressed by use of an "effective" bearing length. For connections where the loading direction is parallel to grain for the layer at the shear plane, the dowel bearing length should be reduced by multiplying the bearing length in each crossing layer (perpendicular to grain) by the ratio of $F_{e\perp}/F_{e\parallel}$. For connections where the loading direction is perpendicular to grain for the layer at the shear plane, the dowel bearing length can conservatively remain unadjusted or it can be increased in the crossing layers (parallel to grain) by the ratio of $F_{e\parallel}/F_{e\perp}$. Actual penetration lengths should be used for checking minimum penetration requirements. For connections loaded at an angle to grain, the procedures in NDS Appendix J for developing design values based on parallel and perpendicular to grain design values should be used with these "effective" bearing lengths. Methods of installation should avoid placing fasteners in gaps between adjacent boards in a lamination, especially where they might occur in the lamination at the shear plane.

C12.3.5.3 An analysis provided in Technical Report 12 (137) shows that the NDS requirement closely approximates results from the more detailed evaluation of the influence of a tapered tip on bearing resistance. For wood screws, nails and spikes, the length of the tapered tip is not generally standardized, but for purposes of accounting for the tip length in the bearing length calculation, E, is permitted to be taken as 2 diameters (2D). For lag screws, E is permitted to be taken from NDS Appendix L, Table L2.

C12.3.6 Dowel Bending Yield Strength

The dowel bending yield strength, F_{yb}, of fasteners such as nails (79), wood screws, lag screws, and bolts are given in NDS Appendix I. For most steel fasteners, F_{yb} equal to 45,000 psi is a conservative value and is equivalent to the bolt strength reported in the original bolt test research (146).

C12.3.7 Dowel Diameter

Reference lateral design values for both smooth shank and deformed shank nails are based on the shank diameter, D. In prior editions of the Specification, lateral design values for deformed shank nails used the root diameter, D_r, and a F_{yb} value associated with hardened medium carbon steel nails.

A change in ASTM F 1575 (205) clarified that nail bending yield strength, F_{yb}, is based on the shank diameter, D, not on the root diameter, D_r. This change in ASTM 1575 facilitated simplification of nail moment resistance in the NDS yield equations for nails specified in ASTM F1667 since D is provided for all nail types.

The reduced moment resistance in the threaded portion of dowel-type fasteners, other than nails, can be accounted for by use of root diameter, D_r, in calculation of reference lateral design values. Use of diameter, D, is permitted when the threaded portion of the fastener is sufficiently far away from the connection shear plane(s). For more information, see NDS Appendix I.5.

Reference lateral design values for reduced body diameter lag screw and rolled thread wood screw connections are based on root diameter, D_r, to account for the reduced diameter of these fasteners. These values, while conservative, can also be used for full-body diameter lag screws and cut thread wood screws. For bolted connections, reference lateral design values are based on diameter, D.

One alternate method of accounting for the moment and bearing resistance of the threaded portion of the fastener and moment acting along the length of the fastener is provided in AWC's *Technical Report 12–General Dowel Equations for Calculating Lateral Connection Values* (137). A general set of equations permits use of different fastener diameters for bearing resistance and moment resistance in each member.

C12.3.8 Asymmetric Three Member Connections, Double Shear

Conservatively, the Specification requires the use of minimum side member bearing length and minimum dowel diameter in the calculation of design values for asymmetric three member connections. Inherent in this calculation is the assumption that the load to each side member is equivalent. Where other load distributions occur, more complex analysis may be needed.

C12.3.9 Multiple Shear Connections

The Specification requires evaluation of each individual shear plane using the yield limit equations of NDS 12.3.1 and then assigning the lowest value to the other shear planes. Interior members should be checked for the combined loading from the adjacent shear planes to ensure that sufficient bearing capacity exists (such as would exist in a double shear connection limited by Mode I_m).

C12.3.10 Load at an Angle to Fastener Axis

Two member connections in which the load acts at an angle to the axis of the fastener are checked using the component of the load acting at 90° to the axis and member thicknesses equal to the length of the fastener in each member measured at the centerline of the fastener (see NDS Figure 12E). Reference design values for connections in which the load acts at an angle to the fastener axis are based on the yield limit equations of NDS 12.3.1. The lowest value of Z obtained, using t_m and t_s equal to the length of the fastener in each member, divided by the cosine of the angle of intersection of the two members is the maximum reference design value for the connection.

The adequacy of the bearing area under washers and plates to resist the component of force acting parallel to the fastener axis can be checked using adjusted compression design values perpendicular to grain, $F_{c\perp}'$.

C12.3.11 Drift Bolts and Drift Pins

Reference lateral design values for drift bolts or pins (181) are 75 percent of the reference design value for common bolts of the same diameter to compensate for the absence of head, nut, and washer. End distance, edge distance, and spacing requirements, and group action adjustments that are applicable to bolts, are also applicable to drift bolts and drift pins.

C12.4 Combined Lateral and Withdrawal Loads

C12.4.1 Lag Screws and Wood Screws

Results of lag screw tests indicated that loading at an angle to the fastener axis to induce lateral and withdrawal components did not reduce the maximum connection capacity. However, when joint resistance was evaluated at the design load level, an interaction of the load components was observed with larger diameter screws at load angles less than 45° (87). Analysis at design load level was performed due to the differences in design level to maximum capacity ratios for lateral and withdrawal. NDS Equation 12.4-1 can also be used to determine the reference design value of lag screws or wood screws embedded at an angle to grain in the wood member and loaded in a direction normal to the wood member. For this condition, α, would be defined as the angle perpendicular to the fastener axis.

C12.4.2 Nails and Spikes

It is assumed that current adjustments for toe-nailed connections address the effects of combined lateral and withdrawal loading and do not require further modification.

Research on the effects of combined lateral and withdrawal loading on nailed connections (37) involved tests of Engelmann spruce, Douglas fir, and red oak single shear connections made with 8d common nails. Nail penetration depths of 6, 10, and 14 diameters into the main member and load angles of 0 degrees, 90 degrees, and six intermediate directions were investigated. Two tests were conducted at each load angle. The interaction equation found to best describe maximum connection load results for each species and penetration depth was of the form:

$$P = \frac{(1 + K \sin 2\alpha)(W'pZ')}{(W'p)\cos\alpha + (Z')\sin\alpha} \qquad \text{(C12.4.2-1)}$$

where:

P = maximum load at angle to grain

W' = maximum load at 90° (withdrawal load perpendicular to grain per inch of penetration in the main member)

p = depth of penetration

Z' = maximum load at 0° (lateral load)

α = angle between wood surface and direction of applied load

K = factor based on least squares analysis of test data for each species-penetration group

The average value of K for the six species and penetration groups evaluated was 0.535, and ranged from 0.151 to 1.406. Average K values by species were 0.432, 0.864, and 0.309 for Douglas fir, Engelmann spruce, and red oak, respectively. When K is conservatively assumed to equal 0, Equation C12.4.2-1 reduces to NDS Equation 12.4-2 or, in another format the following:

$$\frac{R_W}{(W'p)} + \frac{R_Z}{Z'} \leq 1 \qquad \text{(C12.4.2-2)}$$

where:

R_W = connection withdrawal force

R_Z = connection lateral force

C12.5 Adjustment of Reference Design Values

C12.5.1 Geometry Factor, C_Δ

C12.5.1.1 For dowel-type fasteners with diameters less than ¼", no reduction for geometry is specified.

C12.5.1.2 For dowel-type fasteners with diameters equal to or greater than ¼", the geometry factor provides a proportionate reduction of reference lateral design values for less than full end distance or less than full spacing distance. The lowest geometry factor for any fastener applies to all other fasteners in that same connection, not just to the end fastener or a pair of fasteners in a row. It should be noted that further reductions may be necessary when checking stresses in members at connections (see NDS 11.1.2).

The requirement that fastener design values for multiple shear plane connections or asymmetric three member connections be based on the application of the lowest geometry factor for any shear plane to all fasteners in the joint assumes that the total joint capacity is proportional to the number of shear planes.

End Distance: Requirements in NDS 12.5.1.2 (a) and NDS Table 12.5.1A for parallel to grain loading are based on early recommendations (146). For tension loads (fasteners bearing toward the member end), the minimum end distances of 7D for softwoods and 5D for hardwoods for $C_\Delta = 1.0$ were established by test. For compression loads (fasteners bearing away from the member end), the minimum end distance of 4D for $C_\Delta = 1.0$ was based on the minimum spacing of fasteners in a row for $C_\Delta = 1.0$ (146). End distances for angle to grain tension loadings may be linearly interpolated from those for perpendicular to grain and tension parallel to grain design values.

The provisions for use of reduced end distances for connections when proportionate reductions ($0.5 \leq C_\Delta \leq 1.0$) are made in design values are supported by early research (184, 181, 146) which showed a linear relationship between end distance and joint proportional limit strength. A subsequent study showed that a minimum end distance of only 5D was sufficient to develop the full proportional limit load of Douglas fir joints made with metal side plates and loaded in tension parallel to grain (119). Other research further substantiates the adequacy of the end distance requirements for connections loaded in both compression and tension parallel to grain (102, 110). End distances less than 50 percent of those required for C_Δ =1.0 are not allowed.

Shear Area: Requirements in NDS 12.5.1(b) are for members loaded at an angle to the fastener axis. End distance requirements are expressed in terms of equivalent shear areas. Shear area for such a joint is defined as the triangular area in the thickness plane of the member which is enclosed between the tip of the member and the centerline of the fastener (NDS Figure 12E). This shear area for the angled member is compared to the shear area of a joint in which both members are loaded perpendicular to the fastener axis (members parallel to each other) and which meet end distance requirements. The equivalent shear area for the parallel member joint is the product of the required end distance and the length of the fastener in the member.

As with end distance requirements for parallel member connections, reduced shear areas less than 50 percent of those required for $C_\Delta = 1.0$ are not allowed. It is recommended as good practice that the distance between the fastener axis and the inside juncture of the angled side member and the main member (see NDS Figure 12E) be at least 1.5*D*.

Spacing Requirements for Fasteners in a Row: For fasteners in a row, the spacing requirements contained in NDS 12.5.1(c) and NDS Table 12.5.1B are assumed to be sufficient to cover the effects of non-uniform distribution of shear stresses through the thickness of the member (concentrated at the edges) that occur as the fastener bends (146). Reduced spacings less than 75 percent of those required for $C_\Delta = 1.0$ are not allowed.

If the direction of loading is perpendicular to grain, the minimum spacing for $C_\Delta = 1.0$ is based on the attached member. If the attached member is steel, then steel spacing controls from the appropriate steel standards (125). If the attached member is a wood member loaded parallel to grain, then parallel to grain spacing controls. If the attached member is wood loaded perpendicular to grain, then 4D should be adequate. Evaluating the wood members for shear per NDS 3.4.3.3 would also be advisable.

C12.5.1.3 For dowel-type fasteners with diameters equal to or greater than ¼", the connections need to be designed to comply with several related limitations, including edge distance and spacing between the rows of fasteners and the maximum perpendicular to grain distance between outermost fasteners.

Edge Distance: Requirements in NDS Table 12.5.1C for parallel to grain loading of 1.5*D* or the greater of 1.5*D* or 1/2 the spacing between rows for ℓ/D greater than 6, and for loaded edge–perpendicular to grain loading of 4*D* are based on early research (146). The unloaded edge–perpendicular to grain minimum of 1.5*D* is a good practice recommendation.

NDS 12.5.1 does not provide specific guidance on edge distance requirements for loads applied at angles other than 0° and 90°, nor does it provide specific geometry factors for reduced edge distances.

The ratio of the fastener length in side member to fastener diameter, ℓ/D, in NDS Table 12.5.1A is based on the total thickness of both wood side members when connections of three or more wood members are involved. For connections involving metal main or side members, only the ℓ/D ratio for the wood members are considered for determination of edge distance requirements in this section. Metal parts must still be designed per NDS 11.2.3.

Avoidance of heavy or medium suspended loads below the neutral axis of a beam was added as a result of several reported field problems involving glued laminated timber beams subject to a line of concentrated loads applied through bolted hangers or ledger strips attached in the tension zone or at the bottom edge of the beam. Concentrated loads less than 100 pounds and spaced more than 24 inches apart may be considered a light load condition.

For perpendicular to grain connections, the member is required to be checked for shear in accordance with 3.4.3.3 of the Specification using a reduced depth, d_e, equivalent to the beam depth (d) less the distance from the unloaded edge of the beam to the center of the nearest fastener.

Spacing Requirements Between Rows: For perpendicular to grain loading, NDS Table 12.5.1D provisions are based on early research (146). These requirements relate the tendency of the fasteners to bend and cause non-uniform bearing stresses and the resistance of the wood between rows to resist splitting. It is for this reason that staggering of fasteners loaded perpendicular to grain is desirable (see NDS 12.6.1). In computing the ℓ/D ratio for determining the appropriate minimum spacing between rows for perpendicular to grain loading, the ratio for side members is based on the sum of the bearing length in each side member where three or more wood member joints are involved.

For parallel to grain loading, NDS Table 12.5.1D permits rows of fasteners to be spaced 1.5D; however, additional spacing may be required when installing bolts and lag screws to accommodate larger head and washer dimensions and clearance requirements for wrench sockets. Note that the steel industry recommends a minimum center-to-center spacing between holes of 2.67D, with a preferred distance of 3D (125).

The limitation on row spacing applies to metal as well as wood side plates, to members loaded perpendicular as well as parallel to grain, and to three or more member connections occurring at truss panel points.

Maximum Perpendicular to Grain Distance Between Outermost Fasteners: For parallel or perpendicular to grain loading, limiting the maximum distance between outer rows of fasteners on the same splice plate to 5" avoids splitting that could occur in members at connections as a result of restraint of shrinkage associated with drying in service. Table 12.5.1F was added in the 2012 edition of the Specification in recognition that structural glued laminated timber is manufactured at lower moisture contents which reduces the amount of shrinkage during drying in service. The 10" spacing was based on judgment following review of several analyses that accounted for effects of moisture content change, shrinkage rate, hole oversize and hole alignment on potential restraint of shrinkage between connected members. The proposed 10" was based on an analysis and the following assumptions: 1) a maximum moisture content at time of fabrication of 16% and an in-service moisture content of 6%; 2) a reduced shrinkage rate applicable to structural glued laminated timbers versus sawn lumber to account for a mixture of tangential and radial shrinkage in the varying layers of glulam; and 3) recognition of the combined effect of bolt hole oversizing and alignment resulting in 1/32" movement.

Special detailing can be utilized in cases where distances between outer rows of bolts exceed the limits in Table 12.5.1F, such as use of multiple splice plates or a single splice plate with slotted holes to allow shrinkage. Such an example of multiple splice plates is shown in Figure C12.5.1.3.

Figure C12.5.1.3 Connection Illustrating Use of Multiple Splice Plates

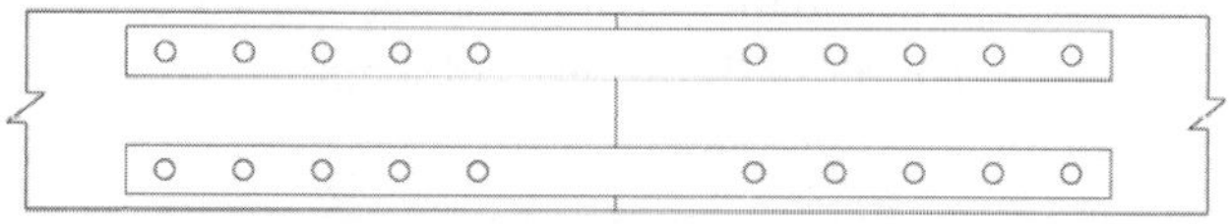

C12.5.1.4 For fasteners installed in the edge of cross-laminated timber panels, special end distance, edge distance and fastener spacing conditions are provided in NDS Table 12.5.1G, while all other requirements follow the general provisions of NDS 12.5.1. For fasteners installed in the wide face of cross-laminated panels, end distances, edge distances, and fastener spacing requirements should follow the requirements for other wood products in NDS 12.5.1. Placement of fasteners in gaps should be avoided.

C12.5.2 End Grain Factor, C_{eg}

C12.5.2.1 Reducing reference withdrawal design values for lag screws 25 percent when the screw is inserted in the end grain (radial-tangential plane) of the main member rather than the side grain (radial-longitudinal or tangential-longitudinal plane) is based on lag screw joint tests (100).

Early tests of wood screws in withdrawal from end grain surfaces of oak, southern pine, maple, and cypress gave somewhat erratic results relative to those for withdrawal from side grain (43). These irregular results were attributed to the tendency of the screw to split the wood in the end grain configuration. Average ratios of end grain withdrawal resistance to side grain withdrawal resistance ranged from 52 to 108 percent (43). Because of this variability, structural loading of wood screws in withdrawal from end grain has been prohibited. Where splitting is avoided, use of an end grain to side grain withdrawal design value ratio of 75 percent has been suggested (184, 183).

Reduction of withdrawal design values up to 50 percent have been reported for nails driven in end grain surfaces (radial-tangential plane) as compared to side grain (radial-longitudinal or tangential-longitudinal planes) surfaces (184, 118). When coupled with the effects of seasoning in service after fabrication, such reductions are considered too great for reliable design. It is considered to be on this basis that loading of nails and spikes in withdrawal from end grain has been prohibited.

C12.5.2.2 The use of a 0.67 adjustment factor on reference lateral design values for lag screws, wood screws, nails, or spikes driven in the end grain is based on early research on joints made with softwood species (181, 184).

C12.5.2.3 For fasteners with $D \geq 1/4"$, the use of a 0.67 adjustment factor for fasteners installed in the edge of a cross-laminated timber panel is based on the assumption that fasteners will be installed into end grain of the cross-laminated timber lamination (see Commentary C12.3.3.6) regardless of whether installation is actually into end grain. Testing of large fasteners installed into end-grain or between laminations with end-grain and side-grain indicated that the 0.67 adjustment factor was sufficiently conservative, even when gaps were present (198). For smaller diameter fasteners with $D < 1/4"$, the end grain factor in 12.5.2.2 applies where installation is into end grain (see Commentary C12.5.2.2) of a cross-laminated timber lamination.

C12.5.3 Diaphragm Factor, C_{di}

Diaphragms are large, flat structural units acting like a deep relatively thin beam or girder. Horizontal wood diaphragms consist of floor or roof decks acting as webs, and lumber, structural glued laminated timber, SCL, or I-joist members acting as the flanges. Such assemblies distribute horizontal forces acting on the flanges to vertical resisting elements (103). Shear walls consisting of wall sheathing materials attached to top and bottom plates and vertical framing members also are diaphragms. Such shear walls or vertical diaphragms act to transfer loads from horizontal diaphragms down to the supporting foundation. The diaphragm factor, C_{di}, applies to both horizontal and vertical diaphragms (144, 145).

C12.5.4 Toe-Nail Factor, C_{tn}

C12.5.4.1 The 0.67 adjustment of reference withdrawal design values for toenailing is based on the results of joint tests comparing slant driving and straight driving (184) and of typical toenailed and end nailed joints used in frame wall construction (118) where the attached member is pulled directly away from the main member. It is applicable to joints fabricated at all levels of seasoning. This includes multiple nail joints fabricated of unseasoned wood and then loaded after seasoning (184, 183, 118). Toenailing with cross slant driving can produce stronger joints than end or face nailing. For example, a stud to plate joint made of four 8*d* toenails was reported to be stronger than the same joint made with two 16d end nails (181, 118). Where toenailed connections are resisting withdrawal, the depth of penetration, p_t, of the nail in the member holding the point may be taken as the actual length of nail in the member as shown in Figure C12.5.4-1.

Figure C12.5.4-1 Effective Penetration and Side Member Thickness for Toe-Nails Subject to Lateral Loads

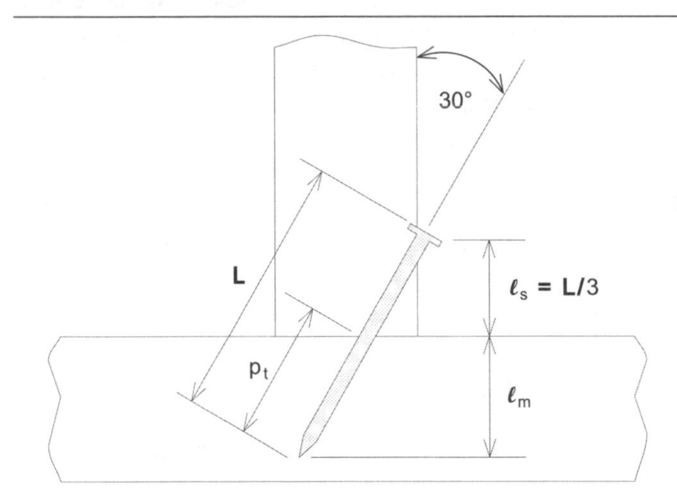

C12.5.4.2 The toe-nail factor of 0.83 is an adjustment based on the intermediate condition between the full lateral design value for side-grain connections and the full lateral design value for end-grain conditions where C_{eg} = 0.67. Where toe-nailed connections are resisting lateral loads, the bearing length, ℓ_m, of the nail in the member holding the point may be taken as the vertically projected length of nail in the member (see Figure C12.5.4-1) calculated as:

$$\ell_m = L\cos 30° - L/3 \qquad \text{(C12.5.4-1)}$$

where:

L = length of nail, in.

For purposes of establishing the single shear reference lateral design value applicable to a toe-nailed connection, the side member bearing length, L_s, of the nail (see Figure C12.5.4-1) shall be taken as:

$$\ell_s = L/3 \qquad \text{(C12.5.4-2)}$$

Equation C12.5.4-2 only applies to nails driven at an angle of approximately 30° to the face of the member being attached and one-third the nail length from the end of that member.

C12.6 Multiple Fasteners

C12.6.1 Symmetrically Staggered Fasteners

See C12.5.1.3 Spacing Requirements Between Rows.

C12.6.2 Fasteners Loaded at an Angle to Grain

General provisions for the placement and spacing of fasteners to cover all directions of loading and any number of members in a connection are beyond the scope of the Specification. For this reason, the gravity axis of all members must pass through the center of fastener resistance to maintain uniform stress in main members and uniform distribution of load to all fasteners. If it is not possible to achieve intersection of member gravity axes with the center of resistance of the fastener group, the designer has the responsibility to fully evaluate and account for the effects of the resultant eccentric loading on both the load-carrying capacity of the members and the capacity of the connection (see C11.1.3).

C12.6.3 Local Stresses in Connections

See C11.1.2.

C13 SPLIT RING AND SHEAR PLATE CONNECTORS

C13.1 General

C13.1.1 Scope

Split ring and shear plate connectors act like dowels or keys in distributing loads from one member to another in a joint (184). The large diameters of the rings or plates, relative to the diameters of bolts, and the relatively shallow depth of the connectors in the members provide for increased bearing areas without penalizing reductions in net section areas. As a result, these connectors can develop significantly higher design values than those obtainable from bolts alone.

Split ring connectors are installed in precut grooves made with a special power-driven drill and cutting tool. They are used in wood-to-wood joints where high lateral joint loads are involved; such as in bowstring trusses, arches, and bridges. The bolt or lag screw passing through the center of the ring holds the faces of the joint members in contact.

Similar to split rings, shear plates are installed in precut grooves but are flush to the surface when fully seated. Two shear plates are the equivalent of one split ring, with the load being transferred from one plate to the other in the joint through shear in the bolt or lag screw. Shear plates are primarily used in wood-to-steel connections; such as steel gusset plate joints or column-foundation connections where the metal replaces one of the plates, and in demountable wood-to-wood connections, such as stadium bleachers (142).

The design provisions for split ring and shear plate connectors in the Specification are based on early research (104, 117).

C13.1.2 Terminology

A connector unit is described in terms of the metal parts required for a single shear plane. For a split ring connection, one ring is used in matching grooves in the members adjacent to one plane. For shear plate connections, two matching shear plates, one in appropriate grooves in each member, are used in wood-to-wood joints. In a wood-to-metal joint, the steel strap or plate replaces one of the shear plates. In all three cases, the bolt or lag screw tying the joint together is considered loaded in single shear. Where more than one connector unit is on the same bolt, as in the case of a three member joint where the main member has connectors on the same bolt on both faces, an adjusted single shear design value for each shear plane is provided in the design value tables (see NDS Tables 13.2A and 13.2B).

C13.1.3 Quality of Split Ring and Shear Plate Connectors

C13.1.3.1 The split ring is wedge shaped (beveled toward the edges) to facilitate installation and assure a tight fit when fully seated. The diameter of the inside groove for the split ring is 2 percent larger than the inside diameter of the ring, thus requiring the ring to be sprung slightly when inserted. This provides for any subsequent shrinkage of the members and for simultaneous bearing of the inner surface of the connector against the inner core of wood created by the grooving operation and bearing of the outer surface of the connector on the opposite side against the outside wall of the groove (117, 142). The position of the tongue-slot joint in the ring relative to the direction of loading is not significant (117).

The two small perforations in the central portion of pressed steel shear plates serve to facilitate temporary attachment of the connector to the joint member when off-site fabrication is employed and in the erection and dismantling of temporary structures in the field. The perforations do not affect plate load-carrying performance.

C13.1.3.2 Design values in NDS Tables 13.2A and 13.2B correspond to the dimensions for split rings and shear plates, respectively, in Appendix K of the Specification. In addition to connector diameter, the depth of the connector in the member and its thickness affect joint load-carrying capacity. Only those split rings that have equivalent or larger inside diameter, metal depth, and metal thickness than those given in NDS Appendix K qualify for the connector design values provided in NDS Table 13.2A. Similarly, only those shear plates that have equivalent or larger plate diameter, plate depth, and plate thickness than those given in NDS Appendix K qualify for the connector design values provided in NDS Table 13.2B.

The projected areas given in NDS Appendix K for split rings are calculated as the sum of the inside groove diameter and twice the groove width times the groove depth. The projected areas for shear plates given in NDS Appendix K are based on the groove diameter times the groove depth for the nominal shear plate dimensions shown. Tabulated projected areas for split ring and shear plate connectors given in NDS Appendix K are to be used in checking localized wood stresses in accordance with NDS 11.1.2 and 13.3.4.3.

C13.1.3.3 Bolts used with split rings or shear plates are required to meet the quality provisions of NDS 12.1.2 for full body diameter bolts to prevent use of undersized fasteners that do not provide full bearing with the connectors.

C13.1.3.4 Lag screws used with split rings or shear plates are required to meet the quality provisions of NDS 12.1.3 for full body diameter lag screws to prevent use of undersized fasteners that do not provide full bearing with the connectors.

C13.1.4 Fabrication and Assembly

C13.1.4.1 Cutterheads should be designed specifically for the dimensions provided by the particular connector manufacturer.

C13.1.4.3 Washers may be used in shear plate connections involving steel straps and plates when use of a longer bolt or lag screw is necessary to avoid bearing of the threaded portion of the bolt or screw on the strap or plate.

C13.1.4.4 Reference design values for split ring and shear plate connectors apply to joints in which the members are in contact, are fabricated of wood having a moisture content of 15 percent or lower to a depth of at least 3/4 inch from the surface, and will remain dry in service. Effects of normal variations in moisture content that occur in dry conditions of service are accounted for in the reference values.

When connectors are installed in unseasoned or partially seasoned wood intended for use in dry conditions of service, reference design values are to be adjusted in accordance with the factors in NDS 11.3.3. Such joints will need to be tightened as the members season in service by periodically turning down the nuts on the bolts until service equilibrium moisture content is reached.

It is good practice to exclude visible face knots within a distance of one-half the connector diameter along the grain from the edge of the connector unit (181, 117). Where visible knots are included within a one-half connector diameter distance of the critical section, the net section based on the projected area of the connector unit and bolt or screw should be further reduced for the cross-sectional area of such included knots (see NDS 3.1.2.3).

C13.2 Reference Design Values

C13.2.1 Reference Design Values

Early connector tests of joints made with Douglas fir, southern pine, white oak, and other representative species showed that joint load-carrying capacity was directly related to the specific gravity of the wood members (184, 181, 104, 117).

Reference design values in NDS Tables 13.2A and 13.2B represent maximum joint test loads reduced by a factor of 3.6 that includes adjustments for variability and load duration (184, 181, 117). These reference design values, applicable to normal loading conditions, are considered to be less than 70 percent of proportional limit test loads (181, 117). Reference design values apply only to those joint designs which meet the minimum thickness requirements in NDS Tables 13.2A or 13.2B and the end distance, edge distance, and spacing requirements corresponding to C_Δ=1.0 in NDS Table 13.3. Net thickness requirements refer to the actual thickness of the member before grooving.

C13.2.1.1 Reference design values for split ring connections in NDS Table 13.2A and for shear plate connections in NDS Table 13.2B are given in terms of the number of faces a member has with a connector on the same bolt and on the thickness of that member. The lowest reference design value for the two members being joined is the reference design value for the shear plane.

C13.2.1.2 The 2900 pound limit for the 2-5/8 inch shear plate is the maximum reference bearing load for a pressed steel plate without a reinforcing hub about the bolt hole. The 4400 and 6000 pound limit for the 4 inch plates used with 3/4 and 7/8 inch bolts, respectively, are the maximum reference shear design values for A307 bolts of these diameters. The 4 inch plates have integral re-enforcing hubs about the central bolt hole. The limiting values specified in footnote 2 of NDS Table 13.2B are based on metal strength; therefore, these metal parts should be designed per NDS 11.2.3. The strength of metal parts should not be adjusted by factors given in NDS 11.3.1 (e.g., ASD Load Duration Factor, C_D).

C13.2.2 Thickness of Wood Members

C13.2.2.1 The minimum member thicknesses required for use of the split ring and shear plate connector values in NDS Tables 13.2A and 13.2B have been established from the results of joint tests (117).

C13.2.2.2 The provision for use of linear interpolation between minimum thicknesses and those required from maximum design values is based on the original connector research (117).

C13.2.3 Penetration Depth Factor, C_d

Adjustments for reduced lag screw penetration depths are permitted to be interpolated between the values for $C_d = 1.0$ and $C_d = 0.75$ using the corresponding penetrations, respectively, for each species group.

C13.2.4 Metal Side Plate Factor, C_{st}

Increases for metal side plates used with 4 inch shear plate connectors are based on original connector research involving claw plates (117). The increased values for 4 inch shear plates loaded parallel to grain are still limited by footnote 2 of NDS Table 13.2B.

C13.2.5 Load at Angle to Grain

Use of the standard bearing angle to grain equation (NDS Equation 13.2-1 and NDS Appendix J) to determine reference design values for split ring and shear plate connectors located in a shear plane that is loaded at an angle to grain between 0° and 90° are based on claw plate connector research (117). In this same study, tests of split ring connectors showed the relationship between maximum design value and grain angle could be described by a linear relationship without appreciable error. For consistency with the provisions for other fastener types, the standard angle to grain equation is conservatively used in the Specification to adjust both split ring and shear plate connector reference design values for grain angle.

C13.2.6 Split Ring and Shear Plate Connectors in End Grain

Design of connectors in end grain surfaces are frequently encountered in practice, such as those at the peak of A-frames or similar arches. Reference design values for split ring and shear plate connectors in end grain surfaces are keyed to use of a reference design value for connectors in square-cut end surfaces equal to sixty percent of the reference design value for connectors in side grain surfaces loaded perpendicular to grain.

The use of 0.60 Q' as the reference design value for a square-cut end surface was originally based on experience with connector design with glued laminated timber (140). Available data from a comprehensive study of the capacity of shear plates in sloping grain end surfaces in Douglas fir (80) generally confirm the use of the 0.60 ratio. This ratio is slightly more conservative than the 0.67 value assumed for square-cut end surface design values in Canada (32, 75).

For split ring and shear plate connectors used in sloping end grain surfaces, the thickness of the member is taken as the distance between the edge of the connector and the nearest point on the outside edge of the member located on a line parallel to the bolt or lag screw axis. Where the end grain surface is square cut, the thickness of the member may be taken as the length of the dowel in the member.

C13.3 Placement of Split Ring and Shear Plate Connectors

C13.3.1 Terminology

Edge and end distances and spacings for split ring and shear plate connectors are referenced to the center not the edge of the connectors.

C13.3.2 Geometry Factor, C_Δ, for Split Ring and Shear Plate Connectors in Side Grain

The geometry factor adjusts reference design values for split ring and shear plate connectors installed in side grain with end distances, edge distances, and/or spacings less than those required for $C_\Delta = 1.0$. The smallest geometry factor for any split ring or shear plate connector in a joint is to be applied to all connectors in that joint regardless of their alignment relative to one another.

C13.3.2.1 Values for geometry factors presented in Table 13.3 were determined from original connector research on split rings and claw plates (117). Most values have remained unchanged for decades, but geometry factor values for edge distances were modified in the 2012 edition of the Specification as discussed below.

Geometry Factors for Edge Distance

Prior to the 2012 edition of the Specification, the minimum edge distance was 1.75 inches for 2-1/2" split rings and 2-5/8" shear plates and 2.75 inches for 4" split rings and 4" shear plates. This was based on the assumption that the smaller connectors would be used in lumber with a nominal width of 4 inches (3.5 in.) or larger, and the larger connectors would be used with in lumber with a nominal width of 6 inches (5.5 in.) or larger. However, these connectors are commonly used in structural glued laminated timbers with widths as narrow as 3 inches and 5 inches for the smaller and larger connectors, respectively.

The original research (117) included tests on material with widths as small as the outside diameter of the connector. This data was reviewed to determine appropriate geometry factors for connectors with edge distances as small as 1.5 inches for the smaller connectors and 2.5 inches for the larger connectors. These are considered to be practical minimums for good practice.

Significant differences were observed in the behavior of claw plates and split rings with decreasing loaded edge distances, so separate geometry factor values are tabulated for split rings and shear plates (which are similar to claw plates) for minimum loaded edge distance. Interpolation is permitted for unloaded edge distances between the minimum value and the values corresponding to a geometry factor of 1.0.

Geometry Factors for Spacing

Spacing requirements in NDS Table 13.3 are based on original connector research (17, 142) with the following exceptions:

The factor for the perpendicular loading and spacing case was reduced to 0.50 as part of an effort to simplify adjustment of connector design values for end distances and longitudinal spacing (181).

C13.3.2.2 (Connectors Loaded at an Angle to Grain) NDS 13.3.2.2 was introduced in the 2012 edition of the Specification and clarifies requirements for split ring and shear plate connectors loaded at an angle to grain. Separate geometry factors for end and edge distance are calculated for the parallel and perpendicular components of the resistance.

The original connector research indicated that the load-carrying capacity of a joint made with two or more connectors aligned parallel-to-grain but loaded perpendicular-to-grain, was less than the sum of the maximum design values for the same connectors acting singly (181, 117). Staggering or offsetting connectors along the grain of the transverse loaded member was found to give somewhat higher design values (181). When such offsetting is used, the line connecting the centers of two or more connectors located in the same contact face–the connector axis, φ–may not be oriented parallel or perpendicular to the grain of the member or to the direction of load, θ. Prior editions of the NDS referenced methods presented in the TECO design manual (142) and the AITC Timber Construction Manual (140) for determining spacing between connectors with connector axes at angles other than parallel-to-grain or perpendicular-to-grain. NDS Equation 13.3-1 and Table 13.3.2.2 were taken from the AITC Timber Construction Manual (140) and provide identical results to the graphical method presented in the TECO design manual (142). Equation 13.3-1 and Table 13.3.2.2 define elliptical transition functions between parallel-to-grain spacing requirements and perpendicular-to-grain requirements for various angles of load.

C13.3.3 Geometry Factor, C_Δ, for Split Ring and Shear Plate Connectors in End Grain

NDS 13.3.3 clarifies that a single geometry factor, C_Δ, is determined and applied to both the parallel and perpendicular components of the resistance. Beginning with the 2012 edition of the Specification the same elliptical transition equation for spacing of connectors in side grain is applied to connectors in sloped end grain surfaces. These new provisions remove a large discontinuity from previous requirements and provide a better transition between the parallel-to-grain provisions and the perpendicular-to-grain provisions. Prior to the 2012 edition of the Specification, the perpendicular-to-grain spacing, end distance, and edge distance requirements were applied for all sloped cuts between 45 and 90 degrees and the parallel-to-grain provisions for sloped cuts less than 45 degrees. These provisions resulted in large differences in spacing and end/edge distance requirements between members with sloped cuts of 45 and 46 degrees.

C13.3.3.1 Procedures for establishing geometry factors. C_Δ, for connectors in end grain surfaces follow the same logic as that employed to establish reference design values for such configurations in NDS 13.2.6.

C13.3.3.2 Shear capacity of members supported by connectors in end grain surfaces should be checked using provisions of NDS 3.4.3.3. Where the slope of the surface cut, α, is other than 90°, the component of the vertical force on the connector shear plane that is normal to the outside or uncut edge of the member should be taken as the shear force, V. The effective depth of the member, d_e, should be taken as the component of the distance from the loaded edge of the member to the unloaded edge of the connector that is normal to the outside or uncut edge of the member.

C13.3.4 Multiple Split Ring or Shear Plate Connectors

C13.3.4.1 The group action factor, C_g, applies only to a row of two or more connectors which are in the same shear plane, are aligned in the direction of load, and are on separate bolts or lag screws (see C11.3.6). The factor need not be applied to connections involving two or more connector units on two or more contact faces concentric to the same bolt axis.

C13.3.4.2 When two sizes of split ring grooves are cut concentrically on the same wood surface and rings are installed in both grooves, the total load on the joint is limited to the reference design value for the larger ring only.

C13.3.4.3 Localized wood stresses should be checked in accordance with NDS 11.1.2.

Table 13.3 Geometry Factors, C_Δ, for Split Ring and Shear Plate Connectors

Geometry factors, C_Δ, in Table 13.3 were revised in the 2012 edition of the Specification to account for reduced edge distance associated with structural glued laminated timbers with faces as narrow as 3" and 5" rather than 3.5" and 5.5" assumed previously (e.g., edge distances of 1.5" and 2.5" rather than 1.75" and 2.75"). Tabular values for loaded edge distance were removed for the Parallel to Grain Loading case as technically there is no loaded edge in parallel to grain loading. Values had been provided previously in order to accommodate linear interpolation, however new provisions described in NDS 13.3.2.2 eliminate the need for these values.

Based on a re-evaluation of the Scholten data (117) for narrower widths, the minimum unloaded edge distance for 2-1/2" split rings and 2-5/8" shear plates was reduced from 1-3/4" to 1-1/2" with the corresponding geometry factor, C_Δ, being reduced from 1.0 to 0.88. Similarly, the minimum unloaded edge distance for 4" split rings and 4"shear plates was reduced from 2-3/4" to 2-1/2", with the corresponding geometry factor, C_Δ, being reduced from 1.0 to 0.93.

Also, as a consequence of using narrower widths, Table 13.3 was revised in the 2012 edition of the Specification to tabulate separate geometry factors, C_Δ, for split rings and shear plates with regard to loaded edge distance for perpendicular to grain loading.

C14 TIMBER RIVETS

C14.1 General

C14.1.1 Scope

The Specification presently limits use of timber rivets to attachment of steel side plates to structural glued laminated timber.

Timber rivets, also known as glulam rivets, were originally developed in Canada more than 35 years ago to connect pre-drilled steel plates to structural glued laminated timber (41). Typical applications include tension splices, beam hangers, and moment splices. The rivets have flattened-oval shanks with tapered heads that, when driven, wedge tightly into holes in the steel plate (see Appendix M in the Specification). The resulting head fixity adds to the strength and stiffness of the connection. The number of rivet rows in each plate and the number of rivets per row can both range from 2 to 20 (see NDS Figure 14A and NDS Tables 14.2.1A through 14.2.1F and Tables 14.2.2A and 14.2.2B.

C14.1.2 Quality of Rivets and Steel Side Plates

Provisions of the Specification are applicable only to timber rivets that are hot-dipped galvanized. Rivets are made with fixed shank cross-section and head dimensions (NDS Appendix M) and vary only by length.

Steel plates used in timber rivet connections must be a minimum of 1/8" thick and, when used in wet service conditions, must be hot-dipped galvanized. Strength reductions apply for steel plates less than 1/4" thick (see NDS Table 14.2.3). Due to rivet and plate hole dimensions and tolerances, fabrication of joints with plates greater than 1/4" is not practical and is generally avoided. Also, the reduced penetration of the rivet into the wood associated with greater plate thickness can limit connection capacity by reducing the area of wood available to resist the tension and shear loads being applied around the rivet group.

C14.1.3 Fabrication and Assembly

C14.1.3.1 Rivets, whose shank dimensions are nominally 1/4" by 1/8", must be driven with the wider dimension oriented parallel to the grain of the wood member. This orientation provides maximum connection capacity for both parallel and perpendicular to the grain loading and minimizes any splitting that may occur (41). Further, rivets are not driven flush with the plate but only to the point where the tapered heads wedge tightly into the predrilled holes in the plate. It is assumed that approximately 1/8" of the rivet head will protrude from the face of the plate after driving (see NDS Appendix M).

To minimize splitting in rivet groups involving more than two rows and more than two rivets per row, rivets are driven around the perimeter first and then in successive inner rectangles toward the center.

C14.1.3.2 The limit on maximum penetration of rivets of 70% of wood member thickness is intended to prevent through splitting of the piece.

C14.1.3.3 Connections in which rivets driven through plates on both sides of a member penetrate beyond the midpoint of the member are not generally used. Where such overlap of rivets does occur, the length of overlap is limited to 20% of the member thickness (see NDS 14.1.2.2) and the rivets on both sides are required to be spaced (see NDS 14.3.1) as though they were all driven from one side. The capacity of the connection is then determined as if all rivets were driven from one side and with spacings parallel (s_p) and perpendicular (s_q) to grain (see Figure 14A in the Specification) determined as the distances between adjacent rivets (one from each side but assumed on one side) at their points. Under these provisions, NDS Equations 14.2-1 and 14.2-2 and NDS Tables 14.2.1A through 14.2.1F and 14.2.2A and 14.2.2B are entered with twice the number of rows and twice the number of rivets per row as those actually driven from one of the sides. Also, NDS Tables 14.2.1A through 14.2.1F are entered with the member dimension of a connection with only one plate, which as footnoted in these tables, is twice the thickness of the wood member.

The procedure for determining the capacity of plates on two sides with rivets overlapping is based on the derivation of the design methodology and supporting data for single plate connections.

C14.2 Reference Design Values

C14.2.1 Parallel to Grain Loading

Design equations for timber rivets are based on Canadian research (24, 47, 45, 48, 69). The ultimate load capacity of such connections are limited by rivet bending and localized crushing of wood at the rivets or by the tension or shear strength of the wood at the perimeter of the rivet group (45). As load is applied to the connection, end rivets carry a larger portion of the load than rivets in the center. As yielding occurs, the load is redistributed to the less-loaded fasteners, until at maximum connection load, all the individual rivets are considered to have reached their ultimate bearing capacity (45). This mode of failure will occur as long as the tension and shear strengths of the wood around the group of rivets is sufficient to resist the total applied load. However, if shear failure of the wood on the side and bottom of the rivet group occurs, followed by tension failure at the interior end of the group perimeter, the block of wood into which the rivets have been driven can be pulled out of the member before the maximum rivet bending load has been reached (45). Thus timber rivet design loads are based on the lower of the maximum rivet bending load and the maximum load based on wood strength.

In the 2012 edition of the Specification, the constant in NDS Equation 14.2-1 for rivet connection design values parallel to grain was changed from 280 to 188. This adjustment results in NDS timber rivet design values that are more consistent with other NDS connection designs for both ASD and LRFD. The constant of 188 in NDS Equation 14.2-1 is based on tests of single rivets in Douglas fir at penetrations of 1, 2, and 3 inches (47). The rivet connection design values (P_r and Q_r) obtained from the equation using a constant of 188 represents the average ultimate test values reduced by a factor of 5.0 to better account for the proportional limit basis of NDS dowel connector values under lateral loads. This adjustment enables consistent application of the load duration factor to rivet capacity which is influenced by both fastener bending and wood bearing stresses. The factor of 5.0 increases the original adjustment of 3.36 (45) on ultimate test values.

NDS Equation 14.2-1 also includes an additional adjustment of 0.88 to account for specifying use of rivets of lower hardness and associated lower ultimate tensile and yield strength than rivets used in the original research (48, 41). The change in rivet specification was made to avoid the possibility of hydrogen embrittlement occurring in service conditions involving high temperature and high humidity (48).

Because of the complexity of the equations used to check wood capacity in timber rivet connections loaded parallel to grain, only tabular values for a range of rivet penetrations, spacings and rivet group sizes are given in the Specification (NDS Tables 14.2.1A through 14.2.1F). In the 2018 edition of the Specification, the number of rivet rows per side in Tables 14.2.1A through to 14.2.1F was revised to reflect the 12" limit on maximum distance perpendicular to grain between outermost rows of rivets per section 14.3.1. The loads in these tables are the lesser of the reference wood tension capacity or the reference wood shear capacity as determined from the equations developed in the original research and verified by tests of full-size connections representing a range of rivet group sizes and spacings in Douglas fir structural glued laminated timbers (45).

The maximum normal (tension) stress is checked assuming an area equal to the rivet penetration times the width of the rivet group. The induced stress on this area is calculated as a function of coefficients which are derived from equations involving the variables of rivets per row, number of rows, spacing between rivets, spacing between rows, and the ratio of member thickness to rivet penetration (45). The lower the ratio, the larger the load component resisted by the normal stress and the lower the load component resisted by shear stress. It is this effect that is being accounted for by entering NDS Tables 14.2.1A through 14.2.1F with a wood member dimension for a single plate connection which is twice the member thickness of a connection with plates on both sides.

In the original research involving evaluation of rivet connections made with Douglas fir members, an average ultimate tension stress parallel to grain of 5600 psi was found in connections whose ultimate load was either a result of rivet bending or wood shear failure (45). For determination of reference connection capacity limited by normal stress, this tension ultimate was reduced to 1600 psi to account for variability (1.6) and load duration and factor of safety (approximately 2.1).

The maximum shear stress in the rivet connection is checked assuming an area equal to twice the rivet penetration times the length of the rivet group. The load on this area is calculated as a function of coefficients which are based on different equations but involving the same variables as those used to determine normal stress plus end distance. These equations account for shear resistance on the bottom of the rivet group acting on the plane at the rivet tips as well as the lateral shear on the sides by proportioning the total shear loads carried by the bottom and side surfaces (45).

Rather than use shear stress values based on the ASTM D 143 block shear specimen, the reference shear stress used in the shear checking equation for rivet connections was developed using a Weibull weakest link model in which strength is inversely related to volume. Based on experimental data, it was determined that the shear strength of a unit volume of Douglas fir under uniform shear at 0.5 survival probability was 2526 psi (45). Employing this value in the equation developed in the original research for maximum lateral shear stress and reducing the equation constants by a factor of 3.36 (1.6 variability and 2.1 load duration and factor of safety) gives a reference shear stress for evaluating shear loads in rivet connections of 745 psi. As verification of the shear checking equation, a mean ratio of estimated to observed ultimate loads of 1.03 was obtained for eight rivet connection configurations in Douglas fir that exhibited wood shear failure. Test connections involved configurations containing 25, 50, 100, and 150 rivets and rivet spacings of 0.5", 1", and 1.5" (45).

It is to be noted that calculated P_r values and P_w values tabulated in NDS Tables 14.2.1A through 14.2.1F apply to connections made with 1/4" side plates and to one plate with associated rivets. For connections with thinner side plates, the adjustments in NDS Table 14.2.3 apply. Where connections involve plates on two sides of the wood member, the limiting P_r or applicable tabular P_w value is doubled to determine the reference capacity of the connection.

Because of the species test results and property values used to develop the rivet bending and wood capacity equations, use of reference design values based on the provisions of NDS 14.2.2 should be limited to Douglas Fir-Larch and Southern Pine structural glued laminated timber.

C14.2.2 Perpendicular to Grain Loading

As with parallel to grain loading, design loads for timber rivet connections in which the loads act perpendicular to the grain of the wood member are based on the lower of the maximum rivet bending load and the maximum load based on wood strength. However, strength in tension perpendicular to grain is the controlling wood property rather than tension parallel and shear strength properties. The mode of wood failure in the perpendicular load case is a separation along the grain just above the first line of rivets nearest the unloaded edge, as contrasted to the pull out of the block of wood containing the rivet group that occurs in the parallel load case (45).

NDS Equation 14.2-2 is the same as that for the parallel to grain loading case (NDS Equation 14.2-1) except for the value of the constant, 108 compared to 188. The ratio of the two values (0.57) represents the ratio of the average ultimate lateral load-carrying capacities of single rivet joints in Douglas fir structural glued laminated test specimens loaded perpendicular to grain and parallel to grain (47, 69). In the 2012 edition of the Specification, the constant in NDS Equation 14.2-2 for rivet connection design values perpendicular to grain was changed to 108 (see C14.2.1).

The wood capacity of rivet connections loaded perpendicular to the grain is a function of penetration, number and configuration of rivets, rivet spacings, and unloaded edge distance (45). Checking equations assume the connection load acts on an area equal to the width of the rivet group times the rivet penetration. However, the distribution of stress is not uniform over this area, but is a maximum at the surface of the member and decreases sharply along the penetration depth and on either side of the center of the rivet group (24). This non-uniform distribution is accounted for in the basic design equations.

Based on tests that showed tension perpendicular to grain strength decreases with increase in cross-section area and/or length, a Weibull brittle fracture model was used to establish a reference wood stress for checking wood capacity in rivet connections loaded perpendicular to grain. Using results from tests of blocks cut from Douglas fir structural glued laminated timber beams and ranging from 16 to 3600 in.^{3} in volume, a tension perpendicular to grain strength for unit volume under uniform stress at a 95% survival probability of 267 psi was established (24). Reducing this value by a factor of 2.1 for load duration and factor of safety gives a reference tension perpendicular to grain stress of 127 psi. This unit value is adjusted in the checking equations for volume through introduction of a variable based on the distance between the unloaded edge of the member and the first line of rivets in the connection.

In lieu of presenting the complex equations required to determine wood capacity for perpendicular to grain loading, a simplified equation (NDS Equation 14.2-3) is given in the Specification enabling such capacity to be calculated for any rivet penetration and plate thickness using loads and factors from NDS Tables 14.2.2A and 14.2.2B that account for the effects of a range of rivet configurations, spacings, and unloaded edge distances. The unit load values given in NDS Table 14.2.2A include an adjustment factor to account for stress distribution effects in connections with two side plates; thus the load values in this table are conservative for a single plate application. In the 2018 edition of the Specification, the number of rivets per row in Table 14.2.2A was revised to reflect the 12" limit on maximum distance perpendicular to grain between outermost rows of rivets per section 14.3.1. It is to be noted that Equations 14.2-2 and 14.2-3 in the Specification provide reference design values for connections with one side plate. Reference design values obtained from either equation are doubled for connections having two side plates.

Because of the species test results and property values used to develop the rivet bending and wood capacity equations, use of reference design values based on the provisions of NDS 14.2.2 should be limited to Douglas Fir-Larch and Southern pine structural glued laminated timber.

C14.2.3 Metal Side Plate Factor, C_{st}

Supporting experimental data for timber rivet design equations involved tests of connections made with 1/4" thick steel side plates (45, 69). Use of thinner plates reduces the amount of fixity of the rivet head which in turn reduces rivet bending capacity.

Reference design values determined in accordance with NDS 14.2.1 and 14.2.2 assume 1/4" side plates are used. For connections made with 3/16" and 1/8" plates, reference design values based on rivet capacity (P_r and Q_r) are adjusted by the side plate factors of 0.90 and 0.80 given in NDS Table 14.2.3.

C14.2.4 Load at Angle to Grain

The equation for calculating reference design values for timber rivet connections loaded at angles to grain other than 0° and 90° is the same form as the bearing angle to grain equation (see NDS Appendix J).

C14.2.5 Timber Rivets in End Grain

The 50 percent reduction for timber rivets used in end grain is based on Canadian design practice (41). It can be compared with the end grain adjustment factor of 0.67 for nails and spikes (see C12.5.2).

C14.2.6 Design of Metal Parts

Timber rivet connections can carry relatively high loads. It is the responsibility of the designer to assure the metal side plates on such connections are of adequate strength to carry the total load being transferred.

C14.3 Placement of Timber Rivets

C14.3.1 Spacing Between Rivets

In the 2012 edition of the Specification, a limit on the maximum distance perpendicular to grain between outermost rows of rivets of 12 inches was added to parallel requirements in the new Table 12.5.1F which specifies the maximum spacing between outer rows of dowel-type fasteners in structural glued laminated timber connections.

C14.3.2 End and Edge Distance

Effects of rivet spacing and edge and end distances have been evaluated using the basic rivet design equations (45). For parallel to grain loading and with other variables constant, wider rivet spacings are associated with the rivet bending failure mode while closer spacings induce wood shear failures. Similarly, with other factors constant, longer end distances allow rivet bending to control while shorter end distances cause wood shear capacity to control.

Minimum spacings and minimum end and edge distance requirements given in NDS 14.3 and NDS Table 14.3.2 minimize the occurrence of premature wood failure in favor of more ductile rivet yielding based on Canadian design standards (41).

C15 SPECIAL LOADING CONDITIONS

C15.1 Lateral Distribution of a Concentrated Load

C15.1.1 Lateral Distribution of a Concentrated Load for Moment

The lateral distribution of concentrated loads is particularly important to obtain efficient design of bending members in structures such as bridges and warehouse or industrial buildings where heavy wheel loads are involved. Easily applied methods for determining the maximum moment and maximum shear in bending members subject to concentrated wheel loads are given in NDS 15.1 of the Specification. These methods, which are based on the thickness of the flooring or decking involved (two to six inches thick) and the spacing of the beams or stringers, have long been used in timber bridge design (129). The procedures have been verified through test and shown to be generally conservative, particularly when the portion of the load distributed to adjacent members is 40 percent or less (42).

The lateral distribution factors for moment in NDS Table 15.1.1 are keyed to the stiffness of the flooring or decking through use of nominal thickness and spacing of beams. These factors are based on recommendations of the American Association of State Highway and Transportation Officials (129). For cases where the lateral load distribution factor exceeds 1.0 (i.e., S/denominator > 1.0) the load is assumed to be fully on the beam. Where the concentrated load is applied to the deck between the beams, the load is distributed to the adjacent beams assuming the deck acts as a simply-supported beam. For cases where the factor is less than or equal to 1.0 and the concentrated load is applied to the deck between the beams, provisions of NDS 15.1.1 can be conservatively used or a more rigorous method of analysis should be considered.

The two-inch plank floor refers to one made of pieces of lumber laid edge-to-edge with the wide faces bearing on the supporting beams or stringers. The four-inch and six-inch laminated floors refer to those made of pieces of lumber laid face-to-face with the narrow edges bearing on the supporting beams or stringers, with each piece being nailed to the preceding piece (129). Nails typically penetrate into two adjacent pieces, are staggered and are alternated on the top and bottom edges (42). Flooring is typically attached to stringers by toe-nailed connections.

The lateral distribution factors apply to bridges designed for one traffic lane and to interior beams and stringers only. The computed factor gives the fraction of the wheel load (both front and rear of tractor or trailer axles on one side) positioned to give maximum bending moment at mid-span of the beam or stringer closest to the wheel load (129, 42).

The live load bending moment for outside beams or stringers is calculated using a load equal to the reaction of the wheel load assuming the flooring or decking between the outside and adjacent stringer is acting as a simply-supported beam (129).

Lateral distribution factors determined in accordance with NDS Table 15.1.1 can be used for any type of fixed or moving concentrated load. The lateral distribution factors determined from the table have been verified by field tests on five timber bridges ranging from 15 to 46 feet in span and by laboratory tests on three full-size bridge deck and stringer assemblies 16 to 28 feet in span (42). These tests indicate the factors are somewhat conservative, particularly at ratios greater than 0.60.

For bridges of two or more traffic lanes, the American Association of State Highway and Transportation Officials (129) provides other lateral distribution factors.

Generally all designs involving multiple parallel bending members that are loaded through transverse elements such as flooring, decking, or sheathing are capable of some lateral distribution of a concentrated load on one member to adjacent members on either side. The repetitive member factor (see NDS 4.3.9, 7.3.6, and 8.3.7) partially accounts for such load redistribution.

C15.1.2 Lateral Distribution of a Concentrated Load for Shear

The lateral distribution factors for shear relate the lateral distribution of concentrated load at the center of the beam or stringer span as determined under NDS 15.1.1, or by other means, to the distribution of load at the quarter points of the span. The quarter points are considered to be near the points of maximum shear in the stringers for timber bridge design.

The tabulated values of the percentage of a concentrated load on the center beam at the quarter point of the span and the percentage of the same load on the center beam at mid-span is closely described by the following relation:

$$P_{1/4} = -1.807 + 1.405 \log(P_m) \qquad \text{(C15.1-1)}$$

where:

$P_{1/4}$ = percentage of load at 1/4 point of center beam

P_m = percentage of load at mid-span of center beam

= S/denominator from NDS Table 15.1.1 or other basis

Values of $P_{1/4}$ from NDS Table 15.1.2 are used to determine the actual shear stress from the wheel or other concentrated load being considered. Field and laboratory tests of full-size timber bridges verify the appropriateness of the NDS Table 15.1.2 values and indicate they are conservative at S/denominator ratios above 0.50 (42).

C15.2 Spaced Columns

C15.2.1 General

Spaced columns refer to two or more individual members oriented with their longitudinal axis parallel, separated at the ends and in the middle portion of their length by blocking and joined at the ends by split ring or shear plate connectors capable of developing required shear resistance (181). The end fixity developed by the connectors and end blocks increases the buckling resistance of the individual members in the direction perpendicular to the wide faces when loaded in compression parallel to grain (parallel to the d_1 dimension in Figure 15A of the Specification).

C15.2.1.1 In the design of spaced columns, the adjusted compression stress for an individual member is determined in accordance with the provisions of NDS 15.2 and other applicable provisions of the Specification. The actual compression stress parallel to grain, f_c, on the members of the spaced column is not to exceed the adjusted compression design value parallel to grain, F_c', for these members based on all provisions of NDS 3.6 and 3.7 except as modified or extended by the provisions of NDS 15.2. The net section requirements of NDS 3.6.3 are to be applied to the members of spaced columns.

C15.2.1.2 The advantage of a spaced column is the increase in the critical buckling design value for compression members obtained by the partial end fixity of the individual members. This increase in capacity, 2-1/2 or 3 times the value for a solid column with the same slenderness ratio, applies only to buckling in the direction perpendicular to the wide face of the members (buckling limited by the ℓ_1/d_1 ratio). If there was no slip in the end connections and full fixity of the ends were provided by the end block fastenings, the buckling stress would be 4 times that of a solid column because of the 50 percent reduction in effective column length (141).

The increase in the critical buckling stress associated with the ℓ_1/d_1 slenderness ratio obtained through the use of spaced column design may make capacity in the direction parallel to the wide face of the members (buckling associated with the ℓ_2/d_2 ratio) the limiting case. The adjusted compression design value parallel to grain in this direction is not affected by spacing the individual members and, therefore, must be checked in accordance with NDS 3.7.

C15.2.2 Spacer and End Block Provisions

C15.2.2.1 Where more than one spacer block is used, the distance ℓ_3 (see NDS Figure 15A) is the distance from the center of one spacer block to the centroid of the connectors in the nearest end block.

C15.2.2.2 Spacer blocks located within the middle one-tenth of the column length are not required to be joined to the compression members by split ring or shear plate connectors. Such blocks should be fastened to assure the compression members maintain their spacing under load (181). A web member joined by connectors to two truss chords making up a spaced truss chord (spaced column) may be considered a spacer block.

Where it is not feasible to use a single middle spacer block, two or more spacer blocks joined to compression members by split ring or shear plate connectors may be required to meet the ℓ_3/d_1 ratio limit of 40 (see NDS 15.2.3.2). Connectors used in such spacer blocks must meet the same requirements as those applicable to end blocks and the distance between two adjacent spacer blocks is not to exceed one-half the distance between the centroids of connectors in the end blocks. Connectors are required for spacer blocks not located in the middle of the column length to provide the shear resistance necessary to assure the two members act as a unit under load.

C15.2.2.3 Spaced columns are used as compression chords in bowstring and other large span trusses (141). In this case, the web members of the truss serve as the end blocks. The distance between panel points, which are laterally supported, is taken as the length of such columns. Spaced-column web members may be designed using the procedures of NDS 15.2 if the joints at both ends of the web member are laterally supported.

C15.2.2.4 The thickness of end and spacer blocks is required to be equal to or larger than the thickness of the compression members and meet the minimum requirements for split ring or shear plate connections in NDS Chapter 13 (181). The length of end blocks and spacer blocks located at other than mid-length of the column should be sufficient to meet the end distance requirements for split ring or shear plate connectors given in NDS Chapter 13. In this regard, the load on the connectors in the end blocks shall be considered applied in either direction parallel to the longitudinal axes of the compression members.

C15.2.2.5 Connectors used in spaced columns are designed to restrain differential displacement between the individual compression members. Since the forces causing differential movement decrease as the ℓ/d of the individual members decrease, connector design value requirements vary with slenderness ratio (181).

The equations for end spacer block constants in NDS 15.2.2.5 are based on K_S of zero when $\ell_1/d_1 \leq 11$ and a K_S equal to one-fourth of the clear wood compression design value parallel to grain for the species group when ℓ_1/d_1 is ≥ 60 (181). The equations give K_S values for intermediate slenderness ratios based on linear interpolation between these limits.

The limiting K_S values of 468, 399, 330, and 261 for species groups A, B, C, and D (defined in Table 13A of the Specification), respectively, represent one-fourth the normal load, unseasoned clear wood compression design value parallel to grain applicable to representative species in each group in 1955 (181). The representative species were dense Douglas fir and dense southern pine for Group A, Douglas fir and southern pine for Group B, western hemlock for Group C, and white fir-balsam fir for Group D.

The connector or connectors on each face of each end spacer block should be able to carry a load equal to the cross-sectional area of one of the individual compression members (without reduction for cuts made to receive connectors) times the end spacer block constant, K_S.

C15.2.3 Column Stability Factor, C_P

C15.2.3.1 Effective column length for spaced columns is determined in accordance with NDS Figure 15A and adjusted by any applicable buckling length coefficient, K_e, greater than one as specified in NDS Appendix G. It is to be noted that ℓ_1 is the distance between points of lateral support restraining movement perpendicular to the wide faces of the individual members, and ℓ_2 is the distance between points of lateral support restraining movement parallel to the wide faces of the individual members. ℓ_1 and ℓ_2 are not necessarily equal.

C15.2.3.2 The slenderness ratio (ℓ_1/d_1) limit of 80 for the individual members is a conservative good practice recommendation recognizing that the individual members are continuous at the bracing locations. The limit of 50 on the slenderness ratio ℓ_2/d_2 is the limit applied to solid columns (see NDS 3.7.1.4). The limit of 40 on the ℓ_3/d_1 ratio also is a conservative good practice recommendation to assure the length between end and spacer blocks in a spaced column is not a controlling factor in the column design.

C15.2.3.3 The column stability factor for an individual member in a spaced column is calculated using the slenderness ratio ℓ_1/d_1 and the same equation as that applicable to solid columns (see NDS 3.7.1.5) except that the critical buckling design value for compression, F_{cE}, is modified by the spaced column fixity coefficient, K_x.

The actual compression stress parallel to grain, f_c, calculated by dividing the total load on the spaced column by the sum of the cross-sectional areas of the individual members, is checked against the product (F_c') of the column stability factor (C_P), the reference compression design value parallel to grain (F_c), and all other applicable adjustment factors (see NDS 2.3). If connectors are required to join spacer (interior) blocks to individual members, and such blocks are in a part of the column that is most subject to potential buckling, f_c is to be calculated using the reduced or net section area remaining at the connector location (see NDS 3.1.2) when comparing with the C_P adjusted compression design value parallel to grain, F_c'.

In spaced-column designs, the actual compression stress parallel to grain, f_c, based on the net section area of the individual members at the end blocks is checked against the product of the reference compression design value parallel to grain and all applicable adjustment factors except the column stability factor (see NDS 3.6.3).

C15.2.3.4 Use of the lesser adjusted compression design value parallel to grain, F_c', for a spaced column having members of different species or grades for all members is conservative. Where the design involves the use of compression members of different thicknesses, the F_c' value for the thinnest member is to be applied to all other members.

C15.2.3.5 The actual compression stress parallel to grain, f_c, in spaced columns also is to be checked in all cases against the adjusted compression design value parallel to grain, F_c', based on the slenderness ratio ℓ_2/d_2 and a

C_P factor calculated in accordance with the provisions of NDS 3.7 without use of the spaced column fixity coefficient, K_x. Use of connectors to join individual compression members through end blocks is assumed to only increase the load-carrying capacity of spaced columns in a direction perpendicular to the wide face of the members. When the ratio of the width to thickness of the individual compression members is less than the square root of the spaced column fixity coefficient, K_x, the adjusted compression stress parallel to grain, F_c', based on the slenderness ratio ℓ_2/d_2 may control.

C15.2.3.6 See C3.7.1.6.

C15.2.3.7 Design provisions for spaced beams joined by end blocks and connectors are not included in the Specification. The beam-column equations of NDS 3.9, therefore, apply only to those spaced columns that are subject to loads on the narrow edges of the members that cause bending in a plane parallel to their wide face.

C15.3 Built-Up Columns

As with spaced columns, built-up columns obtain their efficiency by increasing the buckling resistance of the individual laminations. The smaller the amount of slip occurring between laminations under compressive load, the greater the relative capacity of that column compared to a solid column of the same slenderness ratio made with the same quality of material. Based on tests of columns of various lengths (114, 116), the capacity of two equivalent column types can be expressed as a percentage of the strength of a solid column made with material of the same grade and species. For mechanically-connected built-up columns, efficiencies ranged from a value of 82 percent at an ℓ/d ratio of 6, decreasing to a low of 65 percent at an ℓ/d of 18, and then increasing to 82 percent at an ℓ/d of 26.

The NDS design provisions for built-up columns made with various types of mechanical fasteners are based on more recent modeling and testing (82, 83). This model can be used to determine the strength of any built-up column on the basis of the slip between members of the column in both the elastic and inelastic ranges. The theoretical formulas were verified through extensive testing including 400 column tests and evaluation of the load-slip properties of 250 different types of connections. The formulas are entered with fastener load-slip values based on beam-on-elastic-foundation principles (71).

C15.3.1 General

The provisions of NDS 15.3 apply only to multi-ply columns in which the laminations are of the same width and are continuous along the length. The limitations on number of laminations are based on the range of columns that were tested (83) that met the connection requirements of NDS 15.3.3 and 15.3.4. The minimum lamination thickness requirement assures use of lumber for which reference design values are available in the Specification.

C15.3.2 Column Stability Factor, C_P

Provisions in NDS 15.3.2 are the same as those applicable to solid columns in NDS 3.7.1 except for the addition of the column stability coefficients, K_f, in NDS Equation 15.3-1.

When nailed in accordance with the provisions of NDS 15.3.3, the capacity of built-up columns has been shown to be more than 60 percent of that of an equivalent solid column at all ℓ/d ratios (82). Efficiencies are higher for columns in the shorter ($\ell/d < 15$) and longer ($\ell/d > 30$) slenderness ratio ranges than those for columns in the intermediate range.

The efficiency of bolted built-up columns conforming to the connection requirements of NDS 15.3.4 is more than 75 percent for all ℓ/d ratios (82). As with nailed columns, efficiencies of short and long bolted built-up columns are higher than those for intermediate ones. The greater efficiency of bolted compared to nailed columns is reflective of the higher load-slip moduli obtainable with bolted connections.

In accordance with NDS 3.7.1.3, NDS Equation 15.3-1 is entered with a value of F_{cE} based on the larger of ℓ_{e1}/d_1 or ℓ_{e2}/d_2, where d_2 is the dimension of the built-up member across the weak axis of the individual laminations (sum of the thicknesses of individual laminations). Research (82) has shown that buckling about the weak axis of the individual laminations is a function of the amount of slip and load transfer that occurs at fasteners between laminations. When the controlling slenderness ratio is the strong axis of the individual laminations, ℓ_{e1}/d_1, then $K_f = 1.0$. It is also necessary to compare C_P based on ℓ_{e1}/d_1 and $K_f = 1.0$ with C_P based on ℓ_{e2}/d_2 and $K_f = 0.6$ or 0.75 to determine the adjusted compression design value parallel to grain, F_c'.

Due to the conservatism of using a single factor for all ℓ_{e2}/d_2 ratios, F_c' values for individual laminations designed as solid columns can be greater than F_c' values for built-up columns for relatively small ℓ_{e2}/d_2 ratios. In these cases, the column capacity should not be limited to the built-up column capacities.

C15.3.3 Nailed Built-up Columns

C15.3.3.1 Nailing requirements (a), (b), and (g) and the maximum spacing requirements of (d) and (e) are based on the conditions for which the column stability coefficient, K_f, of 60 percent was established (82). The maximum spacing between nails in a row of 6 times the thickness of the thinnest lamination minimizes the potential for buckling of the individual laminations between connection points. End, edge, and minimum spacing requirements are good practice recommendations for preventing splitting of members (32) and for assuring fasteners are well distributed across and along the face of the laminations.

The requirement for adjacent nails to be driven from opposite sides of the column applies to adjacent nails aligned both along the grain of the laminations and across their width.

The requirement that all nails penetrate at least ¾ of the thickness of the last lamination was further clarified in the 2012 edition of the Specification by making clear that all nails need to penetrate all laminations including the last outermost lamination.

In the nailing requirements of NDS 15.3.3.1, a nail row refers to those nails aligned parallel to the grain of the laminations and in the direction of the column length. Where only one longitudinal row of nails is required, such nails are required to be staggered along either side of the center line of the row. Adjacent offset nails in such a configuration should be driven from opposite faces.

Where three rows of nails are required by spacing and edge distance requirements, nails in adjacent rows are to be staggered and adjacent nails beginning with the first in each row driven from opposite sides as if nails were aligned across the face of the laminations.

C15.3.4 Bolted Built-up Columns

C15.3.4.1 Maximum spacing limits for bolts and rows, and number of row requirements in (d), (e), and (g), respectively, are based on conditions for which the bolted built-up column efficiency factor, K_f, was established (82). Maximum end distance limits in (c) are good practice recommendations (32) to assure end bolts are placed close to the ends of the column where interlaminar shear forces are largest. Minimum end distance, spacing between adjacent bolts in a row, spacing between rows, and edge distance in (c), (d), (e), and (f) correspond to provisions governing bolted joints in NDS 12.5.

As with nailed columns, a bolt row refers to those bolts aligned parallel to the grain of the laminations and in the direction of the column length. The maximum spacing of bolts in a row of six times the lamination thickness minimizes the potential for buckling of individual laminations between connection points.

C15.4 Wood Columns with Side Loads and Eccentricity

C15.4.1 General Equations

Equations for wood columns are based on theoretical analyses (186). The equation in NDS 15.4.1 for combined bending and eccentric axial compression loads is an expansion of the interaction equation given in NDS 3.9.2 to the general case of any combination of side loads, end loads, and eccentric end loads (189).

For the case of a bending load on the narrow face and an eccentric axial load producing a moment in the same direction as the bending load, the general interaction equation in NDS 15.4-1 reduces to:

$$\left(\frac{f_c}{F_c'}\right)^2 + \frac{f_{b1} + f_c(6e_1/d_1)[1 + 0.234(f_c/F_{cE1})]}{F_{b1}'[1-(f_c/F_{cE1})]} \leq 1.0 \quad \text{(C15.4-1)}$$

or

$$\left(\frac{f_c}{F_c'}\right)^2 + \frac{f_{b1} + f_c(6e_1/d_1)[1.234 - 0.234C_{m1}]}{C_{m1}F_{b1}'} \leq 1.0 \quad \text{(C15.4-2)}$$

where:

C_{m1} = moment magnification factor = $1 - f_c / F_{cE1}$

A limit on $(f_c/F_{cE2}) + ([f_{b1} + 6f_ce_1/d_1]/F_{bE})^2$ is given in Equation 15.4-2 to clarify a limitation on flatwise bending in the stress interaction equation (see C3.9.2).

For the case of a bending load on the wide face and an eccentric axial load producing a moment in the same direction as the bending load, the general interaction equation in NDS 15.4-1 reduces to:

$$\left(\frac{f_c}{F_c'}\right)^2 + \frac{f_{b2} + f_c(6e_2 / d_2)[1 + 0.234(f_c / F_{ce2})]}{F_{b2}'[1 - (f_c / F_{cE2})]} \leq \quad \text{(C15.4-3)}$$

or,

$$\left(\frac{f_c}{F_c'}\right)^2 + \frac{f_{b2} + f_c(6e_2 / d_2)[1 + 0.234C_{m2}]}{C_{m2}F_{b2}'} \leq 1.0 \quad \text{(C15.4-4)}$$

where:

C_{m2} = moment magnification factor = $1 - f_c / F_{cE2}$

An alternative formulation of Equation C15.4-4 in terms of induced axial load and induced bending moment follows:

$$\left(\frac{P}{P'}\right)^2 + \frac{M_2 + P\Delta_2[1 + 0.234\frac{P}{P_{cE2}}]}{M_2'(1 - \frac{P}{P_{cE2}})} \leq 1.0 \quad \text{(C15.4-5)}$$

where:

P = induced axial compression load, lbs

P' = adjusted axial compression resistance (i.e. $F_c'A$), lbs

M_2 = induced bending moment in the weak axis, in.-lbs

M_2' = adjusted weak axis moment resistance (i.e. $F_{b2}'S_2$), in.-lbs

Δ_2 = eccentricity of axial load, measured perpendicular to the plane of the weak axis, in.

P_{cE2} = critical column buckling resistance in the weak axis, lbs (see C3.7.1.5)

For cases where loading is concentric (i.e. $\Delta_2 = 0$ in.), equation C15.4-5 reduces to the following:

$$\left(\frac{P}{P'}\right)^2 + \frac{M_2}{M_2'(1 - \frac{P}{P_{cE2}})} \leq 1.0 \quad \text{(C15.4-6)}$$

where

$$P < P_{cE2} = \frac{\pi^2 E_{min}' I_2}{\ell_{e2}^2} \quad \text{(C15.4-7)}$$

C15.4.2 Columns with Side Brackets

The procedure for calculating the portion of an axial load applied through a bracket that is assumed to act as a side load at mid-height of the column is based on early recommendations (184). The application of a side load, P_s, acting at mid-span of a simply-supported beam is assumed to produce a maximum moment ($P_s\ell/4$) equal to three-fourths of the moment produced by the eccentric load on the bracket, P(a), times the ratio of the bracket height (ℓ_p) to the column length (ℓ).

When the bracket is at the top of the column, results obtained by entering NDS Equation 15.4-1 (or NDS Equation 3.9-3) with a concentric axial load and the calculated side load, P_s, will give a 25 percent lower combined stress index than that obtained from the eccentric axial end load formula, NDS Equation 15.4-2. This difference is a result of the latter being based on the assumption of eccentric loads on both ends of the column (constant moment along the length of the column) whereas the procedure in NDS 15.4.2 assumes the moment due to the bracket load decreases linearly from the point of application to zero at the column base.

C16 FIRE DESIGN OF WOOD MEMBERS

C16.1 General

The design provisions in the Specification are intended for use in allowable stress design (ASD) of structural wood members exposed to fire. These provisions do not address procedures for evaluating members for continued service following fire damage.

The topic of fire safety is broad and is addressed extensively in building codes. Other important topics such as flame spread, fire prevention, control of fire growth, fire suppression, fire extinguishment, and compartmentalization of fire are not addressed in the NDS. Other publications of interest from AWC include:

- *DCA No. 1-Flame Spread Performance of Wood Products*
- *DCA No. 2-Design of Fire-Resistive Exposed Wood Members*
- *DCA No. 3-Fire Rated Wood Floor and Wall Assemblies*
- *DCA No. 4-Component Additive Method (CAM) for Calculating and Demonstrating Assembly Fire Resistance*

Fire-Resistance-Rated Assemblies

Some buildings and occupancies require the use of fire-resistance-rated assemblies or members to prevent collapse or fire spread from one compartment of a building to another or from one building to another.

Members and assemblies are rated for their ability either to support design loads during fire exposure or to prevent the spread of fire. Such ratings are arrived at either by calculation or experiment for both members and assemblies. The standard fire exposure is defined in ASTM E119. A 1-hour fire-resistance rating for wall, floor, and floor-ceiling assemblies using light-frame wood members can be accomplished through the use of fire-resistive membranes such as gypsum wallboard. However, material requirements and construction details are critical for assembly performance and are carefully specified. For some wood assemblies, 2-hour ratings have been achieved.

Fire-resistance ratings are available in building codes and reference documents for several generic assemblies. Fire-resistance ratings for assemblies using proprietary materials are typically supplied by either wood products manufacturers or gypsum manufacturers. Selected fire-resistance-rated assemblies for walls and floors are provided in AWC's *DCA No. 3–Fire Rated Wood Floor and Wall Assemblies*, available at www.awc.org. In addition, DCA 3 includes details for the intersection of fire-resistance-rated walls and floors.

Analytically Rated

As an alternative to determining the fire-resistance-rating of members and assemblies by testing for every situation, building code provisions provide for acceptance of fire-resistance-ratings based upon engineering principles and material properties developed from standardized testing. This applies to the rating of previously untested members or assemblies, or in cases where it is desired to substitute one material or component for another. Although calculation procedures may be conservative, they have the advantage of quickly determining a fire-resistance-rating for an assembly or member and allowing interpolation or some extrapolation of expected performance. Additional details regarding the analytical approach are provided in AWC's *DCA No. 4 - Component Additive Method (CAM) for Calculating and Demonstrating Assembly Fire Resistance,* and *Technical Report 10: Calculating the Fire Resistance of Exposed and Protected Wood Members* (136), available at www.awc.org.

Exposed Timber Members

Using calculations, exposed timber members of sawn lumber, glued-laminated softwood timber, laminated veneer lumber, parallel strand lumber, laminated strand lumber, and cross-laminated timber can be designed for desired fire-resistance ratings. Additional details regarding the analytical approach are provided in NDS Chapter 16 and AWC's Technical Report 10 available at www.awc.org.

C16.2 Design Procedures for Exposed Wood Members

The mechanics-based design procedures in the Specification for exposed wood members are based on research described in AWC's *Technical Report 10: Calculating the Fire Resistance of Exposed and Protected Wood Members* (136). The design procedure calculates the capacity of exposed wood members using basic wood engineering mechanics. Section properties are computed assuming an effective char depth, a_{eff}, at a given time, t. Reductions of strength and stiffness of wood in the heated zone adjacent to the char layer are accounted for by assuming the effective char depth, a_{eff}, is equal to 1.2 times the char depth, a_{char} (See C16.2.1.4). Average member strength properties are approximated from accepted procedures used to calculate design properties. Finally, wood members are designed using accepted engineering procedures found in NDS for allowable stress design. The design procedures presented in Chapter 16 are not intended to evaluate wood members for continued use after a fire event.

C16.2.1 Char Rate

C16.2.1.1 Extensive one-dimensional char rate data is available for wood slabs. Two-dimensional char data is also available for timbers, but most of this data is limited to larger cross-sections. Evaluation of linear char rate models using one-dimensional char rate data suggests that charring of wood is nonlinear, and estimates using linear models tend to underestimate char depth for short time periods (< 60 minutes) and overestimate char depth for longer time periods (> 60 minutes). To account for char rate nonlinearity, a nonlinear, one-dimensional char rate model based on the results of 40 one-dimensional charring tests of wood slabs of various species was developed (154). This non-linear model addressed accelerated charring which occurs early in the fire exposure by applying a power factor to the char depth, a_{char}, to adjust for char rate nonlinearity:

$$t = m(a_{char})^{1.23} \qquad \text{(C16.2-1)}$$

where:

t = exposure time (hr.)

m = char slope (hr./in.$^{1.23}$)

a_{char} = char depth (in.)

However, application of this model is limited since the char slope (hr./in.$^{1.23}$), m, is species-specific and limited data exists for different wood species fit to the model. In addition, the model is limited to one-dimensional slabs.

To develop a two-dimensional, nonlinear char rate model, the one-dimensional non-linear char rate model was modified to enable values for the slope factor, m, to be estimated using nominal char rate constants (in./hr.), β_n. The nominal char rate constant, β_n, is estimated using measured char depth at approximately one hour. The non-linear char rate constant, β_t, is estimated from the nominal char rate constant, β_n. The relationship between β_t, and β_n is as follows:

$$\beta_t = \beta_n \text{ (1 hr.)/(1 hr.)}^{0.813} \text{ in./hr.}^{0.813} \qquad \text{(16.2-1)}$$

Substituting and solving for the char depth, a_{char}, in terms of exposure time, t:

$$a_{char} = \beta_t t^{0.813} \qquad \text{(C16.2-2)}$$

C16.2.1.2 For sawn lumber, structural glued-laminated softwood timber, laminated veneer lumber, parallel strand lumber, and laminated strand lumber, the char depth can be directly estimated using NDS Equations 16.2-1 and 16.2-2 assuming a nominal char rate constant, β_n, of 1.5 inches/hr. The char depth, a_{char}, for each exposed surface can be calculated as:

$$a_{char} = 1.5t^{0.813} \qquad \text{(C16.2-3)}$$

C16.2.1.3 For cross-laminated timber manufactured with certain adhesives, fall-off of laminations has been noted in some full-scale tests. The fall-off appears to occur as the char front approaches the glueline. To model this effect, the time required for the char front to reach the glueline of each lamination, starting from the time the char front reaches the prior lamination, can be calculated as:

$$t_{gi,i} = \left(\frac{h_{lam,i}}{\beta_t}\right)^{1.23} \qquad \text{(C16.2-4)}$$

where:

$t_{gi,i}$ = time for char front to reach glued interface for each lamination (hr.)

h_{lam} = lamination thickness (in.)

The number of laminations that could potentially fall off is estimated by subtracting each t_{gi} from the total time until the last partial lamination is determined. The value of n_{lam} is the maximum value in which the following equation is true:

$$t-\sum_{i=1}^{n_{lam}} t_{gi,i} \geq 0 \tag{C16.2-5}$$

where:

n_{lam} = number of laminations charred (rounded down to an integer value)

The values of $t_{gi,i}$ and n_{lam} determined in the above are used to calculate the char depth, a_{char}:

$$a_{char} = \sum_{i=1}^{n_{lam}} h_{lam,i} + \beta_t \left(t - \sum_{i=1}^{n_{lam}} t_{gi,i} \right)^{0.813} \tag{C16.2-6}$$

For cross-laminated timber manufactured with laminations of equal thickness, calculation of the char depth, a_{char}, can be simplified as follows:

$$a_{char} = (n_{lam})(h_{lam}) + \beta_t \left(t - (n_{lam})(t_{gi}) \right)^{0.813} \tag{C16.2-7}$$

where:

$$t_{gi} = \left(\frac{h_{lam}}{\beta_t} \right)^{1.23}$$

and

$$n_{lam} = \frac{t}{t_{gi}}$$

C16.2.1.4 For sawn lumber, structural glued-laminated softwood timber, laminated veneer lumber, parallel strand lumber, and laminated strand lumber, section properties can be calculated using standard equations for area, section modulus, and moment of inertia using reduced cross-sectional dimensions. The dimensions are reduced by the effective char depth, a_{eff}, calculated per NDS Equation 16.2-4 for each surface exposed to fire. Cross-sectional properties for a member exposed on all four sides are shown in Table C16.2-1. Other exposures can be calculated using this method.

Effective char depths, a_{eff}, for cross-laminated timber with equal lamination depths have been calculated in NDS Table 16.2.1B.

C16.2.1.5 For cross-laminated timbers, reduced cross-section dimensions are calculated using the effective char depth, a_{eff}, calculated per 16.2.1.3 and 16.2.1.4; however, due to the cross laminations and proprietary nature of cross-laminated timber layups, the effect of charring on capacity should be checked with the manufacturer. Alternatively, the capacity of the charred cross-laminated timber can be conservatively estimated by limiting the post-fire capacity to that of a panel with the same number of full-depth strong axis laminations remaining after a given fire resistance time.

C16.2.2 Member Strength

To approximate an average member strength using a reference design value, the reference design value is multiplied by an adjustment factor, K, to adjust from a 5% exclusion value allowable design value to an average ultimate value. F_b^* is multiplied by the adjustment factor, K, prior to calculation of the beam stability factor, C_L (Equation 3.3-6). Similarly, F_c^* is multiplied by the adjustment factor, K, prior to calculation of the column stability factor, C_P (Equation 3.7-1).

The adjustment factor, K, has two components, the inverse of the applicable design value adjustment factor, 1/k, and the inverse of the variability adjustment factor, c. To develop general design procedures for sawn lumber, structural glued laminated softwood timber, laminated veneer lumber, parallel strand lumber, laminated strand lumber, and cross-laminated timber, the following design value adjustment factors and estimates of COV were used to conservatively develop an allowable design stress to average ultimate strength adjustment factor, K, shown in Table C16.2-2.

C16.2.3 Design of Members

The induced load cannot exceed the average member capacity of a wood member exposed to fire for a given time, t. The average member capacity is estimated using cross-sectional properties reduced for fire exposure and average ultimate strength properties derived from reference design values.

C16.2.4 Special Provisions for Structural Glued Laminated Softwood Timber Beams

The outer laminations of glued laminated timber bending members in Table 5A of the NDS Supplement are typically higher strength laminations. When the beam is exposed to fire, these laminations are the first to be charred. In order to maintain the ultimate capacity of the beam when these laminations are completely charred, core laminations must be replaced with the higher strength laminations in the beam layup. For unbalanced beams, only the core laminations adjacent to the tension side lamination need to be replaced as shown in Figure C16.2.4A(b) and C16.2.4A(c), respectively. For balanced beams, the core laminations adjacent to the tension laminations on both sides need to be replaced as shown in Figure C16.2.4B(b) and C16.2.4B(c), respectively.

Figure C16.2.4A Typical Unbalanced Beam Layup

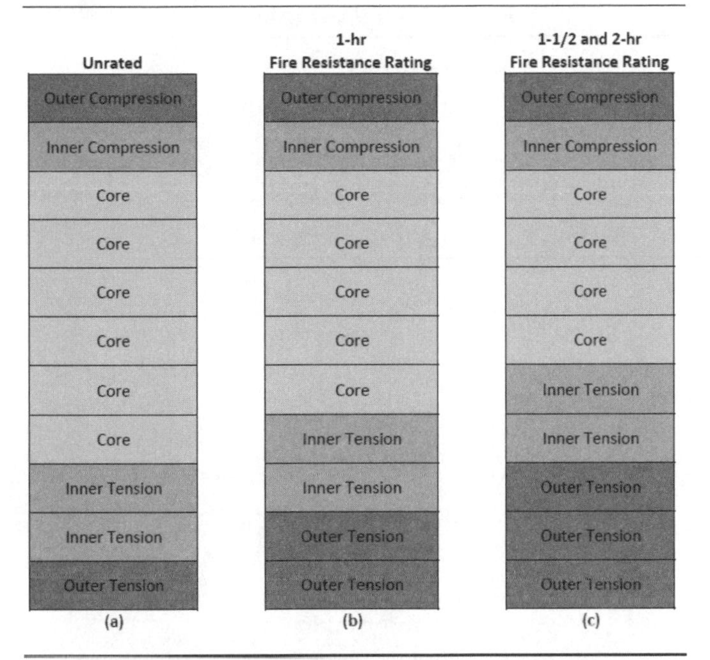

Figure C16.2.4B Typical Balanced Beam Layup

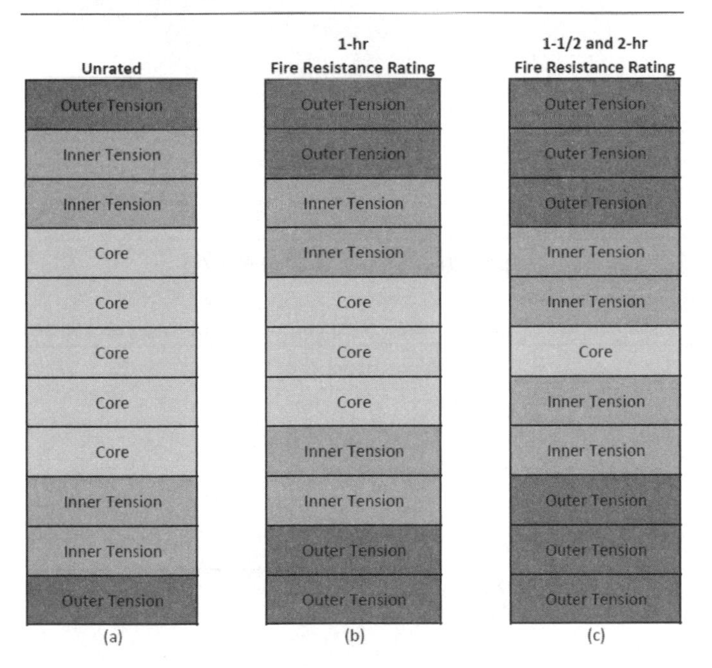

C16.2.5 Provisions for Timber Decks

Sides of individual timber decking members are shielded from full fire exposure by adjacent members collectively acting as a joint. Partial exposure occurs as members shrink and joints between members open. The degree of exposure is a function of the view angle of the radiant flame and the ability of hot volatile gases to pass through the joints. When the joint is completely open, such as can occur with butt-jointed timber decking, hot gases will carry into the joint and the sides of the decking members will char. This charring can be conservatively approximated assuming the sides of a member along the joint char to a depth of a_{eff}. When the joint is open but covered by sheathing, as with butt-jointed timber decking covered with wood structural panels, passage of hot gases is limited, and tests have shown that charring can be approximated assuming a partial exposure char rate along the joint , such that it chars to a depth of $a_{eff}/3$. For joints which are not open, as with tongue-and-groove timber decking, tests have shown that charring of the sides of members is negligible and can be ignored.

C16.3 Wood Connections

In the 2018 edition of the Specification, this section was revised to clarify that all components of the connection, including wood members, connectors, and fasteners, must be protected from fire exposure. Portions of the wood members included in the connection design must be fully protected against charring during the required fire resistance period to ensure that the design strength of the connection is maintained. Protection must be provided by wood, fire-rated gypsum board, other approved materials, or a combination thereof. Where wood is used as a protective cover, use of a_{char} will ensure that the connection elements are shielded from radiative heating and the temperature behind the char front will be less than 550 degrees F (300 degrees C). If the strength of the wood member in the connection is being evaluated (NDS 16.2.2), then use of a_{eff} will ensure no strength loss in the elevated temperature zone behind the char front. Connections located at ends of members must be detailed to ensure that char contraction is addressed to prevent premature loss of protection.

The loss of thickness at any location within the char layer can be estimated by multiplying the char depth, a_{char}, at that location by a *Char Contraction Factor*, C_{CF} (See Ref. 136), equal to 0.3 as shown in Figure C16.3. For a wood member with a char depth of approximately 1 inch in the face of the member, the loss of char thickness would be approximately 0.3 inches.

Table C16.2-1 Cross-Sectional Properties for Four-Sided Exposure

Cross-sectional Property	Four-Sided Example
Area of the cross section, $in.^2$	$A(t) = (D_{min} - 2a_{eff})(D_{max} - 2a_{eff})$
Section Modulus about major-axis, $in.^3$	$S(t) = (D_{min} - 2a_{eff})(D_{max} - 2a_{eff})^2/6$
Section Modulus about minor-axis, $in.^3$	$S(t) = (D_{min} - 2a_{eff})^2(D_{max} - 2a_{eff})/6$
Moment of Inertia about major-axis, $in.^4$	$I(t) = (D_{min} - 2a_{eff})(D_{max} - 2a_{eff})^3/12$
Moment of Inertia about minor-axis, $in.^4$	$I(t) = (D_{min} - 2a_{eff})^3(D_{max} - 2a_{eff})/12$

Figure C16.3 Char contraction

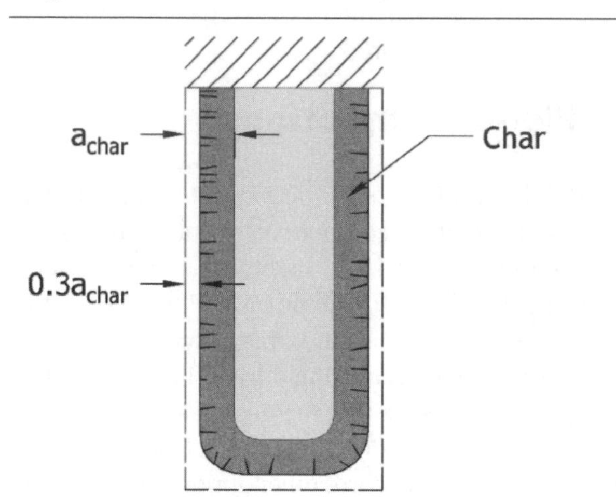

Table C16.2-2 Allowable Design Stress to Average Ultimate Strength Adjustment Factors

	F	1/k	c	Assumed COV	K
Bending Strength	F_b	2.1 [1]	$1 - 1.645\ COV_b$	0.16 [2]	2.85
Tensile Strength	F_t	2.1 [1]	$1 - 1.645\ COV_t$	0.16 [2]	2.85
Compression Strength	F_c	1.9 [1]	$1 - 1.645\ COV_c$	0.16 [2]	2.58
Buckling Strength	E_{05}	1.66 [3]	$1 - 1.645\ COV_E$	0.11 [4]	2.03

1. Taken from Table 10 of ASTM D245 *Standard Practice for Establishing Structural Grades and Related Allowable Properties for Visually Graded Lumber,* Table 1 of ASTM D3737 *Standard Practice for Establishing Allowable Properties for Structural Glued Laminated Timber (Glulam), and* Table 1 of ASTM D5456 *Standard Specification for Evaluation of Structural Composite Lumber Products.*
2. Taken from Table 5-6 of 2010 *Wood Handbook* for bending clear wood values.
3. Taken from Appendices D and H of 2018 *National Design Specification for Wood Construction.*
4. Taken from Appendix F of 2018 *National Design Specification for Wood Construction.*

REFERENCES

1. Aplin, E. N., Factors Affecting the Stiffness and Strength of Metal Plate Connector Joints, Information Report OP-X-57, Ottawa, Ontario, Department of Environment, Canadian Forestry Service, Eastern Forest Products Laboratory, 1973.

2. ANSI Standard A190.1-2012, Structural Glued Laminated Timber, APA-The Engineered Wood Association, Tacoma, WA 2012.

3. ASCE Standard 7-16, Minimum Design Loads and Associated Criteria for Buildings and Other Structures, American Society of Civil Engineers, Reston, VA, 2016.

4. ASTM Standard D 2915-10, Standard Practice for Sampling and Data Analysis for Structural Wood and Wood Based Products, ASTM, West Conshohocken, PA, 2010.

5. ASTM Standard D 143-14, Standard Test Methods for Small Clear Specimens of Timber, ASTM, West Conshohocken, PA, 2014.

6. ASTM Standard D 1760-01, Standard Specification for Pressure Treatment of Timber Products (Withdrawn 2006), ASTM, West Conshohocken, PA, 2001.

7. ASTM Standard D 1990-14, Standard Practice for Establishing Allowable Properties for Visually Graded Dimension Lumber from In-Grade Tests of Full-Size Specimens, ASTM, West Conshohocken, PA, 2014.

8. ASTM Standard D 245-06 (2011), Standard Practice for Establishing Structural Grades and Related Allowable Properties for Visually Graded Lumber, ASTM, West Conshohocken, PA, 2011.

9. ASTM Standard D 2555-06 (2011), Standard Practice for Establishing Clear Wood Strength Values, ASTM, West Conshohocken, PA, 2011.

10. ASTM Standard D 25-12, Standard Specification for Round Timber Piles, ASTM, West Conshohocken, PA, 2012.

11. ASTM Standard D 2899-12, Standard Practice for Establishing Allowable Stresses for Round Timber Piles, ASTM, West Conshohocken, PA, 2012.

12. ASTM Standard D 3200-74 (2012), Standard Specification and Test Method for Establishing Recommended Design Stresses for Round Timber Construction Poles, ASTM, West Conshohocken, PA, 2012.

13. ASTM Standard D 3737-12, Standard Practice for Establishing Allowable Properties for Structural Glued Laminated Timber (Glulam), ASTM, West Conshohocken, PA, 2012.

14. ASTM Standard D 4761-13, Standard Test Methods for Mechanical Properties of Lumber and Wood-Based Structural Material, ASTM, West Conshohocken, PA, 2013.

15. ASTM Standard D 5055-13, Standard Specification for Establishing and Monitoring Structural Capacities of Prefabricated Wood I-Joists, ASTM, West Conshohocken, PA, 2013.

16. ASTM Standard D 5456-14, Standard Specification for Evaluation of Structural Composite Lumber Products, ASTM, West Conshohocken, PA, 2014.

17. ASTM Standard D 5457-12, Standard Specification for Computing Reference Resistance of Wood-Based Materials and Structural Connections for Load and Resistance Factor Design, ASTM, West Conshohocken, PA, 2012.

18. ASTM Standard D 5764-97a (2013), Standard Test Method for Evaluating Dowel-Bearing Strength of Wood and Wood-Base Products, ASTM, West Conshohocken, PA, 2013.

19. ASTM Standard D 6555-03 (2014), Standard Guide for Evaluating System Effects in Repetitive-Member Wood Assemblies, ASTM, West Conshohocken, PA, 2014.

20. Auune, P. and M. Patton-Mallory, Lateral Load-Bearing Capacity of Nailed Joints Based on the Yield Theory: Experimental Verification, Research Paper FPL 470, Madison, WI, U.S. Department of Agriculture, Forest Service, Forest Products Laboratory, 1986.

21. Auune, P. and M. Patton-Mallory, Lateral Load-Bearing Capacity of Nailed Joints Based on the Yield Theory: Theoretical Development, Research Paper FPL 469, Madison, WI, U.S. Department of Agriculture, Forest Service, Forest Products Laboratory, 1986.

22. AWPA Book of Standards, American Wood Preservers' Association, Selma, AL, 2003.

23. Barrett, J. D., R. O. Foschi, and S. P. Fox, Perpendicular to Grain Strength of Douglas-fir, Ottawa, Ontario, Canadian Journal of Civil Engineering, Vol. 2, No. 1: 50-57, 1975.

24. Barrett, J. D., Effect of Size on Tension Perpendicular to Grain Strength of Douglas-fir, Wood and Fiber, 6(2), pp. 126-143, 1974.

25. Bearing Strength of OSB to be Used for the EYM Design Method, APA-The Engineered Wood Association, Tacoma, Washington, 1996.

26. Bendsten, B. A. and W. L. Galligan, Mean and Tolerance Limit Stresses and Stress Modeling for Compression Perpendicular to Grain in Hardwood and Softwood Species, Research Paper FPL 337, Madison, WI, U.S. Department of Agriculture, Forest Service, Forest Products Laboratory, 1979.

27. Bendsten, B. A. and W. L. Galligan, Modeling the Stress-Compression Relationships in Wood in Compression Perpendicular to Grain, Madison, WI, Forest Products Research Society, Forest Products Journal, Vol. 29, No. 2: 42-48, 1979.

28. Bonnicksen, L. W. and S. K. Suddarth, Structural Reliability Analysis of Wood Load-Sharing System, Paper No. 82, Philadelphia, PA, ASTM, Fifth Pacific Area National Meeting, 1965.

29. Borkenhagen, E. H. and H. J. Kuelling, Clinching of Nails in Container Construction, Report No. R1777, Madison, WI, U.S. Department of Agriculture, Forest Service, Forest Products Laboratory, 1948.

30. Buchanan, A. H., Strength Model and Design Methods for Bending and Axial Load Interaction in Timber Members, Thesis, Vancouver, British Columbia, University of British Columbia, Department of Civil Engineering, 1984.

31. Call, R. D. and R. Bjorhawde, Wood Connections with Heavy Bolts and Steel Plates, New York, NY, American Society of Civil Engineers, Journal of Structural Engineering, Vol. 116, No. 11, 1990.

32. Canadian Standards Association, Engineering Design in Wood (Working Stress Design), CAN/CSA-086-M89, Rexdale, Ontario, Canadian Standards Association, 1989.

33. Cline, M. and A. L. Heim, Tests of Structural Timbers, Bulletin 108, Washington, DC, U.S. Department of Agriculture, Forest Service, 1912.

34. Clouser, W. S., Creep of Small Wood Beams Under Constant Bending Load, Report No. 2150, Madison, WI, U.S. Department of Agriculture, Forest Service, Forest Products Laboratory, 1959.

35. Cramer, C. O., Load Distribution in Multiple-Bolt Tension Joints, New York, NY, Proceedings of the American Society of Civil Engineers, Journal of the Structural Division, Vol. 94, No. ST5: 1101-1117, 1968.

36. Criswell, M. E., New Design Equations for Tapered Columns, Portland, OR, Wood Products Information Center, Wood Design Focus, Components, Vol. 2, No.3: 4-7, 1991.

37. DeBonis, A. L. and J. Bodig, Nailed Wood Joints Under Combined Loading, Springer-Verlag, Wood Science and Technology, Vol. 9: 129-144, 1975.

38. Design/Construction Guide — Diaphragms and Shear Walls, Form L350, APA-The Engineered Wood Association, Tacoma, WA, 2001.

39. Doyle, D. V., Performance of Joints with Light Bolts in Laminated Douglas-Fir, Research Paper FPL 10, Madison, WI, U.S. Department of Agriculture, Forest Service, Forest Products Laboratory, 1964.

40. Doyle, D. V. and J. A. Scholten, Performance of Bolted Joints in Douglas-Fir, Research Paper FPL 2, Madison, WI, U.S. Department of Agriculture, Forest Service, Forest Products Laboratory, 1963.

41. Engineering Design in Wood (Limit States Design), CAN/CSA-086.1-M89, Rexdale, Ontario, Canadian Standards Association, 1989.

42. Erickson, E. C. O. and K. M. Romstad, Distribution of Wheel Loads on Timber Bridges, Research Paper FPL 44, Madison, WI, U.S. Department of Agriculture, Forest Service, Forest Products Laboratory, 1965.

43. Fairchild, I. J., Holding Power of Wood Screws, Technologic Papers of the Bureau of Standards No. 319, Washington, DC, Department of Commerce, Bureau of Standards, 1926.

44. Forest Products Laboratory, Communication of August 13, 1935 to National Lumber Manufacturers Association, Madison, WI, U.S. Department of Agriculture, Forest Service, Forest Products Laboratory, 1935.

45. Foschi, R. O. and J. Longworth, Analysis and Design of Griplam Nailed Connections, New York, NY, American Society of Civil Engineers, Journal of the Structural Division, Vol. 101, No. Stp12: 2536-2555, 1974.

46. Foschi, R. O. and S. P. Fox, Radial Stresses in Curved Timber Beams, New York, NY, Proceedings of the American Society of Civil Engineers, Journal of the Structural Division, Vol. 96, No. ST10: 1997-2008, 1970.

47. Foschi, R. O., Load-Slip Characteristics of Nails, Madison, WI, Forest Products Research Society (Forest Products Society), Wood Science, Vol. 9, No. 1: 69-76, 1974.

48. Fox, S. P., Connection Capacity of New Griplam Nails, Ottawa, Ontario, Canadian Journal of Civil Engineering, Vol. 6, No. 1: 59-64, 1979.

49. Freas, A. D. and M. L. Selbo, Fabrication and Design of Glued Laminated Wood Structural Members, Technical Bulletin No. 1069, Washington, DC, U.S. Department of Agriculture, Forest Service, 1954.

50. General Observations on the Nailing of Wood, Technical Note 243, Madison, WI, U.S. Department of Agriculture, Forest Service, Forest Products Laboratory, 1940.

51. Gerhards, C. C., Effect of Moisture Content and Temperature on the Mechanical Properties of Wood: an Analysis of Immediate Effects, Madison, WI, Society of Wood Science and Technology, Wood and Fiber, Vol. 14, No. 1: 4-36, 1982.

52. Gerhards, C. C., Time-Dependent Bending Deflections of Douglas-Fir 2 by 4's, Madison, WI, Forest Products Research Society (Forest Products Society), Forest Products Journal, Vol. 35, No. 4: 18-26, 1985.

53. Goodman, J. R. and J. Bodig, Contribution of Plywood Sheathing to Buckling Stiffness of Residential Roof Truss Chord Members, Report and Supplemental Report to National Forest Products Association, Fort Collins, CO, Colorado State University, Department of Civil Engineering, 1977.

54. Goodman, J. R. and J. Bodig, Orthotropic Strength of Wood in Compression, Madison, WI, Forest Products Research Society (Forest Products Society), Wood Science, Vol. 4, No. 2: 83-94, 1971.

55. Goodman, J. R. and M. E. Criswell, Contribution of Plywood Sheathing to Buckling Stiffness of Residential Roof Truss Chord Members, Supplemental Report to National Forest Products Association, Fort Collins, CO, Colorado State University, Department of Civil Engineering, 1980.

56. Gopu, V. K. A., J. R. Goodman, M. D. Vanderbilt, E. G. Thompson, and J. Bodig, Behavior and Design of Double-Tapered Pitched and Curved Glulam Beams, Structural Research Report No. 16, Fort Collins, CO, Colorado State University, Civil Engineering Department, 1976.

57. Grenoble, H. S., Bearing Strength of Bolts in Wood, Project I-228-7, Madison, WI, U.S. Department of Agriculture, Forest Service, Forest Products Laboratory, 1923.

58. Gurfinkel, G., Wood Engineering, New Orleans, LA, Southern Forest Products Association, 1973.

59. Hankinson, R. L., Investigation of Crushing Strength of Spruce at Varying Angles of Grain, Material Section Paper No. 130, McCook Field, NE, United States Army Engineering Division, U.S. Air Service Information Circular, Vol. III, No. 257, 1921.

60. Hooley, R. F. and B. Madsen, Lateral Stability of Glued Laminated Beams, New York, NY, Proceedings of the American Society of Civil Engineers, Journal of the Structural Division, Vol. 90, ST3: 201-218, 1964.

61. Hooley, R. F. and R. H. Duval, Lateral Buckling of Simply Supported Glued Laminated Beams, Report to Laminated Timber Institute of Canada, Vancouver, British Columbia, University of British Columbia, Department of Civil Engineering, 1972.

62. Hoyle, R. J., Jr., M. C. Griffith, and R.Y. Itani, Primary Creep in Douglas-Fir Beams of Commercial Size and Quality, Madison, WI, Society of Wood Science and Technology, Wood and Fiber Science, Vol. 17, No. 3: 300-314, 1985.

63. Hunt, G. M. and G. A. Garratt, Wood Preservation, 2nd ed. New York, NY, McGraw Hill, 1953.

64. Hyer, O. C., Study of Temperature in Wood Parts of Homes Throughout the United States, Research Note FPL-012, Madison, WI, U.S. Department of Agriculture, Forest Service, Forest Products Laboratory, 1963.

65. In-Grade Testing Program Technical Committee, In-Grade Testing of Structural Lumber, Proceedings 47363, Madison, WI, Forest Products Research Society (Forest Products Society), 1989.

66. Isyumov, N., Load Distribution in Multiple Shear-Plate Joints in Timber, Departmental Publication No. 1203, Ottawa, Canada, Department of Forestry and Rural Development, Forestry Branch, 1967.

67. Johansen, K. W., Theory of Timber Connections, Zurich, Switzerland, Publications of International Association for Bridge and Structural Engineering, Vol. 9: 249-262, 1949.

68. Johns, K. C. and A. H. Buchanan, Strength of Timber Members in Combined Bending and Axial Loading, Boras, Sweden, International Union of Forest Research Organizations, Proceedings IUFRO Wood Engineering Group S5.02, 343-368, 1982.

69. Karacabeyli, E. and H. Fraser, Short-Term Strength of Glulam Rivet Connections Made with Spruce and Douglas-Fir Glulam and Douglas-Fir Solid Timber, Ottawa, Ontario, Canadian Journal of Civil Engineering, Vol. 17, 166-172, 1990.

70. Kolberk, A. and M. Birnbaum, Transverse Strength of Screws in Wood, Ithaca, NY, Cornell University, The Cornell Civil Engineer, Vol. 22, No. 2: 31-41, 1913.

71. Kuenzi, E. W. Theoretical Design of a Nailed or Bolted Joint, Report No. D1951, Madison, WI, U.S. Department of Agriculture, Forest Service, Forest Products Laboratory, 1955.

72. Kunesh, R. H. and J. W. Johnson, Strength of Multiple-Bolt Joints: Influence of Spacing and Other Variables, Report T-24, Corvallis, OR, Oregon State University, School of Forestry, Forest Research Laboratory, 1968.

73. Kass, A.J. Effects of Incising on Bending Properties of Redwood Dimension Lumber. Re.Pap 75. U.S. Department of Agriculture, Forest Service, Forest Products Laboratory, 1975.

74. Lam, F. and P. I. Morris, Effect of Double-Density Incising on Bending Strength of Lumber, Madison, WI, Forest Products Research Society (Forest Products Society), Forest Products Journal, Vol. 41, No. 9: 43-47, 1991.

75. Laminated Timber Institute of Canada, Timber Design Manual, Ottawa, Ontario, Laminated Timber Institute of Canada, 1980.

76. Lane, W. W., A Study of the Effects of Lag Screw Spacing on the Strength of Timber Joints, Building Research Laboratory Report No. BR 4-1, Columbus, OH, Ohio State University, Engineering Experiment Station, 1963.

77. Lantos, G., Load Distribution in a Row of Fasteners Subjected to Lateral Load, Madison, WI, Forest Products Research Society (Forest Products Society), Wood Science, Vol. 1, No. 3: 129-136, 1969.

78. Larsen, H. J., The Yield of Bolted and Nailed Joints, South Africa, International Union of Forest Research Organizations, Proceedings of Division 5 Conference, 646-654, 1973.

79. Loferski, J. R., and T. E. McLain, Static and Impact Flexural Properties of Common Wire Nails, Philadelphia, PA, ASTM, Journal of Testing and Evaluation, Vol. 19, No. 4: 297-304, 1991.

80. Longworth, J., Behavior of Shear Plate Connections in Sloping Grain Surfaces, Madison, WI, Forest Products Research Society (Forest Products Society), Forest Products Journal, Vol. 17, No. 7: 49-63, 1967.

81. Malhotra, S. K., A Rational Approach to the Design of Solid Timber Columns, Study No. 7, Applications of Solid Mechanics, Waterloo, Ontario, University of Waterloo, 1972.

82. Malhotra, S. K. and A. P. Sukumar, A Simplified Procedure for Built-Up Wood Compression Members, St. John's, Newfoundland, Annual Conference, Canadian Society for Civil Engineering, June 1-18, 1989.

83. Malhotra, S. K. and D. B. Van Dyer, Rational Approach to the Design of Built-Up Timber Columns, Madison, WI, Forest Products Research Society (Forest Products Society), Wood Science, Vol. 9, No. 4: 174-186, 1977.

84. Markwardt, L. J. and T. R. C. Wilson, Strength and Related Properties of Woods Grown in the United States, Technical Bulletin No. 479, Washington, DC, U.S. Department of Agriculture, Forest Service, 1935.

85. McLain, T. E., Influence of Metal Side Plates on the Strength of Bolted Wood Joints, Blacksburg, VA, Virginia Polytechnic Institute and State University, Department of Forest Products, 1981.

86. McLain, T. E., Strength of Lag Screw Connections, Blacksburg, VA, Virginia Polytechnic Institute and State University, Department of Wood Science and Forest Products, 1991.

87. McLain, T. E. and J. D. Carroll, Combined Load Capacity of Threaded Fastener-Wood Connections, New York, NY, American Society of Civil Engineers, Journal of Structural Engineering, Vol. 116, No. 9: 2419-2432, 1990.

88. McLain, T. E. and S. Thangjithan, Bolted Wood-Joint Yield Model, New York, NY, American Society of Civil Engineers, Journal of Structural Engineering, Vol. 109, No.8: 1820-1835, 1983.

89. McLain, T. E., P. Pellicane, L. Soltis, T. L. Wilkinson and J. Zahn, Comparison of EYM-Predicted Yield Loads and Current ASD Loads for Nails, Bolts and Screws, Washington, DC, National Forest Products Association, 1990.

90. Moody, R. C., R. H. Falk, and T. G. Williamson, Strength of Glulam Beams–Volume Effects, Tokyo, Japan, Proceedings of the 1990 International Timber Engineering Conference, Vol. 1: 176-182, 1990.

91. Murphy, J. F., Strength and Stiffness Reduction of Large Notched Beams, New York, NY, American Society of Civil Engineers, Journal of Structural Engineering, Vol. 112, No. 9: 1989-1999, 1986.

92. Murphy, J. F., Using Fracture Mechanics to Predict Fracture in Notched Wood Beams, Vancouver, British Columbia, Forintek Canada Corporation, Western Forest Products Laboratory, Proceedings of the First International Conference on Wood Fracture, 1978.

93. Murphy, J. F., B. R. Ellingwood, and E. M. Hendrickson, Damage Accumulation in Wood Structural Members Under Stochastic Live Loads, Madison, WI, Society of Wood Science and Technology, Wood and Fiber Science, Vol. 19, No. 4: 453-463, 1987.

94. Nail Holding Power of American Woods, Technical Note 236, Washington, DC, U.S. Department of Agriculture, Forest Service, Forest Products Laboratory, 1931.

95. Nail-Withdrawal Resistance of American Woods, Research Note FPL-093, Madison, WI, U.S. Department of Agriculture, Forest Service, Forest Products Laboratory, 1965.

96. National Design Specification for Stress-Grade Lumber and its Fastenings, Leesburg, VA, National Lumber Manufacturers Association (American Wood Council), 1944.

97. Neubauer, L. W., Full-Size Stud Tests Confirm Superior Strength of Square-End Wood Columns, Annual Meeting Paper No. 70-408, St. Joseph, MI, American Society of Agricultural Engineers, 1970.

98. Newlin, J. A. and G. W. Trayer, Form Factors of Beams Subjected to Transverse Loading Only, Report No. 1310, Madison, WI, U.S. Department of Agriculture, Forest Service, Forest Products Laboratory, 1941, (Also Report 181 of the National Advisory Committee for Aeronautics, 1924).

99. Newlin, J. A. and G. W. Trayer, Stresses in Wood Members Subjected to Combined Column and Beam Action, National Advisory Committee for Aeronautics Report 188 (Forest Products Laboratory Report No. 1311), Madison, WI, U.S. Department of Agriculture, Forest Service, Forest Products Laboratory, 1924.

100. Newlin, J. A. and J. M. Gahagan, Lag-Screw Joints: Their Behavior and Design, Technical Bulletin No. 597, Washington, DC, U.S. Department of Agriculture, Forest Service, Forest Products Laboratory, 1938.

101. Parker, J. E., A Study of the Strength of Short and Intermediate Wood Columns by Experimental and Analytical Methods, Research Note FPL-028, Madison, WI, U.S. Department of Agriculture, Forest Service, Forest Products Laboratory, 1964.

102. Patton-Mallory, M., End Distance Effects Comparing Tensile and Compression Loads on Bolted Wood Connections, Seattle, WA, Proceedings of the 1988 International Conference on Timber Engineering, Vol. 2: 313-324, 1988.

103. Perkins, N. S., Plywood: Properties, Design and Construction, Tacoma, WA, Douglas fir Plywood Association (APA-The Engineered Wood Association), 1962.

104. Perkins, N. S., P. Landsem, and G. W. Trayer, Modern Connectors in Timber Construction, Washington, DC, U.S. Department of Commerce, National Committee on Wood Utilization and U.S. Department of Agriculture, Forest Service, Forest Products Laboratory, 1933.

105. Perrin, P. W., Review of Incising and its Effects on Strength and Preservative Treatment of Wood, Madison, WI, Forest Products Research Society (Forest Products Society), Forest Products Journal, Vol. 28, No. 9: 27-33, 1978.

106. Plywood Design Specification and Supplements, Form Y510, APA-The Engineered Wood Association, Tacoma, WA, 1997.

107. Polensek, A. and G. H. Atherton, Compression-Bending Strength and Stiffness of Walls Made with Utility Grade Studs, Madison, WI, Forest Products Research Society (Forest Products Society), Forest Products Journal, Vol. 26, No. 11: 17-25, 1976.

108. Popov, E. P., Mechanics of Materials, Englewood Cliffs, NJ, Prentice-Hall, 1976.

109. Radcliffe, B. F. and A. Sliker, Effect of Variables on Performance of Trussed Rafters, Research Report 21, East Lansing, MI, Michigan State University, Agricultural Experiment Station, 1964.

110. Rahman, M. V., Y. J. Chiang, and R. E. Rowlands, Stress and Failure Analysis of Double-Bolted Joints in Douglas- Fir and Sitka Spruce, Madison, WI, Society of Wood Science and Technology, Wood and Fiber Science, Vol. 23, No. 4: 567-589, 1991.

111. Rosowsky, D. and B. Ellingwood, Reliability of Wood Systems Subjected to Stochastic Loads, Madison, WI, Society of Wood Science and Technology, Wood and Fiber Science, Vol. 24, No. 1: 47-59, 1992.

112. Schniewind, A. and D. E. Lyon, Further Experiments on Creep-Rupture Life Under Cyclic Environmental Conditions, Madison, WI, Society of Wood Science and Technology, Wood and Fiber, Vol. 4, No. 4: 334-341, 1973.

113. Schniewind, A. P. and D. E. Lyon, A Fracture Mechanics Approach to the Tensile Strength Perpendicular to Grain of Dimension Lumber, New York, NY, Springer-Verlag, Wood Science and Technology, Vol. 7: 45-49, 1973.

114. Scholten, J. A., Built-Up Wood Columns Conserve Lumber, New York, NY, Engineering News Record, Vol. 107, No. 9, 1931.

115. Scholten, J. A., Rounding Notches Makes Stronger Joist, Chicago, IL, Pacific Logging Congress, American Lumberman, Vol. 46, 1935.

116. Scholten, J. A., Tests of Built-Up Wood Columns, Project L-273-1J4, Madison, WI, U.S. Department of Agriculture, Forest Service, Forest Products Laboratory, 1931.

117. Scholten, J. A., Timber-Connector Joints, Their Strength and Design, Technical Bulletin No. 865, Washington, DC, U.S. Department of Agriculture, Forest Service, Forest Products Laboratory, 1944.

118. Scholten, J. A. and E. G. Molander, Strength of Nailed Joints in Frame Walls, Madison, WI, U.S. Department of Agriculture, Forest Service, Forest Products Laboratory, 1950.

119. Snodgrass, J. D. and W. W. Gleaves, Effect of End-Distance on Strength of Single-Bolt Joints, Corvallis, OR, Oregon State University, Oregon Forest Research Center, 1960.

120. Soltis, L. A., European Yield Model for Wood Connections, New York, NY, American Society of Civil Engineers, Proceedings of Structures Congress 1991, Indianapolis, Indiana, 60-63, 1991.

121. Soltis, L. A. and T. L. Wilkinson, Bolted Connection Design, General Research Report FPL-GRT-54, Madison, WI, U.S. Department of Agriculture, Forest Service, Forest Products Laboratory, 1987.

122. Soltis, L. A. and T. L. Wilkinson, Timber Bolted Connection Design, New York, NY, American Society of Civil Engineers, Proceedings of Structural Congress 1987, Orlando, Florida, 205-220, 1987.

123. Soltis, L. A., W. Nelson, and J. L. Hills, Creep of Structural Lumber, New York, NY, American Society of Mechanical Engineers, Proceedings of 3rd Joint ASCE/ASME Mechanics Conference, San Diego, 216-221, 1989.

124. Special Design Provisions for Wind and Seismic (SDPWS-05), American Wood Council, Leesburg, VA, 2005.

125. Specification for Structural Steel Buildings (ANSI/AISC 360-10), American Institute of Steel Construction (AISC), Chicago, IL, 2010.

126. North American Standard for Cold-Formed Steel Framing, American Iron and Steel Institute (AISI), Washington, DC, 2007.

127. Stamm, A. J., Wood and cellulose science, New York, NY, Ronald Press, 1964.

128. Standard Appearance Grades for Structural Glued Laminated Timber, AITC 110-2001, American Institute of Timber Construction, Centennial, CO, 2001.

129. Standard Specifications for Highway Bridges, American Association of State Highway and Transportation Officials (AASHTO), Washington, DC, 2002.

130. Standard Specifications for Structural Glued Laminated Timber of Hardwood Species, AITC 119-96, American Institute of Timber Construction, Centennial, CO, 1996.

131. Standard Specifications for Structural Glued Laminated Timber of Softwood Species, AITC 117-2004, American Institute of Timber Construction, Centennial, CO, 2004.

132. Stieda, C. K. A., Stress Concentrations in Notched Timber Beams, Contribution No. P-49, Vancouver, British Columbia, Department of Forestry of Canada, Vancouver Laboratory, Forest Products Research Branch, 1964.

133. Structural Glued Laminated Timber, Commercial Standard CS 253-63, U.S. Department of Commerce, National Bureau of Standards, Washington, DC, 1963.

134. Structural Glued Laminated Timber, Voluntary Product Standard PS 56-73, U.S. Department of Commerce, National Bureau of Standards, Washington, DC, 1973.

135. Suddarth, S. K., Test Performance of 1-1/2 Inch Bolts in Glulam–Row Effects and Effect of Subsequent Drying, Portland, OR, Wood Products Information Center, Wood Design Focus, Components, Vol. 1, No.1, 1990.

136. Technical Report 10–Calculating the Fire Resistance of Exposed Wood Members, American Forest & Paper Association, Washington, DC, 2015.

137. Technical Report 12–General Dowel Equations for Calculating Lateral Connection Values, American Forest & Paper Association, Washington, DC, 2015.

138. Technical Report 14–Designing for Lateral-Torsional Stability in Wood Members, American Forest & Paper Association, Washington DC, 2003.

139. Tiemann, H. D., Some Results of Dead Load Bending Tests by Means of a Recording Deflectometer, Philadelphia, PA, Proceedings of the American Society for Testing Materials, Vol. 9: 534-548, 1909.

140. Timber Construction Manual, American Institute of Timber Construction (AITC), John Wiley & Sons, 2012.

141. Timber Engineering Company, Design Manual for TECO Timber-Connector Construction, Washington, DC, National Lumber Manufacturers Association (American Forest & Paper Association), Timber Engineering Company, 1955.

142. Timber Engineering Company, Timber Design and Construction Handbook, New York, NY, F.W, Dodge, 1956.

143. Tissell, J. R., Horizontal Plywood Diaphragm Tests, Laboratory Report No. 106, Tacoma, WA, American Plywood Association (APA-The Engineered Wood Association), 1967.

144. Tissell, J. R., Plywood Diaphragms, Research Report 138, Tacoma, WA, American Plywood Association (APA-The Engineered Wood Association), 1990.

145. Tissell, J. R., Structural Panel Shear Walls, Research Report 154, Tacoma, WA, American Plywood Association (APA-The Engineered Wood Association), 1990.

146. Trayer, G. W., The Bearing Strength of Wood Under Bolts, Technical Bulletin No. 332, Washington, DC, U.S. Department of Agriculture, Forest Service, Forest Products Laboratory, 1932.

147. Trayer, G. W. and H. W. March, Elastic Instability of Members Having Sections Common in Aircraft Construction, Report No. 382, Washington, DC, National Advisory Committee for Aeronautics, 1931.

148. Truss Plate Institute, Commentary and Recommendations for Bracing Wood Trusses, BWT-76, Madison, WI, Truss Plate Institute, 1976.

149. Vanderbilt, M. D., J. R. Goodman, and J. Bodig, A Rational Analysis and Design Procedure for Wood Joist Floor Systems, Final Report to the National Science Foundation for Grant GK-30853, Fort Collins, CO, Colorado State University, Department of Civil Engineering, 1974.

150. Voluntary Product Standard (PS 1-09), Structural Plywood, United States Department of Commerce, National Institute of Standards and Technology, Gaithersburg, MD, 2009.

151. Voluntary Product Standard (PS 2-10), Performance Standard for Wood-Based Structural-Use Panels, United States Department of Commerce, National Institute of Standards and Technology, Gaithersburg, MD, 2011.

152. Voluntary Product Standard (PS 20-15), American Softwood Lumber Standard, United States Department of Commerce, National Institute of Standards and Technology, Gaithersburg, MD, 2015.

153. War Production Board, National Emergency Specifications for the Design, Fabrication and Erection of Stress Grade Lumber and its Fastenings for Buildings, Directive No. 29, Washington, DC, War Production Board, Conservation Division, 1943.

154. White, R. H., Charring Rates of Different Wood Species, PhD Thesis, University of Wisconsin, Madison, WI, 1988.

155. Wilkinson, T. L., Analyses of Nailed Joints with Dissimilar Members, New York, NY, American Society of Civil Engineers, Journal of the Structural Division, Vol. 98, No. ST9: 2005-2013, 1972.

156. Wilkinson, T. L., Assessment of Modification Factors for a Row of Bolts in Timber Connections, Research Paper FPL 376, Madison, WI, U.S. Department of Agriculture, Forest Service, Forest Products Laboratory, 1980.

157. Wilkinson, T. L., Bolted Connection Allowable Loads Based on the European Yield Model, Madison, WI, U.S. Department of Agriculture, Forest Service, Forest Products Laboratory, 1991.

158. Wilkinson, T. L., Dowel Bearing Strength, Research Paper FPL-RP-505, Madison, WI, U.S. Department of Agriculture, Forest Service, Forest Products Laboratory, 1991.

159. Wilkinson, T. L., Elastic Bearing Constants for Sheathing Materials, Research Paper FPL 192, Madison, WI, U.S. Department of Agriculture, Forest Service, Forest Products Laboratory, 1974.

160. Wilkinson, T. L., Formulas for Working Stresses for Timber Piles, Madison, WI, U.S. Department of Agriculture, Forest Service, Forest Products Laboratory, 1969.

161. Wilkinson, T. L., Strength Evaluation of Round Timber Piles, Research Paper FPL 101, Madison, WI, U.S. Department of Agriculture, Forest Service, Forest Products Laboratory, 1968.

162. Wilkinson, T. L., Strength of Bolted Wood Joints with Various Ratios of Member Thickness, Research Paper FPL 314, Madison, WI, U.S. Department of Agriculture, Forest Service, Forest Products Laboratory, 1978.

163. Wilkinson, T. L. and T. R. Laatsch, Lateral and Withdrawal Resistance of Tapping Screws in Three Densities of Wood, Madison, WI, Forest Products Research Society (Forest Products Society), Forest Products Journal, Vol. 20, No. 7: 35-41, 1971.

164. Williamson, T. G. and B. Hill, Waiver of Metal Hanger Torsional Restraint Requirements, Communication to ICBO Evaluation Service, Vancouver, WA, American Institute of Timber Construction, (November), 1989.

165. Williamson, T. G., R. Gregg, and H. Brooks, Wood Design: A Commentary on the Performance of Deep and Narrow Re-Sawn Glulam Purlins, Los Angeles, CA, Structural Engineers Association of Southern California, From Experience, (June), 1990.

166. Wilson, T. R. C., Glued Laminated Wooden Arch, Technical Bulletin No. 691, Washington, DC, U.S. Department of Agriculture, Forest Service, 1939.

167. Wilson, T. R. C., Guide to the Grading of Structural Timbers and the Determination of Working Stresses, U.S. Department of Agriculture Miscellaneous Publication 185, Washington, DC, U.S. Department of Agriculture, 1934.

168. Winandy, J. E., ACA and CCA Preservative Treatment and Redrying Effects on Bending Properties of Douglas-fir, Stevensville, MD, American Wood-Preservers' Association Proceedings, Vol. 85: 106-118, 1989.

169. Winandy, J. E., CCA Preservative Treatment and Redrying Effects on the Bending Properties of 2 by 4 Southern Pine, Madison, WI, Forest Products Research Society (Forest Products Society), Forest Products Journal, Vol. 39, No. 9: 14-21, 1989.

170. Winandy, J. E., Effects of Treatment and Redrying on Mechanical Properties of Wood, Madison, WI, Forest Products Research Society (Forest Products Society), Proceedings 47358 of Conference on Wood Protection Techniques and the Use of Treated Wood in Construction, 54-62, 1988.

171. Winandy, J. E. and H. M. Barnes, Influence of Initial Kiln-Drying Temperature on CCA-Treatment Effects on Strength, Stevensville, MD, American Wood-Preservers' Association Proceedings, Vol. 87, 1991.

172. Winandy, J. E. and R. S. Boone, The Effects of CCA Preservative Treatment and Redrying on the Bending Properties of 2 x 6 Southern Pine Lumber, Madison, WI, Society of Wood Science and Technology, Wood and Fiber Science, Vol. 20, No. 3: 350-364, 1988.

173. Winandy, J. E., Influence of Time-to-Failure on Strength of CCA-Treated Lumber, Madison, WI, Forest Products Research Society (Forest Products Society), Forest Products Journal, Vol. 45, No. 2: 82-85, 1995.

174. Winandy, J. E., J. J. Morell, and S. T. Lebow, Review of Effects of Incising on Treatability and Strength, Madison, WI, Forest Products Society Conference, Savannah, GA, Wood Preservation: In the 90's and Beyond, 1994.

175. Winandy, J. E., R. S. Boone, and B. A. Bendsten, Interaction of CCA Preservative Treatment and Redrying: Effect on the Mechanical Properties of Southern Pine, Madison, WI, Forest Products Research Society (Forest Products Society), Forest Products Journal, Vol. 35, No. 10: 62-68, 1985.

176. Wolfe, R. W., Allowable Stresses for the Upside-Down Timber Industry, Madison, WI, U.S. Department of Agriculture, Forest Service, Forest Products Laboratory, 1989.

177. Wolfe, R. W., Performance of Light-Frame Redundant Assemblies, Tokyo, Japan, Proceedings of the 1990 International Timber Engineering Conference, Vol. 1: 124-131, 1990.

178. Wolfe, R. W., Research Dealing with Effects of Bearing Length on Compression Perpendicular to the Grain, Madison, WI, U.S. Department of Agriculture, Forest Service, Forest Products Laboratory, 1983.

179. Wolfe, R. W. and T. LaBissoniere, Structural Performance of Light-Frame Roof Assemblies, II, Conventional Truss Assemblies, Research Paper FPL-RP-499, Madison, WI, U.S. Department of Agriculture, Forest Service, Forest Products Laboratory, 1991.

180. Wood Construction Data 1 (WCD 1) Details for Conventional Wood Frame Construction, Washington, DC, American Forest & Paper Association, 2001.

181. Wood Handbook, Agriculture Handbook No. 72, Washington, D.C, U.S. Department of Agriculture, Forest Service, Forest Products Laboratory, 1955.

182. Wood Handbook, Agriculture Handbook No. 72, Washington, D.C, U.S. Department of Agriculture, Forest Service, Forest Products Laboratory, 1974.

183. Wood Handbook, Agriculture Handbook No. 72, Washington, D.C, U.S. Department of Agriculture, Forest Service, Forest Products Laboratory, 1987.

184. Wood Handbook, Washington, DC, U.S. Department of Agriculture, Forest Service, Forest Products Laboratory, 1935.

185. Wood, L. W., Behavior of Wood Under Continued Loading, New York, NY, Engineering News Record, Vol. 139, No. 24: 108-111, 1947.

186. Wood, L. W., Formulas for Columns with Side Loads and Eccentricity, Report No. R1782, Madison, WI, U.S. Department of Agriculture, Forest Service, Forest Products Laboratory, 1950.

187. Zahn, J. J., Combined-Load Stability Criterion for Wood Beam-Columns, New York, NY, American Society of Civil Engineers, Journal of Structural Engineering, Vol. 114, No. 11: 2612-2618, 1986.

188. Zahn, J. J., Design Equation for Multiple-Fastener Wood Connections, Madison, WI, U.S. Department of Agriculture, Forest Service, Forest Products Laboratory, 1991.

189. Zahn, J. J., Design of Wood Members Under Combined Load, New York, NY, American Society of Civil Engineers, Journal of Structural Engineering, Vol. 112, No. 9: 2109-2126, 1986.

190. Zahn, J. J., Interaction of Crushing and Buckling in Wood Columns and Beams, Madison, WI, U.S. Department of Agriculture, Forest Service, Forest Products Laboratory, 1990.

191. Zahn, J. J., Progress Report to NFPA on Column Research at FPL, Madison, WI, U.S. Department of Agriculture, Forest Service, Forest Products Laboratory, 1989.

192. Zahn, J. J., Proposed Design Formula for Wood Beam Columns, Paper No. 87-4002, Baltimore, MD, Proceedings of American Society of Agricultural Engineers, 1987.

193. Zahn, J. J., Strength of Lumber Under Combined Bending and Compression, Research Paper FPL 391, Madison, WI, U.S. Department of Agriculture, Forest Service, Forest Products Laboratory, 1982.

194. Zahn, J. J., Strength of Multiple-Member Structures, Research Paper FPL 139, Madison, WI, U.S. Department of Agriculture, Forest Service, Forest Products Laboratory, 1970.

195. Wilkinson, T. L., Moisture Cycling of Trussed Rafter Joints, Research Paper FPL 67, Madison, WI, U.S. Department of Agriculture, Forest Service, Forest Products Laboratory, 1966.

196. Rammer, D.R., Withdrawal Strength Design Expression of Bright Annularly Threaded Nails Conforming to ASTM F1667 Table 45, Madison, WI, U.S. Department of Agriculture, Forest Service, Forest Products Laboratory, 2010.

197. ANSI/APA PRG 320-2017, Standard for Performance-Rated Cross-Laminated Timber, APA-The Engineered Wood Association, Tacoma, WA, 2017.

198. Uibel, T and H. J. Blass. Edge Joints with Dowel Type Fasteners in Cross Laminated Timber. Proceedings of International Council for Research and Innovation in Building Construction, Working Commission W18 – Timber Structures, Bled, Slovenia, August 2007.

199. Winandy, J.E., and Hernandez, R. An Anlaytical Approach to Determining the Effects of Incising on Bending Strength and Stiffness of Glue-laminated Beams. Proceedings of the American Wood Preservers' Association. Vol. 94:98-115. Granbury, TX, 1998.

200. Hernandez, Roland, Winandy, Jerrold E. Evaluation of a Reduced Section Modulus Model for Determining the Effects of Incising on Bending Strength and Stiffness of Structural Lumber. Forest Products Journal 55(9):57-65, 2005.

201. ASTM Standard F 6555-03 (2014), Standard Guide for Evaluating System Effects in Repetitive-Member Wood Assemblies, ASTM, West Conshohocken, PA, 2014.

202. ASTM Standard F 1667-17, Standard Specification for Driven Fasteners: Nails, Spikes, and Staples, ASTM, West Conshohocken, PA, 2017.

203. Rammer, Douglas, Zelinka, Samuel. Withdrawal Strength and Bending Yield Strength of Stainless Steel Nails. ASCE Journal of Structural Engineering, Volume 141, Issue 5, 2015.

204. Douglas, Bradford, K, Line, Philip, Douglas, Mary K. Evaluation of Fastener Head Pull-Through. American Wood Council. 2018.

205. ASTM Standard F 1575-17, Standard Test Method for Determining Bending Yield Moment of Nails, ASTM, West Conshohocken, PA, 2017.

206. Morell, J.J., and Winandy, J.E. Characteristics of Incising Patterns and Densities of Douglas-fir and Hem-Fir Lumber Produced by Treating Plants in the Western United States. Department of Wood Science and Engineering, Oregon State University, Corvalis, OR. Final Report Prepared for the Western Wood Preservers Institute, Vancouver, WA, 2017.